HANDBOOK
OF
MEDICAL
SOCIOLOGY

second edition

HANDBOOK OF MEDICAL SOCIOLOGY

Edited by

HOWARD E. FREEMAN
Morse Professor of Urban Studies, Florence Heller Graduate School for Advanced Studies in Social Welfare, Brandeis University, and Sociologist, Russell Sage Foundation

SOL LEVINE
Chairman and Professor, Department of Behavioral Sciences, School of Hygiene and Public Health, The Johns Hopkins University, and Director, Center for Urban Affairs, The Johns Hopkins University

LEO G. REEDER
Professor of Public Health and Sociology, School of Public Health, University of California at Los Angeles

PRENTICE-HALL, INC., Englewood Cliffs, New Jersey

ISBN: 0-13-380311-2

Library of Congress Catalog Card No.: 78-152864

10 9 8 7 6 5 4 3 2 1

PRINTED IN THE UNITED STATES OF AMERICA

PRENTICE-HALL INTERNATIONAL, INC., *London*
PRENTICE-HALL OF AUSTRALIA, PTY. LTD., *Sydney*
PRENTICE-HALL OF CANADA, LTD., *Toronto*
PRENTICE-HALL OF INDIA (PRIVATE) LIMITED, *New Delhi*
PRENTICE-HALL OF JAPAN, INC., *Tokyo*

The first edition of the Handbook
was dedicated to our friend, Benjamin D. Paul.
He joins with us in dedicating this edition to
the late EDWARD A. SUCHMAN.

CONTENTS

part four *STRATEGY, METHOD, AND STATUS OF MEDICAL SOCIOLOGY*

ACKNOWLEDGEMENTS

The editors of course wish to thank the contributors to this handbook: their task was made more difficult in this revision because of the increased volume of theoretical and empirical literature in medical sociology. The patience and understanding of the contributors with respect to the many problems in producing this volume are greatly appreciated.

The editors shared equally in the planning and development of this book. Individual contributors are responsible, of course, for any opinions or views in their own chapters. Unless the authors are not alphabetical, the writing of the chapters, like the editing of the book, is a joint and equal responsibility of the contributors.

Mrs. Kara Rosenberg and Mrs. Dora Alaoui typed drafts of the manuscript and were responsible for coordinating the flow of materials among contributors, editors, and the publisher. Mrs. Kara Rosenberg and Miss Linda Reitman assisted in the editing.

We are grateful to the many investigators and publishers who granted us permission to use their materials, and to the editorial staff of Prentice-Hall, Inc.

INTRODUCTION TO THE FIRST EDITION

Hugh R. Leavell

In recent years a phenomenal expansion of interest has developed in the study of the aspects of health problems with which the social sciences have tools to deal. Among the reasons for this new increase of interest are a number of forces which require special mention. Some of these forces are to be found on the health side of the relationship, and some lie on the side of the social sciences. Certain forces in the general environment of the times are also noteworthy.

On the health side, professionals are reviving past interest in the importance of the multiple causation of disease and disorder. The microbiological era introduced by Pasteur brought an enormous change in medical thinking. Searches began for the one specific microbe which was thought to be the prime causative agent for each disease. Research for specific cures became almost frantic, following the dramatic development of the vaccines and immune sera which provided prevention for a number of diseases and cures for others. Knowledge of antibiotics, hormones, and specific nutrients such as vitamins and minerals further fanned the unitary-causation flame. Science all but lost sight of the individual patient living in his social environment. Social medicine, which had been developing even before all this, became sidetracked.

Of course, the early optimism about specific causation of and specific treatment for all man's ills had to be tempered. Accumulating experience showed the fallacy of extrapolating too far from the unquestionably good results found in a limited number of situations. The importance of the environment in all its aspects, of genetic factors, and of the mental and emotional aspects of illness was recognized once more. The concepts of the "whole man," of psychosomatic illness, and of various socio-economic factors in producing or contributing to disease once again became more widely accepted. However, physicians were not trained in these areas of investigation. So, led by mental health workers, medical people called on social scientists for help.

A parallel situation existed in organized community health work—that is, public health. Much of the productive health research that was going on could be applied on a mass basis to the community's benefit. Various governmental and voluntary organizations—including hospitals—were set up to provide the needed community services and to educate people to use them. At first, there was little realization that health organization and administration was comparable in any significant way with other organizations to be found in the community. Gradually, it became apparent that people in organizations act in somewhat comparable ways, even though the objectives of the organizations differ considerably. Executives and others responsible for health organizations, many of whom were physicians, found that their training in the natural sciences provided little basis upon which to design and conduct studies of organization, of the community itself, and of how the public might be educated to avail itself of the health knowledge pouring out of the rapidly expanding laboratories in hospitals and in medical schools. Once again the social scientists were called upon.

While all these things were going on among health workers, social science was coming of age and proving itself in numerous fields of application. Concepts were being clarified and research tools with greater applicability were becoming available. Looking about for new research areas, a number of social scientists found receptive hosts and collaborators among health workers. Hospitals, with their complex organizational ramifications, were found to be fertile fields for study. Health education of the public obviously involved problems that were interesting to social scientists. Occasional difficulties in collaborative work which developed in some situations only served to prove that sufficient collaboration was being attempted to bring the difficulties to light and to make them of sufficiently broad interest to warrant publication.

The general environment of the times has also had a great influence in bringing the social sciences and health together for their mutual benefit and for the public good. International activities carried on at a greatly increased tempo have made obvious the need to understand the other fellow if international educational exchange and technical cooperation are to be successful, not to mention international military operations. The public's expectation of scientific miracles has led to geometric expansion of funds to support research. Greater public sophistication about things medical, while helping the physician with the health education of his patients, has also impelled the physician himself to carry on this education in a more sophisticated way. Expansion of health insurance and the introduction of other third parties into the patient-physician relationship have introduced factors that make the relationship one which can best be studied by social science techniques. Finally, the rapidly rising costs of health care have aroused people to the point that they insist on having a stake in the matter and demand that the economics and other aspects of the problem be investigated.

It is unnecessary to document here the expansion of interest in health and the social sciences. However, one may point to the establishment in 1955 by the American Sociological Association of a section on medical sociology and note that there are several hundred names of both social scientists and health workers included on a roster of people with special interest in these fields.

Great credit is due the Russell Sage Foundation, The Milbank Fund, The Commonwealth Fund, The Ford Foundation, The Social Science Research Council, and others, for fostering this collaboration. Public health schools, medical schools and schools of nursing were assisted in adding social scientists to their teaching and research staffs; fellowships were provided for social scientists who wished to become more familiar with the health subculture; the publication of pertinent books was encouraged, and so forth. The National Institute of Mental Health also had an early interest in the enterprise, and has done much to strengthen it, as have other elements in the National Institutes of Health.

The field is ripe, then, for the harvest. This book represents a broad cross-section of part of the fund of information and concepts which are already at hand. A good deal of data, too, are included in the various chapters, much of it coming from the work of the authors themselves. Much more data will became available later on as the suggestions made here for further research are followed up. Certainly, one of the major reasons for the existence of the book is the conviction on the part of the editors that much more research is needed, and the hope that this book will help stimulate both health workers and social scientists to get on with the job.

The social science-health field is developing on so many fronts that it is hardly possible for a single person to present its many facets. Hence the device of inviting a number of authors, physicians, and social scientists, who are experts and investigators in their specialties, to write individual chapters. This book draws together a wealth of fresh material which will be important to the work of physicians, nurses, social workers, community organizers, and social scientists interested in health.

INTRODUCTION TO THE SECOND EDITION

John H. Knowles

We have reached a watershed in American medicine. In 1970, children died of diphtheria and malnutrition in the United States, while a man walked on the moon and another heart was transplanted. Science and technology are praised and blamed in the same breath. As we search for new knowledge, we are unable to use existing knowledge. From 1960 to 1970, expenditures on health in the United States more than doubled from 28 billion to 62 billion dollars. Yet health statistics belie our massive investment, leading many to question priorities, allocation of resources, and the effectiveness of our system of health services. Major public health problems have evolved from the nineteenth-century menace of infectious diseases to the degenerative and chronic diseases, accidents, drug ingestion and alcoholism, and mental illness of the twentieth century.

Rising expectations that health professionals will solve the problems are matched by rising costs. Massive governmental programs to relieve medical indigency find the level of medical indigency rising, as inflation in hospital and doctor bills far exceeds the general inflation. And public interest, frustration, and criticism grow apace with skyrocketing costs and expectations. Maldistribution of services; inefficient organization and questionable utilization of facilities, institutions, and health workers; increasingly critical shortages of manpower in the health field; the uncertain state of quality controls; the precarious and complex financing of health services and medical schools; the increasingly inefficient and grinding encounters of private and public interests; the conservative posture of "organized medicine" and "organized faculties" as regards changes in the delivery of health services and in medical curricula; the overwhelming need for and the rational uses of medical technology—these and many other problems demand a more effective articulation of the work of medicine with the demands and needs of the people. At the interface of the producers and consumers of health services there exists a rapidly increasing body of knowledge which can point the way to improve services and the resolution of critical conflicts. It is the knowledge contained within the social sciences, in this case called medical sociology.

The social sciences have been underemphasized in medical education in favor of the biological and physical sciences. One must ask whether or not the medical intellect functions only or even best on solely a foundation of natural science. Certainly it is true that those who plan a career in medical research must be knowledgeable about the life and physical sciences. But are mathematics and nuclear physics necessary to the successful practice of medicine? Can intellectual development suitable for a doctor be developed other than through the study of the physical and biological sciences? Why did Virchow say that medicine is a social science and politics is nothing but medicine on a large scale? Why did L. J. Henderson refer to the practice of medicine as "applied sociology"? Could it be that man is, indeed, a social as well as biological animal? Is there *social*, as well as biological ease and disease? And can dis-ease in one system give rise to dis-ease in the other? The answers are obvious.

I believe that medicine is a social science as well as a physical and biological science and that it needs the social sciences and the effects of their study as never before in the history of man.

Why the underemphasis of the social sciences in medical school? Not enough time in an already overcrowded curriculum? The "nonscientific" nature of their results? Perhaps it is all these reasons but just as important has been the complete segregation of schools of public health from the mainstream of medicine. Such schools do utilize the social sciences when considering the subjects of medical administration and the formulation, organization, and implementation of public health programs. Quite clearly, human attitudes, beliefs, and values play a determining role in the utilization of health services by the recipient public as well as in the implementation of programs by the purveying members of the health profession. Sociological research in medical care has given us invaluable information in many spheres. A brief listing of such studies would include the analysis of health wants and needs of communities; the influence of prepaid insurance programs on the utilization of health services; the dynamics of solo versus the group practice of medicine; role expectations amongst the various categories of health workers including doctors, nurses, social workers, dieticians, and medical scientists; the influence of social and economic class on the receipt and utilization of services; the evaluation of types of organizations designed to give comprehensive, continuing medical care in ambulatory clinics; the internal organization of the hospital with its paradoxical arrangements of authority and responsibility; the public's attitude toward the general hospital, the mental institution, the public health unit, and so on; the assessment of medical care programs for special population groups such as the medically indigent, dependents of military personnel, and the chronic and mentally ill; the effect of cultural determinants on the utilization of health service; and the recruitment, development, organization, and retention of health personnel.

Clearly, the results of such studies have tremendous implications for all of us interested in the health of our communities, whether we be the professional purveyors or the nonexpert recipients of medical care. The rational organization, distribution, and utilization of limited and costly health resources is of central importance. The rationalization of the behavior of doctors, nurses, administrators, patients, and so on should facilitate the goal of high-quality medical care for all the people.

I am perplexed and fascinated with the problem—or phenomenon—of why such intellectual activity is *not* a much larger and integral part of all medical schools' programs of teaching and research. The medical school curriculum accelerates the constricting effect of premedical education by its virtually complete emphasis on a foundation of biological science during the first two years. The opportunity still exists to study medicine from the viewpoint of the social sciences, but it is not seized. The history of medicine—its people, its institutions, and its social setting—is neglected, as are the political science, the cultural anthropology, and the economics of medicine. The student is relentlessly forced to focus on the individual doctor-patient relation and the science of disease as objects, and his own subjective self-understanding and his understanding of the world around him flags. At the end of four years he is a highly individualistic person cloaked with the charismatic robes of the profession, trained to take immediate action with the individual patient and to expect immediate rewards, with his knowledge firmly grounded in science.

The primary purpose of medical education—that is, to understand disease and to be able to comprehend and manage the problems of sick people from the perspective of biological science—has been fulfilled. But the broader issues of the physician's place and problems in the world at large have been neglected. The world of the health profession and its institutions—the givers and the receivers of care—has been left undescribed and unstudied. The social environment surrounding the sick person and its effects on the causation and/or course of disease is virtually unknown.

Why has this happened? Is the launching pad already too crowded with the physical and biological sciences to permit room for the social sciences? Is the inherently utilitarian nature of the social sciences incompatible with the truly scientific nature of present-day medical education? Do the social sciences really qualify as science, i.e., hard factual knowledge concerning predictable and reproducible natural phenomena?

Some of the confusion surrounding the social sciences should be dispelled. Popularly when one speaks of the social sciences, several points of view are conjured up in confused minds, which hinder rational consideration. These are (1) the confusion of the social science of medicine with *socialized* medicine and socialism and the belief that social scientists advocate socialized medicine, particularly true of elements of the medical profession and the AMA; (2) the quaint and misguided belief that knowledge of medical social science is designed somehow to make the student more "humane," sympathetic, and tactful; (3) the idea that the intellectual development of the medical student would be subverted and hindered by an overloading of vocational subjects with the notion that *medical* economics concerns itself mainly with the costs of starting an office practice and the pricing of drugs and is taught so that the student will be able to handle his *own* financial business; (4) the belief that social science, like social work, is concerned only with the impoverished, illiterate, and uneducated, in short, the disadvantaged individual; (5) the peculiar insistence that the same paradigm of evaluation be applied to the social sciences that is used in the biological and physical sciences, and the resulting hesitation of biologists to accept social sciences as "science," (the Hawthorne effect is used widely in this context); and finally (6) the confused idea that the study of traditional psychiatry includes the social sciences.

The idea of control and power over human behavior, with improvement guaranteed, as a result of social science study has been flagged, and I can do no better than to quote from a contemporary critic who notes the changeless hope that individuals can be guided for their own good by science when he says:

> The . . . dangerous superstition abroad today is that if behavioral science did progress our problems could be solved. This plausible proposition is fraught with calamity. Our so-called problems are due in part to the willfulness, stupidity, greed, and fears of men; in part also to the presence in life of real choices and hence of ineducable conflicts! Washington in 1774 was not willful, stupid, greedy, or afraid; he simply preferred independence and was a problem to the British. He did not need to be cured or saved, but satisfied—like his opponents. How could behavioral science have helped—and on which side?[1]

One should state here that the doctor, like Washington, prefers independence and seems to have become, at least collectively, a problem to the United States government, as he has at times to the governments of Belgium, Italy, Great Britain, and Saskatchewan.

[1] Jacques Barzun, *Science: The Glorious Entertainment* (New York, Harper & Row, Publishers 1964), p. 186.

Barzun sounds his final note of judgment with the following blast:

> The social sciences today have yet to show one universal or controlling 'law,' one unit of measurement, one exactly plotted universal variable, or one invariant relation. The ologies in their latest avatar are not so much young as unborn. I am of course speaking of the social sciences as quantitative and predictive disciplines having general truth, not of the local descriptions and statistics found in sociology, economics, anthropology, and psychology which were well-advanced in these ways as far back as 1890.[2]

Barzun calls the social sciences "not a pseudo-science, . . . but an *after science*."

All of these criticisms are important and should be understood by those who hope for the establishment of social science in medical education, if only to meet each criticism and either do away with it or do something about it. The arguments surrounding utility, pragmatism, and improvement in human behavior can be met simply. If the health profession understands as much of its history, economy, political science, social psychology, cultural anthropology, and behavioral psychology as is available, at least part of the behavior of doctors, patients, politicians, and so on can be understood, and rational choices for action or inaction can be taken on the basis of understanding through knowledge. Perhaps short-term, vested interests can be overcome more often by long-range decisions (or ideas, which ultimately are more powerful than vested interests) in the public, or over-all interest through the moral suasion of knowledge. Where there is ignorance, there is mischief. I must add, however, that I am still unable to answer in every instance, Barzun's question of which side is right in the struggle for power. I am convinced that "the local descriptions and statistics found in sociology, economics, anthropology, and psychology" are central to the work of medicine and should be a part of the intellectual development of the doctor. The fact that it is not "science" and will not necessarily result in better behavior disturbs me not one whit. I do believe that better understanding of this body of knowledge *will* help improve health services. I also believe (to paraphrase Brandeis and Santayana) that one page of history is worth a volume of logic and that he who knows no history is doomed to relive it. I also tend to agree with Keynes, who is quoted by Paul Samuelson in his textbook of economics, that

> The ideas of economists and political philosophers, both when they are right and when they are wrong, are more powerful than is commonly understood. Indeed, the world is ruled by little else. Practical men, who believe themselves to be exempt from any intellectual influences, are usually the slaves of some defunct economist.[3]

[2] Ibid., p. 185.

[3] Paul A. Samuelson, *Economics*, 6th ed. (New York: McGraw-Hill Book Company, 1964), p. 12.

Can anyone argue today that the health profession, along with its various institutions, is not being ruled by the ideas of economists and political philosophers? Is it not possible that the medical profession could play a larger, more constructive role in its future if it at least understood the issues and arguments?

Perhaps the crux of the situation is the necessity of bring the medical school and medical education back into the university, where the other university disciplines, and particularly the social sciences, can be used as powerful research tools in medicine and will be available for the intellectual development of the medical student. These needs for the social sciences are not peculiar to medical education. The graduate schools of business, law, education, and theology are also recognizing the need for a more complete approach to their highly specialized and vocational pursuits. They recognize the need for knowledge of human behavior and the social sciences for two reasons: (1) to increase the understanding of one's self and the professional socioeconomic system in which one works and (2) to understand better the objects of one's professional work, be they patients, clients, employees, or students. More truly university work will further the aims of a true university education, and the social science disciplines can add much to the perspective of the student and to the development of knowledge in specialized areas.

The *Handbook of Medical Sociology* achieves these ends admirably. It can be used to enlarge the understanding of all who work in the health field. It will also be useful to the experts of other disciplines. It is such a book that will assure medical sociology the important position it deserves in the medical curriculum.

CONTRIBUTORS TO THIS EDITION

RONALD M. ANDERSEN is Research Associate and Assistant Professor in the Center for Health Administration Studies, University of Chicago.

ODIN W. ANDERSON is Director and Professor in the Center for Health Administration Studies, University of Chicago.

EMIL BERKANOVIC is Assistant Research Sociologist, Survey Research Center, and Assistant Professor in Residence, School of Public Health, University of California at Los Angeles.

HOWARD S. BECKER is Professor in the Department of Sociology, Northwestern University.

SAMUEL W. BLOOM is Professor of Sociology in Community Medicine at the Mount Sinai School of Medicine of The City University of New York.

JOHN A. CLAUSEN is Professor in the Department of Sociology at the University of California at Berkeley.

SYDNEY H. CROOG is Professor in the School of Dental Medicine and the School of Medicine, University of Connecticut Health Center.

BRUCE K. ECKLAND is Associate Professor in the Department of Sociology at the University of North Carolina.

JACK ELINSON is Professor and Director, Division of Sociomedical Sciences, School of Public Health and Administrative Medicine, Columbia University.

HOWARD E. FREEMAN is Morse Professor of Urban Studies at The Florence Heller Graduate School for Advanced Studies in Social Welfare, Brandeis University, and Sociologist, Russell Sage Foundation.

ELIOT FREIDSON is Professor of Sociology at New York University.

BLANCHE GEER is Professor, Department of Sociology and Anthropology, Northeastern University.

SAXON GRAHAM is Professor, Departments of Sociology and Preventive Medicine, State University of New York at Buffalo.

PATRICIA KENDALL is Professor and Chairman of the Department of Sociology, Queens College of The City University of New York.

STANLEY H. KING is Director of Research and Lecturer, University Health Services, Harvard University.

JOHN H. KNOWLES is President of the Rockefeller Foundation.

HUGH R. LEAVELL, is Consultant to the Ford Foundation and the Indian Government, New Delhi, India.

SOL LEVINE is Chairman and Professor of the Department of Behavioral Sciences, School of Hygiene and Public Health, The Johns Hopkins University.

HANS O. MAUKSCH is Professor of Sociology, Department of Sociology and Department of Community Health and Medical Practice, University of Missouri.

STEPHEN J. MILLER is Associate Dean, Harvard Medical School, Harvard University.

GEORGE G. READER is Professor, Department of Medicine, The New York Hospital-Cornell Medical Center.

LEO G. REEDER is Professor of Public Health and Professor of Sociology, University of California at Los Angeles.

GEORGE ROSEN is Professor in the Department of History of Science and Medicine, School of Medicine, Yale University.

IRWIN T. SANDERS is Professor and Chairman of the Department of Sociology and Anthropology, Boston University.

OZZIE G. SIMMONS is Associate Program Director, Ford Foundation.

LAWRENCE SMITH, JR., is Research Assistant Professor, Department of Pediatrics and Community Medicine, School of Medicine, Temple University.

EDWARD A. SUCHMAN (deceased) was Professor in the Department of Public Health Practice, Graduate School of Public Health, University of Pittsburgh.

BERT E. SWANSON is Professor of Political Science and Urban Studies, University of Florida.

DONNA VER STEEG is a graduate student, Department of Sociology, University of California at Los Angeles.

WALTER I. WARDWELL is Professor of Sociology at the University of Connecticut.

PAUL E. WHITE is Associate Professor in the Department of Behavioral Sciences, School of Public Health, The Johns Hopkins University.

RICHARD H. WILLIAMS is Assistant to the Director for Special Projects, National Institute of Mental Health.

ROBERT N. WILSON is Professor and Chairman of the Department of Mental Health, School of Public Health, The University of North Carolina.

WESLEY O. YOUNG is Professor of Community Dentistry, Department of Community Dentistry, University of Alabama at Birmingham.

HANDBOOK OF MEDICAL SOCIOLOGY

CONTRIBUTIONS OF SOCIOLOGY TO MEDICINE

Patricia L. Kendall and George G. Reader

Sociology has already contributed much to medicine and gives promise of making an even greater contribution in the future. For a number of years it has had a considerable impact through those social scientists who have "walked the wards" with physicians and nurses, those who have interviewed patients, and those who have taught medical students. Now, however, it has developed a distinct body of knowledge and even added to general social theory. It has, in fact, reached a position where it can contribute substantially to decision making in medicine. Each chapter in this volume deals with the contributions of sociology—and to a lesser extent, other behavioral sciences—to a particular aspect of medicine. Among these are the social factors involved in illness, the behavior of patients with regard to illness, the medical profession and related health workers, and different types of medical organizations.

CRITERIA FOR A CONTRIBUTION

When work in any scientific field is considered for application to practice, the question is asked implicitly: What good is it to the practitioners? Engineering research, for instance, presumably devotes itself to formulating basic principles; development is concerned with the application of these principles to bridge construction, or automotive propulsion, or the generation of electricity. Development is application of basic principles in practice, but it also contains the element of design—the innovative application of fundamental principles. Design in engineering is in many ways akin to the "art" of a practice such as medicine, an individualistic and intuitive approach to the solution of some practical and immediate problem. The style of the performer makes his application of principles individualistic; his internalized knowledge, based on experience, makes it intuitive. Occasionally, engineering development as well as medical practice results in the formulation of new basic principles or the modification of old ones. Often, in fact, the problems encountered by the practitioner determine the strategy of investigation. Then the dichotomy between research and development becomes less clear. Scientists do more than discover principles, and practitioners do more than merely apply them. Research is inseparable from good practice; each contributes to the other.

Social science research contributions, by their very nature, deal with human relationships: interpersonal or intergroup relationships, individual personality differences, the perceptions and reactions of people to their internal as well as to their external milieu. Social science does not deal with pathological lesions, nor with alterations in biological structure, nor with physiological function, nor with the invasive effects of microorganisms; it concerns itself with people who are well or ill, not with the disease process itself. On the other hand, it most specifically has to do with society—with people living in groups and with the structure, function, and change or action of such groups.

Medicine has at times been called a social science, but of course it is not that any more than it is a physical science. Medicine is a synthesis of many disciplines; it is essentially the practice of knowledge and skills and attitudes helpful in the care of the sick. There is a certain body of knowledge unique to this activity, which might be termed a science of medicine and which grows by accretion from applications of the physical, natural, and social sciences. Physicians with training in these other disciplines may add to knowledge in the basic sciences as well as in the applied; by the same token, other scientists may contribute to knowledge in medicine and in their own field as well. Both, as they provide principles on which practice is based, can modify techniques of practice and help to build a "science of medicine."

In order to understand the nature of a contribution in this field, however, it is important to examine the field from the point of view of the practitioner. What is the body of knowledge unique to medical practice? It may perhaps best be considered in terms of the interests of the health professional. He concerns himself with the prevention, diagnosis, prognosis, and treatment of illness in individuals if he is a clinician; in communities if he is a public health officer. *Prevention* implies an understanding of causation—both a knowledge of specific etiology and a recognition of circumstances that promote or detract from good health. *Diagnosis* is the identification and categorization of clinical or epidemiological entities. For generations the clinical entity has been the organizing principle which has directed the clinician's activity. It ranges from the syndrome (a recognizable constellation of signs and symptoms) to a more or less fully understood disease process. Sometimes, as in many dermatological conditions, it is merely a descriptive name; often, as in the infectious diseases, it indicates an understanding of the cause as well as of the course of the illness. *Prognosis* is the prediction of outcome in an illness. It implies a knowledge of the natural history of a disease and the probable response of the particular individual or group to the disease process. *Treatment*, or management, includes rehabilitation and requires knowledge of the various factors that may modify the natural course of the illness—from specific drugs and physical agents to the salubrious effects of encouragement, support, optimism, rewards, and a beneficial environment. In order to be considered useful contributions by the medical practitioner, social science findings must, therefore, describe more fully and accurately these phases of his dealings with health and illness, or they must increase his ability to predict what he will find as to cause, type of diagnosis, outcome, or success of treatment, or they must modify his methods of practice in some useful way.

CONTRIBUTIONS OF SOCIOLOGY

It would be needlessly repetitious, as well as hopelessly cumbersome, to try to summarize here all of the specific contributions which are described and analyzed in the chapters that follow. Instead, we shall attempt to provide a broad overview within which these contributions can be located. To achieve this, we shall start with a useful proposal made in an earlier phase of medical sociology. We shall then go on; first, to indicate how this initial suggestion was refined, and second, how recent sociological concerns have made for increasingly sophisticated contributions to medicine.

Some years ago, Robert Straus proposed the helpful distinction between sociology *in* medicine and sociology *of* medicine [93]. Sociology *in* medicine may be described as the application of sociological concepts, knowledge, and techniques in efforts to clarify medical and social-psychological problems in which the medical profession and its allied workers are interested. In this instance, sociological knowledge supplements medical knowledge, in order to find solutions to what are essentially medical problems.

Those concerned with the sociology *of* medicine, on the other hand, raise questions about medical workers, their institutions and organizations, and their relations with others in their orbits of activity, in an effort to clarify what are essentially sociological questions. In this instance, application of a sociological perspective to the medical world parallels the sociological examination of other areas of activity in our society, such as business organizations, educational institutions, and the like.[1]

[1] Helmut Schelsky has suggested that these two categories be paralleled by their reverse forms: medicine in sociology and medical aspects of sociology [86]. In the first instance, he suggests that medical variables be introduced to help explain sociological phenomena. He cites as possible examples the notion that investigators carrying out community studies include, as part of the research team, persons who would be able to assess the health status of community residents, or that the mental health of individuals exhibiting antisocial attitudes be examined.

Schelsky suggests that the medical study of sociology would consider medical correlates of particular kinds of sociological work.

Despite the utility of this broad distinction, the proliferation of studies in the field of medical sociology made it desirable, almost from the beginning, to develop a number of subcategories. A first step in this direction followed soon after Straus' article appeared, and subsequent refinements have continued [51, 54, 97].

We propose that this elaborated scheme can serve as a useful framework within which to review and illustrate various subclasses of studies. In the course of this review, we shall emphasize those instances in which new kinds of studies or new sociological interests have led to advances in the nature of sociology's contributions to medicine.

I. SOCIOLOGY IN MEDICINE

Sociology in medicine has been concerned with two distinct, although interrelated, topics.

A. Ecology and Etiology of Disease

Even before sociology was recognized as a separate branch of inquiry, investigators studied how the incidence and prevalence of illnesses were related to the location of individuals in the society. For example, in an article on the "Historical Background of Industrial and Occupational Disease," Henry Sigerist points out that as early as ancient Egypt and Greece, there were accounts of the special illnesses and disabilities associated with particular occupations, and that such studies were undertaken more systematically in the eighteenth and nineteenth centuries [89].

As sociology developed, its practitioners became more active in the study of the distribution and determinants of disease in men (epidemiology). The number of such studies carried out in the last several decades runs into the hundreds. Some have been rather broad ranging, seeking to ascertain the health problems and medical experiences of nationwide samples of the population [10, 100]. Others have focused on the ecological distribution of particular diseases and the social factors related to their incidence. Thus, there have been numerous studies dealing with coronary disease, cancer, peptic ulcer, and so on. (See Chapter 3 in this volume. See also [13].)

By now there can be little question as to the correlation between social factors and the incidence of a wide variety of illnesses. But one thorny problem has remained. This concerns the directionality of the relationship that is found. In some cases, on common-sense grounds if on no others, the question seems easily answered. For instance, if it is found that members of a particular ethnic group are especially susceptible to a blood disease, it would be difficult to argue that the blood condition had led to ethnic status. There are other cases, however, where the cause and effect sequence is not so clear.

For example, it is a well-established fact that there is a correlation between social class and mental illness or, at least, some forms of mental illness. But how does this correlation come about? Is it the case that individuals who undergo the hardships and frustrations of being in a lower-class position develop psychological difficulties? Or,

---

For example, investigators working in applied fields may become psychologically disturbed by the possibility that their findings will be used to the detriment of the groups they are studying. Or participant observers who have disguised their identities may develop anxieties because of the constant need to maintain a pretense about themselves.

does the relationship come about via the opposite route? Do individuals with mental problems become increasingly unable to retain jobs, to take care of themselves and their families, to behave in acceptable middle-class ways, so that gradually, whatever their initial class position, they tend to become déclassé? The Dohrenwends have reviewed epidemiological studies on the relationship between social class and mental illness with these questions in mind [17]. Even though their findings were not entirely conclusive, their efforts to disentangle cause and effect represent real progress in studies of the ecology and etiology of disease. (See also [49]).

B. Variations in Attitude and Behavior Regarding Health and Illness

A second major area that falls under the general rubric of sociology in medicine deals with variations in response to and behavior regarding problems of health and illness. Relevant here are such diverse topics as public information about illness, definitions of who is ill and who not, conceptions among different parts of the population as to what their health needs are, and their differential utilization of various kinds of medical facilities.

Some of the recent contributions which sociology has made to an understanding of such variations grow out of earlier traditions in medical sociology and, thus, represent continuities in sociological theory and research; others can best be characterized as a reflection of reoriented interest in topics that have long concerned sociologists but which now bring with them newly emerging theoretical interests.

We shall confine ourselves to these two types of contributions. Doing so has the advantage of providing a focus for our discussion; it has the obvious disadvantage that we shall be forced to omit a number of important topics and studies.

1. *Sociological continuities: the case of social class.* Among the earliest studies in medical sociology were several that stressed the importance of social class in information about and attitudes toward health and disease, as well as in the use made of available health resources. Perhaps the classic study of this kind was that carried out by Koos in Regionville [59]. He found large and consistent class differences in knowledge about disease, in attitudes toward health care, in the number of families claiming to have a family doctor, and in the use of nonmedical personnel for advice in health matters. Much the same results were replicated a decade later in a nationwide survey carried out by the National Opinion Research Center [21].

Since those early days, similar studies have been conducted, sometimes in different settings but nonetheless leading to essentially the same conclusions. Rather than review what must be, by now, rather well-known literature, we propose here to highlight some of the new developments in this continuing tradition. Essentially, these developments have involved refinements in the processes linking social class to the several dependent variables under consideration here.

We begin with the relationship between social class and attitudes toward and information about illness. A study by Suchman and his colleagues uncovered familiar kinds of findings: The blue-collar workers in their sample were considerably less well informed than white-collar workers about the symptomatology of disease and considerably more likely to express skepticism about different aspects of medical care [82]. Having anticipated these results, the investigators were prepared to go further, and to test an important possible interpretation of the relationship. They stated their hypothesis as follows:

> Our original position held that blue-collar workers are more alienated than white-collar workers from the large-scale modern medical care system. Almost all of the findings presented above are consistent with this formulation. It now becomes necessary to learn whether or not those blue-collar workers who are more generally oriented toward "sophistication" and are more liberated from their primary groups also differ in their attitudes and information toward the sociomedical factors previously discussed. Our hypothesis is that the more "cosmopolitan" blue-collar workers will score more positively on the sociomedical factors than will the more "parochial" blue-collar workers.

So that they could test their hypothesis, the investigators built into their survey instrument a series of questions which enabled them to assess the "cosmopolitan" or "parochial" orientations of their subjects. Among these were such items as the following: "In my family we think the old-time customs and traditions are important"; "Almost all of my friends are people I grew up with"; "I prefer to deal in stores where clerks are the same kind of people as we are"; and also several measures of religiosity.

By and large, the expectations of the investigators were supported by the data. Although the intervening variable in which they were interested did not do away completely with the original class differences they had observed, it did emerge as an important factor in the information and attitudes of the workers they studied.

Attitudes toward illness may be extended to include concerns with one's own physical well-being. Here again, some recent work suggests that such preoccupations with sickness provide a useful way of explaining or accounting for the epidemiological findings that there is more illness among the lower social strata.[2]

For example, Levine, in a carefully conducted study which took into account the availability of medical facilities, concluded that members of the lower class worry more about their health status, and "are more unnerved when confronted with the [possibility of serious disease]" [61]. Rosengren, in a small-scale qualitative study of obstetrical patients, found that those in the lower strata were more likely to define pregnancy as an illness and to develop the concerns and self-attitudes appropriate to a sick person [83]. Finally, Kadushin contends that although there is very little association between social class and becoming ill, the lower classes feel more sick and are more concerned about illness [48].

Do these negative feelings about their physical well-being on the part of the lower classes become translated into action? That is, do the lower socioeconomic groups make greater use of available medical resources? Most of the evidence is to the contrary.[3] As we have already seen, Koos found that the lower classes were con-

[2] Elements of cultural relativity seem to enter here. In a survey carried out about a decade ago dealing with the attitudes of French people toward their health and toward the medical care they received, it was found that farmers were least likely and free professionals most likely to say that, at one time or another, they had worried about being afflicted with a serious illness [46].

[3] Ann Cartwright, in her study of the medical situation in Great Britain, reports inconsistent findings: in the youngest age group, working-class patients made a somewhat larger number of visits to their general practitioners than did members of the middle class; in the middle age group, there was virtually no class difference; in the oldest age group, middle-class patients saw

siderably less likely to have a family doctor. More recently, a study by Hyman has shown that the rate of untreated illness (of which the potential patient was aware) was definitely higher among those classified as having low economic status [45].

Here, we are less interested in the statistical relationship between class position and the utilization of medical resources than we are in understanding how that relationship comes about. There have been a limited number of sociological contributions to such understanding. For example, Rosenblatt and Suchman have offered a number of interesting, although by now not very startling, speculative answers to this question [81]. They suggest, for instance, that blue-collar workers in urban slums encounter a number of barriers which discourage their use of existing medical services. Among these are language problems, cultural traditions which predispose the prospective patient to seek help from medically unorthodox sources, the impersonality with which patients are treated in many clinic settings, the inconveniences they encounter, and so on. (In a later section of this chapter we shall consider some recent developments in systems of medical care which may help to eliminate some of these problems.)

In his more systematic study, Hyman sought to encompass a range of these barriers in the notion of "medical-social discontent." His measure of this was based on the frequency with which the subjects voiced complaints about the clinic in which they were being seen, physicians in general, and the social quality of the neighborhood in which they lived. Hyman expected such discontent to be more prevalent among those with lower economic status, and it was—to a substantial degree. (See [45], Table 3.) More important for our present purposes, Hyman was able to show that it was an intervening variable, linking socioeconomic status and untreated illness. When it was introduced as a "test factor," the original relationship virtually disappeared. (See [45], Table 4.)

2. *Reoriented sociological concerns: the cases of deviance, labeling, and stigma*. Sociologists have long been interested in deviance—sometimes referred to as social problems or social pathology. (One reason for this is that the ability to identify the kind of behavior which is socially defined as deviant helps specify the norms which are expected to guide the behavior of the "normal" members of society.) Reflecting this interest, Parsons has consistently characterized the sick role as a form of deviance [74]. (We shall not consider Parsons' treatment of the sick role further, in part because it has been extensively discussed elsewhere and in part because it is ably analyzed in the chapter by Wilson and Bloom in this volume.) But Parsons' strong interests in positive normative patterns and mechanisms of social control have led him to deemphasize the elements of deviance involved in patients' assumption of the sick role.

It was not until recently that sociologists have returned to and elaborated the relevance of deviance to illness and, by extension, to problems of disability. Among the foremost treatments are those by Freidson [26] and Mechanic [67]. A review of some of this material, while necessarily abbreviated and oversimplified, may help to clarify some emerging contributions of sociology to the field of medicine.

their doctors considerably more often than did members of the working class. See [12], Table 10, p. 34.

Because, in our opinion, Freidson's article is especially provocative, we shall focus on it. (Even so, space limitations require us to deal only with selected portions of his discussion.) He starts with three basic assumptions.[4] First, deviance

> is an *imputed* condition, and the imputation may or may not rest on physical reality. Not all handicapped people are called handicapped or act like handicapped people. [Freidson justifies this assumption on the fact that what is considered deviant varies under different historical and cultural conditions.]
>
> Second, insofar as deviance constitutes a role, it implies a process of labeling and therefore the likely existence of a set of epithets connected with it. . . .
>
> Third, insofar as deviance is secondary, it is likely to be generally recognized as a "social problem," and thus, in complex societies such as ours, there will be connected with it a set of offices or organizations devoted to identifying and dealing with it—agents of social control. . . . [26]

According to Freidson, the implications of these assumptions, and especially the second and third, are that deviant roles may actually be created. The individual identified as a deviant may not consider himself such to begin with. But once he has been so labeled, and once control agencies bring him within their orbit so that they can cure or help him, he may gradually adopt their designation of him as a deviant and accept the stigma that goes with it.

Freidson's objective in raising these issues is on two levels. First, as a compassionate human being, he is apprehensive about the creation of "damaged identities." Second, and more germane to our discussion here, he is concerned lest agencies charged with the responsibility of rehabilitation inadvertently do more harm than good. Although he makes no concrete suggestions on how to prevent this, he apparently hopes that his analysis will lead to greater awareness and gradual alleviation of the problems that he sees.

In a recent paper, Hyman reports findings which have direct implications for medical practice [44]. When patients feel themselves stigmatized because of their illness, not only do they experience psychological difficulties but also their medical progress is adversely affected. Hyman studied 110 stroke patients who subsequently were treated in a rehabilitation center. He found that patients who believed themselves stigmatized differed from patients without such self-images in three significant ways: Whatever the actual severity of their disability, the stigmatized patients were less motivated to undergo physical rehabilitation; they manifested less functional improvement during rehabilitation; and, following discharge from the rehabilitation center, they were less likely to resume the activities which had been a part of their normal routines prior to their strokes.

II. THE SOCIOLOGY OF MEDICINE

As we turn from sociology in medicine to the second major branch in our framework, that which deals with the sociology of medicine, we find ourselves concerned with quite different problems. Now we are dealing with questions which belong within the traditions of the sociology of the profes-

[4] Throughout his discussion, Freidson refers to a large number of monographs and articles, not all of which are familiar in traditional medical sociology. The interested reader should consult the citations in Freidson's article, as well as several works by Becker [1, 2] and Goffman [34, 35].

sions and organizational sociology. Relevant topics include recruitment into and training for the profession, the organization of the profession, and, finally, its relations to external pressures and agencies.

In approaching these topics, we have adopted a fairly arbitrary ground rule, which needs to be spelled out. Recent considerations of the medical profession have included in their purview groups which do not have the M.D. degree. The present volume follows this trend. (See, for example, Chapters 9, 10, and 11.) For a number of reasons, not the least of which is the enormous amount of pages that would be required to analyze recent sociological contributions to all professions and occupations engaged in the field of health, we have chosen to focus only on physicians, and the ways sociology has contributed to an understanding of their profession.

A. The Recruitment of Physicians

In recent years a number of forces have impinged on the medical profession to make changes in the number and kind of doctors that are produced. These pressures for change in recruitment policies are based on two sets of facts: (1) There is a serious shortage of doctors in the United States and (2) several social groups are markedly underrepresented in the medical profession at the present time.

As Rashi Fein has demonstrated in his monograph, the population of this country has grown tremendously over the last several decades, while the production of doctors has remained fairly constant [20]. In addition, compared with the situation in the past, the public is now more affluent, better educated, and more likely to be covered by some form of third-party health insurance. As a result, the demand for physicians' services has sharply increased.

Two other trends—in the medical profession itself—have contributed to the public's experience that there are not now enough doctors and that, consequently, more should be produced. One of these is the increasing inclination of young doctors to go into specialized fields. As Stevens [92] and Kendall [58], among others, have shown, the proportion of young physicians seeking certification by one or another of the specialty boards has greatly increased over the last several decades, with a parallel decline in the number of men going into general practice. One effect of this is that physicians who, in earlier decades, treated "ordinary" patient problems are no longer available. As Fein points out in his analysis, the number of physicians who might be considered potential family doctors (pediatricians, internists, and general practitioners) declined from 94 per 100,000 in 1931 to 50 per 100,000 in 1965. See [20], Table III-4.

A related development has been the marked growth in medical and health-related research that has taken place over the last two decades. According to a report of the National Institutes of Health, expenditures for such research totaled $148 million in 1950; in 1961, the corresponding figure was $890 million [77]. And according to an even more recent report [8], approximately $1,100 million was appropriated to the research institutes and divisions of NIH in 1970.

While the amount of money spent on research is probably not a completely accurate indication of the number of people engaged in it, there is undoubtedly a close correspondence. To the extent that energies which might be devoted to patient care are siphoned off into research, it can be said that medical research, however necessary and meritorious, contributes to the doctor shortage.

There are two main ways of responding to these pressures to produce more doctors. One is by opening new medical schools; the other is by increasing the enrollment of students in existing schools. At the present time both types of change are under way.

The creation of a new medical school is a tremendously complex undertaking. Not only are large sums of money involved, but faculties have to be assembled, curricula developed, and appropriate clinical facilities arranged for. The magnitude of these problems always leads to lengthy debate and discussion.[5] Nonetheless, despite the thorniness of these problems, a number of new medical schools have opened in the last few years, and others are now being developed. These include schools in New Mexico; at Hershey, Pennsylvania; in East Lansing, Michigan; in Lexington, Kentucky; in New York City and Stony Brook, New York; in Hartford, Connecticut; in New Brunswick, New Jersey; and in Providence, Rhode Island.

The second major way to turn out a larger number of doctors is to increase the number of students accepted by existing schools. There is obvious concern that any such enlargement not compromise current standards of medical education. To guard against this, much money would have to be spent on the expansion of classroom and laboratory space, on the addition of new faculty members, and so on.[6]

Sociologists are not renowned as fund-raisers. But once the money necessary to build new medical schools or to enlarge existing ones is found, sociologists can join medical educators in planning how these funds can be most effectively used. In a small but growing number of instances this has taken place. Perhaps the prototypical case is that of Robert Straus. When Willard was invited to set up a new medical school at the University of Kentucky in Lexington, he brought with him a number of people with whom he had previously worked at Syracuse; among these was Straus. As one of the few who has described his experiences in the role of consulting sociologist, Straus reports that he participated in designing the hospital wards and clinics, as well as in planning the curriculum [94, 95, 96]. More recently, Bloom at Mount Sinai and Coser at the State University of New York at Stony Brook have played similar roles.

The medical profession is facing other pressures in connection with efforts to alleviate the doctor shortage. These deal with questions concerning the kinds of individuals who should be trained to become members of the medical profession. There are some who believe that the prospective student's preparation and intellectual qualifications for a career in medicine should be the main, if not the only, considerations. There are others—and their numbers seem to be growing—who argue that special efforts should be made to recruit members of social groups which, up to now, have been underrepresented in the medical pro-

[5] At the time the Mount Sinai School of Medicine was being developed, it, in collaboration with the New York Academy of Sciences, sponsored a conference on many of these problems. The published proceedings of the conference give a good indication of the range of topics considered [71].

[6] For a recent discussion of some of these problems, see the paper by Rose [79], read before the 66th Annual Congress of Medical Education in February, 1970.

fession. Several such groups can be identified, but probably those which have received most attention are Negroes and women.

There can be little doubt that, at the present time, neither group is represented in the medical profession or among current medical students to a degree that approaches its representation in the total population. To cite some recent figures, of the 10,371 students who entered medical schools in the fall of 1969, 440 (4.2 percent) were black; moreover, blacks constitute only about 2 percent of the approximately 230,000 physicians currently practicing in the United States. And, in a study of women in medicine [63], it was found that, in recent years, women made up from 4 percent to 8 percent of the total student body in medical schools.

It would undoubtedly be an oversimplification to attribute these facts merely to racial prejudice or "male chauvinism." As a recent conference on Negroes in medicine reported [14], many black students are not well prepared for the requirements of most medical schools; those charged with the admission of students to the schools may feel, therefore, that, if poorly qualified black students are admitted, they will present the faculty with the twin challenges of *preparing* the students to undertake their medical studies at the same time that they are expected to be engaged in them. Schools are, accordingly, reluctant to admit such students. There is also the point that occupations other than medicine may offer more immediate rewards to the intelligent, well-educated black.

The case of women is somewhat different. Some women medical students and physicians, when faced with the conflicting demands of marriage and child rearing, either temporarily interrupt or totally abandon their medical careers. Or, if they practice, they may do so only on a part-time basis. (For relevant data, see [63], p. 179.) As a result, the medical schools may feel that the return on their investment in training women is insufficient.

But it is unlikely that these pressures to recruit more members of underrepresented social groups into the medical profession will abate. The question then is, can sociology help in any way to meet these pressures? Several such contributions seem possible, although they have not yet been achieved on any large scale. For example, in the last few years, a small number of programs designed to prepare Negro students for entrance into medical school have been set up. One of these, sponsored by the Josiah Macy Foundation, brings a group of fifteen or so black graduates of predominantly Negro colleges to a summer session on the campus of a liberal arts college such as Haverford or Oberlin; during the regular academic year, they either remain on these campuses or go on to similar colleges where they are offered a fifth year of college preparation. Other programs with similar objectives are located in medical schools—for example, the Albert Einstein School of Medicine and the Cornell Medical College.

Sociological research could contribute to the planning and evaluation of such programs. Their academic success would have to be evaluated by nonsociologists. But there are many aspects which lend themselves to sociological inquiry. For instance, do participants in such preparatory programs have unanticipated experiences? Do they consider themselves—and are they in fact—isolated and set apart from the "regular" students at the colleges? These students generally come from different socioeconomic backgrounds than the usual medical students; do they, as a result, have problems of adjustment once they reach medical school? Data on such questions could be used to modify and improve the programs and the kind of orientation they provide.

No concerted efforts have yet been made to bring more women into medicine. But it is likely that sociology can shed light on obstacles to the recruitment of women physicians, and can thereby contribute to an understanding of ways in which they can be used more effectively.

From the point of view of the women themselves, there is evidence that at the present time few women contemplate a career in medicine. Data on this point are provided in a study carried out by Alice Rossi among a sample of women who graduated from college in June, 1961 [84]. On the basis of their answers to a question on career goals, Rossi divided her sample into three categories: *homemakers,* who reported no career goals other than being a "housewife"; *traditionals,* whose long-range goals involved employment in fields in which women predominate—as elementary and secondary school teachers, nurses, social workers, secretaries, librarians, and so on; and *pioneers,* who aspire to careers in predominantly masculine fields—medicine, law, engineering, the natural sciences, and the like. According to Rossi's data, the homemakers made up approximately one-fifth of her sample and the traditionals nearly half, while the pioneers constituted only about 7 percent of the sample.

The origin of these career goals is not well understood. Undoubtedly, the family plays a major role. Rossi found, for example, that women college graduates attributed to their families virtually the same images of different careers that they themselves had [84]. High school and college counselors probably share some responsibility also.[7] But if more are to be attracted into medical careers, it will be important to study how and through what channels they develop their images of different fields of work.

However, as we have already suggested, it is not enough to persuade more women that medicine is an appropriate career for them. The medical schools must be convinced that training larger numbers of women is a worthwhile enterprise. This calls for still a different kind of inquiry. Here the focus would not be on attitudes, but on the possibility of new types of medical careers and new patterns of medical practice into which women could fit. Probably the medical profession will want to take the initiative in specifying the dimensions of these new patterns. But the experience of sociologists in analyzing professional activities under varied cultural and historical conditions can undoubtedly be useful in this connection.

B. The Training of Physicians

Pressures to increase the number of doctors and to modify existing patterns of recruitment come, by and large, from outside the profession. In contrast, pressures to alter current patterns of training seem to originate among physicians themselves. They focus on three aspects of medical education: Ways in which the *length* of training might be shortened; the new *settings* in which medical education can—and probably will—take place; and changes in the *content* of the training.

[7] See the chapters on "Career Guidance in High Schools" and "Counseling Pre-Meds" in [63].

Alternative ways of shortening the length of medical education have long been discussed, although they continue to be debated today. See [11]. In a recent article [73], the dean of a new medical school which has adopted a three-year curriculum, identifies the main possibilities. These are: "(1) reducing the calendar years in college to less than four, (2) reducing the calendar years spent in medical school to less than four, (3) elimination of the internship, and (4) decreasing the years spent in residency training."

Decisions regarding the adoption of any of these possibilities are properly the responsibility of medical educators. But sociological studies can help the educators anticipate possible reactions to proposed modifications in the length of medical training. For example, the second alternative—to reduce the amount of time spent in medical school—implies that blocks of time formerly devoted to particular courses or particular departments would have to be shortened or entirely eliminated from the curriculum. A study carried out some years ago in connection with a conference on clinical teaching provides data suggesting how such proposals might be responded to [52]. Heads of clinical departments in the medical schools belonging to the Association of American Medical Colleges and a sample of clinical teachers in the same departments were asked whether, in their view, there should be any change in the amount of time allotted to a variety of basic sciences, and, if so, whether this change should involve an increase or decrease in allotted time. Most of the clinicians recommended no change in connection with most of the basic sciences about which they were asked. But where changes were recommended, they seemed to reflect the vested interests of the clinicians. Thus, pathologists suggested, more often than did other clinicians, that more time be devoted to courses in pathology, while radiologists recommended, more frequently than other clinicians, that more time be allotted to courses in radiation biology. Along similar lines, surgeons were more likely than internists to recommend either that no change be made in the amount of time devoted to anatomy or that this time be increased. And psychiatrists, more than surgeons, favored increasing the amount of time allotted to courses in the behavioral sciences. On the basis of findings such as these, it seems unlikely that all medical educators will respond in a completely disinterested fashion to proposals to shorten the length of medical training.

Because university hospitals have only a limited number of positions for house officers (and because nonuniversity hospitals have a corresponding need for interns and residents), much graduate medical education now takes place in hospitals that are not closely affiliated with medical schools.

As new schools are developed and as existing schools expand in size, increasing needs for patients will undoubtedly bring about a closer liaison between medical schools and community hospitals.[8] It therefore becomes strategic to find out how the training which takes place in such institutions compares with that obtained in the traditional university hospital.

One sociological study was undertaken with such questions in mind. This was the Comparative Study of Interns and Residents, carried out between 1958 and 1965 at the Bureau of Ap-

[8] At the present time, although not yet developed into four-year schools, both the medical colleges of Michigan State and Brown Universities rely on community hospitals for the clinical training of their students.

plied Social Research, Columbia University. The project was a large-scale one, divided into several subparts, each of which involved a separate set of research techniques. Much attention was devoted to analyzing questionnaires obtained from more than 3,000 house officers working in a nationwide sample of 167 hospitals. Some of these hospitals were the major teaching units of the medical schools with which they were affiliated; others had some connection with a medical school but could not be considered university hospitals; the final group was not affiliated with any medical school.

The main thrust of the statistical analysis was to compare the learning experiences of house officers working in these different kinds of environments.[9] It was found, for example, that the house staff in closely affiliated hospitals were much more satisfied than their counterparts in unaffiliated hospitals with the opportunities for learning they found in their environments. (Significantly, though, there still was a fair amount of dissatisfaction among the men working in university hospitals.) At the same time, house officers in closely affiliated hospitals felt themselves and their work more highly visible to their colleagues; they experienced a greater degree of competitiveness; and so on.

Another major part of the study, involving a qualitative comparison of a university teaching hospital and a community hospital, was carried out by Mumford and is reported in her recently published book on interns [70]. Her findings also underscore the differences in the learning environments provided by these different kinds of settings. The intern in a university hospital is far down in the medical hierarchy, and therefore less likely to have an opportunity to exercise responsibility or to do more than carry out routine procedures; the patients he sees are more likely to be suffering from exotic "university-type" diseases, as they have been called; his role models are not so much practitioners of medicine as the research-oriented, cosmopolitan leaders of medical science.[10]

Because of growing needs for clinical facilities, community hospitals will almost certainly become the loci for increasing amounts of medical training. Sociological studies of the kind reviewed here point to some ways in which the learning environments they offer differ from those found in more traditional university hospitals. Whether these differences can, or should, be diminished is a matter of policy which medical educators will have to decide.

Medical educators and sociologists have a long tradition of collaboration on matters related to the content of medical training. (For an early statement of some of the features of such collaboration, see [38].) Again, it would not be appropriate here to review just what cooperative efforts have been made or what results have been obtained. (The article in this volume by Becker, Geer, and Miller does this. See also the extensive bibliography provided by Bloom in his review of the sociology of medical education [7].) We do however want to identify the different types of contributions which sociology has made to an understand-

[9] Some of the results of this statistical analysis are found in the following articles: [53, 55, 57]. Others are recorded in unpublished doctoral dissertations [43, 64, 78].

[10] A qualitative study of interns working in the Harvard Unit of Boston City Hospital has recently appeared [69]. While it is an interesting and insightful work, its lack of a comparative base limits its utility for the present issue of the kinds of medical training obtained in different medical settings.

ing of substantive aspects of medical education.

Collaboration has taken place on several levels. On one, the sociologist lends his technical expertise, generally his knowledge of how to carry out evaluation studies. Sometimes these studies are quite limited in scope—confined, perhaps, to the contents of a single course in medical school. In other instances, the evaluation studies are much broader. For example, during the 1950's especially, a number of medical schools undertook large-scale experiments in medical education. For a review of nine of the experiments, see [60]. Several of these—those at Cornell University Medical College, at the University of North Carolina, at the University of Colorado, and at Temple University—were designed to teach medical students the principles of comprehensive medical care and to instill in them more humanistic attitudes toward patients. At the University of Colorado and at Cornell, these experimental programs were extensively evaluated; the individuals primarily responsible for carrying out the evaluation were a social psychologist in the case of Colorado [42] and several sociologists in the case of Cornell [76].

On a different level, sociologists have selected medical schools as strategic research sites in which to raise a number of sociological questions. The best-known examples of such studies are those carried out by Becker, Geer, and their colleagues at the medical school of the University of Kansas [3] and that carried out by Merton and his associates at Cornell Medical College, the University of Pennsylvania, and Western Reserve University [68]. Similar studies have been carried out on a smaller scale at Downstate Medical Center and are currently going on at the Medical College of Ohio, Michigan State College of Human Medicine, and Mount Sinai Medical School. Such investigations contribute as much to the field of sociology as to medicine.[11] They have added to our understanding of the conditions under which group perspectives are developed and to theories of adult socialization. From their findings, medical educators can learn something of the changes in attitudes and values their students experience in the course of their medical training; they can then decide whether these changes are desirable, from the point of view of what they are trying to achieve in medical school, and whether some modification of teaching methods or of the curriculum seems called for.

Finally, sociologists contribute directly to the training of medical students. They do this in one of two ways: (1) by helping educators from various departments in the medical school introduce sociological knowledge and perspectives into courses taught in these departments or (2) by teaching courses in sociology (or more often, behavioral science) that have been tailored to the needs of medical students.

In most medical schools, it was the department of psychiatry which first encouraged the incorporation of sociological materials into the courses for which it was responsible. Generally also, departments of psychiatry first gave sociologists full-time positions on the medical school staff. As other departments have followed suit, the close alliance between sociologists and teachers of psychiatry has been maintained. A concrete demonstration of this was a recent conference on teaching psychiatry in medical school, sponsored jointly by the American Psychiatric Association and the Association of

[11] For critiques of the sociological significance of these studies, see the articles by Bloom [7] and Levinson [62].

American Medical Colleges. Among the participants invited to prepare papers to serve as a basis for the discussion of goals and methods in courses of psychiatry were a number of sociologists: Bloom, Erikson, Simmons, Srole, and Straus [18].

Gradually, the occasional and isolated lectures by sociologists (or other behavioral scientists) began to evolve into entire courses,[12] complete with their own teaching staffs and texts. See, for example, the books by Bloom [6] and Wilson [103]. Sometimes these have been under the aegis of existing departments in the medical school (again, typically, the department of psychiatry). More recently, separate departments of behavorial science have been created; they have usually been assigned the dual tasks of teaching medical students and of carrying out medically relevant social research.

Through direct contributions of the kind described here, sociologists are collaborating with medical educators in continuing efforts to make sure that medical training keeps pace with the changing needs of society.

C. Relations of Physicians to Others in Role-set

A third major line of inquiry concerns the relations of physicians to others in their role-set. The variety of such "others"—patients, family, colleagues, and collaborators—indicates at once the impossibility of considering here the contributions which sociology has made, or might make, to an understanding of all of these relationhsips. Again, canons of selectivity will have to be invoked.

In the pages which follow, we shall not consider the relations between physicians and other members of the team responsible for patient care, such as nurses, social workers, technicians, and the like. Instead, we shall focus, first, on selected aspects of the doctor-patient relationship and, second, on some recent sociological contributions to an understanding of collegial relationships.

As is made amply clear in Chapter 13 in this volume, which deals with the doctor-patient relationship, the analysis of that relationship has received considerable attention from varied points of view. Nonetheless, until recently, there have been significant omissions. Just as the traditional models of the transactions between doctors and their patients have not generally considered the relationships which obtain when patients are chronically ill or, which may be synonymous, suffer from progressively degenerative diseases, so the more familiar models do not take into account the special conditions of the relationship of physicians to dying patients.

In the last few years, the tendency not to consider the dying patient has been dramatically altered. First came

[12] The rapid proliferation of such courses had, as one result, the creation of a Committee on Teaching Sociology in Schools of Medicine and Public Health, as part of the Medical Sociology Section of the American Sociological Association. This committee, along with representatives from the fields of anthropology and psychology, has recently undertaken a study of the teaching of behavioral sciences in schools of medicine, with support from the National Center for Health Services Research and Development. There have also been a series of conferences at which the most appropriate content and methods of teaching behavioral sciences to medical students have been jointly discussed and debated by behavioral scientists and more traditional kinds of medical educators. The fourth and most recent of these conferences, sponsored by the Division of Physician Manpower of National Institutes of Health and the National Institute of Child Health and Human Development, was held in the fall of 1970.

two studies by Glaser and Strauss [31, 32]; next came a study that Sudnow conducted in two general hospitals [98]. There followed a conference on the treatment of patients with fatal illnesses [72], and the trend has recently culminated in a collection of articles on the dying patient [9].

It is interesting to speculate on some of the sociological reasons why death and the dying patient have recently assumed such importance among medical sociologists. Several explanations seem relevant. In the first place, a new social climate has developed over the last few years; this has involved, in part, the relaxation of taboos which prevailed earlier. We are all familiar with the freedom with which sexual matters once considered "indecent" can now be discussed in polite company and the frankness with which they can be depicted in the mass media. So it is with earlier proscriptions against talking openly about death and dying persons. What previously was considered indelicate is now held to be an acceptable topic for discussion.

This first explanation pertains to society as a whole, and not to sociologists specifically. A second way of accounting for the newly developing openness in talking about death involves new trends among sociologists themselves. As social problems grow both in number and severity, the sociological profession is increasingly expressing its compassionate concern toward some of society's victims. There is growing attention to slum dwellers, to members of oppressed minority groups, and to the swelling number of the aged. According to some recent authors, dying patients fall into the same category because physicians tend to lose interest in them once they are convinced there is nothing more that can be done medically to keep them alive.[13] As a result, many dying patients are allowed to linger on relatively unattended until death occurs.

There is still another explanation for the recent sociological interest in dying patients: Such patients offer strategic opportunities for studying the extent to which norms assumed to govern the doctor-patient relationship actually do so. According to the familiar Parsonian model, physicians are expected to maintain an attitude of affective neutrality toward their patients, and they are also expected to treat all patients alike. Most physicians would probably accept these prescriptions for their behavior, although there is no research which documents this. But the work of several sociologists, especially Sudnow [98], has indicated that these norms do not always operate in the care of dying patients. For example, heroic efforts are made to maintain the life of a stricken leader; they are less likely to be applied in the case of a dying alcoholic. Mouth-to-mouth artificial respiration will ordinarily be used in attempts to resuscitate a dying child; this medically preferred method is less likely to be applied in the case of a derelict from skid row. Differences such as these enable the sociologist to specify the conditions under which physicians behave according to ideal norms and those under which they behave differently. The dying patient thus provides an occasion for elaborating elements that characterize the doctor-patient relationship.

As we turn to the relations of the doctor to his colleagues, we find that the sociological contributions to an

[13] The reasons for this form a vast topic for inquiry that are beyond the scope of this chapter. It seems quite clear, however, that the behavior of physicians vis-à-vis dying patients is not simply a matter of callousness. See the article by White [102].

understanding of this aspect of the medical profession are quite different. Traditionally, the study of collegial relations has stressed cooperative arrangements between physicians and the effects that these may have. Thus, Hall analyzed the importance of colleague networks in advancing the career of the young doctor [40, 41]. Coleman, Katz, and Menzel demonstrated how the adoption of new medical practices —in their instance, a new drug—depended on the friendship patterns that existed among physicians [15]. And Freidson has carried out long-term studies of types of medical practice involving collaboration between doctors [27].

One recent study, however, attempted to identify some sources of conflict between physicians, especially between medical educators and medical practitioners [56]. The research was carried out in eight communities having medical schools, and it involved interviews with both faculty members of the schools and local practitioners. The most universal source of conflict was the complaint, on the part of practitioners, that to the extent that faculty members were allowed to see private patients and receive fees from them, they constituted unfair economic competition. The variations on this theme were numerous and complex; their specific form and content suggested a number of ways that sociologists might propose resolving the conflict. Space limitations, however, prevent us from reviewing those that were discussed in the monograph.

But there are other dimensions of the conflict between medical educators and practitioners for which solutions do not seem easily possible. Here the sociologist can only suggest that, given the conditions he has analyzed, modes of accommodation will have to be developed. It turns out, for example, that processes of displacement have characterized the recent histories of medical schools and of the medical communities in which they are located. Within the medical schools, the part-time faculties that formerly were dominant have now been replaced by full-time professors and chiefs, and the clinicians who not so long ago commanded top respect have lost some of their prominence to those engaged primarily in research. In the community at large, general practitioners have been progressively displaced by specialists, and their practices have been gradually limited by newly instituted restrictions on what they may and may not do in community hospitals. It should also be noted that this phenomenon of displacement is aggravated by associated developments. Significantly, a generational conflict is involved: The full-time faculty member is usually younger than the part-time colleague whose position he assumes; similarly with the researcher who displaces the previously dominant clinicians and the specialist who takes over from the general practitioner. Thus, in addition to losing positions of power and authority they formerly had, these displaced groups find themselves subordinate to men younger than they are.

A related sociological observation is that, as a group, the new brand of medical educators generally have a cosmopolitan rather than a local orientation. This involves, among other things, no strong commitment to the community in which they are located at any particular time. They are likely to have come from another community, and to feel free to move on to yet another should a more attractive opportunity present itself. According to many practitioners, this lack of local commitment on the part of medical educators means a lack of involvement of the medical school in local community needs. However, as we shall consider in the last section of this chapter, community pressures may be changing this situation.

The sociologist can identify these trends. But it is not likely that he can —or should—think of ways of reversing them. Probably the most that he can do is to suggest ways in which the consequences of these changes can be anticipated and modes of accommodation developed.

D. Medical Organizations—The Case of Hospitals

The sociology of medicine is not only concerned with questions of how physicians are recruited and trained or how they relate to their patients on the one hand or to their colleagues on the other. It also is interested in investigating the medical institutions and organizations to which doctors belong. As we suggested at the outset, in this sense the sociology of medicine is a branch of organizational sociology, which focuses on medical organizations rather than on schools, business firms, or other kinds of institutions [75].

Hospitals are undoubtedly the most familiar medical institutions, and in this section of the chapter we shall focus on them, with particular emphasis on sociological contributions to an understanding of their functioning.

The history of hospitals has been well documented. (For a concise summary, see the article by George Rosen [80]. See also Chapter 12 in this volume.) In medieval times they were created as havens for the ill and homeless who had nowhere else to go and no one to care for them. They soon earned a rather unsavory reputation as places where one went to die: If the patient was not fatally ill when he entered, the primitive sanitary conditions and lack of precautions against contagion might very well produce such a terminal outcome. Gradually, as medical notions of antisepsis and the mechanisms of contagion advanced, conditions found in hospitals improved. And they began to enjoy a correspondingly better reputation: They were thought of as institutions to which one went when he needed expert medical and nursing care. Interestingly enough, however, the clientele they served, even under these improved conditions, did not change significantly. Those who had families and who were affluent enough to bring in extra help to nurse the patient through his illness remained at home, and, depending on the severity of the illness, were visited there daily—or more often—by the family physician.[14]

It was not until quite recently that the hospital came to be thought of as the logical place to treat all seriously ill patients, of whatever social class or financial standing. One might say that the impetus for this development was an unanticipated consequence of the growth in medical science and technology. As diagnostic and therapeutic devices have become both more complex and more expensive, physicians have become progressively less comfortable about relying on the contents of their little black bags, or even on the limited amount of equipment they have in their offices. Increasingly, then, they have turned to the diverse equipment —and the varied personnel—of the hospital to assist them, not only in treating seriously ill patients, but also in arriving at a diagnosis for those who present more than routine problems. In this sense, then, the modern hospital

[14] That hospitals were still considered charitable institutions in this phase of their history is indicated by the fact that many of them were called "dispensaries" and that their boards of directors were often composed of the social leaders of the community.

has taken on a major function that it did not previously have. Parallelling this are other developments which have contributed to the nature of the hospital as we know it today.

Starting about fifty years ago, many of the most prestigious hospitals associated with medical schools began to expand their teaching functions. Even in the early stages of medical education in this country, medical students made bedside rounds with their teachers and performed some of the simpler procedures in the clinics and wards. But as medical specialization began to develop, and as the various specialty boards outlined the kinds of training required for certification in their fields [30], a whole new kind of hospital-based medical education—that involving interns and residents—developed at a rapid pace. At first, as we have indicated, this educational function was confined to hospitals closely affiliated with medical schools. Gradually, however, other hospitals began to realize that, in the course of advancing their training, such interns and residents could render useful services to the hospital in the providing of patient care. Gradually, then, these hospitals began to set up educational programs for interns and residents. According to recent figures, there are now nearly 3,000 different internship programs, and more are added each year.

The growth of medical research represents a third major function that has been developing in and affecting the character of the modern hospital. As we had occasion to note earlier, the amounts of money devoted to medical and health-related research have increased dramatically, especially since the end of the Second World War. Not all of this research takes place in medical schools and their related hospitals; a substantial portion goes on in various governmental agencies, such as the National Institutes of Health and the National Institute of Mental Health. Still other medical research is conducted in independent institutes and organizations. The fact remains, however, that a significant part, if not the bulk, of such research is located in medical schools and their associated hospitals. (One clear indication of this is that, as a result of recent cutbacks in research funds for the medical field, a number of medical schools have found themselves in financial straits.) And research-oriented hospitals have acquired all sorts of new and (to the layman) exotic equipment, and have added to their staffs specially trained individuals capable of operating it.

These, then, are the main developments that differentiate the modern hospital from its predecessors or from what it was like in earlier periods. As we have suggested, the trends apply mainly to hospitals associated with medical schools. But as other hospitals increasingly seek to emulate university hospitals, it can be assumed that these characteristics will become more widespread.

Sociologists, faced with a set of developments such as these, typically ask what consequences can be discerned. They are interested not only in the fact that social changes take place but also in tracing out the implications of such changes.

So it is with certain sociological studies of the modern hospital. The reader should be forewarned that we are not making any attempt here to provide an exhaustive survey of all sociological studies of hospitals. They are many and varied. Those who wish to pursue the topic further are referred to the bibliographies in Chapter 12 in this volume and in the article by Perrow [75]. Here we shall focus on what appear to be two important consequences of the developments we outlined. The first has to do with the increasing bureaucratization of hospitals, and what sociologists have been able to contribute to an understanding of this process. The second implication, which seems to be related to the first, concerns the feeling on the part of many patients that hospitals—especially university hospitals—have become impersonal institutions in which they do not feel comfortable.

Every large-scale organization—hospitals included—is a bureaucratic structure. There are hierarchical levels, each assigned a specific set of functions and a particular degree of authority. At the top of this hierarchy is a director who is responsible for seeing that assigned tasks are carried out, that the proper kinds of personnel are available to perform the tasks, that the organization remains solvent, that the physical plant is maintained, and so on.

But this simplistic model of bureaucratic structure has never applied easily in the case of hospitals, because there have almost always been dual lines of authority. On the one hand, there is the hospital administrator, generally a layman, who is responsible to a board of trustees, generally composed of laymen. On the other hand, there is the medical staff who are inclined to think that the hospital is "theirs," and that they should have ultimate authority as to how the institution is run.

Traditionally, therefore, there have been conflicts between these two chains of command [90]. These may arise when physicians begin to undermine the authority of the administrator, by bypassing the proper channels of communication, by breaking rules which the administrator has established, or by other similar behavior.[15] Moreover, the professional staff and the administrator may have divergent views about the hospital itself. Staff physicians are likely to view it as their special province and to want to see it supplied with the most modern equipment, regardless of cost. The administrator, on the other hand, is more likely to regard the hospital as a "business" which should, if possible, maintain itself economically; he is therefore apt to resist efforts by the medical staff to bring in expensive equipment, unless its utility can be fully justified.

It seems likely that the trends we have traced will exacerbate these bureaucratic problems. As hospitals expand their functions of patient care, medical education, and medical research, the need for coordination of all activities will greatly increase. One cannot bring into the hospital ever larger numbers of patients without making sure that adequate staffs of nurses, aides, and other support personnel are available to care for them. One cannot expand the number of interns and residents unless provision has been made for their training and for supervising their work with patients. One cannot accept large-scale research grants until appropriate research space and appropriate research assistants have been found.

There is a sociological study which suggests that, at least in one university hospital, efforts have been made to anticipate some of these problems and to accommodate to them. In the institution she studied, Goss [36] found that although the physicians generally disliked administrative work and considered it less prestigious than their more orthodox professional activites, some of them agreed to devote at least a portion of their time to bureaucratic

[15] An interesting study relating conformity to hospital regulations to social status was carried out by Julius Roth [85]. He found that the higher the status of the personnel, the less likely they were to obey rules set down by the hospital administration.

problems. It seems likely that, in order to cope with the increasing number of such problems, this accommodative solution will be extended to hospitals where it does not now exist.

Related to the increasing bureaucratization of hospitals and its attendant problems is the feeling on the part of some patients that hospital care, especially in the university hospitals, has become impersonal and something to be avoided if at all possible. It is not that they doubt the quality of care they will receive in such institutions; there is considerable evidence that it is actually higher in hospitals which have teaching as one of their primary goals. (See the recent article by Goss [37].) But they are afraid of how they are going to be treated. Elling, for example, found that such fears were one major deterrent to the utilization of high-quality medical facilities [19]. And in a study carried out for quite different purposes [56], it was not uncommon to hear practitioners describe their patients' reluctance to be hospitalized in a university-connected medical center. They were afraid they would be used as "guinea pigs" in the hospital, or that if they did have some medically complicated problem, they would be visited repeatedly by different members of the house staff on the look out for "interesting cases." As a kind of crucial experiment in this connection, one of the practitioners who was visited undertook a small research project for the field worker. It is perhaps best described in an excerpt from the interview that was conducted with him:

> I think the best way to tell you how the local people feel about the [university] hospital is to give you a notion of the ease with which you can get private beds in these three different hospitals. It's almost always harder to get a bed at St. Mary's or at Baptist than it is at the medical center. I think that gives you a pretty good idea of how people generally feel about going to the medical center. Let's just try something. [At this point, the respondent called Baptist Hospital and asked for a private room; he was told that the first reservation he could get would be exactly one week later. He then called St. Mary's; there he was told that he could have a private room in three days. Finally, he called the medical center and was told that he could have a private bed immediately.] During the winter, on an average day, you have to wait about two weeks for a private room at Baptist Hospital, about one week for a room at St. Mary's, and one or two days for a private room at university hospital [56].

Sociologists can help identify some of the problems that have developed as a result of changes in hospital organization and goals; hopefully, they will also be able to suggest appropriate solutions. Up to this point, however, sociological contributions of this latter kind have been rather few and far between. Recent developments to be considered in the next section, however, suggest some promising lines of progress.

E. Development of Community Health

During the decade of the sixties a new concept came into prominence in the delivery of health services—that of considering the community, rather than the individual patient, as the entity for which services are needed. This came about in part because of the interest of social scientists in studying the organization of health services and in part because of the developing concern with ecology. In its simplest terms, a community is conceived of as a population group residing in a defined geographic area. Demographic and epidemiologic studies identify the types of people, their statuses, occupations, fertility, mobility, and the incidence and prevalence of their illnesses. Ecologic studies survey environmental influences, sanitation, and the food supply. This holistic view of people and their environment transcends the problem of the individual patient.[16]

The rising costs of medical care, however, have perhaps attracted the greatest attention to the study of the way services are delivered to large groups of people and focused the attention of economists and legislators, as well as health professionals, on the interaction of health providers and consumers in the community setting instead of on the traditional doctor-patient relationship. The civil rights movement, with its concern for discrimination, has focused its spotlight on the underprivileged or slum community, where health services are notoriously deficient. Consumer rights, as they have become an issue and a force, have also served to enhance the importance of the community view over the personal view.

For some years too medical school deans and prominent medical educators have been speaking of the importance of changing the curriculum with the aim of providing greater attention to the patient and his family in their natural setting rather than to the disease itself. Some notable steps were, in fact, taken during the last twenty years. However, student militancy, fostered by growing dissatisfaction with unmet social problems, has recently brought relatively rapid change in medical teaching and in the concern of universities and their medical schools with social problems.

Social scientists have become relatively commonplace on medical faculties, in medical care programs, in research organizations devoted to analysis of the health care system, and in government agencies. Economic forces, consumer demand, professional concern, and educational interest have converged to develop what has come to be labeled "Community Medicine." With the focus of attention on the community rather than the individual, the need for sociologists to participate in defining the population to be served and in establishing benchmarks to determine progress in improving health care has become evident.

The *Annals of the American Academy of Political and Social Science* for March, 1963, entitled "Medicine and Society" reviewed the converging trends, and the New York Academy of Science's conference "Medical Schools and Teaching Hospitals" [71] provided a forum for the discussion of community medicine, among other topics. The Rockefeller Foundation sponsored a conference on community medicine in September, 1968, which "provided the first occasion for community medicine to be considered in a systematic and thorough way" [59a].

Most United States medical schools today have departments or sections on community medicine, which are striving to develop a body of knowledge in the field as well as to reorient the teaching hospital towards providing direct service to a community. The Regional Medical Program and Comprehensive Health Planning, as they interact with the medical schools, are also having the effect of heightening the concern of medical educators with the need for social science concepts and methods and for faculty positions for sociologists [5, 91].

Few studies of community health have yet been completed or published except those designed primarily for epidemiological purposes such as Tecumseh [22, 23], but Kark reviewed the pos-

[16] That the same sorts of concern exist in other countries as well is documented by a recent study on medicine and urbanization in France [39].

sibilities and recommended techniques in the Brogden Memorial Symposium at Johns Hopkins in November, 1968 [50].

One of the leading innovations in community medicine has been the development of the neighborhood health center. The first was established by Tufts University with funds from the Office of Enocomic Opportunity at Columbia Point, an isolated low-income public housing project on the edge of Boston Harbor [4, 29]. There are now some eighty centers on the same or similar models throughout the United States, most of them funded by the OEO but some by the Health Services and Mental Health Administration. As a means of delivering health services conveniently to an underprivileged community, they have been the focus of much attention. They solve the problem of geographic accessibility, and standards of care are maintained by association with a backup hospital that provides both staff appointments for the health workers and complex diagnostic and treatment facilities. There have been many problems in relating to community groups, however, and the issue of community control has often thwarted the mission of the center. Davis and Tranquada have reported on this in detail as it occurred in the Watts Neighborhood Health Center [16]. The final solution to the role of the professional providers versus that of the indigenous consumers has yet to be found, although it is being actively sought and studied in many places.

Whether the neighborhood health center in its current form is the best answer to the problem of delivery of health services in urban and rural ghettos and elsewhere is a subject for debate. The effectiveness of existing neighborhood health centers has not yet been measured systematically, nor have they been adequately compared with other delivery arrangements. The question of their usefulness is also tied in with the larger one of the proper type of health care system for the entire country.

A number of schemes have been proposed, and the next few years will likely see one or another of these or some combination introduced. One approach is to extend the Medicare insurance principle to cover all age groups; another, favored by the American Medical Association, is to offer tax credits for health insurance premiums. Neither of these would alter the present system of delivery, and with the current and anticipated shortage of physicians and facilities, the costs of health care would probably continue to increase rapidly. For that reason many favor a plan which would alter the arrangements for delivery by emphasizing group practice, particularly with prepayment. The present pluralistic approach, dependent as it is on large numbers of solo practitioners and called by some a nonsystem, would be replaced by a more bureaucratic organization of health providers based on medical centers with satellite hospitals and clinics; most of the provider physicians would be on salary. The question of what type of arrangement will be least costly and most efficient and satisfying to the consumer, as well as acceptable to the powerful professional interest groups, such as the American Medical Association and the American Nursing Association, will be grist for sociological research for some time to come.

It is likely that the impetus for legislative solutions at the national level, however, will not permit the delay necessary for study, planning, and rational decision making about the proper choice of system. Nevertheless, the role of sociologists in both analysis and implementation of new systems is bound to grow both in stature and importance.

REFERENCES

1. BECKER, HOWARD S., *Outsiders: Studies in the Sociology of Deviance.* New York: The Free Press, 1963.
2. ———, ed., *The Other Side: Perspectives on Deviance.* New York: The Free Press, 1964.
3. ———, BLANCHE GEER, EVERETT C. HUGHES, AND ANSELM L. STRAUSS, *Boys in White.* Chicago: University of Chicago Press, 1961.
4. BELLIN, SEYMOUR S. AND H. JACK GEIGER, "Actual Public Acceptance of the Neighborhood Health Center by the Urban Poor," *Journal of the American Medical Association,* 214 (1970), 2147–53.
5. BELOFF, J. S., P. S. SNOKE, AND E. R. WEINERMAN, "Yale Studies in Family Health Care: II. Organization of a Comprehensive Family Health Care Program," *Journal of the American Medical Association,* 204 (1968), 355–60.
6. BLOOM, SAMUEL W., *The Doctor and His Patient.* New York: The Free Press, 1965.
7. ———, "The Sociology of Medical Education: Some Comments on the State of a Field," *Milbank Memorial Fund Quarterly,* 43 (1965), 143–84.
8. BRAZDA, JEROME, *Washington Report on Medicine and Health.* New York: McGraw-Hill Book Company, 1969.
9. BRIM, ORVILLE G., HOWARD E. FREEMAN, SOL LEVINE, AND NORMAN A. SCOTCH, eds., *The Dying Patient.* New York: Russell Sage Foundation, 1970.
10. BRITTEN, R. H. et al., "The National Health Survey: Some General Findings as to Disease, Accidents, and Impairments in Urban Areas," *Public Health Reports,* 55 (1940), 444–70.
11. Carnegie Commission on Higher Education, *Higher Education and the Nation's Health: Policies for Medical and Dental Education.* New York: McGraw-Hill Book Company, 1970.
12. CARTWRIGHT, ANN, *Patients and Their Doctors: A Study of General Practice.* New York: Atherton Press, Inc., 1967.
13. COE, RODNEY M., *Sociology of Medicine.* New York: McGraw-Hill Book Company, 1970.
14. COGAN, LEE, *Negroes for Medicine: Report of a Macy Conference.* Baltimore: The Johns Hopkins Press, 1968.
15. COLEMAN, JAMES S., ELIHU KATZ, AND HERBERT MENZEL, *Medical Innovation: A Diffusion Study.* Indianapolis: The Bobbs-Merrill Company, Inc., 1966.
16. DAVIS, MILTON S. AND ROBERT E. TRANQUADA, "A Sociological Evaluation of the Watts Neighborhood Health Center," *Medical Care,* 7 (1969), 105–17.
17. DOHRENWEND, BRUCE AND BARBARA, *Social Status and Psychological Disorder: A Causal Inquiry.* New York: John Wiley & Sons, Inc., 1969.
18. EARLEY, L. W. et al., eds., *Teaching Psychiatry in Medical School.* Washington, D.C.: American Psychiatric Association, 1969.
19. ELLING, RAY, "The Design and Evaluation of Planned Change in Health Organizations," in Arthur B. Shostak, ed., *Sociology in Action.* Homewood, Ill.: Richard D. Irwin, Inc., Dorsey Press, 1966.
20. FEIN, RASHI, *The Doctor Shortage.* Washington, D.C.: The Brookings Institution, 1967.
21. FELDMAN, JACOB J., *The Dissemination of Health Information: A Case Study in Adult Learning.* Chicago: Aldine Publishing Company, 1966.
22. FRANCIS, THOMAS, JR., "Aspects of the Tecumseh Study," *Public Health Reports,* 76 (1961), 963–66.
23. FRANCIS, T. AND F. H. EPSTEIN, "Tecumseh, Michigan," *Milbank Memorial Fund Quarterly,* 43 (1965), Part 2, 333.
24. FREEMAN, HOWARD E., SOL LEVINE, AND LEO G. REEDER, eds., *Handbook of Medical Sociology,* Second Edition. Englewood Cliffs, N.J.: Prentice-Hall, Inc., 1972.

25. FREIDSON, ELIOT, ed., *The Hospital in Modern Society.* New York: The Free Press, 1963.
26. ———, "Disability as Social Deviance," in Marvin B. Sussman, ed., *Sociology and Rehabilitation.* Washington, D.C.: American Sociological Association, 1965.
27. ———, *Profession of Medicine: A Study of the Sociology of Applied Knowledge.* New York: Dodd, Mead & Company, 1970.
28. GEE, H. H. AND C. G. CHILD III, eds., "Second Institute on Clinical Teaching," *Journal of Medical Education,* 36 (1961), Part 2, 1–199.
29. GEIGER, H. JACK, "The Neighborhood Health Center," *Archives of Environmental Health,* 14 (1967), 912–16.
30. GIBBON, J. H., JR., "Two Views of the Specialty Boards: A. A Surgeon's Views," in H. H. Gee and C. G. Child III, eds., "Second Institute on Clinical Teaching," *Journal of Medical Education,* 36 (1961), Part 2, 1–199.
31. GLASER, BARNEY G. AND ANSELM L. STRAUSS, *Awareness of Dying.* Chicago: Aldine Publishing Company, 1965.
32. ———, *Time for Dying.* Chicago: Aldine Publishing Company, 1968.
33. GLOCK, CHARLES Y., ed., *Survey Research in the Social Sciences.* New York: Russell Sage Foundation, 1967.
34. GOFFMAN, IRVING, *Asylums: Essays on the Social Situation of Mental Patients and Other Inmates.* Garden City, New York: Doubleday & Company, Inc., 1961.
35. ———, *Stigma: Notes on the Management of Spoiled Identity.* Englewood Cliffs, N.J.: Prentice-Hall, Inc., 1963.
36. GOSS, MARY E. W., "Patterns of Bureaucracy Among Hospital Staff Physicans," in Eliot Freidson, ed., *The Hospital in Modern Society.* New York: The Free Press of Glencoe, 1963.
37. ———, "Organizational Goals and Quality of Medical Care: Evidence from Comparative Research on Hospitals," *Journal of Health and Social Behavior,* 11 (1970), 255–68.
38. GOSS, MARY E. W. AND GEORGE G. READER, "Collaboration between Sociologist and Physician," *Social Problems,* 4 (1956), 82–89.
39. GOUST, FRANCOIS, *Médecine et Urbanisation.* Paris: Les Éditions Ouvrières, 1969.
40. HALL, OSWALD, "The Informal Organization of the Medical Profession," *Canadian Journal of Economics and Political Science,* 12 (1946), 30–44.
41. ———, "The Stages of a Medical Career," *American Journal of Sociology,* 53 (1958), 327–36.
42. HAMMOND, KENNETH AND FRED KERN, JR., *Teaching Comprehensive Medical Care.* Cambridge: Harvard University 1959.
43. HARRISON, BARBARA, "Foreign Doctors in American Hospitals: A Sociological Analysis of Graduate Medical Education." Unpublished Ph.D. dissertation, Columbia University, 1968.
44. HYMAN, MARTIN D., "Illness, Disability and Stigma: Some Implications for Medical Practice," *Geriatrics,* in Press.
45. ———, "Some Links between Economic Status and Untreated Illness," *Social Science and Medicine,* 4 (1970), 387–99.
46. Institut Français d'Opinion Publique, "Les Français et Leur Médecin," *Sondages,* 22 (1960).
47. JACO, E. GARTLEY, ed., *Patients, Physicians, and Illness.* New York: The Free Press, 1958.
48. KADUSHIN, CHARLES, "Social Class and the Experience of Ill Health," *Sociological Inquiry,* 35 (1964), 67–80.
49. ———, *Why People Go to Psychiatrists.* New York: Atherton Press, Inc., 1969.
50. KARK, SIDNEY L., "Community Health Research," *Johns Hopkins Medical Journal,* 124, 5 (1969), 258–70.
51. KENDALL, PATRICIA L. AND ROBERT K. MERTON, "Medical Education as Social Process," in E. Gartley Jaco, ed., *Patients, Physicians, and Illness.* New York: The Free Press, 1958.
52. KENDALL, PATRICIA L., "Clinical Teachers' Views of the Basic Science Curriculum," *Journal of Medical Education,* 35 (1960), 148–57.

53. ———, "Impact of Training Programs on the Young Physician's Attitudes and Experiences," *Journal of the American Medical Association*, 176 (1961), 102–7.

54. ———, "Medical Sociology in the United States," *Social Science Information*, 2 (1963), 1–13.

55. ———, "The Learning Environment of Hospitals," in Eliot Freidson, ed., *The Hospital in Modern Society*. New York: The Free Press, 1963.

56. ———, *The Relationship between Medical Educators and Medical Practitioners*. Evanston, Ill.: Association of American Medical Colleges, 1965.

57. ———, "Consequences of the Trend toward Specialization," in Clark Vincent and Robert Coombs, eds., *Psycho-Social Aspects of Medical Training*. Springfield, Ill.: Charles C. Thomas, 1971.

58. ———, "Medical Specialization: Trends and Contributing Factors," in Clark Vincent and Robert Coombs, eds., *Psycho-Social Aspects of Medical Training*. Springfield, Ill.: Charles C. Thomas, 1971.

59. KOOS, EARL LOMON, *The Health of Regionville: What the People Thought and Did about It*. New York: Columbia University Press, 1954.

59a. LATHEM, WILLOUGHBY AND ANNE NEWBURY, eds., *Community Medicine*. New York: Meredith Corp., 1970.

60. LEE, PETER V., *Medical Schools and the Changing Times: Nine Case Reports on Experimentation in Medical Education, 1950–1960*. Evanston, Ill.: Association of American Medical Colleges, 1962.

61. LEVINE, GENE N., "Anxiety about Illness: Psychological and Social Bases," *Journal of Health and Human Behavior*, 3 (1962), 30–34.

62. LEVINSON, DANIEL J., "Medical Education and the Theory of Adult Socialization," *Journal of Health and Social Behavior*, 8 (1967), 253–65.

63. LOPATE, CAROL, *Women in Medicine*. Baltimore: The Johns Hopkins Press, 1968.

64. MAHONEY, ANNE R., "Career Orientations of Physicians: A Sociological Study of Plans for Medical Practice." Unpublished Ph.D. dissertation, Columbia University, 1970.

65. MARCH, JAMES G., ed., *The Handbook of Organizations*. Skokie, Ill.: Rand McNally & Company, 1965.

66. MATTFELD, JACQUELYN A. AND CAROL VAN AKEN, *Women and the Scientific Professions*. Cambridge: The M.I.T. Press, 1965.

67. MECHANIC, DAVID, *Medical Sociology: A Selective View*. New York: The Free Press, 1968.

68. MERTON, ROBERT K., GEORGE G. READER, AND PATRICIA L. KENDALL, eds., *The Student-Physician*. Cambridge, Mass.: Harvard University Press, 1957.

69. MILLER, STEPHEN J., *Prescriptions for Leadership: Training for the Medical Elite*. Chicago: Aldine Publishing Company, 1970.

70. MUMFORD, EMILY, *Interns: From Students to Physicians*. Cambridge: Harvard University Press, 1970.

71. New York Academy of Sciences, "Medical Schools and Teaching Hospitals: Curriculum, Programming, and Planning," *Annals of the New York Academy of Sciences*, 128 (1965), 457–720.

72. ———, "Care of Patients with Fatal Illness," *Annals of the New York Academy of Sciences*, 164 (1969), 635–896.

73. PAGE, ROBERT G., "The Three-Year Medical Curriculum," *Journal of the American Medical Association*, 213 (1970), 1012–15.

74. PARSONS, TALCOTT, *The Social System*. New York: The Free Press, 1951.

75. PERROW, CHARLES, "Hospitals: Technology, Structure, and Goals," in James G. March, ed., *The Handbook of Organizations*. Skokie, Ill.: Rand McNally & Company, 1965.

76. READER, GEORGE G. AND MARY E. W. GOSS, eds., *Comprehensive Medical Care and Teaching*. Ithaca, N.Y.: Cornell University Press, 1967.

77. *Research: Requirements and Resources, 1965–1970*. Washington, D.C.: National Institutes of Health, 1962.

78. ROGERS, THERESA A., "Competence and Careers: A Study of Interns and

Residents." Unpublished Ph.D. dissertation, Columbia University, 1969.
79. Rose, John C., "Maintaining Standards of Education while Expanding Physician Production," *Journal of American Medical Association*, 213, 4 (1970), 597–99.
80. Rosen, George, "The Hospital: Historical Sociology of a Community Institution," in Eliot Freidson, ed., *The Hospital in Modern Society*. New York: The Free Press, 1963.
81. Rosenblatt, Daniel and Edward A. Suchman, "The Underutilization of Medical-Care Services by Blue-Collarites" in Arthur B. Shostak and William Gomberg, eds., *Blue-Collar World: Studies of the American Worker*. Englewood Cliffs, N.J.: Prentice-Hall, Inc., 1964.
82. ———, "Blue-Collar Attitudes and Information toward Health and Illness," in Arthur B. Shostak and William Gomberg, eds., *Blue-Collar World: Studies of the American Worker*. Englewood Cliffs, N.J.: Prentice-Hall, Inc., 1964.
83. Rosengren, William R., "Social Class and Becoming 'Ill'," in Arthur B. Shostak and William Gomberg, eds., *Blue-Collar World: Studies of the American Worker*. Englewood Cliffs, N.J.: Prentice-Hall, Inc., 1964.
84. Rossi, Alice, "Barriers to the Career Choice of Engineering, Medicine or Science among American Women," in Jacquelyn A. Mattfeld and Carol Van Aken, eds., *Women and the Scientific Professions*. Cambridge: The M.I.T. Press, 1965.
85. Roth, Julius, "Ritual and Magic in the Control of Contagion," *American Sociological Review*, 22 (1957), 310–14.
86. Schelsky, Helmut, "Die Soziologie des Krankenhauses im Rahmen einer Soziologie der Medizin," in *Auf der Suche nach Wirklichkeit*. Düsseldorf–Köln: Eugen Diederichs Verlag, 1965.
87. Shostak, Arthur B., ed., *Sociology in Action*. Homewood, Ill.: Richard D. Irwin, Inc., Dorsey Press, 1966.
88. ——— and William Gomberg, eds., *Blue-Collar World: Studies of the American Worker*. Englewood Cliffs, N.J.: Prentice-Hall, Inc., 1964.
89. Sigerist, Henry B., *On the History of Medicine*, ed. Felix Marti-Ibanez. New York: MD Publications, Inc., 1960.
90. Smith, Harvey L., "Two Lines of Authority Are One Too Many," *Modern Hospital*, 84 (1955), 59–64.
91. Snoke, P. S. and E. R. Weinerman, "Comprehensive Care Programs in University Medical Centers," *Journal of Medical Education*, 40 (1965), 625–57.
92. Stevens, Rosemary, *Medical Practice in Modern England: The Impact of Specialization and State Medicine*. New Haven: Yale University Press, 1966.
93. Straus, Robert, "The Nature and Status of Medical Sociology," *American Sociological Review*, 22 (1957), 200–204.
94. ———, "A Department of Behavioral Science," *Journal of Medical Education*, 34 (1959), 662–66.
95. ———, "A Role for Behavioral Science in a University Medical Center," *Annals of the American Academy of Political and Social Science*, 346 (1963), 99–108.
96. ———, "Planning a University Medical Center for the Student and the Patient," *Journal of Health and Human Behavior*, 4 (Spring, 1963), 36–44.
97. Suchman, Edward A., "The Survey Method Applied to Public Health and Medicine," in Charles Y. Glock, ed., *Survey Research in the Social Sciences*. New York: Russell Sage Foundation, 1967.
98. Sudnow, David, *Passing On: The Social Organization of Dying*. Englewood Cliffs, N.J.: Prentice-Hall, Inc., 1967.
99. Sussman, Marvin B., ed., *Sociology and Rehabilitation*. Washington, D.C.: American Sociological Association, 1965.
100. U.S. National Health Service, "Limitation on Activity and Mobility Due to Chronic Conditions, U.S., July, 1957–June, 1958," *Public Health Service Publication* 584, Series B, 11 (1959).
101. Vincent, Clark and Robert Coombs, eds., *Psycho-Social Aspects of Medical Training*. 1971.
102. White, Laurens P., "Self-Image of

the Physician and the Care of Dying Patients," in New York Academy of Sciences, "Care of Patients with Fatal Illness," *Annals of the New York Academy of Sciences*, 164 (1969), 636–896.

103. WILSON, ROBERT N., *The Sociology of Health: An Introduction*. New York: Random House, Inc., 1970.

2

THE EVOLUTION OF SOCIAL MEDICINE

George Rosen

Social scientists tend to emphasize the newness of medical sociology. But viewed as the study of the relationships between health phenomena and social factors and contexts, medical sociology is seen to have deep historical roots.[1] Long before social scientists identified medical sociology as a specialty, men concerned with affairs of state and matters of policy—administrators, politicians, economists, physicians, and social reformers—were preoccupied with sociomedical problems and had made significant contributions to their solution. Indeed, sociology partly owes its origin as a science to this stream of development.

Health problems have always been intimately related to the political, economic, and social conditions of particular groups of people, but in earlier periods these relationships were not the subject of systematic investigation. In particular, the influence of social structure, and especially of its class divisions,

[1] This chapter is based to a large extent on studies in the history of social medicine carried out by the author over a period of some twenty years [140, 142, 143, 144, 148, 149, 150, 152].

on the provision of health care was plainly recognized by ancient authors, although the point was not developed. Nonetheless, sporadic observations linking social and cultural factors or situations with the health of the members of a community were recorded in antiquity and in medieval times [11, 12, 73, 84, 125, 126, 127, 169]. During the Renaissance, and later, in the seventeenth and eighteenth centuries, the need to provide medical care produced other observations about the relation between social factors and health [4, 80, 107, 109, 130, 196].

By the early eighteenth century some of the basic elements of a concept of social medicine had been brought together. These included the need to study the relation between the health of a given population and the living conditions determined by its social position, the noxious factors that act in a particular way or with special intensity on a group because of its social position, and the elements that exert a deleterious influence on health and which impede improvement of general well-being. The emergence of such ideas, however, was not an isolated phenomenon. They were part of a scheme of policy and organization of which the supreme aim was to place social and economic life in the service of the power politics of the state. This was the system that came to be known generally as *mercantilism* or, in its specifically German form, as *cameralism* [38, 51, 96, 108, 165, 175].

MERCANTILISM AND THE CONCEPT OF MEDICAL POLICE

Within the cameralist framework, a key concept in relation to problems of health and disease is the idea of *police*, derived from the Greek *politeia*. Characteristically, the theory and practice of public administration came to be known as *Polizeiwissenschaft* (police science), and the branch of this discipline dealing with health administration was designated *Medizinalpolizei* (medical police) [16, 31, 76, 80, 121, 138]. Although the beginnings of this concept were already evident in the early seventeenth century, the crystallization of the idea of medical police by the latter part of the eighteenth century heightened and fostered interest in health as a matter of public policy [46, 81, 91, 92, 133, 137, 149, 174, 178].

This trend culminated in the monumental work on medical police of Johann Peter Frank. Best known today as a pioneer in public health and social medicine, his reputation among his contemporaries was based to an equal if not greater degree on his activities as a clinician, medical educator, and hospital administrator. In 1766, he conceived a plan for the measures to be taken by government for the protection of individual and group health—that is, for medical police. The first volume of his *System einer vollstandigen medicinischen Polizey* appeared in 1779, and the sixth in 1817. Three more volumes appeared posthumously. The work is a landmark in the history of thought about the social relations of health and disease.

The system of public and private hygiene presented by Frank was based on enormous erudition and rich practical experience. A spirit of enlightenment and humanitarianism pervades the entire work but, as might be expected from a public medical official who spent his life in the service of absolute rulers, great and small, the exposition serves not so much for the instruction of the people—or even of physicians—as for the guidance of the officials who are supposed to regulate and supervise for the benefit of society all the spheres of human activity [141]. Frank's *System* appropriately opens with a consideration of population, followed by a detailed consideration of procreation, marriage, and pregnancy. According to him, it was the duty of public officials to promote marriage, and so he proposed a tax on bachelors, a suggestion realized in our time. He was convinced also of the importance of training and education for marriage, urged that a midwife be consulted prior to an expected confinement; and that all childbirths be attended by trained persons. Frank proposed legislation to enforce a reasonable period of bed rest during the puerperium and to free the mother for several weeks from any work in or outside the house which might prevent her from giving the necessary attention to her child. When necessary, he felt the state should support the mother for the first six weeks after the delivery.

He also considered problems of infant and child health. It is not possible to deal here with the multifarious details of the child-welfare program outlined by Frank; but mention must be made of his discussion of the care of schoolchildren and the necessary supervision of educational institutions. With his customary thoroughness, Frank covered the welfare of schoolchildren, ranging from accident prevention to mental hygiene, and from the lighting, heating, and ventilation of schoolrooms to the provision of athletic programs.

Frank then turned to food, clothing, recreation, and housing. Food was considered in even greater detail than maternal and child health. Problems of sanitation were examined in relation to housing, sewage disposal, and water supply. Of considerable interest is Frank's discussion of accidents and his position that many accidents are preventable. From this premise, he concluded that the health authorities should initiate a program to deal with factors responsible for such occurrences. Modern public health authorities have only recently realized the importance of accident prevention. The supplementary volumes that appeared from 1822 to 1827 deal with, among other topics, vital statistics, hospitals, military medicine, epidemic and communicable diseases, and venereal diseases. Difficult as it is to summarize a work as vast as Frank's *System*, it is clear that he achieved his objective of formulating and presenting systematically a coherent, comprehensive health policy.

The publication of Frank's *Medicinische Polizey* exerted an unusually strong influence and helped to spread the idea of medical police beyond the borders of the German states. Evidence of his influence is to be found in countries such as Hungary, Italy, Denmark, and Russia, where cultural contact with the Germanies was close. Moreover, during the late eighteenth century and well into the nineteenth, the idea of medical police appeared not only in the countries mentioned above but also in France, Great Britain, and the United States [150].

Nevertheless, neither his concept of medical police nor the solutions developed on this basis were equally applicable in all countries. The idea of medical police as employed by Frank was rooted in a particular political, economic, and social system. Based on cameralistic promises, the concept of medical police as developed by Frank and other German writers was authoritarian and paternalistic. At the end of the eighteenth century, social and political conditions obtaining in Great Britain, France, and the United States were markedly different from those in Germany. It was inevitable, therefore, that the concept would be materially altered by the impact of fundamentally different political and social institutions. Insofar as the concept of medical police was adopted outside of Germany and brought to bear upon specific problems, it tended to be limited to those areas of community life in which governmental action was most easily accepted, chiefly in the control of communicable disease and in sanitation.

In the Germanies, and also in Italy, economic progress and the social change which it entailed did not keep pace with England's and France's. While Britain and Western Europe moved away from the pattern woven out of absolutism and mercantilism, this evolution was retarded in Central Europe [21]. Reinforced by the inertia of tradition, the ideal of orderly efficiency remained the goal of public administration, and the concept of medical police continued to be applied within this framework. In terms of the progressive social aspirations connected wth the French Revolution and the problems created by the emergent industrial civilization, the idea of medical police faced the past. As part of an ideological and administrative structure whose chief function was to buttress an antiquated edifice, it lost the creative aspects which had characterized it during the eighteenth century. German administrators and authors of the first half of the nineteenth century continued to deal with questions of medical police along the lines drawn by Frank and his contemporaries, but by the middle of the nineteenth century the concept had in large measure become a sterile formula. Such practical significance as it still retained resided largely in administrative and regulatory activities concerned with the control of communicable disease, the organization and supervision of medical personnel, environmental sanitation, and the provision of medical care to the indigent. But the broad social approach—the keen awarencess of the social relations of health and disease which had characterized the thinking and writing of Johann Peter Frank and his more significant contemporaries—had been drained from the idea of medical police. As a result, when Germany encountered the health problems connected with the new industrial order, a new approach was necessary.

This does not mean, however, that medical police achieved nothing of importance or permanence. In practice, it meant a program of social action for health and welfare intended primarily to augment the power of the state. Within these limits there undoubtedly was a real concern for social welfare. Frank was fully aware of the impact of poverty among the lower classes—stunted and distorted physical development, lowered resistance to disease, and unfortunate social effects [48]. The most significant attempt to put Frank's ideas into practice was made by Franz Anton Mai, humanitarian and professor of obstetrics at the University of Heidelberg, in a health code submitted to the government of the Palatinate in 1800 [46, 113]. Mai's proposal was not realized, largely because of political conditions. Less ambitious endeavors, however, were more successful, so that even though Frank's name is not associated with them, he stimulated the enactment of various salutory laws in Europe.

In short, the development and application of the concept of medical police was a pioneer attempt at a systematic analysis of the health problems of community life. In the course of this endeavor a body of knowledge was collected, further stimulating the study of the social relations of health and disease. To France, however, fell the task of developing theoretically, under the new conditions of the early and middle-nineteenth century, the social problems of health defined by Johann Peter Frank and the other workers who created the concept of medical police.

REVOLUTION, INDUSTRIALISM, AND SOCIAL MEDICINE IN FRANCE

Mercantilism, as has been pointed out, played a major role in shaping the seventeenth and eighteenth centuries, and French views on the social relations of health are marked by its influence [152]. Although the French did not during this period arrive at a systematic formulation comparable to the concept of medical police, they were nevertheless aware of the implications of the concept. (In fact the term "police" is itself of French origin.) As early as 1711, for instance, the Abbé Claude Fleury, tutor to the grandsons of Louis XIV, referred to the subject of health police, indicating its significance for the welfare of the State and the duty of the monarch to concern himself with its problems [161]. However, the term "medical police" was not widely accepted by the French. Although a few, like F. E. Fodéré and C. C. Marc, were in some degree influenced by Frank, the majority of French medical men interested in the social aspects of health and disease pursued an independent course. When French hygienists studied the relation of social and political conditions to health, they did so within a framework very different from that in which the concept of medical police had originated and developed.

By the last decade of the eighteenth century, it was obvious to many Frenchmen that profound changes were needed to deal effectively with problems of health and welfare. This was one of the problems with which the revolutionary governments had to deal in their twofold task of liquidating the old regime and constructing the new France. The acts of the Convention represent the most advanced point attained by the French Revolution in dealing with problems of health and social welfare [148]. In 1793 and 1794, the Convention passed a series of laws establishing a national system of social assistance which included medical care. The application of those laws was incomplete, however, for the available resources were limited, and the need to provide the instruments of war took precedence over all else. After the downfall of the Robespierrists, the Convention, and then the Directory, retreated from this policy. Nonetheless, certain goals had been set. Ideas on public policy had been developed which were to influence France profoundly (and, through her, other countries) during the first half of the nineteenth century. Ideas of public service, public interest, and social utility provided the seedbed in which germinated new views on the relations among health, medicine, and society [15, 94]. The men of 1789 and 1793 could not foresee the consequences of their thoughts and acts. The triumph of the machine and the concentration of capital were still in the future, but it was in terms of the situation created by these developments that the men of 1848 endeavored to apply the ideas of their predecessors. In this attempt they carried the ideas to a more advanced level. *Social medicine*, the idea of 1848, must be seen as the fruit of this historical process, a process which has continued in a variety of circumstances to our own day.

The Revolution and the needs of the Napoleonic regime had gradually begun to industrialize France. But it was only after the Restoration, and particularly during the reign of Louis Philippe (1830–1848), that the French economy created its first railroads and heavy industries. The process of economic development imposed stresses and strains which endured until the 1870's, and which were reflected in the evolution of French thought and action on health. During this period, France faced many of the health problems that had already been encountered in England and which were being met contemporaneously in Belgium, Germany, and the United States. As in England, the introduction of steam power and machinery threw craftsmen out of work; the prospect of work and wages attracted them to urban industrial centers. The French urban population increased from 15 per cent of the total in 1830 to 25 per cent in 1846. Lack of proper housing, overcrowding, and the effects of periodic unemployment combined to make the life of the worker and his family a living death. After the Napoleonic Wars, wages declined steadily. Buret, a contemporary statistician, estimated that from 1816 to 1840 wages fell by 25 per cent [25]. It was estimated that only a third of the French people could afford to eat meat. To earn his meager wage the French worker labored from thirteen to sixteen hours a day; and it was absolutely necessary for women and children to work, also [166]. As Buchez wrote in 1833:

> In the wage-earning class, children work as soon as they are strong enough to stand on their feet, otherwise they would be too great a burden for their parents to support.... Parents have tried to have large families and have considered many children a benefit, for these little unfortunates eat less than they earn, and when they are old enough to insist on keeping their wages, they leave the house and are on their own [22].

These terrible conditions existed throughout the July Monarchy, and it was not until the 1840's that the French government took any remedial action on a national basis. The first piece of labor legislation in French history, a law regulating child labor in factories, was passed in 1841. Meanwhile, the baneful consequences of factory work and of the industrial slums forced themselves upon the attention of physicians, writers, economists, and public officials. Baudelaire asked:

> How can anyone, whatever party one may belong to and whatever prejudices one may have been brought up on, fail to be touched at the sight of this sickly multitude breathing the dust of the factories, swallowing cotton floss, their systems saturated with white lead, mercury and all the poisons necessary to the creation of works of art, sleeping amid vermin in quarters where the greatest and simplest of human virtues nestle by the side of the most hardened vices and the vomit of the penitentiary? [10].

During the same period a vigorous group of physicians and hygienists had been carrying out surveys and statistical studies of living conditions among workers in urban communities and the circumstances under which they labored in shops and factories. Practical experience both at home and abroad, acquired during the Revolutionary and Napoleonic Wars, had made many French physicians alert to health problems—especially those of the community.

This orientation was further reinforced by the fact that during the first half of the nineteenth century France was the country most advanced in political and social theory. This was the period of Fourier, Saint-Simon, Comte, Buchez, Leroux, Blanc, Proudhon, Considérant, and Pecqeur, and there was a considerable amount of cross-fertilization between social philosophy and medicine. As a result, French medicine was to a considerable degree permeated with a spirit of social change. An outbreak of cholera in Paris in 1831 (and the desire to propagate their doctrine) led the Saint

Simonians to establish a free medical service covering the twelve arrondissements of Paris and staffed by physicians belonging to the group. Then, in 1832, the *Globe,* a newspaper of Saint-Simonian persuasion, proposed that the city be provided with an adequate supply of good water, a proper sewerage system, and other facilities calculated to improve sanitary conditions and the health of the people [28, 34]. In turn, physicians participated actively in the various groups dedicated to social change. Most important, perhaps, was Philippe Buchez, who was also a historian, radical politician, and social philosopher [32, 33, 52, 55]. Other physicians were Auguste Boulland, a disciple of Buchez; Ulysse Trélat, with whom Buchez issued a *Journal des progrès des sciences et institutions médicales*; and Ange Guépin, who followed Saint-Simon and in 1835 published a survey of Nantes, his native city [62, 124]. To investigate the problems created by the new social order, numerous statistical analyses were made. As a tool for observation, the survey was well-known; it had been employed during the eighteenth and early-nineteenth centuries, particularly in the form of the regional health survey, or medical topography. This trend was encouraged by the publication of Frank's work and the appearance (between 1792 and 1795) of the first medical geography by L. L. Finke. The third volume of the latter work contains a manual for the preparation of medical topographies [139].

It is not possible to mention all the significant contributions that were made in the ensuing fifty years, but in general these monographs dealt with the physical geography and natural history of the area: the nutrition, housing, and customs of the inhabitants; health institutions and personnel; and the relation of these factors to the occurrence of endemic, epidemic, and sporadic diseases. In 1830, for instance, a committee of the New York State Medical Society proposed a plan for a "Medical Topographical Survey of the State" and pointed out that since the chief object of medical topography is "to ascertain the influences of climate, soil, different occupations, and moral and physical causes in the production or modification of diseases," attention must be directed to the age, sex, constitution, occupation, and diet of those most liable to be affected "by endemic or epidemic diseases" [183].

Throughout this period, the methods available for the study of social problems of health were rational empiricism, critical observation, the survey and, from the late 1820's onward, statistical analysis [146]. Statistical methods were eagerly accepted and applied with considerable vigor, so that increasing numbers of studies of health problems based on numerical data began to appear. Some of the studies were undertaken in the course of official inquiries, others by private citizens whose interest was attracted to a specific social or heath problem. Many were concerned with the question of differential mortality and the effect on health of such factors as social class, occupation, rate, imprisonment, intemperance, and lack of proper sanitation.

France, a leader in medicine and hygiene during the first half of the nineteenth century, produced numerous such studies [2].[2] The outstanding figure of the period was the physician Louis René Villermé, best known for his study of the health conditions of textile workers. His report, published in 1840, aroused public opinion and led to the child-labor law of 1841. Villermé was interested, as well, in the

[2] An invaluable source of material is the *Annales d'hygiène publique*, which began to appear in 1829.

relation between social circumstances and differential mortality and morbidity. In 1828, he showed that mortality rates in France were closely linked to the living conditions of the different social classes [185]. Two years later, he published his study of mortality in different sections of Paris, which pointed to a clear relationship between poverty and disease [187]. This point was reinforced by his study (which appeared in the same year) of infant and child mortality in two districts of Paris [188]. Villermé was likewise concerned with all the factors that enter into the standard of living and with their effect on physical growth and development. In 1829, he reported on the influence of income, nutrition, and housing on growth and physique [162, 186]. He also studied the mean duration of illness at different ages so as to apply this knowledge to the organization of mutual-aid societies.

These interests were shared by other investigators. L. F. Benoiston de Chateauneuf studied the differential mortality of rich and poor [29]. He also dealt with the influence of different occupations on pulmonary tuberculosis, a subject investigated by H. C. Lombard as well. The other great French hygienist of this period, A. J. B. Parent-Duchâtelet, who is best known today for his treatise on prostitution in Paris, also gave considerable attention to the health problems of various occupational groups [114, 115]. He dealt with the health problems of sewer workers, and together with D'Arcet studied the effects of tobacco on the health of workers handling it. In 1838, L. Tanquerel des Planches published his classic treatise on lead poisoning, and in 1846, Th. V. J. Roussel published a book on the diseases of workers in match factories, a pioneer study of occupational phosphorus necrosis. Nor were these the only health problems involving social factors that were investigated. Efforts were made to determine why the working-class population and the peasants did not readily accept vaccination against smallpox [7, 30]. Medical indices or aspects of social disintegration received attention [19, 37, 182]. In 1828, for example, Étienne de Sainte-Marie surveyed the problems faced by the Health Council of Lyon. In his report, he discussed abortion, alcoholism, prostitution, factory work, and poisoning [159]. Indeed, the conclusion reached by Durkheim that suicide is indicative of a lack of social integration had already been reached by students of the problem earlier in the nineteenth century.

New conditions led to the emergence of new ideas—products of direct contact with the social reality of industrialism and the lives of the workers. And with them came new or unfamiliar terms to designate these concepts. "Socialism" became generally current after 1834, having appeared in a historic article by Pierre Leroux [44, 123]. There was a recognition that the good of society, the welfare of the individual, and the interests of the state are not necessarily identical and that it is therefore necessary to study how these may be coordinated for the greatest benefit and to substitute social questions for political questions [45, 161]. It is in this sense that Jules Leroux, in 1833, asserted that the practical purpose of political economy is "the same as that of political science, namely, to found *social* science." It is "the *human factor* . . . which dominates both economic and political factors. And the science which treats of it, or *social science* properly so called, likewise dominates both political and economic science" [44].

These views were the soil within which the idea of *social medicine* germinated and out of which the term emerged in 1848. An early use of the term *social hygiene* occurs in a thesis presented by J. A. Rochoux in 1838 [136]. Pointing out that man is a social animal who necessarily exists in society, he asserted that hygiene may be divided into two major branches: private or individual hygiene, which may be left entirely to the initiative of the individual; and public or social hygiene, which requires legal and administrative action. However, Rochoux recognized that such a sharp separation cannot always be maintained in practice; not infrequently the community must take action in the interest of the group which will affect the individual whether or not this is desired.

In 1844, the physician Fourcault used the term "social hygiene" in a work concerned with the prevention of chronic diseases, especially pulmonary phthisis [47]. He was particularly interested in providing for children who had to work and for adults who labored under unhealthful conditions. Such action, he claimed, would lead to improved moral conditions among workers, for unemployment and poverty lead to illness, vice, theft, crimes of violence, and suicide. Thus, the use of the adjective "social" in connection with medical problems was by no means new when Jules Guérin introduced the term and the concept "social medicine" in March, 1848. At a time when revolutionary hopes were still running high, Guérin appealed to the French medical profession to act for the public good, to help create the new society for which the February Revolution had opened the way [63, 64, 65]:

> We have already had occasion to indicate the numerous relations which exist between medicine and public affairs.... Instead of those halfhearted and uncoordinated approaches which we have tended to include under such rubrics as medical police, public health, and forensic medicine, the time has come to collect these separate parts into an organized whole and to raise them to their highest potential under the designation of *social medicine*, which better expresses their purpose....

Guérin divided social medicine into four parts: social physiology, social pathology, social hygiene, and social therapy. These were to deal, respectively, with the relation between the physical and mental condition of a population and its laws or other social institutions; the study of social problems in relation to health and disease; the determination of measures for health promotion and disease prevention; and the provision of medical and other measures to deal with social disintegration and other conditions that societies may experience. In this sense, Guérin saw social medicine as "the key to the most important issues of our period of regeneration . . ." and the medical profession as the most appropriate group to use this tool.

This emphasis on the role of the physician in social matters was the result of several factors. On the one hand, some felt that the doctor was closer than anyone else to the problems of the day; on the other, the situation of the medical profession in most European countries was unsatisfactory both socially and economically, and physicians wished to improve it. Owing to the insufficient number of fully qualified physicians, auxiliary and ancillary groups were trained and given permission to practice. Prussia, for example, had not only physicians, but also *Wundärzte* (surgeons), first and second-grade; Austria had its *Landärzte*; Britain had physicians, surgeons, and apothecaries; and France had *officiers de santé* for its rural districts. In most European countries at this time there was a demand for a unified medical profession, all of whose members would be qualified by similar training and would receive adequate compensation for their work. It was also felt, by some in France and Germany, that such an organization of the medical profession might also be used to provide more and better medical care for most of the population. Buchez made such a proposal for a national medical service in 1839, and again in 1848. Raspail, a chemist, advanced a similar idea in 1843, and Küntzli, a physician, offered a plan for such a service in 1846 [87, 90]. Indeed, the problem of medical care for the masses was so urgent that Louis Napoleon, in his bid for power, endeavored to ingratiate himself with the workers by offering a program of social legislation, including old-age pensions, free medical care for the indigent, and a compensation scheme for injured workers.

"MEDICINE IS A SOCIAL SCIENCE": 1848 IN GERMANY

The ideas and proposals that were advanced in France before and during the revolutionary movement of 1848 were not limited to that country. From Paris, liberal ideas spread to Germany. Arnold Ruge, a democratic German journalist, wrote in 1844 that "Every attempt to make science serviceable to the world, every association of science with politics is directly linked to France" [156]. Various French investigators studied the influence of poverty, occupation, nutrition, housing, and other factors on health, and these studies influenced German medical men and others concerned with similar matters. During the revolutionary years of 1848 they joined forces to secure overdue health reforms. Prominent among the leaders of this movement were Salomon Neumann, Rudolf Virchow, and Rudolf Leubuscher. These men were keenly aware of the role of social factors in health problems. Basic to their thinking is the view vigorously asserted by Neumann in 1847, that "medical science is intrinsically and essentially a *social* science, and as long as this is not recognized in practice we shall not be able to enjoy its benefits and shall have to be satisfied with an empty shell and a sham" [111]. Or, as Virchow formulated the idea: "Medicine is a social science, and politics nothing but medicine on a grand scale."

The proponents of the idea of medicine as a social science were not dreaming of some vague utopia; they employed it, rather, as a convenient conceptual formulation under which to sum up definite principles upon which they based a program of action [1]. The first of these principles is that the health of the people is a matter of direct societal concern, and that society has an obligation to protect and assure the health of its members [189].

The second, as noted by Neumann, is that social and economic conditions have an important and—in many instances—crucial impact on health and disease, and that these relations must be subjected to scientific investigation [111, 112]. Virchow's basic standpoint was very similar. His investigation of the Silesian typhus epidemic of 1847 led him to conclude that its causes were as much social, economic, and political as they were biological and physical. He later elaborated this view in a series of articles on public health, in which he discussed the relation of medical problems to social and political developments. Virchow conceived the scope of public health as broadly as possible: "For if medicine is really to accomplish its great task, it must intervene in political and social life. It must point out the hindrances that impede the normal functioning of vital processes, and effect their removal" [190].

The third principle that follows logically is that the steps taken to promote health and to combat disease must be social as well as medical. The broad outlines of the program of action proposed on the basis of these principles are probably best represented by a draft for a Public Health Law submitted to the Berlin Society of Physicians and Surgeons on March 30, 1849 [86]. According to this document, public health has as its objectives: (1) the healthy mental and physical development of the citizen; (2) the prevention of all dangers to health; and (3) the control of disease. Public health must care for society as a whole by considering those conditions that may adversely affect health—such as soil, industry, food, and housing—and it must protect each individual by considering those conditions that prevent him from caring for his health. These may be considered in two major categories: conditions (such as poverty and infirmity) in which the individual has the right to request assistance from the state; and conditions (such as transmissible disease and mental illness) in which the state has the right and the obligation to interfere with the personal liberty of the individual. Public health can fulfill these duties by supplying well-trained medical personnel in sufficient numbers and by providing adequate organization and appropriate institutions within which their work can be performed.

It should be clear that during this period the terms "public health," "social hygiene," and "social medicine" were used interchangeably by many. Nor is this surprising, for as long as public health was focused on the improvement of environmental circumstances and permeated with a spirit of social reform, its goals, to a considerable extent, coincided with and overlapped those advocated by proponents of social medicine [151]. Only as sanitary reform began, in a narrow sense, to achieve its aims, and developments in medical bacteriology turned attention away from the control of the social and physical environment to the control of specific communicable diseases, did public health begin to achieve a distinctive character. In the course of the twentieth century, however, concern with the social aspects of health has again become a prominent feature of public health and has tended to bring it closer to social medicine and to a second, new discipline: medical sociology.

While the Germans did not specifically divide their concept of medicine as a social science into social physiology, pathology, prophylaxis, and therapy, much of what they wrote—and the specific proposals they made for action—imply such a framework. Thus, as an extension of his views on the relations of medicine to society, Virchow developed a theory of epidemic disease as a manifestation of social and cultural maladjustment [191]. He differentiated between natural and artificial epidemics, basing the distinction on the degree to which cultural factors interpose themselves between nature and man. He defined artificial epidemics as "attributes of society, products of a false culture, or of a culture which is not available to all classes. . . . Here belong typhus, scurvy, the sweating sickness, and tuberculosis" [189]. Furthermore, these artificial "epidemics occur not only as a result of social contradictions, but also as significant manifestations of the historical process." He believed that such outbreaks occur at nodal points in history, during periods of political and intellectual revolution. Interestingly a very similar view was expressed by Sigerist in 1928 [168].

At the same time, voices were raised

for governmental action, and many specific measures were proposed. An important problem was the provision of medical care for the indigent, and proposals were made by Virchow and others for public medical services, including free choice of physician. It was realized, however, that provision of medical care was not enough, that it must go hand in hand with social prophylaxis. In consequence Virchow proclaimed *the right of the citizen to work* as a fundamental principle to be included in the constitution of a democratic state [105]. Here Virchow was no doubt influenced by the action of the French provisional government of 1848 [99].

The probem of the industrial worker also demanded attention. Although industrialization began later in Germany than in England and France, and proceeded at a slower pace during the first half of the nineteenth century, by 1848 the existence of a wage-earning class —an industrial proletariat—could no longer be overlooked. As in England and France, industrialization was ushered in by a slaughter of the innocents. Those that survived the cradle were given over to the tender mercies of the factory and the mine. It was plain, said Virchow, that "the proletariat in ever increasing degree became the victim of disease and epidemics, its children either died prematurely or developed into cripples" [105]. To deal with this problem, his colleague, the psychiatrist Leubuscher, proposed a program of industrial hygiene which emphasized the legislative regulation of working conditions [105]. Particularly important was the question of limiting the working day. Leubuscher advocated the prohibition of labor by children under fourteen, reduction of the working day in dangerous occupations, protection of pregnant women, the establishment of standards for ventilation of workrooms, and the prevention of industrial poisoning through the use of nontoxic materials.

Demands were also made for uniform licensure of medical practitioners, entitling them to practice in every German state; appointment of physicians to official positions on the basis of competitive examinations; and the establishment of a National Ministry of Health [1, 105]. Very important was the recognition of the necessity for reliable statistics in the investigation of the causal relations between social conditions and health problems. Neumann was most active in agitating for the collection of accurate statistics, and for statistical data on all elements of social life that in any way have a bearing on problems of health and illness [111, 112].

The revolution of 1848 was defeated in Germany, as it had been in France, and with this development the medical reform movement came to a quick end. The medical leaders of 1848—Virchow and Neumann—remained active in politics and loyal to their principles. In the decades that followed 1848, the broad program of health reform was transformed into a more limited program of sanitary reform that was practically attainable. Not until the end of the century were the views of Virchow and the other reformers to come to fruition in a new discipline.

FROM VIRCHOW TO GROTJAHN

Some awareness of the social problems of health and disease in terms of medical police existed in Great Britain throughout the earlier nineteenth century. Nevertheless, the idea came to be limited more and more to the control of epidemic disease and the supervision of environmental sanitation [150]. The concept of medical police as developed in Germany could hardly be expected to flourish in Britain, where economic liberalism was the prevailing doctrine. This philosophy, with its acceptance of social atomism and its belief in the manifestation—thorugh inexorable economic laws—of a predetermined harmony of man and nature, carried with it a stubborn insistence on the absolute necessity of submission to the alleged laws of society. Discrepancy between social fact and social theory was not generally accepted as affecting the hard core of economic liberalism, and it was not until the latter nineteenth century that the gradual and peripheral erosion which had been carried on in practice began to receive recognition.

Such an intellectual environment was hardly conducive to analyses of the social aspects of health and disease, and no theoretical formulations comparable to those of the French and the Germans were developed. Nevertheless, stubborn facts intruded themselves into public consciousness as the Industrial Revolution inexorably changed the living conditions of millions of people. Questions of ill health, poor housing, dangerous and injurious occupations, and excessive morbidity and mortality could not be overlooked, and investigations of these social problems were undertaken, often by medical men, to find out how they had arisen and what could be done about them.

The high incidence of communicable disease led to a study by James Philips Kay, in 1832, of the condition of workers in the cotton mills of Manchester [82]. Vice, physical degradation, poverty, and illness were found to be intimately interlocked. For proof of the relation of ill health to other forms of social pathology, Kay cited the records of the medical charities of Manchester. After reviewing the statistical data, he concluded, for example, that more than half of the inhabitants of Manchester were "either so destitute or so degraded as to require the assistance of public charity, in bringing their offspring into the world" [74]. Kay saw no necessary connection between the existing socioeconomic organization and the various social maladjustments that he had observed, yet his observations remain acute throughout. Discussing Irish immigration and the consequent effect on conditions in Manchester, he indicates an awareness—though as yet unclear and lacking precise formulation—that the dismal scenes in his portrayal are the product of a cultural cataclysm.[3]

Some physicians, however, did recognize that social and economic institutions, especially industrialism, had significant and necessary connections with the problems of the factory workers. Outstanding in this respect was C. Turner Thackrah, whose pioneer treatise on occupational health appeared in 1831. His book became a bible for the factory reformers, and he actively supported the struggle to restrict child labor [39]. During the 1830's and into the 1840's, a gradual but definite shift in thought and attitude about the social aspects of health and disease became evident. The creation of the Poor Law Commission and the studies initiated by its secretary, Edwin Chadwick, provided the basis for this ideological development [68].

Empirical recognition of the relation between social problems and medical care went hand-in-hand with programs for remedial action. Testimony before Lord Ashley's Committee on Medical Poor Relief indicated that pauperism

[3] Social scientists have recently recognized that the experiences of a large part of European society in the early days of industrial capitalism are comparable to the changes experienced by various African peoples after contact with European civilization and its representatives [180].

in the legal sense was a relatively small matter, compared with medical indigence. On the basis of testimony by the physicians—Southwood Smith, W. P. Alison, and others—the conclusion "that the *preventive* should be combined with the *remedial* provision for the health of the poorer classes" seemed inevitable [20, 68, 95, 129]. One witness, Henry W. Rumsey, recommended that "medical care and inspection should be brought as near as possible to the habitations of the poor. In towns it must be forced upon them, both for their own benefit, and for the safety of the community" [68].

Few efforts, however, were made to develop a systematic theoretical basis for such programs. An outstanding exception is Rumsey's endeavor to formulate a theory of public health and medical care within a framework of social organization and action—in short, a social policy for health care. In 1856, he published *Essays on State Medicine,* in which he emphasized that the promotion of health and the prevention of disease were matters of social concern and required governmental action. Rumsey pointed out that various diseases were caused by factors in the social environment; he laid great stress on health education and urged that "district medical officers" be appointed to carry out the proposed programs [157].

At the time Rumsey expressed these views, the health officer was still a novelty, the first such official having been appointed in 1847 at Liverpool. The appointment of health officers for various towns and districts, as well as increased interest in public health, led the authorities of St. Thomas's Hospital (in 1856) to establish a course of lectures on public health, the first of its kind in England. Edward Headlam Greenhow was appointed to this lectureship, and in preparation for his lecture undertook to collect statistical information on the preventable causes of disease. Greenhow concluded that numerous environmental factors cause diseases that can be prevented, and that "some of these causes of preventable sickness and premature death arise necessarily from the circumstances of our social system." As an example, he discussed the relation of infant mortality to the employment of mothers in factories. From 1862 to 1865, John Simon, Medical Officer to the Privy Council, undertook various medical studies on its behalf, concerning himself particularly with the investigation of food supply, housing and physical environment, and industrial circumstances. The studies showed that these factors were related to the prevalence of ill health among British workers [56, 172, 173].

By the end of the 1860's, a considerable advance had been made in Britain toward a socially oriented view of health and disease. Various administrators, physicians, and philanthropists recognized that the greater or lesser prevalence of disease was intimately related to social and economic factors, and that these relations could be studied precisely, using, for the most part, statistical data and methods. Economic liberalism was still the dominant social philosophy, but in practice and to a lesser degree in theory, it was being challenged as untenable for an industrial society. However, it was not until the 1880's that the interplay of long-term trends and particular events came to a focus in new formulations of social problems and societal values. Out of this recasting of social goals and ideologies, a theory of social medicine was to emerge in Great Britain in the twentieth century [3, 4, 27, 97, 184, 192].

During the last quarter of the nineteenth century, the basic lines of thought that had been developed earlier in the century and which had been sharply formulated in the concepts of "social medicine" and of "medicine as a social science" were kept alive by far-seeing, socially minded men [140]. An interesting, well-developed system of social medicine was presented in 1865 by Armand-Joseph Meynne, a Belgian army doctor. Studies of the social, economic, and health status of the Belgian people during the preceding thirty years placed at Meynne's disposal a considerable mass of data [14, 41, 42, 79]. His *Topographie médicale de la Belgique* [106] is divided into four parts: the first deals with the geography, geology, and climatology of Belgium; the second, with the morbidity and mortality of the Belgian population (and includes a discussion of the causes of the most prevalent or most serious diseases); the third, with the relations of the diseases to soil, climate, poverty, nutrition, housing, and alcoholism; the fourth, various measures designed to alleviate or remove the conditions previously described. Special attention must be called to Chapter 6 of Meynne's treatise. Here he takes up the diseases of greater importance, analyzes each in terms of its causation, and indicates the social factors involved. This section is unique; not until Grotjahn's *Soziale Pathologie* (1915) does one find anything comparable [60].

A number of other medical men recognized the influence of social conditions on health and discussed it from various points of view. In Russia, Friedrich Erismann spoke of the artificial environment imposed upon man by his social condition and of the role of hygiene in preventing or mitigating problems related to this factor [167]. The Swiss physician, Fridolin Schuler, turned his attention to numerous sociomedical problems, but especially to those of factory workers [24]. In France, Alexandre Layet published a sociomedical study of rural populations in 1882 [88]. Six years later, Jules Rochard published a treatise on social hygiene, in which he dealt with housing, consumer cooperation, anti-alcoholism, industrial hygiene, and school health [135].

Among the German representatives of this period, one of the most interesting and least known is Eduard Reich, an eccentric and peripatetic medical scholar. In his *System der Hygiene* which appeared in 1870–1871, Reich set up four branches of hygiene: moral; social; dietetic; and police. Although his categories are not entirely congruent with those in use at present, Reich's "social hygiene" may be considered an early combination of social medicine and social work. Social hygiene, he asserted, studies phenomena of social life in order to maintain the well-being of the community [46, 134].

The ideas of Eduard Reich remained almost unknown, but similar views were expressed by Max von Pettenkofer, his better-known contemporary. Von Pettenkofer made hygiene an experimental laboratory science, yet he was fully aware that man's health is influenced not only by his physical environment but also by the social world in which he lives. Customs, habits, political and socioeconomic conditions influence the health and mortality of a population [120].

The significant influence that social institutions and conditions exert upon health was also pointed out in 1874 by Nikolaus Alois Geigel, professor of hygiene at Würzburg. He dealt with the effects of the rise of capitalism, the growth of an industrial proletariat, increasing urbanization, and the unhygienic conditions under which workers were compelled to live, and with the relations of these changing social and economic conditions to health and illness. Like many of his predecessors and contemporaries, Geigel insisted on the need for accurate statistics that would throw light on social phenomena [50].

Nevertheless, the last decades of the nineteenth century in Germany were not favorable for the development of a clearer conceptual formulation of health and illness in social terms. After 1871, the movement of 1848 had little relevance to most Germans. At the same time, the natural sciences developed rapidly and achieved enormous prestige in medicine, and the emergence of medical bacteriology seemed to answer the problem of disease causation. Under these conditions it was not difficult to overlook the patient and his environment, and to emphasize the cause-and-effect relationships between germs and disease. As Emil Behring declared in 1893, the study of infectious diseases could now be pursued unswervingly without being sidetracked by social considerations and reflections on social policy [13].

Yet at the very peak of its triumph, interest in the significance of social conditions in the causation of disease led various physicians to react against the exaggerated bacteriological standpoint. Among these were Max Rubner in Germany, Ferdinand Hueppe in Austria, and Émile Duclaux in France. Hueppe summed up their viewpoint in 1899 with the statement: "Hygiene is a social art which has developed in response to social need; consequently it must and will always be social hygiene, or it will not exist at all" [75]. Duclaux pointed out that the spread, severity, and duration of communicable diseases involved not only the infectious agents but a number of other factors such as nutrition, working and living conditions, education, and income [40].

ALFRED GROTJAHN AND SOCIAL HYGIENE

At the very time that Emil Behring was ardently proclaiming bacteriology as the ultimate medical truth and Koch as its prophet, a young German medical student conceived the idea of systematically investigating medical problems in the light of social science so as "to arrive finally at a theory of social pathology and social hygiene, which with its own methods . . . would be used to investigate and to determine how life and health, particularly of the poorer classes, are dependent on social conditions and the environment" [60, 61, 66]. The student was Alfred Grotjahn, who, in pursuit of this aim, produced a concept of social hygiene (he reserved the term "social medicine" for medical care) which stimulated the theoretical development of social medicine during the first half of the twentieth century.

This was also the period during which the term *medical sociology* made its appearance, a development which was by no means purely coincidental. At the turn of the century many of those engaged in health and social work were not entirely satisfied with what they saw. Booth's investigations in London from 1889 to 1902 and Rowntree's study of York in 1899 showed that a substantial portion of the English laboring population was living at a subsubsistence level. The more the condition of the poorer classes was studied, the more unsatisfactory their health and social situation was found to be. To be sure, the crude death rate had declined, but maternal mortality was still high. Although infant mortality had declined, the condition of children attending school as well as that of preschool children was found to be extremely poor. Malnutrition was rife, and the health and physical fitness of the more poorly paid members of the working class were defective. Similar evils were present in the slum districts of great cities in the United States and in Europe. The inescapable fact that poverty, disease, vice, and suffering were large-scale urban phenomena brought forth groups and programs for reform of social and health conditions in England, America, Germany, and other similarly situated countries. These developments must be seen in the perspective of a worldwide historical evolution that has brought into being the modern state, with its concern for the needs of the individual, family, and community for organized social security and health services. By the first decade of the present century, it was no longer possible to consider poverty the "natural" punishment of the poor for their shortcomings, and poverty came to be diagnosed as a social disease. It was equally clear that the consequences of poverty on health must be dealt with if the community was to be maintained in a healthy state. This was the context out of which both social medicine and medical sociology first emerged.

Grotjahn's theory received its fullest expression in the best-known of his publications, the classic *Soziale Pathologie*, which first appeared in 1911 [60]. In it he advanced a number of principles that are fundamental to a systematic study of human disease from a social viewpoint:

1. The significance of a disease from a social point of view is determined in the first place by the *frequency* with which it occurs.
2. It is necessary to know the *form*, as well as the frequency, with which the particular disease occurs most often.
3. The etiological relationship between social conditions and disease may be expressed in four ways. Social conditions may: (a) create or favor a predisposition for a disease; (b) cause disease directly; (c) transmit the causes of disease; and (d) influence the course of disease.
4. Not only are the origin and causes of diseases determined by social factors, but these diseases may in turn exert an influence on social conditions, particularly through their outcome.
5. In the case of a disease which is important from a social viewpoint, it must be established whether medical treatment can exert an appreciable influence on its prevalence, and whether such therapeutic success as may be achieved is important from a social point of view.
6. Preventing diseases or influencing their course by social measures requires attention to the social and economic environment of the patient.

Grotjahn realized that many diseases of social importance were chronic in character, and that a large number of these were preventable or could at least be controlled. He felt that health education could be an extremely important factor in this connection, and was of the opinion that the physician should use his position to promote developments in social hygiene so that the benefits of medical knowledge could be applied to all the people. For the physician to understand these responsibilities, Grotjahn saw that the teaching of social hygiene would have to become a part of the medical curriculum [58].

Grotjahn emphasized that investigations in social hygiene would make use of the methods of statistics, demography, anthropology (especially anthropometry), economics, and sociology. His own formal training in social science had been obtained by attending the seminar of Gustav Schmoller. Here he acquired the social-science methodology of the period and prepared a paper on the changes in food consumption by workers that had occurred in

Germany and other countries as a part of the process of industrialization. In it he warned against judging diets too exclusively on the basis of caloric adequacy [57]. Grotjahn also considered physical and social degeneration one of the major problems of social hygiene. With this in mind he emphasized the importance of eugenics [59].

Despite Grotjahn's insistence on the need for sociological analysis of health problems, he could not move beyond the scientific level of the period. Sociology in Germany was formal, theoretical, and involved in controversies over values. At a time when Max Weber demanded a sharp separation between basic research and applied science, between social science and social policy, there could hardly be much contact with a social hygiene that Grotjahn regarded as having two aspects: *descriptive* and *normative* [193, 194]. For Grotjahn, social hygiene reached its apogee in its "conscious purpose to spread hygienic measures, which at first always benefit a preferred minority, to the entire population and thus carry on a progressive improvement of existing conditions." From a sociological point of view, social hygiene remained incomplete.

Grotjahn (who taught at the University of Berlin) was the outstanding figure of a group of men who developed, during the first three decades of the twentieth century, a concept of social medicine that could be used in medical education and medical practice. An important initial impulse toward the development of the field had derived from Bismarck's social-insurance program, itself a product of the problems attendant upon industrialism and urbanism. A number of physicians realized, however, that to restrict the field of social medicine to the medical aspects of social insurance was to take too restricted a view of the matter. Consequently, many of those who concerned themselves with social medicine endeavored to define the field so as to broaden it and yet keep it within clear conceptual and practical bounds.

The literature on social medicine that appeared during the period from 1900 to 1930 is extensive, and one can do no more in this survey than to select several authors who in some respect contributed to the development of the field. Prominent in this group were Ludwig Teleky, Adolf Gottstein, Alfons Fischer, and J. Kaup. A survey of social medicine as it had developed in Germany prior to World War I is available in a 1913 volume edited by Mosse and Tugendreich [109]. On the whole, the editors follow the ideas and system of Grotjahn. But where the latter believed that social-hygiene measures should culminate in eugenic action, the former regarded the equalization of life expectancy for all socioeconomic classes as the goal of social medicine.

The level of development attained by social medicine in Germany up to the outbreak of World War I is summed up in the statement made in 1913 by Adolf Gottstein: "Social etiology can now be regarded as accepted" [53, 177]. He and his peers believed that research methods were receiving too little attention and agreed on the preeminent significance of statistical materials and methods. Teleky pointed out that the effects of social conditions on health can be determined directly by observation as well as indirectly with the help of statistics. This emphasis may be related to the fact that Teleky's major interest was industrial medicine and hygiene, which also require observation. Furthermore, Teleky's emphasis on the pivotal role of social class in health differentials may serve as a clue to an understanding of the lack of emphasis on empirical, firsthand investigations. Social structure manifested itself so prominently in terms of class position and its economic, educational, and other correlates that it seemed to many a fixed variable.

The period following World War I did not add much to the theory of social medicine. Manuals and handbooks for medical administrators, students, and practicing physicians were published, but for the most part these did not concern themselves extensively with theory. A volume by Ickert and Weicksel (1932) is noteworthy because of its division of the field of social medicine into four parts—social physiology and pathology, social diagnosis, social therapy, and social prophylaxis—which are reminiscent of Jules Guérin. Also of interest is their reference to Mary Richmond's concept of social diagnosis, from which stem social therapy and social prophylaxis [78].

Social medicine as it developed in Germany, in particular the ideas of Grotjahn, had a wide influence on the development of this field in other countries, notably in Central and Eastern Europe. Social medicine has been extensively developed in the Scandinavian countries and in Italy, France, Switzerland, Holland, Belgium, Czechoslovakia, and Yugoslavia. In the Soviet Union, all health problems are considered from a social angle. The developing nations are now beginning to move into this field as they experience increasingly the problems attendant on economic development.

In general, developments in different countries may be regarded as reflecting the conditions, traditions, and problems of the particular country. Italians, for example, have tended to emphasize the physiology and pathology of occupation; in France and Belgium, attention has been directed to the social hygiene of infancy and childhood, control of tuberculosis and venereal diseases, and occupational health. In Yugoslavia, under Andrija Stampar, the emphasis was on the problems of a rural population; since World War II there has been a shift to problems connected with industrialization and the movement of a rural population to urban centers. A review of social medicine in various countries of the world from the turn of the century to 1950 is to be found in a useful compendium by René Sand [162], one of the leading representatives of social medicine of the last generation [160].

SOCIAL MEDICINE IN GREAT BRITAIN AND THE UNITED STATES

In Great Britain, as in the United States, interest in social medicine is relatively recent. Social factors in health and disease had been recognized by physicians and laymen, but little or no concerted effort had been made to organize and apply such knowledge systematically.[4] Indeed, as we shall see, in the United States such problems tended to emerge as those of medical sociology rather than as problems of social medicine. In Great Britain, influences within medicine itself and in society as a whole led to the appearance, in the 1940's, of both theoretical and practical sociomedical developments. It was recognized that the rise and expansion of medical specialism tended to compartmentalize the thought and action of the physician.

[4] Contributions to specific social aspects of health or to medical problems having social implications are to be found scattered throughout American medical and public health literature. One need only consult, for example, the early volumes of the reports of the American Public Health Association, or to recall the names of Daniel Drake, John H. Griscom, Stephen Smith, Lemuel Shattuck, Joseph Goldberger, and C. E. A. Winslow. Nevertheless, it is true that these data were never brought together as a basis for a theory of social medicine.

The sick person—the patient—had to be seen as a unity involving his environment if the best medical care was to be provided [98, 110]. Moreover, by the 1930's, the ideology of individualism had worn exceedingly thin and a consciousness of social and economic problems was acute. Various studies on the social aspects of health and disease appeared: G. C. M'Gonigle and Kirby's *Poverty and Public Health*; J. B. Orr's *Food, Health, and Income*; and R. M. Titmuss's *Poverty and Population*. Another significant undertaking was the work of the Peckham Health Centre in London, started in 1926 by G. Scott Williamson and Innes H. Pearse [117, 118, 119]. At this institution, the attempt was made to develop health as a positive social value on the basis of a fundamental social unit: the family.

Suggestions and proposals for the teaching of the social aspects of disease under the name *preventive medicine* came from a variety of governmental and private agencies. By 1943 these ideas had advanced so far that an Institute of Social Medicine was set up at Oxford with John A. Ryle as the first professor of social medicine. Some two years later, F. A. E. Crew was appointed to a chair of social medicine at Edinburgh. Since then a number of other chairs of social medicine have been created in Great Britain [102]. Ryle defined social medicine as including "the whole of the public and industrial health services, the social services and the remedial services of a community" [158].

Although social medicine is today a recognized subject of instruction in British medical schools, the social element apparently does not involve explicit inclusion of the social sciences (sociology, social anthropology, social psychology). The content of such a course is essentially the same as that offered by a department of preventive medicine in the United States [54, 101, 179]. Meanwhile, research has been carried on very actively. The Medical Research Council's Social Medicine Unit, headed by J. N. Morris, has carried out numerous studies of peptic ulcer, perinatal mortality, coronary heart disease, and hypertension. For the most part the emphases in the sociomedical studies are statistical and epidemiological, although clinical studies have been undertaken. Investigations from the viewpoint of social administration have largely been the product of Titmuss and his associates at the London School of Economics, while social psychiatry has been advanced by studies at Maudsley Hospital under the leadership of Sir Aubrey Lewis.

The roots of social medicine in the United States are to be found generally in public health and organized social work, which emerged out of organized charity during the 1890's. It was here that health work and the social science of the period found a common ground for action—in the prevention of tuberculosis and the fight for decent working conditions in factories and mines, improved nutrition, and better housing. These efforts emerged as public health and medical sociology; social medicine came later. As early as 1879, John Shaw Billings linked the study of hygiene with sociology [17]. In 1895, Charles McIntire defined medical sociology as:

> [1] the science of the social phenomena of the physicians themselves as a class apart and separate; and the science which investigates the laws regulating the relations between the medical profession and human society as a whole; treating of the structure of both, how the present conditions came about, what progress civilization has effected and indeed everything relating to the subject [100].

In some degree McIntire anticipated Straus's distinction between "the sociology of medicine" and "sociology in medicine." Elizabeth Blackwell used the term *medical sociology* in 1902 as the title for a collection of essays ranging in subject from sex hygiene and education to medical education and the religion of health [18]. In 1910, James P. Warbasse published a book entitled *Medical Sociology*, in which he advocated various reform measures, including health education. Warbasse was also an ardent exponent of cooperation between producers and consumers, and endeavored to apply these principles to health problems. The same year also saw the formation of a Section on Sociology in the American Public Health Association which lasted until 1921, when it was disbanded. Its members were physicians and social workers. Among the subjects it considered were the labor of women and children, housing, and the use of the referendum in obtaining needed health legislation. It reflected the sociology of the period, which was concerned with social problems associated with immigration, race relations, slums, rural life, and related matters. It was closely identified with philanthropy, social work, and that development of liberal Protestantism known as the social gospel [116]. The keynote for the period from the health viewpoint was struck by Hermann Biggs in 1911. He wrote:

> Disease is largely a removable evil, it continues to afflict humanity, not only because of incomplete knowledge of its causes and lack of individual and public hygiene, but also because it is extensively fostered by harsh economic and industrial conditions and by wretched housing in congested communities. These conditions and consequently the diseases which spring from them can be removed by better social organization.

Out of this same context others began to speak of social medicine. Francis Lee Dunham in 1925 tried to develop such a concept. Basic to its origin, according to Dunham, was the need in welfare work "for a field of preventive medicine to which social sciences, psychology, psychiatry, and various other departments shall contribute but upon no one of which shall the entire burden of responsibility fall" [43]. In defining the function of social medicine, Dunham put the emphasis on personal and social adjustment. Social medicine, he said, helps to harmonize human behavior, and to organize conduct. The eugenic approach to social problems is clearly evident in Dunham's thinking. But this venture was stillborn.

One might expect that the advent of the Depression would have turned the minds of some in this direction. Nevertheless, with one outstanding exception, this was not the case. It may be that the almost exclusive concentration on the economic aspects of medical care which occupied many students of health problems militated against the development of a theory of social medicine. The exception was Edgar Sydenstricker, who in 1933 brought out his study on *Health and Environment*—a masterly analysis which broke down the idea of environment into its component aspects, and then showed the relation of each of these to health problems. Sydenstricker thus laid the basis for a theory of social medicine, but unfortunately he never went on to develop such a theory.

Sporadic references to social medicine occur during the 1930's. Michael M. Davis called attention to the possibilities for social research in medicine [35, 36]. The importance of a concept of social medicine was repeatedly emphasized by Henry E. Sigerist [170]. After World War II this idea gained increased interest. In 1947 the New York Academy of Medicine held a three-day Institute on Social Medicine and the papers given on this occasion were published in 1949 under the title *Social Medicine: Its Derivations and Objectives.* In 1947, also, the Milbank Memorial Fund devoted its annual conference to social medicine and published the proceedings in its quarterly.

It was during this period too that the social and health sciences began to converge to produce what has come to be known as "medical sociology." Both developments—the interest in social medicine and the emergence of medical sociology—result to a considerable extent from converging trends in the health field and in social science. On the medical side, the acute communicable diseases had come under relatively effective control, and chronic diseases and other noninfectious conditions began to demand attention. Demographic change had led to an increase in the proportion of aged in the population. As the hospital obtained a central role in medical care, the physician became essential for its operation and the institution itself became indispensable for the practice of good medicine. These developments, in turn, have felt the impact of new patterns of hospital utilization and financing of medical care. As a result, organizational relationships within the hospital have been disturbed and have become unstable. These and many other problems led to a recognition that the social sciences in terms of theory, knowledge, or method might be able to shed light on and help solve some of these problems [154]. On the social-science side, interest had developed in the study of the professions and of formal organizations, social factors in perception and attitude formation, and cultural patterns and value systems of large and small groups. Although many of these areas of interest had been studied earlier, the mobilization of social scientists in World War II and the utilization of their skills hastened the process [83].

Interest in social medicine grew because of the new medical and health problems and the need to deal with them in institutional, family, and community terms. Problems involving chronic illness, the aged, the mentally and emotionally ill, the physically handicapped, the provision of medical care, and the like were the stimuli. As a result, for example, Montefiore Hospital developed a Division of Social Medicine—a pioneer achievement. The development of home-care programs, attention to nursing homes, the provision of medical care, and similar activities are all part of the route social medicine has taken in the United States. Along this route, many have had to turn to the social sciences for collaborative action.

SOCIAL MEDICINE AND MEDICAL SOCIOLOGY

To a very large extent the history of social medicine is the history of social policy and social action (welfare). In this sense, social medicine is an applied discipline. Basically, it has been medically oriented even where its proponents have emphasized its basis in social science. Obviously, at any given period those interested in the social problems of health have had to use social science as they found it. To a very large extent, social medicine has been pragmatic, and has used whatever methods were available and seemed to suit its purposes. Thus, the availability of statistical data and survey methods led to their use. Social medicine, throughout its history, has used methods that did not involve analysis of social structures, but today it is possible to apply such methods to problems of social medicine. Indeed, a great deal of research has already been done along these lines [8, 26, 49, 89, 128, 131, 132, 153, 155, 195].

The field of interest designated as medical sociology has expanded greatly. In the United States, the process of evolution is gradually leading to a meeting and collaboration of the social sciences—as represented by medical sociology—and social medicine. This has been particularly evident in such areas of investigation and action as aging, psychiatry, and medical care [9, 74, 93, 181]. As yet, however, the broad range of the social sciences, and more specifically of sociology, has not been completely related to the concerns of health workers. That only a few authors have attempted general works on medical sociology reflects this situation [67, 103, 122, 171]. In part, it is due to a lack of agreement among physicians and sociologists as to how medicine and social science might best join forces and about what should be the subject matters of research and teaching, to differences in scientific values between the fields of sociology and medicine as well as differences in values concerning such crucial areas of medical practice as patient care. A perceptive review of these problems has been prepared by Hyman [77].

Despite all problems, however, the number of social scientists and specifically sociologists engaged in teaching and research in the health field has increased in the past decade. In 1957, Straus found only 34 sociologists occupying some position in schools of medicine or public health [176]. Buck, in 1961, reported 96 in medical schools [23]. In 1965, the newsletter of the Medical Sociology Section of the American Sociological Association reported that 218 social scientists had formal appointments in schools of medicine or public health. A number of other studies have revealed that a growing number of social scientists are involved in research, teaching consultation, or administration. Of these functions, research has received the greatest emphasis [5, 6, 104, 176].

The development of social medicine and medical sociology in the United States reflects both the state of the health and social sciences and the nature of the problems presented by a complex industrial society. In this sense, one can draw an analogy between the role of cameralism and medical police in relation to eighteenth-century enlightened absolutism and medical sociology in relation to the rationalization and bureaucratization of health services in twentieth-century industrial America. In part at least, this helps to explain why medical sociology appeared in the United States and why its evolution in Europe has been so slow. Since World War II, however, West Germany has begun to develop a medical sociology. There had been some tendencies in this direction earlier in the century [70, 71, 72], but more recently—under American influence—a definite field of study has appeared [85, 164].

A review of the literature clearly shows that the term *medical sociology* is not satisfactory. Actually, as the field so designated has developed (see Chapter 21 for an appraisal of the present status of the field), it is concerned with the sociology of health institutions, health personnel and their problems, and the role of sociology (or, more broadly, the social sciences) in elucidating the social and medical aspects of health and disease. Perhaps, one should endeavor to introduce a new designation: *the sociology of health.*

REFERENCES

1. ACKERKNECHT, ERWIN H., "Beiträge zur Geschichte der Medizinalreform von 1848," *Archiv für Geschichte der Medizin*, 25 (1932), 61–109, 112–83.
2. ———, "Hygiene in France: 1815–1848," *Bulletin of the History of Medicine*, 22 (March–April, 1948), 117–55.
3. ACLAND, HENRY W., *National Health.* Oxford: James Parker, 1871.
4. ———, Health (Address delivered at the Social Science Congress at Plymouth). Oxford: James Parker, 1873.
5. ANDERSON, ODIN W. AND MILVOY S. SEACAT, *An Analysis of Personnel in Medical Sociology.* New York: Health Information Foundation, 1962.
6. ———, *The Behavioral Scientists and Research in the Health Field: A Questionnaire Survey.* New York: Health Information Foundation, 1957.
7. *Annuaire des cinq départements de l'ancienne Normandie.* Caen: 1835. Reviewed in *Annales d'hygiène publique* (1835), p. 233.
8. APPLE, DORRIAN, "Sociology and Anthropology," *Bibliographies on Nursing* (National League for Nursing), 3 (1957), 69–114.
9. AXELROD, S. J., *Public Assistance Medical Care: Areas of Research and an Annotated Bibliography.* Chicago: American Public Welfare Association, 1959.
10. BAUDELAIRE, CHARLES, "L'Art romantique," in *Oeuvres*, Pléiade, II. Cited in D. O. Evans, *Social Romanticism in France: 1830–1848.* Oxford: Clarendon Press, 1951, pp. 7–8.
11. BEER, KARL, ed., *Die Reformation Kaiser Sigmunds. Eine Schrift des 15. Jahrhunderts zur Kirchen-und Reichsreform.* Stuttgart: Beiheft zu den Deutschen Reichstagsakten herausgegeben durch die historiche Kommission bei der Bayerischen Akademie der Wissenschaften, 1933.
12. ———, "Was ein Reformer vor einem halben Jahrtausend vom Ärztestand erwartete," *Gesnerus*, 11 (1954), 24–36.
13. BEHRING, E., *Gesammelte Abhandlungen zur ätiologischen Therapie von ansteckenden Krankheiten.* Stuttgart: Georg Thieme Verlag, 1893, p. xix.
14. DE BELGIQUE, ROYAUME, *Enquête sur la condition des classes ouvrières et sur le travail des enfants.* Bruxelles: 1848.
15. BELIN, J., *La logique d'une idée-force. L'idée d'utilité sociale pendant la Révolution française: 1789–1792.* Paris: Gallimard, 1939.
16. *John Bellers, 1654–1725: Quaker, Economist and Social Reformer.* (His writings, reprinted, with a memoir by A. Ruth Fry). London: Cassell & Co., Ltd., 1935.
17. BILLINGS, JOHN SHAW, in ALBERT HENRY BUCK, ed., *Treatise on Hygiene and Public Health.* New York: Wood, 1879, pp. 5–6.
18. BLACKWELL, ELIZABETH, *Essays in Medical Sociology.* 2 vols. London: Ernest Bell, 1902.
19. DE BOISMONT, BRIERRE, "De l'influence de la civilization sur le suicide," *Annales d'hygiène publique* (1835).
20. BROTHERSTON, J. H. F., "Williams Pulteney Alison, Scottish Pioneer of Social Medicine," *Medical Officer* (June 6, 1958), pp. 331–36.
21. BRUNSCHWIG, HENRI, *La Crise de l'état prussien à la fin du XVIIIe siècle et la genèse de la mentalité romantique.* Paris: Presses Universitaires de France, 1947.
22. BUCHEZ, P. J. B., *Introduction à la science de l'histoire.* Paris: Paulin, 1833.
23. BUCK, ROGER L., "Behavioral Scientists in Schools of Medicine," *Journal of Health and Human Behavior*, 2 (1961), 59–64.
24. BUESS, HEINRICH, "Fridolin Schuler (1832–1903) aus Mollis: Ein Vorkämpfer der Sozialmedizin im 19. Jahrhundert," *Die Praxis*, 47 (December, 1958), 1236–39.
25. BURET, E., *La Misère des classes laborieuses en Angleterre et en France.* 2 vols. Paris, 1845–1846.
26. CAUDILL, WILLIAM, "Applied Anthropology in Medicine," in A. L. Kroeber, ed., *Anthropology Today.* Chicago: University of Chicago Press, 1953, pp. 771–806.

27. Chadwick, Edwin, "Results of Differerent Principles of Legislation and Administration in Europe," *Journal of the Statistical Society of London* (September, 1859), pp. 381–420.
28. Charléty, Sebastien, *Histoire du Saint-Simonisme (1825–64)*. Paris: Paul Hartmann, 1931.
29. de Chateauneuf, L. F. Benoiston, "De la durée de la vie chez le riche et chez le pauvre," *Annales d'hygiène publique*, 3 (1830), 5–85.
30. Chevalier, Louis, *Classes laborieuses et classes dangereuses à Paris pendant la première du XIXe siècle*. Paris: Plon, 1958, pp. 415–20.
31. Cunningham, W., *The Growth of English Industry and Commerce in Modern Times*, Vol. I. Cambridge: Cambridge University Press, 1912.
32. Cuvillier, Armand, *P. J. V. Buchez et les origines du socialisme chrétien*. Paris: Presses Universitaires de France, 1948.
33. ———, *Hommes et idéologies de 1840*. Paris: Marcel Rivière, 1956.
34. d'Allemagne, H. R. *Les Saint-Simoniens: 1827–1837*. Paris: Gründ, 1930.
35. Davis, Michael M., "Wanted: Research in the Economic and Social Aspects of Medicine," *Milbank Memorial Fund Quarterly*, 13 (October, 1935), 339–46.
36. ———, "Social Medicine as a Field for Social Research," *American Journal of Sociology*, 44 (September, 1938), 274–79.
37. Descuret, J. B. F., *La médecine des passions*. Liége, 1844.
38. Dobb, Maurice, *Studies in the Development of Capitalism*. London: Routledge & Kegan Paul, Ltd., 1946, pp. 177–220.
39. Driver, Cecil, *Tory Radical: The Life of Richard Oastler*. Fair Lawn, N.J.: Oxford University Press, 1946, pp. 73, 135–36.
40. Duclaux, Emile, *L'hygiène sociale*. Paris: Felix Alcau, 1902.
41. Ducpetiaux, Edouard, *De la condition physique et morale des jeunes ouvriers et des moyens de les améliorer*. 2 vols. 1843.
42. ———, *Budgets économiques de classes ouvrières en Belgique*. 1855.
43. Dunham, Francis Lee, *An Approach to Social Medicine*. Baltimore: Williams & Wilkins Co., 1925, p. 30.
44. Evans, D. O., *Le Socialisme romantique: Pierre Leroux et ses contemporains*. Paris: M. Rivière, 1941.
45. ———, *Social Romanticism in France: 1830–1848*. Oxford: Clarendon Press, 1951.
46. Fischer, Alfons, *Geschichte des deutschen Gesundheitswesens*. 2 vols. Berlin: F. A. Herbig, 1933, I, 327–28; II, 362–65.
47. Fourcault, A., *Hygiène des personnes prédisposées aux maladies chroniques et spécialement à la phthisie pulmonaire: Ou moyens de prévenir le développement de ces affections*. Paris: B. Dusillon, 1844, pp. 197–224.
48. Frank, J. P., "The People's Misery: Mother of Disease" (Address delivered in 1790), trans. from the Latin, with an Introduction by Henry E. Sigerist, *Bulletin of the History of Medicine*, 9 (January, 1941), 81–100.
49. Freeman, H. E. and Leo G. Reeder, "Medical Sociology: A Review of the Literature," *American Sociological Review*, 22 (February, 1957), 74–81.
50. Geigel, N. A., "Öffentliche Gesundheitspflage," in *Handbuch der öffentlichen Gesundheitspflege und der Gewerbekrankheiten*, Bd. I of H. von Ziemssen, ed., *Handbuch der speziellen Pathologie und Therapie*. Leipzig, 1874.
51. Gershoy, Leo, *From Despotism to Revolution, 1763–1789*. New York: Harper & Row, Publishers, Inc., 1944, pp. 39–43.
52. Godlewski, Henri, "L'étudiant en médecine Philippe Buchez, fondateur du Carbonarisme français," *Bulletin de la Société française d'histoire de la médicine* (1937).
53. Gottstein, A., *Die Medizin der Gegenwart in Selbstdarstellungen*, ed. L. R. Grote. Leipzig: Meiners, 1925, pp. 53–91.

54. GRANT, JOHN B., "Social Medicine in the Curriculum," *British Medical Journal*, 1 (February 21, 1948), 333–36.
55. GREC, EDOUARD, *Un médecin novateur: Philippe Buchez (1796–1865)*. Paris: Vignez, 1938.
56. GREENHOW, EDWARD H., in *General Board of Health: Papers Relating to the Sanitary State of the People of England*. London: Eyre and Spottiswoode, 1858, pp. 131–33.
57. GROTJAHN, ALFRED, *Über Wandlungen in der Volksernährung* (Staatsund socialwissenschaftliche Forschungen Bd. XX, Heft, 2). Leipzig: Duncker & Humblot, 1902.
58. ——— and F. KRIEGEL, *Jahresbericht über die Fortschritte und Leistungen auf dem Gebiete der socialen Hygiene und Demographie, Dritter Band: Bericht über das Jahr 1903*. Jena: Gustav Fischer, 1904.
59. ———, *Geburten-Rückgang und Geburten-Regelung im Lichte der individuellen und der sozialen Hygiene*. Berlin: Louis Marcus Verlagsbuchhandlung, 1914.
60. ———, *Soziale Pathologie* (2nd ed.). Berlin: August Hirschwald Verlag, 1915, pp. 9–18.
61. ———, *Erlebtes und Erstrebtes. Erinnerungen eines sozialistischen Arztes*. Berlin: F. A. Herberg, 1932, p. 72.
62. GUÉPIN, ANGE, *Nantes an XIX siècle, statistique, topographique, industrielle et morale*. Nantes: P. Sebire, 1835.
63. GUERIN, JULES, "Médecine sociale: Au corps médicale de France," *Gazette Médicale de Paris* (March 11, 1848), 203.
64. ———, "Médecine sociale: La Médecine sociale et la médecine socialiste," *Gazette Médicale de Paris* (March 18, 1848), p. 203.
65. ———, "Médecine sociale: De l'association médicale au point de vue de la situation actuelle," *Gazette Médicale de Paris* (March 18, 1848), p. 211.
66. HARMS, B., "Alfred Grotjahn und seine Lebensaufgabe," *Zeitschrift für Sozialhygiene* (1949), pp. 1–4.
67. HAWKINS, NORMAN G., *Medical Sociology: Theory, Scope and Methods*. Springfield, Ill.: Charles C Thomas, Publisher, 1958.
68. *Health and Sickness of Town Populations: Considered with Reference to Proposed Sanitary Legislation and to the Establishment of a Comprehensive System of Medical Police and District Despensaries*. London: John W. Parker, 1846, p. 2.
69. HECKSCHER, E. F., *Mercantilism*. 2 vols. London: George Allen & Unwin, Ltd., 1934.
70. HELLPACH, W., "Nervosität und Kultur," in *Kulturprobleme der Gegenwart*. Bd. V. Berlin: Rade, 1902.
71. ———, "Sozialpathologie als Wissenschaft," *Archiv für Sozialwissenschaft* 21 (1905), 275.
72. ———, *Nervenleben und Weltanschauung: Ihre Wechselbeziehungen im deutschen Leben von Heute* (Grenzfragen des Nerven—und Seelenlebens, Bd. 41). Wiesbaden: Bergmann, 1906.
73. HIPPOCRATES, *Diet*. Littré, VI 594–604.
74. HOCH, PAUL H., "Social Psychiatry," in Gruhle, Jung, Mayer-Gross and Muller, eds., *Psychiatrie der Gegenwart: Forschung und Praxis*. Berlin: Springer-Verlag, 1961, pp. 9–35.
75. HUEPPE, FERDINAND, *Handbuch der Hygiene*. Berlin: Hirschwald, 1899, p. 11.
76. HULL, C. H., ed., *The Economic Writings of Sir William Petty*. Cambridge: Cambridge University Press, 1899, pp. 27, 109–10, 151, 259, 303, 463, 536.
77. HYMAN, MARTIN D., "Medicine," in P. F. Lazarsfeld, W. H. Sewell, and H. L. Wilensky, eds., *The Uses of Sociology*. New York: Basic Books, Inc., Publishers, 1967, pp. 119–55.
78. ICKERT, FRANZ AND JOHANNES WEICKSEL, *Grundriss der Sozialen Medizin*. Leipzig: J. A. Barth, 1932.
79. JACQUEMYNS, G., *Histoire de la crise économique des Flandres*. Bruxelles: Maurice Lamertin, 1929, pp. 295–362.
80. JOHNSON, E. A., *Predecessors of Adam*

Smith. Englewood Cliffs, N.J.: Prentice-Hall, Inc., 1937, pp. 117–38, 259–77.
81. VON JUSTI, J. H. G., *Grundsätze der Policey-Wissenscheft.* Göttingen: 1756, pp. 64–76.
82. KAY, J. P., *The Moral and Physical Condition of the Working Classes Employed in the Cotton Manufacture in Manchester.* London: James Ridgeway, 1832, pp. 40–42.
83. KENDALL, PATRICIA AND ROBERT K. MERTON, "Medical Education as a Social Process," in E. Gartley Jaco, ed., *Patients, Physicians and Illness.* New York: The Free Press, 1958, pp. 321–50.
84. KHALDUN, IBN, *The Muqaddimah: An Introduction to History,* trans. from the Arabic by Franz Rosenthal. New York: Pantheon Books, Inc., 1958, Vol. II, pp. 136–37, 245–46, 376–77.
85. KÖNIG, R. AND M. TONNSEMANN, *Probleme der Medizin-Soziologie* (Köln Z. Soziol. Sonderheft 3). Köln, Opladen, Westdeutscher Verlag, 1958.
86. KROEGER, GERTRUD, *The Concept of Social Medicine as Presented by Physicians and Other Writers in Germany: 1779–1932.* Chicago: Julius Rosenwald Fund, 1937, pp. 14–15.
87. KÜNTZLI, *État de la médecine, position des médecins, garanties sanitaires du peuple en France, et plan d'organisation médicale.* Paris: Chez l'Auteur, 1847.
88. LAYET, A., *Hygiène et maladies des paysans.* Paris: Masson, 1882.
89. LEAVELL, HUGH R., "Chronic Disease and the Behavioral Sciences," *Journal of Chronic Diseases,* 2 (July, 1955), 113.
90. LE BORGNE, G., *Le Médecin.* Paris: J. B. Baillière, 1846, pp. 3–33, 155–221.
91. LEIBNIZ, G. W., *Die Werke von Leibniz,* herausgegeben von Onno Klopp, I. Reihe, Bd. 5. Hannover: 1866, pp. 315 *ff.*
92. ———, *Sämtliche Schriften, Dritter Band: 1680–1683.* Leipzig: K. F. Koehler Verlag, 1938, p. 405.
93. LEIGHTON, A., J. A. CLAUSEN, AND R. WILSON, *Explorations in Social Psychiatry.* New York: Basic Books, Inc., Publishers, 1957.
94. LEROY, MAXIM, *Histoire des idées sociales en France,* t.1 (de Montesquieu à Robespierre). Paris: Gallimard, 1946, pp. 318–24.
95. LIDDLE, JOHN, "On the Connection between Medical Poor Relief and the Sanitary Condition of the People," *Journal of Public Health,* 1 (1848), 92–95.
96. LIPSON, E., "England in the Age of Mercantilism," *Journal of Business History,* 4 (August, 1932), 697–707.
97. LYND, HELEN M., *England in the Eighteen-Eighties.* Fair Lawn, N.J.: Oxford University Press, 1945, pp. 3–19, 61–112.
98. MACKENZIE, JAMES, *The Future of Medicine.* Fair Lawn, N.J.: Oxford University Press, 1919.
99. MARRIOTT, J. A. R., ed., *Louis Blanc's Organisation du Travail: The French Revolution of 1848 in Its Economic Aspect.* Vol. I. Oxford: Clarendon Press, 1913.
100. MCINTIRE, CHARLES, "The Importance of the Study of Medical Sociology," *Bulletin of the American Academy of Medicine,* 1 (February, 1894), 425–34.
101. MCKEOWN, THOMAS, "The Preparation of a Syllabus in Social Medicine," *Journal of Medical Education,* 32 (February, 1957), 110–14.
102. MACKINTOSH, JAMES, *Teaching of Hygiene and Public Health in Europe.* Monograph Series No. 34, 1957. Geneva: World Health Organization.
103. MECHANIC, DAVID, *Medical Sociology: A Selective View.* New York: The Free Press, 1968.
104. Medical Sociology Section, *Medical Sociology Newsletter,* I, No. 5 (1965). American Sociological Association.
105. *Die Medicinische Reform: Eine Wochenschrift, erschienen vom 10 Juli 1848 bis zum 29 Juni 1849.* Berlin: G. Reimer, 1848–1849, pp. 38, 127, 185, 189, 190.
106. MEYNNE, A. J., *Topographie médicale de la Belgique.* Bruxelles: H. Manceaux, 1865, pp. 123–235.
107. MICHELS, ROBERTO, *First Lectures in Political Sociology,* trans. with an In-

troduction by Alfred de Grazia. Minneapolis: University of Minnesota Press, 1949, p. 13.

108. MITCHELL, WESLEY C., *Lecture Notes on Types of Economic Theory*. 2 vols. New York: Augustus M. Kelley, 1949, I, 15–23, 48–61.

109. MOSSE, M. AND G. TUGENDREICH, eds., *Krankheit und soziale Lage*. München: J. F. Lehmanns Verlag, 1913.

110. NEWMAN, GEORGE, *Health and Social Evolution*. London: George Allen & Unwin, Ltd., 1931.

111. NEUMANN, SALOMON, *Die öffentliche Gesundheitspflege und das Eigenthum. Kritisches und positives mit Bezug auf die preussische Medizinalverfassungsfrage*. Berlin: Adolf Riess, 1847, pp. 64–65, 84.

112. ———, "Zur medizinischen Statistik des preussischen Staates nach den Acten des statistischen Bureaus für das Jahr 1846," *Achiv für Pathologische Anatomie, und für klinische Medicin*, 3 (1851), 13–141.

113. OESER, MAX, *Geschichte der Stadt Mannheim*. J. Bensheimer, 1908, pp. 359–70.

114. PARENT-DUCHATELET, A. J. B., "Les ulcères des extremités inférieures des artisans de Paris," *Annales d'hygiène publique*, 4 (1830), 239.

115. ———, *De la prostitution dans la ville de Paris sous le rapport de l'hygiène publique, de la morale et de l'administration*. Paris: Baillière, 1836.

116. PARSONS, TALCOTT, "Some Problems Confronting Sociology as a Profession," *American Sociological Review*, 24 (August, 1959), 547–59.

117. PEARSE, I. H. AND G. S. WILLIAMSON, *The Case for Action*. London: Faber & Faber, Ltd., 1931.

118. ———, *Biologists in Search of Material: An Interim Report on the Work of the Pioneer Health Centre Peckham*. London: Faber & Faber, Ltd., 1938.

119. PEARSE, I. H. AND LUCY H. CROCKER, *The Peckham Experiment: A Study in the Living Structure of Society*. London: George Allen & Unwin, Ltd., 1943.

120. VON PETTENKOFER, MAX, "The Value of Health to a City: Two Lectures, Delivered in 1873," trans. from the German, with an Introduction by Henry E. Sigerist, in *Bulletin of the History of Medicine*, 10 (November, 1941), 593–613.

121. PETTY, WILLIAM, *Some Unpublished Writings of Sir William Petty*, edited from the Bowood Papers by the Marquis of Lansdowne. London: Constable & Company, 1927, I: 33, 35, 36–40, 176, 195, 256–57, 267; II: 55, 170, 176.

122. PFLANZ, M., *Sozialer Wandel und Krankheit. Ergebnisse und Probleme der medizinischen Soziologie*. Stuttgart: Ferdinand Enke Verlag, 1962.

123. PICARD, ROGER, "Sur l'origine des mots socialisme et socialiste," *Revue socialiste*, 51 (1910), 379–80.

124. ———, "Un Saint-Simonien démocrate: Le docteur Ange Guépin," *Revue d'histoire economique et sociale*, 13 (1925), 456–94.

125. PLATO, *Laws*, 720c,d.

126. ———, *Republic*, 3, 406c.

127. PLUTARCH, "Advice about Keeping Well," in *Moralia*, trans. Frank Cole Babbitt. London: William Heinemann, Ltd., 1928, II, 291.

128. POLGAR, STEVEN, "Health and Human Behavior: Areas of Interest Common to the Social and Health Sciences," *Current Anthropology*, 3 (December, 1961), 159–205.

129. POYNTER, F. N. L., "Thomas Southwood Smith: The Man (1788–1861)," *Proceedings of the Royal Society of Medicine*, 55 (May, 1962), 381–92.

130. RAMAZZINI, BERNARDINO, *De morbis artificum diatriba: Diseases of Workers*. The Latin text of 1713 revised, transl. and with notes by Wilmer Cave Wright. Chicago: University of Chicago Press, 1940, pp. 5–11, 347, 449.

131. READER, GEORGE G. AND MARY E. W. GOSS, "The Sociology of Medicine," in R. K. Merton et al., eds., *Sociology Today*. New York: Basic Books, Inc., Publishers, 1959.

132. ———, "Medical Sociology with Particular Reference to the Study of Hospitals," *Transactions of the Fourth World Congress of Sociology*. Louvain:

1959, II, 139–52.

133. Reihe, Erste, *Allgemeiner Politischer und Historischer Briefwechsel* (herausgegeben von der Preussischen Akademie der Wissenschaften). Zweiter Band, 1676–79, "G. W. Leibniz: Sämtliche Schriften und Briefe." Darmstadt: Otto Reichl, 1927, pp. 74–77.

134. Reich, Eduard, *System der Hygiene.* Leipzig: Friedrich Fleischer Verlag, 1870–1871, I, xii, xvi, xxii, 267.

135. Rochard, J., *Traité d'hygiène sociale et de prophylaxie sanitaire.* Paris: Delahaye and Lecrrosiner, 1888.

136. Rochoux, J. A., *Thèse de concours pour la chaire d'hygiène* (presentée et soutenue le janvier 1838). Paris: De Rignoux et Ce, 1838, p. 28.

137. Roscher, Wilhelm, *Geschichte der National-Oekonomik in Deutschland* (2nd ed.). Berlin: R. Oldenbourg, 1924, pp. 238–52.

138. Rosen, George, "An Eighteenth Century Plan for a National Health Service," *Bulletin of the History of Medicine,* 16 (December, 1944), 429–36.

139. ———, "L. L. Finke on the Different Kinds of Geographies, but Chiefly on Medical Topographies and How to Compose Them." trans. from the German, *Bulletin of the History of Medicine,* 20 (November, 1946), 527–38.

140. ———, "What is Social Medicine? A Genetic Analysis of the Concept," *Bulletin of the History of Medicine,* 21 (July–August, 1947), 674–733.

141. ———, "Biography of Dr. Johann Peter Frank . . . Written by Himself, translated from the German, with an Introduction and Notes," *Journal of the History of Medicine,* 3 (Winter and Spring, 1948), 11–46, 279–314.

142. ———, "The Idea of Social Medicine in America," *Canadian Medical Association Journal,* 61 (September, 1949), 316–23.

143. ———, "Medical Care and Social Policy in Seventeenth Century England," *Bulletin of New York Academy of Medicine,* 2nd series, 29 (April, 1953), 420–37.

144. ———, "Political Order and Human Health in Jeffersonian Thought," *Bulletin of the History of Medicine,* 26 (January–February, 1952), 32–44.

145. ———, "Economic and Social Policy in the Development of Public Health," *Journal of the History of Medicine,* 8 (October, 1953), 407–30.

146. ———, "Problems in the Application of Statistical Analysis to Questions of Health: 1700–1880," *Bulletin of the History of Medicine,* 29 (January–February, 1955), 27–45.

147. ———, "The Historical Significance of Some Medical References in the Defensor Pacis of Marsilius of Padua," *Sudhoff's Archiv für Geschichte der Medizin,* 37 (1953), 350–56.

148. ———, "Hospitals, Medical Care and Social Policy in the French Revolution," *Bulletin of the History of Medicine,* 30 (January–February, 1956), 124–49.

149. ———, "Cameralism and Concept of Medical Police," *Bulletin of the History of Medicine,* 27 (January–February, 1953), 21–42.

150. ———, "The Fate of the Concept of Medical Police," *Centaurus,* 5 (1957), 97–113.

151. ———, *A History of Public Health.* New York: M.D. Publications, 1958, pp. 201–20, 236–47.

152. ———, "Mercantilism and Health Policy in Eighteenth Century French Thought," *Medical History,* 3 (October, 1959), 259–77.

153. ———, "The Why and the How of Sociology in Medical Training," *Archives of Environmental Health,* 4 (April, 1962), 638–42.

154. ———, "The Hospital: Historical Sociology of a Community Institution," in Eliot Freidson, ed., *Sociological Studies on the Hospital.* New York: The Free Press, 1963.

155. ——— and E. Wellin, "A Bookshelf on the Social Sciences and Public Health," *American Journal of Public Health,* 49 (March, 1959), 441–54.

156. Ruge, Arnold, "Plan der Deutsch-Französischen Jahrbücher," *Deutsch-Französische Jahrbücher.* Herausgegeben von Arnold Ruge und Karl Marx. Paris: 1844. Reproduced in facsimile in the series *Neudrucke marxistische Selten-*

heiten. Verlag von Rudolf Leibing. Leipzig: L. Franz & Company, 1925, I, 6.
157. RUMSEY, HENRY W., *Essays on State Medicine.* London: John Churchill, 1856, pp. 248, 280–82.
158. RYLE, JOHN A., "Social Medicine: Its Meaning and Its Scope," *British Medical Journal,* 2 (November 20, (November 20, 1943), 633–36.
159. DE SAINTE-MARIE, ÉTIENNE, *Lecture relative à la police médicale faite au Conseil de salubrité de Lyon et du départment du Rhône en 1826, 1827, 1828.* Paris: Baillière, 1829.
160. SAND, RENE, *L'Économie humaine par la médecine sociale.* Paris: Les Editions Rieder, 1934, pp. 11–13.
161. ———, *Vers la médecine sociale.* Paris: J. B. Baillière et fils, 1948.
162. ———, *The Advance to Social Medicine.* London: Staples Press, Ltd., 1952, pp. 515–54.
163. *Social Implications of Industrialization and Urbanization in Africa South of the Sahara.* Paris: UNESCO, 1956.
164. SCHELSKY, H., "Die Soziologie des Krankenhauses im Rahmen einer Soziologie der Medizin," *Krankenhausarzt,* 31 (1958), 169.
165. SCHUMPETER, JOSEPH, *History of Economic Analysis.* Fair Lawn, N.J.: Oxford University Press, 1954, pp. 335–76.
166. SEE, HENRI, *La Vie économique de la France sous la Monarchie censitaire (1815–1848).* Paris: Alcan, 1927, pp. 91–95.
167. SEMASHKO, N. S., "Frederich Erismann: The Dawn of Russian Hygiene and Public Health," *Bulletin of the History of Medicine,* 20 (June, 1946), 1–9.
168. SIGERIST, H. E., "Kultur und Krankheit," *Kyklos,* I (1928), 60–63.
169. ———, "Historical Background of Industrial and Occupational Diseases," *Bulletin of the New York Academy of Medicine,* Series 2, 12 (November, 1936), 597–609.
170. ———, *The University at the Crossroads.* New York: Henry Schuman, Inc., Publishers, 1946, pp. 106–26, 130.
171. SIMMONS, LEO W. AND HAROLD G. WOLFF, *Social Science in Medicine.* New York: Russell Sage Foundation, 1954.
172. SIMON, JOHN, *Public Health Reports.* London: J. and A. Churchill, 1887, II, 97–98.
173. ———, *English Sanitary Institutions.* London: John Murray, 1897, pp. 246–48, 266 (fn), 293.
174. SMALL, ALBION W., *The Cameralists: The Pioneers of German Social Polity.* Chicago: University of Chicago Press, 1909, pp. 60–106.
175. SOMMER, LOUISE, *Die österreichischen Kameralisten in dogmengeschichtlicher Darstellung.* Wien: Carl Konegen, 1920–25. See especially Part I, pp. 43–56.
176. STRAUS, ROBERT, "The Nature and Status of Medical Sociology," *American Sociological Review,* 22 (1957), 200.
177. STÜRZBECHER, M., "Adolf Gottstein als Gesundheitspolitiker," *Medizinische Monatsschrift,* 13 (June, 1959), 374–78.
178. SUDHOFF, KARL, *Jeh. Peter Brinkmann: Ein Niederrheinischer Arzt im 18. Jahrhundert.* Düsseldorf: 1902.
179. TERRIS, MILTON, "Social Medicine as an Academic Discipline," *Journal of Medical Education,* 33 (August, 1958), 565–73.
180. THURNWALD, R. C., *Black and White in East Africa: The Fabric of a New Civilization.* London: Routledge & Kegan Paul, Ltd., 1935.
181. TIBBITTS, CLARK, ed., *Handbook of Social Gerontology: Societal Aspects of Aging.* Chicago: University of Chicago Press, 1960.
182. TISSOT, SIMON, *De la manie du suicide et de l'esprit de révolte.* Paris: 1840.
183. *Transactions of the Medical Society of the State of New York: For the Year 1830.* Albany: Websters and Skinners, 1830, p. 25.
184. TREVELYAN, CHARLES, *Metropolitan Medical Relief.* London: Longmans, Green & Company, Ltd., 1877.
185. VILLERMÉ, L. R., "Mémoires sur la mortalité en France, dans la classe aisée et dans la class indigente" (with a supplement by Benoiston de Chateauneuf), *Memoires de l'Académie royale de médecine,* 1 (1828), 51–99.

186. ———, "Mémoires sur la taille de l'homme en France," *Annales d'hygiène publique*, 1 (1829), 351–99.

187. ———, "De la mortalité dans les divers quartiers de la ville de Paris," *Annales d'hygiène publique*, 3 (1830), 294–341.

188. ———, "Décès à domicile des enfants dans quelques rues du Ier et du XIIe arrondissements," *Annales d'hygiène publique*, 3 (1830).

189. VIRCHOW, RUDOLF, "Die öffentliche Gesundheitspflege," *Medicinische Reform*, 5 (August, 1848), 21–22.

190. ———, *Die Einheitsbestrebungen in der wissenschaftlichen Medicin*. Berlin: G. Reimer, 1849, p. 48.

191. ———, "Die Epidemien von 1848, Gelesen in der Jahressitzung der Gesellschaft für wissenschaftliche Medizin am 27 (November, 1848)," *Archiv für pathologische Anatomie und Physiologie und für klinische Medicin*, 3 (1851), 3–12.

192. WEBB, SIDNEY AND BEATRICE, *The State and the Doctor*. London: Longmans, Green & Company, Ltd., 1910, p. 7.

193. WEBER, MAX, *Gesammelte Aufsätze zur Wissenschaftslehre*. Tübingen: J. C. B. Mohr, 1922.

194. ———, *Gesammelte Aufsätze zur Soziologie und Sozialpolitik*. Tübingen: J. C. B. Mohr, 1924.

195. WELLIN, EDWARD, "Uses of the Behavioral (Social) Sciences in Public Health." Unpublished report submitted to the National Institute of Mental Health, U.S. Public Health Service, 1961.

196. WINCKELMANN, O., *Das Fürsorgewesen der Stadt Strassburg vor und nach der Reformation bis zum Ausgang des 16. Jahrhunderts*. Quellen und Forschungen zur Reformationsgeschichte. Leipzig: 1922, V, 25.

part one

THE SOCIOLOGY OF ILLNESS

3

SOCIAL FACTORS IN THE CHRONIC DISEASES

Saxon Graham and Leo G. Reeder

The chronic diseases today constitute the biggest health problem in the developed nations of the world. And sociological approaches hold promise of solving some of the knottiest aspects of this problem. In this chapter we will deal with the two largest categories of chronic disease, cardiovascular disease and cancer, and with the sociological factors in their development, prevention, and therapy.

The importance of sociological factors to therapy becomes apparent when we consider the man who repeatedly experiences chest pain on exertion, a symptom of heart disease, yet fails to seek advice of a physician. Similiarly, sociological questions arise about persons who do not follow medical advice. And, although both medical and social scientists are preoccupied with therapy, a second set of problems—those involved in the prevention of disease—is perhaps even more important. Most would agree that the social and economic costs, as well as the burdens of individual suffering are much better prevented in the first place, but the prevention of illness frequently requires that individuals change their behavior in a more healthful direction. The contribution of the sociology of behavioral change to the development of means of prevention, then, is obvious.

Neither prevention nor therapy can occur unless there is an understanding of the ways in which given illnesses develop. Much of the traditional biological approach to understanding the development of illness has been based on laboratory studies of animals, and some biologists would express surprise at the idea of studying humans when seeking the cause of disease in humans. Epidemiologists are not surprised, moreover, that some of the major steps in the study of the epidemiology of chronic diseases in the last decade have been in the realm of social epidemiology. In this enterprise, such social factors as geographic mobility, competitiveness, smoking, and diet have been shown to be related to diseases of various sorts. It is only with the information which can be gathered from social epidemiology that effective means of prevention can be designed for many diseases. From such research, clues to essential useful therapies can be obtained.

It is obvious that sociological approaches need to be supplemented by biological and chemical studies. Nevertheless, some of the most important problems in therapy, prevention, and epidemiology can only be approached by sociologists working in concert with other kinds of scientists. In this chapter we will detail the sociological strategy in dealing with these problems as well as some of the useful findings which have resulted from this strategy.

THE INCREASING INCIDENCE OF CHRONIC DISEASE

Had a handbook of medical sociology been produced fifty years ago, it is probable that it would not have contained a chapter on chronic disease. The omission would not necessarily have suggested a lack of interest; it would have been dictated by the necessity of devoting so much space to the infectious diseases that other important concerns would have had to be excluded. The fact that chronic diseases are included in this handbook is evidence of a new emphasis on an old concern, and this, as we will show, is a product in part of developments in medicine over the last hundred years.

The Development of Modern Medicine

Until the latter half of the nineteenth century, relatively little improvement had been made in techniques for protecting the health of mankind. Prior to this time, of course, important discoveries in basic science had been made, such as the possibilities of the microscope by van Leeuwenhoek, the development of the mercury thermometer by Fahrenheit, the beginnings of an important chemistry by Lavoisier and Davy, and the contributions of Lennaeus and Cuvier in biology [98]. Among the most important were the discoveries of Pasteur and Koch. Their work revealed the pathogenic potential of some of the microorganisms and provided the impetus for a line of investigation that has been utilized with increasing fruitfulness ever since. Once the principle was established that specific infectious microorganisms cause particular diseases, it was applied successfully to investigations of a host of illnesses.

Knowledge of the origin and cause of infectious diseases had the effect of stimulating a large number of developments of incalculable benefit to mankind. One of the earliest was aseptic surgery. Pasteur's demonstration, in 1858, that bacteria were responsible for fermentation gave Joseph Lister a clue to the cause of the fermentation of wounds in his surgical wards at Glasgow Infirmary. Up to that time, infections had been the chief cause of death following surgical operations of any sort, and rarely did a surgical patient not develop postoperative infection. Newsholme notes that of the 13,000 amputations performed by French army surgeons during the Franco-Prussian War, no less than 10,000 proved fatal [80]. Lister, however, reasoned upon Pasteur's evidence that everything in the surgical environment should be purified of the fermentation-producing bacteria. Using carbolic acid as an antiseptic, Lister found immediately that infection was prevented and healing permitted in a majority of cases. Operations had been performed for at least 4,000 years, usually with disastrous results, but the simple measure of asepsis created a revolution.

A second outgrowth of the original bacteriological principle was an effective preventive medicine. Even before bacteriology was developed, there had been understanding that contact with a diseased person or with filth was somehow related to acquisition of the disease. Acting on this idea, public-health workers had introduced the quarantine and other measures to prevent the spread of disease. But once it was understood *why* contact with disease led to its contraction, once the agent causing a disease was isolated, steps could be taken to develop substances which, when introduced into an individual, would stimulate his system to manufacture antibodies immunizing him from the disease. Jenner's discovery of a smallpox vaccine, developed before the advent of bacteriology simply on the basis of the observation that it worked, plus research which led to an understanding of why it worked, led ultimately to measures for immunization against diphtheria, yellow fever, whooping cough, tetanus, typhoid fever, cholera, poliomyelitis, some of the influenza viruses, and many other diseases. Mass immunization has produced as dramatic results for the scientist in preventive medicine and public health as the aseptic operating room has for the surgeon.

Bacteriological studies contributed to a third important development, also implemented on the public health level. With the understanding that bacteria could cause illness, and that bacteria could be carried from one person, insect, or animal to another, public-health workers endeavored to discover how to break the chains of contact. The principle was applied in many ways: Enforced pasteurization of milk killed agents of infection borne in the fluid, breaking the chain of contact of many diseases; purification of public drinking water had a similar result; sewage was treated and disposed of in ways that prevented it from carrying infection; swamps were drained or treated so as to destroy the breeding place of malaria-carrying mosquitoes. All these procedures, and many others, were carried out on a massive basis with startling results. We have comparative evidence today of the effectiveness of these mass health measures. At the present time, for example, India uses only rudimentary measures for the purification of its water. Two million Indians die annually from water-borne diseases, while the number in the United States is negligible.

In our time, bacteriologists have developed penicillin, tetracyline, and similar antibiotic drugs. Stimulated by the success of penicillin, drug manufacturers and others are scouring the world for other molds which might be effective against diseases for which good remedies do not yet exist. It is true that such therapeutic advances actually save fewer lives than the routine application of public-health measures such as immunization and the treatment of water, milk, and sewage. Nevertheless, the importance of antibiotics and their dramatic effect in therapy for such dread killers as tuberculosis, appendicitis, rheumatic fever, spinal meningists, and other acute infectious diseases should not be minimized.

Effects of Medical Advances

We are safe in saying that the effects of the aforementioned innovations in medicine have been great. In some cases, to be sure, the evidence that the advances in health are due to the advances in medical science is not clear. The reduction in the incidence of some diseases may result partially from the gradually improving standard of living in the United States as a whole. Nevertheless, there is no doubt that the great steps taken in medicine, especially in the last fifty years, have had much to do with prolonging the lives and lowering the death and disease rates of the population.

Table 3–1 shows, per 100,000 population, death rates from a number of causes in each decade since 1900; it reveals the dramatic decline in deaths from the infectious diseases which were attacked bacteriologically. Immunization has all but wiped out diphtheria and whooping cough, while pasteuriza-

TABLE 3-1 Death Rate 1900–1965 from Selected Causes: United States
*Death Rate per 100,000**

Cause of Death	*1900*	*1920*	*1940*	*1960*	*1965*
All Causes	1,719.1	1,298.9	1,076.4	954.7	943.2
Infectious diseases					
Tuberculosis, all forms	194.4	113.1	45.9	6.1	4.1
Syphilis and its sequelae	12.0	16.5	14.4	1.6	1.3
Typhoid fever	31.3	7.6	1.0	—	—
Dysentery, all forms	12.0	4.0	1.9	0.2	—
Diphtheria	40.3	15.3	1.1	0.0	—
Whooping cough	12.2	12.5	2.2	—	—
Acute poliomyelitis	—	0.9	0.8	0.1	0.5
Measles	13.3	8.8	0.5	0.2	—
Influenza and pneumonia, except pneumonia of newborn	202.2	207.3	70.3	37.3	31.9
Chronic diseases					
Malignant neoplasms	64.0	83.4	120.3	149.2	153.5
Diabetes mellitus	11.0	16.1	26.6	16.7	17.1
Major cardiovascular renal diseases	345.2	364.9	485.7	521.8	516.4
Ulcer of stomach and duodenum	2.7	3.6	6.8	6.3	5.4
Accidents					
Motor vehicle accidents	—	10.3	26.2	21.3	25.4
All other accidents	72.3	59.7	47.0	30.7	30.4

*Based on population enumerated as of April 1 for 1965 and 1960, and estimated as of July 1 for other years. Statistical Abstract of the U.S., 1968. Washington, D.C.: Government Printing Office, 1969.

tion and water purification have had much to do with reducing infant dysentery. Infectious diseases which formerly attacked adults as well as children have been brought under control. Rates of death from tuberculosis, for example, have dropped consistently; a big decrease occurred in pneumonia about twenty-five years ago; syphilis declined by six-sevenths from 1940 to 1959. The use of antibiotic drugs was in large part responsible for these successes, but effective social organization also played an important part in controlling tuberculosis and syphilis. Thus, the efforts of public-health organizations in finding and treating tuberculosis cases and their contacts helped reduce the incidence of this disease. Again, much of the victory over syphilis was won through the efforts of Surgeon General Thomas Parran. He was able to mobilize the entire nation to provide education about the prevention and treatment of syphilis as well as medical facilities for its control. The history of the control of syphilis is graphic proof of the importance of social organization in bringing health to the community. The fact that venereal diseases are on the rise again suggests that new social measures need to be developed to control them.

A look at the other items in Table 3–1 shows that although infectious diseases have increasingly come under control, little success has attended the battle against the diseases of adulthood and old age. The death rate for diabetes and ulcers has not dropped. Cardiovascular-renal diseases and malignant neoplasms (cancers) have actually increased. It is possible that the increases in rates of death from malignant neoplasms and cardiovascular renal diseases are partly a result of changes in diagnostic procedures in the decades since 1910. Some of the increase is the result of the more widespread survival of infants from the infectious diseases; in later years these survivors become victims of chronic diseases. Fifty years ago, few persons lived long enough to die from such illnesses as heart disease and cancer. Still, there can be little doubt that the actual rates, as well as the absolute numbers, of deaths from the cancers and circulatory diseases have increased substantially in the last sixty years.

Medical science today and in the future will be increasingly concerned with the diseases of older age groups, which are usually chronic and often extremely expensive to treat. The problems of chronic disease appear formidable at the moment. The old epidemiological approaches, so suited to the finding of a bacterial cause of disease, may not be as effective in developing our understanding of heart disease, cancer, and mental illness. Medical scientists went a long way on the momentum provided by the findings of early bacteriologists, but now it appears that other basic discoveries must be made to help them solve the newer problems which face them. New approaches to investigating the chronic diseases, including mental illness, must be devised, and it may be that a union of sociology and the medical sciences will produce a new and successful epidemiology.

THE CHRONIC ILLNESSES AND DISABILITY

Any force which disturbs the human organism so profoundly and over such a long period as chronic disease, if affecting a large enough proportion of persons in a community, is bound to have far-reaching effects on that population. It should be emphasized that although we are discussing relatively few chronic diseases, the number of persons they affect in the Western world is large. The effects of these diseases on the population are reflected in its demographic character, in various social and economic burdens levied upon the society, in peculiar problems affecting therapy and physician-patient relationships, in therapeutic organization, and in other ways. These problems are fully discussed in Chapters 12, 13 and 14, and are dealt with in the following section only as they are affected by the chronic diseases.

Demographic Effects

For some years the age distribution of the United States has been changing, a result in part of the advances of medical science against infectious disease. More and more people are living beyond the childhood years into middle and old age. In 1900, the death rate per 1,000 population was 17.2; by 1965 it had dropped to 9.4. The annual mortality rate for white males under one year of age decreased from 133.5 per thousand, in 1900, to 24.2 per thousand in 1965. Thus, in that age group most profoundly affected by successes in the prevention and treatment of communicable disease, death rates plummeted.

What happened in the older groups, on the other hand, was quite different. The mortality rate for white males 65 years of age was 41.7 per thousand in 1900; by 1965 it had dropped to 34.5 [109]. Thus, the decline in the death rate of the oldest group has been only a fraction of that of the youngest. Put another way, mortality in the youngest group declined approximately 82 percent, while among the 65-year-olds it declined only about 20 percent. Heart disease and strokes accounted for more than half the deaths in the United States in 1963. More than 25 percent of these deaths, moreover, are of people under 65—men and women in their prime years. In addition to their dominance as a cause of death, heart diseases are the cause of extremely widespread illness and disability. The National Health Survey of the U.S. Public Health Service estimates that 14,600,000 adults suffered from diagnosed heart disease, and that nearly as many had suspected heart disease.

Cancer, second in importance as a chronic disease, is the cause of 16 percent of all deaths in the United States. It is of interest to note that 45 percent of all deaths from cancer occurred in the age groups under 65 and that about 9 percent of its victims were under 45. Furthermore, cancer is either the first or the second cause of death in children between 1 and 14 years. The illness and disability it creates is enormous: it is estimated, on the basis of current trends, that about 1 out of every 4 people alive in the United States today can be expected to develop cancer at some time during his or her lifetime.[1]

Social and Economic Costs

The social and economic burdens which must be borne when large numbers of people succumb to chronic disease—while of a different nature than those formerly imposed by such diseases as plague, cholera, smallpox, and other scourges—are nevertheless severe. To begin with, the chronic diseases strike middle-aged and older persons in large numbers. These are the people who have mastered their occupations, who have experience, who have dependent children. Their death and disablement entail great losses to society. Lung cancer, for example, is a disease of extremely high and increasing incidence

[1] The data referred to in this section are derived from References 92, 111, and 112.

among middle-aged males. Inasmuch as only 2 or 3 percent of male lung-cancer patients survive more than five years, the social cost is obvious. Coronary disease, of much higher incidence, strikes many adults in their most productive years, as we have already noted.

Even when chronic diseases do not result in the obvious social loss of the death of experienced individuals, the social burden imposed by the disabling of such individuals is just as great. A person who has had a heart attack or cerebral vascular accident is often very limited in his activity. Not only is he frequently not able to function at peak efficiency in the most productive years of his life, but also, to varying degrees, he can become a burden on his family and community. If he is completely incapacitated and requires continual care, the cost of the disability is very high. Disabling diseases, such as the various forms of arthritis, are not severe enough to kill the patient yet render him in various degrees helpless and dependent upon others for care. The considerable costs of disability derive not only from the loss of the services of a productive individual in the prime of his life, but also from the fact that the services of others must be used to support and sustain him.

These diseases impose a tremendous burden on the economy. Heart disease alone is a multibillion dollar expense. Direct expenditures for medical care for persons with heart disease amounted to over three billion dollars in 1969. About 15 percent of the total days of care in the short-term hospitals are for heart-disease patients; these patients account as well for 28 percent of the patient days in nursing homes.

As with heart disease, the costs of cancer also run into billions of dollars annually. In addition to the direct costs, the indirect costs—loss of work days of disabled members of the labor force, and of housewives and others—are staggering.

Stroke ranks third as a cause of death in the United States. It is significant for other reasons—it ranks as the No. 5 killer of people in their most productive years; it claims more female than male victims in the United States and more nonwhite females than white. About eight of every ten stroke victims survive the acute initial phase of the disease, and most of these people survive for some years, usually in a seriously disabled condition, requiring much support from their society.

Special problems are posed to communities and families which must support persons with chronic illnesses. In communities, special hospitals for chronic disease have been opened; indeed, many hospitals once devoted to the treatment of tuberculosis have been altered to care for persons with other chronic diseases. There is also a trend to establish hospitals specializing not in emergency care but in the treatment of chronic diseases and in the long-term care of disabled persons (see Chapters 12 and 16). In addition, the number of nursing homes is increasing, as will special satellite institutions organized and run by general hospitals to provide non-emergency long-term care. Because hospital care is organized today to meet emergency medical and surgical demands, and is very costly, it is probable that ordinary hospital facilities in the future will be used only for acute flare-ups of chronic disease.

In some instances, home-care programs have been developed by hospitals to enable families to care for chronically ill patients. This course is feasible when the care required does not involve too much time or skill and when the facilities of the home are adequate.

Because the therapeutic period for chronic diseases is often so long and because lengthy disability is often entailed, the costs of care are very high in relation to what the average family can pay. It is not unusual for an average case of cancer to cost a family many thousands of dollars. The family is indeed fortunate that has sufficient savings to take care of such an emergency; for the most part, when such savings exist, they have been put aside to pay for the education of children or other family necessities. Frequently, there are no savings and the possessions of the family must be liquidated in order to meet hospital and physicians' bills. When no family resources remain to be liquidated, care must be supported publicly.

Often the problem of the social and economic costs of chronic illness is exacerbated by the attitudes of society. Certainly, this situation has been documented for mental illness, and a substantial effort was made to educate the general public concerning the rehabilitation potential of persons who have been mentally ill. Similarly campaigns have been launched to "hire the handicapped." But there is a lack of recognition of the less patent forms of discrimination practiced against victims of certain chronic disorders, such as coronary heart disease. In one of the early efforts to investigate this problem, Reeder found that the impact of heart disease on a person's occupational and economic standing varies with his occupational status. Men with coronary heart disease who were of lower-ranking occupational status tended to have the greatest problems: long-term disability, reduction or loss of income, the necessity of changing their jobs or occupations. The result is that the disease itself has a critical impact upon social structure: that is, it influences a person's socioeconomic status and life style, and hence must be considered as an independent as well as a dependent variable in social research [89, 90, 91].

When the catastrophic costs of therapy occur after the breadwinner in the family has retired and his income is reduced, as is often the case, it is obvious that the economic problem to the patient, his community, and the therapeutic organization is great. Even though Medicare lessens the burden on the older patient, the burden on society remains considerable.

THEORY OF SOCIAL EPIDEMIOLOGY

A disease may be considered as a tissue change toward a morbid state, brought about by some biochemical or biophysical agent acting directly on the tissue. Usually this action is the last in a series of events that put the host in contact with the disease-producing agent.

Thus, the train of events leading to contraction of scrotal cancer, as Sir Percival Pott found in studying the disease in England in 1755, was somewhat as follows [84]:

1. An environmental need for heated dwellings
2. Was met with a sociocultural response in the form of widespread installation of home space heaters,
3. The preferred fuel for which produced so much smoke and soot that
4. Exhaust passages required frequent cleaning;
5. An occupation, chimney sweep, developed which put the worker into close and frequent contact with soot, which in individuals who were susceptible, caused scrotal cancer.

Thus, as the paradigm in Figure 3–1 shows, the chain of events which may produce a disease may start with an occupational or other group, drawn typically but not necessarily from a given social class, which may engage in a pathogenic pattern of behavior.

FIGURE 3-1 Etiological Chain of Events Producing some Diseases

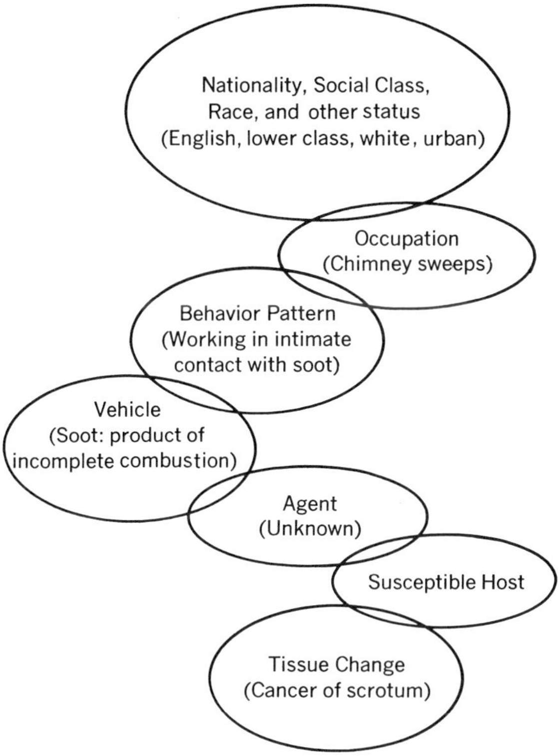

The behavior pattern or social situation may act directly on the organism (as in accidents, mental illness, or sociosomatic disease) or it may put the individual into contact with an agent which can cause disease. In susceptible hosts, tissue change may result. Whether or not the host is susceptible may depend on his genetic makeup, his previous experiences and possible immunities, and his general physical and mental state. The last two factors, of course, may be strongly affected by the social situation. Thus, the ubiquitous tubercle bacillus is more likely to produce clinically recognizable disease in an individual from the lower classes. Nonbehavioral environmental factors (e.g., sunlight) and genetically determined characteristics may figure importantly in the chain, as in the case of skin cancer and diabetes, respectively. Even here, however, it is clear that social factors, in these cases, occupations involving exposure to the sun, and diet, may significantly alter the effect of the nonsocial.

The etiological chain of events may be interrupted at almost any stage, and the disease thereby controlled. Thus, Pott vastly reduced the incidence of scrotal cancer simply by prescribing bathing. It is not necessary, obviously, to recognize the agent that causes the tissue change in order to prevent the disease. From the point of view of understanding the etiology of disease, on the other hand, it is apparent that the whole process of causation—all of the events leading to the disease—must be identified. This may involve epidemiological field work as well as laboratory investigation; the gamut of phenomena from biosocial to biochemical and biophysical must be examined as they relate to the disease. To achieve a coherent and complete theory of causation of a given disease, data of all three sorts must generally be obtained, and each kind determined to be consistent with the others in relation to the disease. Unless this is done, the etiology of a disease remains incompletely understood.

The strategy of epidemiological investigations develops from the etiological chain of events that we have described. Where hints of a relation between a behavior pattern and a disease exist—as, for example, between cigarette smoking and lung cancer—the investigation may proceed from hypothesized behavior. In such instances, hunches are derived from knowledge of the function of a given organ and of behavior that conceivably might affect it.

Often, however, no such hypotheses suggest themselves, and the strategy must be modified. Consider that specific behavior is frequently peculiar to certain segments of the population—that contact with soot, for instance, was peculiar to chimney sweeps. Such a circumstance suggests that investigation of the relative incidences of disease in occupational or other kinds of social groups within a society might be useful. If it is discovered that a singularly *high* incidence of a disease obtains in a given occupational group, as indeed was the case with scrotal cancer, further investigation may reveal specific behavior peculiar to that group that might account for their contact with the disease. The discovery of singularly *low* incidence of a disease in a particular segment of the population suggests that further investigation of that group might uncover the factor that is uniquely shielding or protecting it against contact with the disease.

Population groups that are culturally homogeneous have particularly strategic significance. It is much easier to establish the etiology of a disease in a group well-defined by a single characteristic such as occupation, particularly one as distinctive as chimney sweep, than in aggregates such as socioeconomic or rural-urban groups. But when there are no clues to specific occupational or other relationships, studies of the distribution of disease in socioeconomic, ethnic, racial, religious, or other types of groups can be quite useful.

If a given group is shown to have unusually high or low incidence of the disease in question, the next step is to investigate why. What particular characteristic of the group is producing this unusual incidence? In the answer to this question may lie information about other important links in the etiological chain of events leading to the disease.

Lung Cancer as an Example

One of the most graphic illustrations of the role of social factors is the etiology of lung cancer. In 1604 a member of the court of King James I wrote against the use of tobacco on the grounds that it was inimical to health, and tobacco has been designated as harmful ever since. Much more recently, investigators noted a great increase in the incidence of lung cancer, and cigarettes, which are bronchial irritants, were suspected as a cause. As a result, a large number of retrospective studies of hospital populations were undertaken. In every case, the studies showed a significantly higher incidence of lung cancer among smokers than among nonsmokers [103].

Recently, eight prospective studies of large population groups were carried out with the same results [42]. Figure 3–2 indicates one finding in Hammond

FIGURE 3-2 Carcinoma of Lung Deaths (all reported)

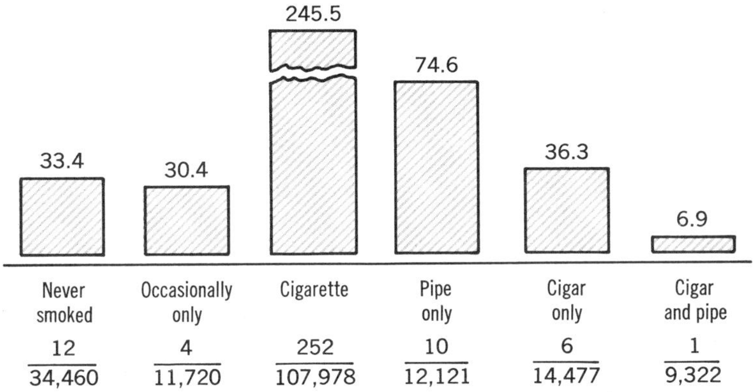

From E. C. Hammond and D. Horn, "A Study of the Relationship between Smoking and Death Rates: Preliminary Report of the 1954 Follow-up," a paper presented at the annual meeting of the American Medical Association in Atlantic City, New Jersey, June 6, 1955.

and Horn's study [43]. Briefly, their procedure was to interview approximately 200,000 males regarding their smoking habits, wait an interval of several years, interview them again about changes in their smoking habits, and measure the mortality rate within the group from various diseases, comparing the smokers and nonsmokers. As is evident from Figure 3–2, cigarette smokers had much higher rates of mortality from lung cancer than others, 245 per 100,000 compared to 33 for nonsmokers. Among the cigarette smokers, the mortality rate increased directly with the number of cigarettes smoked per day. Among persons who had stopped smoking during the years investigated, the mortality rate was lower than among those who continued. These findings, and those of many other researchers, have led the U.S. Surgeon General to warn of the relation between cigarette smoking and lung cancer.

Critics might argue that possible self-selection of smokers is responsible for the finding, or that some *x*-factor is really responsible both for lung cancer and smoking, and thereby creates the association between the two. One way to decide this might be to allocate cigarette smoking randomly within a large group of 12-year-old human males, control their environment, wait 30 years for the slow-acting carcinogen to take effect, and then measure the lung-cancer rate. It is unlikely that such an experiment could take place. But the epidemiological evidence based on behavior can be supplemented by laboratory studies. Such studies have found substances in tobacco smoke that are carcinogenic to animals. One of the more interesting laboratory studies of humans is by Auerbach et al. [4].

Auerbach and his colleagues dissected the tracheobronchial tree out of the lungs of 404 white males who had died of various causes. From each tree they prepared 208 sections for histological study, and systematically selected 55 for microscopic examination. It was found that while much of the bronchial epithelium of nonsmokers was normal, only 0.2 and 0.1 percent, respectively, of the sections of heavy smokers and lung-cancer cases showed normal epithelia. Furthermore, as Figure 3–3 shows, no sections of the epithelia of nonsmokers revealed carcinoma *in situ*, but 11.4 percent of those of heavy smokers did. In terms of individual autopsies, the investigators found that 75 percent of heavy smokers had at least one slide showing carcinoma *in situ*, compared to none for those who did not smoke or who smoked only occasionally (see Figure 3–3).

Recently, other evidence of a dose-response relationship (in which the risk of disease increases with increases in exposure to a pathogen) was garnered by the author [32]. There are variations in puffing patterns, some individuals puffing more and some less frequently, some puffing more immediately after lighting up, others towards the end of the cigarette. The simulation of these behavior patterns on an analytic smoking machine revealed that the patterns yielded considerably varying amounts of tar [36]. Observations were then made of lung-cancer and control patients to determine their smoking patterns. We found that the lung-cancer patients more frequently exhibited the smoking patterns shown by the machine analyses to yield the greatest amount of tar. Taking the same number of puffs over a long period of time carried greater risk than taking them over a short interval; puffing more towards the end of the cigarette produced greater risk than smoking more at the beginning. This micro-behavioral analysis thus provided more evidence of a dose-response relationship. Still other evidence of a dose-response relationship derives from studies of several populations which have shown a decline in risk as the length of time since the individual has stopped smoking increases. Our own studies show that as this period approaches ten years, the risk declines to the minimal level of the individual who has never smoked [39].

In addition, of course, much work with animals has shown the same result: The greater the exposure of the skin of various animals to tobacco tar, the higher is the incidence of tumors. Because traditional medical investigation has involved the bench laboratory and the experimental animal, the num-

FIGURE 3-3 Percentage of Slides with Carcinoma in situ

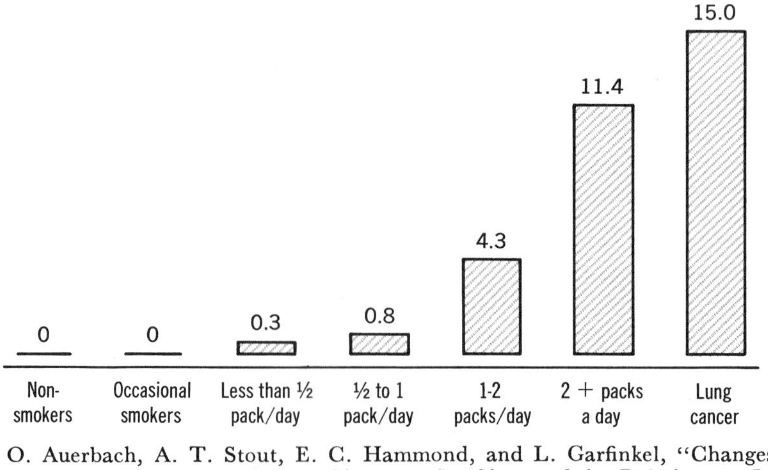

From O. Auerbach, A. T. Stout, E. C. Hammond, and L. Garfinkel, "Changes in Bronchial Epithelium in Relation to Cigarette Smoking and in Relation to Lung Cancer," a paper presented at the Clinical Meeting of the American Medical Association. Dallas, Texas, December 4, 1959.

ber of such studies is incredibly large and the number of human studies is very small in comparison. Nevertheless, it is the behavioral research which has been most convincing in establishing the cigarette-lung cancer relationship. This is truly a triumph for the social-epidemiological approach. Moreover, despite the fact that the biochemical mechanism by which tobacco tar produces lung cancer in humans is unknown, prevention can proceed on the basis of the social-epidemiological findings. Typically, social-epidemiologic findings must be supplemented by laboratory research, and this is certainly true of lung cancer. But the converse is also true: Findings from biochemical and biophysical research must be supplemented by biosocial investigations.

APPLICATIONS AND IMPLICATIONS OF SOCIAL-EPIDEMIOLOGIC THEORY

The etiological chain of events, the natural history of disease as we have been discussing it here, is a model which is more or less efficient depending on the disease to which it is applied. Thus, although modern geneticists agree that even almost wholly genetic diseases are affected by environmental factors, there are diseases in which the genetic susceptibility of the host is extremely prominent and environmental factors unimportant. Retinoblastoma is an example; sickle-cell anemia, which is characteristic of the black race, is another; thalassemia, found mainly in persons of Mediterranean ancestry, is a third.

On the other hand, the class of diseases known variously as psychosomatic or sociosomatic may have genetic components but are primarily a product of immersion in stressful situations which involve certain kinds of behavior and membership in certain kinds of social groups. In both the genetic and sociosomatic diseases, the vector (i.e., vehicle) and agent in the usual sense are missing. (For a fuller discussion of genetics and sociobiology see Chapter 4.)

Diseases may be classified according to the categories contained in our model of the Etiological Chain of Events (Figure 3–1). One classification, typically employed in medical textbooks, is by the type of tissue change, the organs or systems affected, and the type of agent. The table of contents of Cecil and Loeb's *Textbook of Medicine* [14], for example, lists chapters on diseases of collagen, metabolism, ductless glands, the digestive system, the respiratory system, the blood, the nervous system, and so on. Mixed with this is a classification based on type of agent (e.g., virus diseases, rickettsial and bacterial diseases, and spirochetal, protozoan, and metazoan infections). Another section of this text concerns diseases due to physical agents.

Again, diseases may be classified by the social groups evincing them or the behavior patterns associated with them. Thus, a large number of diseases occur more frequently among the lower socioeconomic classes than the upper, as we shall see presently. Similarly, there are diseases associated with particular racial or ethnic backgrounds. There are a number of smoking-related diseases: coronary disease, peptic ulcers, and cancer of the bladder, mouth, and, of course, lung. Moreover, we could cite classifications of disease based on social mobility, status inconsistency, alienation, anomie, crowding, and loss of emotionally significant persons through death, divorce, or mobility. Many of these latter could be related to the general concept of stress, in spite of (or because of) the varieties of use to which that word is put.

One clear implication of these classifications is that we assume no simplistic concept of disease causation, no one-cause–one-disease explanation. There is no reason to assume that each disease has one cause and only one, peculiar to itself and unrelated to the cause of any other disease. Thus, a number of factors can contribute to the development of lung cancer, e.g., exposure to dust in cobalt mining, asbestos dust, industrial smoke, and cigarette smoke. At the same time, smoke is a noxious substance which can also cause other diseases, such as emphysema. Similarly, mobility may be related to coronary disease, as well as to peptic ulcers, hypertension, or arthritis. A number of other factors possibly also contribute to the development of these diseases, such as status inconsistency, overwork, the loss of significant others, and particular behavior patterns.

It obviously does not follow, then, that because a factor is implicated in the development of one disease, it must not be implicated in another. Some writers have asserted, for example, that because smoking is related to lung cancer, it cannot be related to any other pathology. This does not make logical or biological sense. Smoking can influence the cardiovascular system via nicotine's vasoconstrictive effect, and the gastrointestinal system through stimulating the flow of hydrochloric acid in the stomach. It is not unreasonable to suggest that it could thereby contribute to the elevation of blood pressure and to ulcers in the stomach.

The old classifications of some diseases by causes were useful, and classifications based on newer conceptions of cause may be useful as well. For example, the concept of water-borne diseases was valuable because it shed light not only on etiology but also spurred the development of pure-water systems to control those diseases. Similarly, classifications by behavior or social situation may be found useful in the future. There very likely are a number of diseases related to mobility, stress, smoking, and the ingestion of alcohol; preventive steps which deal with these stimuli, therefore, may affect the incidence of several types of disease. Such reasoning provides an argument for an additional focus of future inquiry: The social situation which may foment a number of diseases should be investigated, and this kind of investigation should supplement the traditional research into one disease at a time.

Traditionally, those interested in etiology have focused their attention on using epidemiology to discover the agent or vector bringing about the tissue change. Our paradigm is useful in pointing up the importance of studies of the other factors appearing earlier in the etiological chain. It is true that in many cases we know the agent or vector but we do not know enough about antecedent factors to control the disease. Thus, for example, we know the agent of gonorrhea, we know the immediate behavior pattern, promiscuous sexual intercourse. But we do not know enough about factors leading to promiscuity, the culture of promiscuity. We know that auto accidents cause injuries, but we know little of the social and behavioral characteristics of individuals involved in them. Knowledge of these could be used, perhaps, to prevent such accidents. The tubercle bacillus is an agent of tuberculosis—but it is not sufficient to cause the disease. We know deprivation and isolation are also related, but we do not know enough about "why" to prevent the disease. We know the cause of the disease that might be called hyperfertility; but we know too little of the cultures of the groups afflicted with it. In all of these instances, the traditional concerns with vector and agent have been met; to control the pathology, however, knowledge of other factors in the paradigm is necessary. Very frequently these are social factors.

In the pages that follow, we will discuss diseases related to various social factors, starting at the demographic level, then turning to such social situations as mobility, status inconsistency and loss of status, and finally the concept of stress itself.

Socioeconomic Status

Socioeconomic status, which epidemiologists usually equate with social class, has been correlated with a variety of diseases. Perhaps most familiar is the supposed relationship between social class and the diseases which might be called "the diseases of civilization" or, more specifically, of advanced and urbanized, industrialized societies. In a recent review, Susser [104] notes the wide variability in rates of mortality from peptic ulcer among various populations and the changes in the pattern of the disease over the past 150 years. He notes that in Britain, before 1870, the upper classes had the highest mortality rates from duodenal ulcer and that in later cohorts the lower classes had the higher rates. Susser further states that the better-executed studies are to some extent consistent with each other. He concludes that although no single factor has yet been found to be sufficient to account for the observed variation in rates, "the specific elements that contribute to the variations probably include: diet, alcohol, cigarette smoking, emotional strain, personality and genotype." The consistency of some of these findings may be illustrated with smoking; for example, in Kasanen and Forsstram's recent study [50], and in our own work, it was found that the risk of peptic ulcers among smokers was much higher than among nonsmokers. Recent evidence from English and American studies shows that smoking is more common in the lower social classes. Thus, we may speculate that there is a link between social class and peptic ulcers—perhaps related to the changing pattern of smoking behavior.

Another disease purportedly related to socioeconomic status is hypertension. Although population surveys have demonstrated the relationship between blood-pressure level, on the one hand, and age, race, sex, and weight, on the other, unfortunately there have been few well-designed population studies of blood-pressure distribution and environmental and social characteristics. A recent study of an American population provides some data on this subject, however, Borkman and Borhani show that:

> Socioeconomic status and its various indicators are inversely associated with systolic blood pressure but not with diastolic blood pressure in many age-race-sex groups. Low SES and elevated systolic blood pressure are found in males more than females and Negroes more than whites [9].

These findings tend to be more or less consistent with the data concerning blood pressure among Negroes. It is worth noting that similar findings are reported in a large-scale community-wide study in Bergen, Norway, in which a large percentage of population was observed and an inverse relation between hypertension and social class was found [48].

The relationship of coronary artery disease—the leading cause of death in the United States and associated with high morbidity and mortality rates in other Western nations,—to socioeconomic status is less clear. In an examination of the literature on social class and coronary artery disease, Lehman [60] found that the results were equivocal. In part, this finding reflects the variations in the measures of independent variables employed by different investigators as well as the different social contexts within which the studies were done. There also are variations in how the dependent variable, coronary heart disease, is measured in the several studies Lehman reviewed. While there does not appear to be a linear relationship between social class and coronary disease, nor with occupational status when taken as an indicator of social position, there is some evidence (discussed presently) that the rate of incidence is higher among groups of certain occupational status [97].

Social class has been found to be associated with certain other chronic diseases. In a study of the incidence of cancer at various sites among the entire population of Buffalo, from 1948 to 1952 (see Table 3–2) it was found that lung, cervix, stomach, and esophageal cancer are of increasing incidence as class rank decreases, and that cancer of the breast increases with socioeconomic status [37]. Similar findings about these diseases have been made in New Haven, Connecticut, Denmark, England and Wales.

Although in this chapter we are primarily concerned with the chronic illnesses, it is appropriate to refer to the relationship of social class or socioeconomic status to all illnesses. As the continuing health survey of the National Center for Health Statistics [110] has pointed out, serious illness is appreciably more prevalent among the poor than among any other group in the population. The proportion of serious illness in the family, when related to income, showed that there was two to three times as much serious illness among the poor than among the population as a whole. When we consider the variable that is generally regarded as perhaps the most sensitive indicator of health status currently available, i.e., days of disability spent in bed, the data show that the numbers increase markedly from the high-income group to the low-income group. Similar patterns hold for other measures of disability. Moreover, evidence from the National Health Survey indicates the underreporting of illness by the lower-income groups.

Other evidence indicates that there are differential types of changes in health related to social class and illness. Perhaps the most careful and extensive study of infant mortality, conducted in England and Wales, states:

> One fact stands out from recent social studies of infant mortality, including the present one—the remarkable similarity of the decline among various social groups. There has been no narrowing of the social gap in infant mortality; if anything, it may have widened slightly. This finding was unexpected [77].

As Antonovsky notes, studies are needed of those diseases for which there is a closing of the class gap, those in which the gap appears to be widening, and those in which there seems to be a reversal in the relationship, as in the case of peptic ulcers, noted earlier. In short, social class is a very useful predictor of disease, and an important variable in understanding disease.

As we noted earlier in this chapter, our model of disease causation does not rely simply on what Dubos has called the "specific etiology" approach [20]. Disease is considered a product of the *interaction* among factors noted in the paradigm discussed earlier. Such a complex, multifactorial approach includes such concepts as stress, relative deprivation, anxiety, status inconsistency, and modes of coping. Social class or socioeconomic status thus may be a suggestive or gross indicator of other variables more immediately related to health and health behavior.

TABLE 3-2 AVERAGE ANNUAL AGE STANDARDIZED INCIDENCE RATES IN PATIENTS REPORTED WITH CANCER AT VARIOUS SITES BY SOCIO-ECONOMIC QUARTILE

(Buffalo, New York, 1948–1952)

Site	*Quartile I (Highest)* Number	*Quartile I (Highest)* Rate per 100,000	*Quartile II* Number	*Quartile II* Rate per 100,000	*Quartile III* Number	*Quartile III* Rate per 100,000	*Quartile IV (Lowest)* Number	*Quartile IV (Lowest)* Rate per 100,000
Trachea, bronchus and lung (males only)	129	35.8	105	31.1	137	44.8	182	57.9
Stomach (males only)	70	19.6	83	24.9	87	28.0	119	38.0
Esophagus (males only)	24	6.7	35	10.5	28	9.0	58	18.7
Breast (females only)	353	115.8	230	86.9	237	74.2	153	51.6

From S. Graham et al., "The Socioeconomic Distribution of Cancer at Various Sites in Buffalo, New York: 1948–1952," *Cancer*, 13 (1960), 180 ff.

Ethnicity and Religion

It is probable that ethnicity is related to the epidemiology of a number of diseases. This is because, first, ethnic background implies homogeneity within the group of dietary, hygiene, education, religious, and other customs. Inasmuch as his customary behavior may predispose the individual to a given disease or protect him from it, we would expect ethnic background to be related to several of the chronic diseases. Nevertheless, despite the fact that this characteristic is potentially so fruitful to epidemiological research, very few studies of it have been undertaken. As Figure 3–4 shows, Polish-Americans have been found to be subject to unusually high relative risks of cancer of the esophagus and lungs, while Italian-Americans are subject to high risks of cancer of the bladder, large intestine, and pharynx [38]. This finding has stimulated further research into those dietary, drinking, and other habits of Italian-Americans and Polish-Americans that may be related to the etiology of the disease, not only in these groups but wherever they occur.

The relationship between ethnic background and heart disease has been difficult to study. Investigators have usually had to content themselves with studies of *prevalence* (the number of cases current in a population at a given time) rather than of *incidence* (the number of new cases occurring at a given time). If the investigator's material is limited to prevalence, and he finds that a given nationality has a low rate of prevalence, this may indicate simply that the ethnic group under study gets poor medical care and has a higher mortality rate for this disease than other groups. And high preval-

FIGURE 3-4 Relative Risk of Developing Cancer

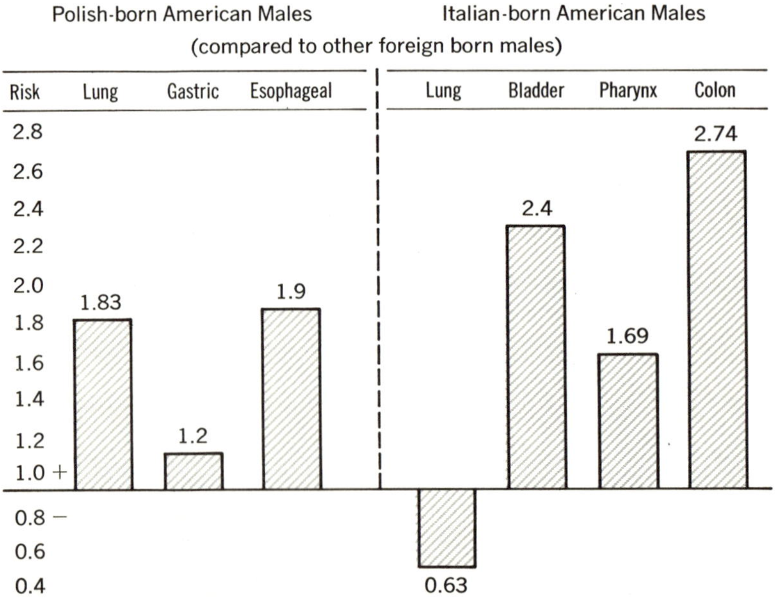

ence may indicate, not higher incidence, but merely a relatively low mortality rate—a result, for example, of good medical care.

Nevertheless, the few studies made of ethnic background as related to the prevalence of coronary disease offer some interesting suggestions. Epstein conducted examinations of about 1,600 persons. He concluded that Jews have a higher prevalence of coronary-artery disease, and also higher serum cholesterol levels, than Italians [24]. Sauer's finding that persons born in the USSR had very high mortality rates from the disease [95] is probably consistent with Epstein's because the largest proportion of Epstein's Jews were Russians. Saucer's finding that the Irish also had high rates is consistent with that of Graham, who studied prevalence in a random sample of Butler County, Pennsylvania [33], and Graham's finding on Southern Europeans is also consistent with that of Epstein. Kjelsberg and Stamler found higher death rates from coronary disease among American males than among Japanese-Americans, Chinese-Americans, and American Indians [56].

In spite of the fact that these studies were solely of data about prevalence, the magnitudes of the observed differentials and the consistency of the findings lend credence to them. What little is known about the diets of high-risk ethnic groups suggests that they are richer in animal fats than those of others; and animal fats have been related to coronary disease in other researches. The findings on diet and ethnic backgound appear to be consistent. More evidence along these lines is offered in our next section, on religion. Other features of the life style, however, such as physical activity, social stress, personality patterns, and smoking, must also be considered as significant. Psychosocial and socioenvironmental factors may also influence cholesterol levels.

It may be well to discuss briefly the relationship between diet and serum cholesterol in the study of coronary heart disease, particularly as it may pertain to certain observed ethnic differences. There are many difficulties in studying the relationship between diet and coronary heart disease. There is no doubt that a high serum-cholesterol level is associated with increased risk of developing coronary heart disease. The basis for the belief in the diet hypothesis rests upon the consistent observation of large quantities of cholesterol in plaques lining the arteries of patients with the disease. The assumption was then made that a diet high in saturated fats raised the level of cholesterol in the blood, which in turn increased the likelihood of plaque formation in the coronary arteries.

Nevertheless, the heart disease–*diet* hypothesis is far from settled. Mann's studies of the Masai in Africa are a case in point [69]. Masai men have a diet which is almost exclusively restricted to highly saturated fats (meat, milk, and blood), at least until they achieve the age of forty-five. But despite this high-fat diet, the Masai cholesterol levels are among the lowest ever recorded in the world, and coronary heart disease is said to be nonexistent among them. Furthermore, as Syme points out:

> . . . not one study in the United States, Canada or England has been able to identify a significant association between what individuals eat and the occurrence of coronary heart disease. Nor has any study in these countries been able to show that specific dietary practices are associated with serum cholesterol levels or other risk factors in individual subjects [105].

Perhaps one of the most striking epidemiologic observations about ethnicity is the differential in mortality from cerebrovascular and cardiovascular disease between the Japanese and persons of Japanese descent living in the United States. Gordon called attention to this startling contrast in mortality patterns in 1957 [30]. Comparing the rates of death from cardiovascular and cerebrovascular diseases in Japan with the rates for Japanese-Americans in Hawaii and in the mainland United States, he found that male residents of Japan, aged 55–64 years, had heart-disease death rates about half those of Japanese-Americans living in the continental United States, while the Hawaiian-Japanese had intermediate rates. A comparable *but inverse* gradient was demonstrated for deaths attributed to vascular lesions of the central nervous system, i.e., strokes. (The Japanese in Japan have the highest mortality rates in the world for strokes.)

A. Keys et al. reported a study of diet and serum lipids of Japanese men in Japan, Honolulu, and Los Angeles [54]. They found that serum lipids were lowest in residents of Japan, next lowest in Hawaiians, and highest in Los Angeles Nisei. It may be worth noting, parenthetically, that the Japanese diet contains little saturated fat.

A number of reports of differences in the incidence of these two diseases among ethnic groups in Hawaii showed that Japanese-Hawaiians had much lower death rates for coronary disease than Caucasians, while their rates for cerebral-vascular disease were moderately higher [6, 57]. More recently, Winkelstein and Syme have followed up Gordon's observations and have initiated a study of stroke and coronary diseases in Japanese-Americans living in Northern California to complement studies under way in Japan and Hawaii by other investigators. The following paragraph from the Winkelstein-Syme study is illustrative of the proposed approach:

> Japanese migrants and their descendants in Hawaii and California have a way of life that is different from that of those Japanese who remained in Japan, and the environmental differences between these geographic areas account for the differences in mortality pattern. Among these factors are diet, occupation, physical activity, etc. Although migrants may be different genetically from nonmigrants, this is not a tenable explanation of the gradient, since the intermediate position of Hawaii is difficult to explain. In matters relating to social and cultural aspects of the environment, Hawaii is intermediate, for here the migrants adhered longer and more tenaciously to Japanese customs and attitudes [116].

This study, while concerned with a particular ethnic group is, in addition, an investigation of the influence of migration. The approach is to compare the health of people who move with: (1) the health of the people in the original area; and (2) the health of the people in the area of destination. Of particular interest is the research concerned with migration of siblings and coronary heart disease. These researches of brothers, one of whom stayed in the country under consideration while the other migrated, should be most useful because they allow assessment of the effect of different cultures on people who are genetically similar [3].

The findings about coronary disease and cerebral-vascular disease among Japanese migrants are reminiscent of those regarding gastric cancer in the same groups. Thus, the Japanese in their homeland have the highest rates of mortality from gastric cancer of all those countries reporting with some reliability. Smith [100] found that Japanese living in Hawaii had somewhat lower rates, but still the highest of any of the Hawaiian ethnic groups. On the West Coast of the United States, the Japanese had still lower rates of gastric cancer, but still higher than the Caucasoid and Negroid populations on the West Coast. The fact that gastric cancer is readily defined and is usually quickly fatal makes it possible to rely on mortality data. These findings have stimulated studies of the diet of the Japanese populations living in Japan, Hawaii, and the Western United States.

Finally, mention might be made of ethnicity and migration in relation to congenital abnormalities. In a recent paper, Leck compared the main immigrant groups in Birmingham, England, with those of similar ethnic origin in other countries, and with the British-born population, in respect to the incidence of malformations among their offspring [58]. His most conclusive finding was "that the children of West Indian immigrants to Birmingham are quite unlike the offspring of Europeans there in respect to the incidence of malformations. . . ." Although Leck argues strongly for a genetic hypothesis, he concludes that both the environmental and the genetic components of the process may vary with the ethnic group. (See also Hobbs [47].)

Like ethnicity the religion of a group may sometimes dictate that it will exhibit certain distinctive behavior patterns. When such behavior patterns are related to the etiology of a disease, a correlation between the specific religion and the disease may be observable. We noted Epstein's finding regarding coronary disease among Jews. Again, the discovery that Jewish women rarely have cancer of the cervix was a very important lead in suggesting further avenues of investigation. Because Jews circumcise, investigations of the relation between circumcision and cancer of the cervix have been undertaken.

Toor has found interesting differences in the incidence of coronary artery disease among different groups of Jews in Israel [107]. The Yemenites (Jews from the Near East, and usually of low economic status) have a lower incidence of coronary artery disease than the Ashkenazim (European Jews, economically much better off). In dietary studies of the two groups, the Ashkenazim were found to ingest significantly larger quantities of animal fats than other Jews. This evidence regarding the diets and the incidence of heart disease among two groups of Israeli Jews still leaves unanswered the question of how socioeconomic status life styles, other than diet, may influence coronary heart disease.

Familial Characteristics

Just as various cultural patterns peculiar to religious groups may be related to a given disease, behavioral traits peculiar to individual families may affect their risk of contracting certain diseases.

Thus, the child-rearing practices adopted by certain families may protect against or foment disease. There may be some association between breast cancer and not nursing offspring [67]. Again, some commentators have hypothesized that the woman who is much burdened with the cares of raising many children is more likely to have hypertension than the woman without children and without such cares. However, evidence to the contrary has been provided by research undertaken in Norway [48]. In a community-wide study of blood tension, it was found that single women have the highest rates of hypertension of any group of females, and the rate decreased progressively among married women with one child, with two children, and with three or more children. In short, the incidence of female hypertension may decline with an increase in familial responsibilities.

A second type of study of disease in families is investigation of the relatives of ill persons in an effort to discover whether certain diseases are inherited. Typically, such studies compare the incidence of a given disease among the kin of patients with the incidence among relatives of control persons not having the disease. In the past, many geneticists concluded that if a disease appeared more frequently among the relatives of control persons, the disease did "run in families" and was inherited genetically.

Currently, most geneticists and sociologists realize that the aggregation of disease in certain families can be attributed to both social and genetic inheritance, with either one type or the other predominating. (See Chapter 4 for a discussion of genetics and social factors.) Thus, for example, dietary behavior peculiar to individual families may help to account for the fact that gastric cancer has been found to occur approximately twice as often in the families of gastric cancer patients as among the relatives of persons without this disease [34]. Again, the intrafamilial transmission of rheumatoid arthritis was discussed by Kasl and his associates [51]. They point out that sociocultural factors—status inconsistency, in the case of women—is implicated along with psychosocial factors involving mother-daughter relationships. A different psychosocial sequence appears to obtain in the case of male rheumatoids. We must emphasize however, that both sociologists and geneticists agree that a given manifestation is almost never the exclusive result of either genetic or social inheritance. Most diseases are the result of a pathologic environmental factor brought into contact with a host genetically, physically, socially, and psychologically susceptible to this factor.

One convenient way to investigate the extent to which a disease is inherited genetically or sociologically is to study its incidence among blood relatives of persons with and without the disease as compared to non-blood relatives of these persons, such as spouses. Inasmuch as mates share from marriage onward the same environment as blood relatives (their children, for example), if the aggregation among blood kin is higher than among mates, evidence is provided that inheritance may be more genetic than sociologic. But equal incidence among blood and non-blood kin living in the same household is evidence to support a hypothesis of essentially sociologic inheritance. Winkelstein demonstrated significant spouse aggregation of systolic blood pressure developing after 10 to 15 years of marriage. "In order to explain this finding on a genetic basis, it would be necessary to assume a high degree of assortative mating with delayed expression of the inherited blood pressure trait." [117]. Parent-child aggregation in this study was limited to families with aggregated parents (both parents had the same systolic blood pressure level).

Cancer of the Uterine Cervix

We have seen that a wide variety of characteristics related to social class, religion, ethnic background, and stress and related social situations are associated with a number of chronic diseases. Such relationships are useful in suggesting areas for future research. Thus, the finding that the Japanese have an unusually high risk of stroke suggests that examination of their behavior patterns might reveal one which is related to the etiology of this disease. In some chronic diseases, many relationships of the kinds already discussed have been discovered; these in turn have suggested the possible existence of additional relationships, and further research to test these newer hypotheses has been undertaken. This is true in the case of the disease which we will discuss in this section, cancer of the *cervix uteri*; we will attempt here to present a brief but comprehensive picture of the epidemiology of this disease.

Cancer is generally thought to be not one disease but a group of different diseases having at least one characteristic in common: the aggregation of abnormal cells at particular sites in the body, such cells having potentialities for invasive growth at the site of origin and for proliferation to other parts of the body. But the various types of cancer differ in many other respects, such as the morphology of the cells involved, the sites which come under attack, and their etiological characteristics. For most purposes and even though there may be some etiological factors which all cancers have in common, most epidemiological research must treat the different kinds of cancer as different disease entities. Thus, it is necessary that we consider the epidemiology of cancer of the cervix as a distinct and separate study.

In 1960, cancer of the cervix of the uterus had an age-adjusted incidence rate of 25 for every 100,000 population in Upstate New York [25]. It ranked second in importance among the various kinds of cancers afflicting females. Primarily a disease of older women, there are sociological factors related to it. Among these are race, social class, religion, circumcision, sexual habits, and family stability. According to most studies, it is a disease found only about two-thirds as often among whites as among nonwhites. Other data from New Haven, Denmark, and England suggest that the disease increases with decreasing socioeconomic status (see Table 3–3).

Several decades ago it was discovered, as we have already mentioned, that Jewish women have a much lower incidence of cancer of the cervix than non-Jews. Figure 3–5, for example, shows incidence differentials between Jews in Israel and a United States population, and between Yemenite and Ashkenazi Jews in Israel. If such a difference among the Jews is sus-

TABLE 3-3 STANDARD INCIDENCE RATIOS, BY INCOME CLASS, FOR WHITE FEMALES, OF CANCER OF THE CERVIX UTERI: UNITED STATES, DENMARK, AND ENGLAND AND WALES

	United States 10 Cities	*Denmark*	*England and Wales*	
Class	*1947*	*1943–47*	*1950*	*1930–32*
1 (lowest)	156	131	150	130
2	113	100	109	106
3	90	79	98	99
4	85	90	69	78
5 (highest)	74	50	61	65

From Harold F. Dorn and Sidney J. Cutler, "Morbidity from Cancer in the United States," Part II, U.S. Public Health Monograph No. 56 (Washington, D.C.: Government Printing Office), 1959.

FIGURE 3-5 CANCER OF THE CERVIX

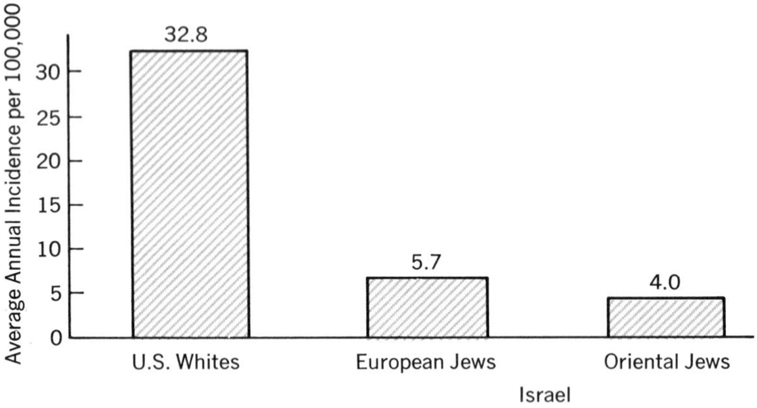

From: H. F. Dorn, "Cancer Morbidity Surveys." Paper read at American Public Health Assn, meetings, Buffalo, Oct. 14, 1954.

TABLE 3-4 CERVICAL CANCER AS A PERCENTAGE OF TOTAL FEMALE CANCER ADMISSIONS AT THE TATA MEMORIAL HOSPITAL, BOMBAY, 1941–1950, AND THE PREMIER RADIOLOGICAL INSTITUTE AND CANCER HOSPITAL, MADRAS, 1950–1952

	TATA MEMORIAL		*PREMIER RADIOLOGICAL INSTITUTE*	
	Total female cancer admissions	*Per cent cervix cancer*	*Total female cancer admissions*	*Per cent cervix cancer*
Hindus	3,828	45	280	53
Christians	575	29	60	29
Moslems	818	16	67	18
Parsis	396	13	—	—

From E. L. Wynder, J. Cornfield, P. D. Schroff, and K. R. Doraiswami, "Study of Environmental Factors and Carcinoma of the Cervix," *American Journal of Obstetrics and Gynecology*, 79 (October, 1954), pp. 1016–52.

tained by replicative studies, it might be related to the more orthodox observance of the Jewish religious practices among the Oriental Jews. Other ethnic relationships have also been discovered in the study of cancer of the cervix: Table 3–4 shows, from a study in India, that Moslems and Parsis had much lower rates than Protestants and Hindus. There have been intimations, furthermore, that Moslems in the East Indies have less cancer of the cervix than other religious groups.

A number of suggestions have been made to account for the low incidence of cancer of the cervix among Jews and Moslems. One factor is the hygienic practices traditional to those groups, described in an imaginative and valuable anthropological work by a physician, E. L. Kennaway [53]; other factors are the circumcision of males and the prescription of abstinence from intercourse during the first week after the cessation of menses, noted in Leviticus. The traditional Jewish ritualistic hygiene of the sex organs is probably no longer widely observed, at least in the United States, and therefore is probably not a factor in the low rates of cervical cancer among women. Abstinence from intercourse during menses and the first week thereafter would of course reduce exposure to any possible cancer-causing agent involved in intercourse by almost half. But such abstinence does not appear to be practiced by large numbers of Jews in the United States. Indeed, Kinsey found a somewhat greater frequency of marital intercourse among Jewish males than among Catholics or Protestants. Because of Jewish endogamy, we are fairly safe in suggesting that the same statement could be made for Jewish females, assuming the accuracy of Kinsey's data.

Circumcision, however, is still common to many of the low-incidence religious and ethnic groups: the Jews, Moslems, and Parsis. Under poor conditions of hygiene, the uncircumcised male may introduce a substance called smegma into contact with the cervix. Inasmuch as human smegma has been found carcinogenic to the mouse cervix, circumcision, and smegma as a possible human carcinogen, are of epidemiological interest.

Studies of the amount of circumcision among mates of cervical cancer as compared to other patients have revealed contradictory findings. The research of Dunn and Buell revealed essentially no differences in exposure of cervical cancer and other patients to circumcised and uncircumcised males [22]. Stewart and associates and Wynder revealed a somewhat greater excess of exposure to uncircumcised males among women with cancer of the cervix as compared to controls [102, 119]. Because of the conflict in the findings of research on this very important question, an answer to why such conflict might exist was sought.

In all the studies, the circumcision of the mates was determined by asking each patient if her husband was circumcised. The validity of such a method of establishing the fact of circumcision was questioned, and further research was undertaken. In this study, physicians giving admission examinations were asked to pay special attention to, and record, the presence or absence of circumcision of each male patient, with *no prior knowledge* of the patient's own statement on the subject. Analysis of about 200 male patient's statements revealed disagreement with the physicians' observation in 34.4 percent. This finding suggests that the methodology of the previous studies makes their conclusions dubious. It is also an interesting commentary on the kind of error that can be made with interview techniques, even those applied to very concrete questions. A better, but certainly more difficult, way to study circumcision as related to cancer of the cervix in the future is to conduct actual examinations of the husbands of patients and control subjects. However, it might well prove difficult to persuade husbands of women with cancer of the cervix to submit to an examination.

Despite these difficulties, Jean Aitken-Swan and Sir Dugald Baird carried out examinations of the husbands of 54 cervical cancer patients and 56 control subjects in Aberdeen [1]. Previous investigators had noted that whether a male has been circumcised or not should not be the question at issue. This is because persons who have not been circumcised may have naturally shorter foreskins than those who have been. Complicating the problem is the fact that some surgical circumcision is perfunctory. Indeed, in comparing circumcision carried out by rabbis with that done by surgeons, Breslow once said that "Surgical circumcision is often little more than ritual; on the other hand, ritual circumcision is often more surgical than ritual."[4]

In light of these problems, Aitken-Swan and Baird compared the husbands in terms of length of foreskin. They found that about 9 percent more of their patients' husbands had long foreskins than the control subjects'. They thus had too few cases to establish a relationship, even though the finding was in the hypothesized direction. Clearly, foreskin length is only one of many factors that may be implicated in this disease.

We have seen how the finding of a simple relationship between a disease and a religious group has stimulated a large number of studies designed to explain the relationship. There is a possibility that still other differences between Jews and non-Jews could explain the different incidences of the disease. To learn more about the problem, the study of groups which are racially similar but culturally different—such as Moslems and Jews in the Near East—should be undertaken to discover possible differences in incidence of cervical cancer. A genetic hypothesis might be tenable, for the groups which have been found to be low in cervical cancer, the Jews in Israel and the Moslems in India, probably derive from similar racial stock. Sachs, for one, has adduced evidence that there is a gene pool held in common by Jews regardless of whether they derive from Eastern or European sources [94]. In frequencies of fingerprint whorls of various types, Jews in one nation show much more similarity to Jews in other nations than to non-Jews in their own country: German Jews, for example, show a greater similarity of frequencies to other Jews than they do to Germans in general. It is possible, therefore, that there is some characteristic protecting Jews against cervical cancer that is inherited genetically within the group.

In addition to factors related to religion and circumcision, a number of other characteristics have been examined as they relate to cervical cancer. With regard specifically to sexual behavior, the findings are equivocal. Thus, Jones and Terris discovered no significance in the frequency of coitus. A number of writers have found evidence that persons with cancer of the cervix married early or had commenced to have intercourse at an earlier age than control patients. A number of studies have provided the consistent finding that cervical cancer patients had their first and last pregnancies at an earlier age than others. In addition, they are more likely to have been married one or more times than others and also less likely to have been childless.

The suggestion that frequent intercourse and intercourse commenced early in life may be related etiologically to cancer of the cervix is consistent with findings that among nuns there is almost no cancer of the cervix, but that among prostitutes the rate is high. Levin's finding that cancer of the cervix is related etiologically to the presence of syphilis might explain in part the high incidence among prostitutes [66]. Of equal sociological interest is the finding of a greater frequency of familial instability and poverty among cervical cancer patients than among others. Paloucek, after interviews in depth with a series of patients, suggests that such conditions do indeed characterize cervical cancer patients as compared to control subjects [81]. Of equal but parenthetical interest is Paloucek's finding that persons with a good social

[4] Personal communication, Lester Breslow, Commissioner of Health, State of California, 1965.

prognosis for those variables also have the best physical prognosis for recovery from cervix cancer.

Although a large number of different variables have been suggested as being positively related to cancer of the cervix, only a few show up in many studies as being possibly important: early age at intercourse and marriage, non-Jewish religion, multiple sex partners, and circumcision. These findings, taken together with the finding of very little cancer of the cervix among nuns and a high risk among prostitutes, suggest a venereal model for this disease. This has become particularly interesting in view of the recent findings of virus-like bodies associated with some human cancer and the transmissibility of cancers in fowls and animals.

Clyde Martin, for example, suggests this hypothesis in assaying the results of this study [71]. In the course of his doctoral dissertation research, Martin studied about forty Jews with cancer of the cervix and compared them with Jews without cancer of the cervix. He would have preferred to include larger numbers but was unable to because of the rarity of the disease among Jewish women. He found that those with cancer of the cervix had had more sex partners and more partners who were not Jewish. One might propose an infectious hypothesis to explain his (and others') findings.

Thus, we might hypothesize that a woman must have close contact with a man carrying an agent which can produce cancer of the cervix. Such an agent would more likely be carried by a man with a long foreskin or one who is uncircumcised, because it would be relatively more difficult for such individuals to maintain good penile hygiene. It could be that the agent is found rarely in Jews because they marry and mate endogamously for the most part, and so the agent has had little opportunity to spread from non-Jews to Jews. Intercourse with a number of partners would increase a woman's chances of coming into contact with a male carrier of the agent. The higher risk associated with intercourse at an early age could be an artifact of an association between early intercourse and intercourse with several partners; it has also been suggested that contact of an agent with less mature tissue may result in increased risk of cervical cancer. It must be emphasized that all of this is speculation. Nevertheless, it would appear that a number of the sociological findings are consistent with an infectious hypothesis.

SOCIAL STRESS AND DISEASE: A SOCIOLOGICAL PERSPECTIVE

The concept that stress is related to medical problems is by no means of recent origin, but in recent years the study of stress and the emotional states of fear, anger, frustration, and anxiety and other depression have received the attention of an increasing number of investigators. (See Chapter 5 for a discussion of this concept from a somewhat different perspective.) The professional literature on stress is impressive in its range and variety, spanning virtually all the fields of the behavioral and medical sciences and the related professions. There is a considerable body of scientific information concerning the responses of the cardiovascular, respiratory, gastrointestinal and endocrine systems to emotional stress, and new evidence is accumulating concerning the chemical changes that occur in the brain under conditions of stress [7, 26, 27, 28, 63, 85, 113, 115, 118].

One of the features of this literature is the extent to which writers of widely divergent backgrounds emphasize sociocultural factors and not just physical sources such as heat, cold, and wounds, in considering the etiology of stress. Indeed, it may be said that the major emphasis, explicit or not, is on a strictly sociological source of stress, i.e., "the structure of social relationships in which contemporary man finds himself enmeshed" [72], or, as Stanley King notes in Chapter 5, on the stress points structured by the social order. We now have considerable experimental evidence, from studies of laboratory-animal populations, that social environments (including those dictated by different population densities, by social-group size and composition, by social status, and by social isolation) may have demonstrable short-term and long-lasting effects upon the metabolism of substances in the central nervous system, and that physiology and behavior cannot be fully understood out of context of the social environment [16, 44].

Similarly, experiments conducted with human populations under laboratory conditions, simulating real-life situations, have produced demonstrable effects in the autonomic and endocrine systems; other studies have indicated a relationship between life-stress situations and the production and secretion of the stress hormones, adrenaline and noradrenaline and cortico-steroids and blood lipids, all of which are important in understanding coronary heart disease [13, 64, 65]. In addition, a substantial number of laboratory, clinical, and field studies have indicated relationships between social stress and other physiological outcomes, e.g., mental disorder. Henry and Cassel, working from laboratory studies and field studies of human populations, suggest that:

> the blocking of aspirations and the uncertainty that the organism will be able to satisfy behavioral urges through programmed goals appear to be important causes of chronic psychosocial stimulation . . . [leading] to progressive and eventually irreversible disturbances such as renal hypertension, heart failure, or cerebrovascular disease [44].

A number of sociological concepts have been employed to indicate a relationship to social stress; these include status inconsistency, alienation, anomie, relative deprivation, cultural change, and sociocultural mobility. In addition, it is recognized that there are mediating factors in the responses to stressful situations. These mediating or intervening variables include personality and characteristic response repertoire as well as individual perceptions of social stress. Hinkle and Wolff put it this way:

> . . . the bulk of psychiatric and physical illness episodes occur at times when individuals perceive their life situations as unsatisfying, threatening, too demanding, and productive of conflict . . . the critical factor in the development of illness is not actual social or environmental stress, but the individual's perception of such stress [45].

The theoretical sociological underpinnings of stress as a response to environmental, i.e., social and situational factors, may most usefully be found in the work of Durkheim, Cooley, Mead, Thomas, and Merton [18, 23, 74, 76, 114]. Thus, Durkheim places great emphasis upon the impact of external constraining forces in establishing and also maintaining an integrated, functional unit. He states that:

> A social fact is to be recognized by the power of external coercion which it exercises or is capable of exercising over individuals, and the presence of this power may be recognized in its turn either by the existence of some specific sanction or by the resistance offered against every individual effort that tends to violate it [23].

According to Durkheim, the lack of integration, or isolation, is the critical factor in the disruption of the social system. In his analysis of anomie, Merton carries Durkheim's conception of isolation further, in his presentation of a paradigm of individual patterns of adaptation to normative stress. He specifically cites the failure of individuals to attain adequate means to reach the prescribed goal of success as a source of stress. According to Merton's paradigm, individuals who are either least able to attain the goal or to control the means of success are defined as "retreaters." The concept of relative deprivation is introduced here as the individual compares himself with others in the situation. Retreatism thus becomes an adaptation to normative stress that may result in "absorption into a world of externally defined stress."[5]

Thomas's view of "conflicting definitions of situations" adds to our conceptualization of stress. He states:

> As long as the definitions of situations remain constant and common we may anticipate orderly behavior reactions. When rival definitions arise . . . we may anticipate social disorganization and personal demoralization . . . the mass of delinquency, crime, and emotional instability is the result of conflicting definitions [114].

Thomas, in fact, fused the notion of "crisis" with that of "situation" and "definition of the situation."[6] When social life is running smoothly, so long as habits are adjustive, "situations" hardly exist. There is nothing to "define" when people behave as anticipated. But when the habitual situation is altered, or when the individual or group is not prepared for an experience, then we may assume that there is a threat, a challenge, a strain, a kind of "crisis." Thomas pointed out that the "*same crisis will not produce the same effect uniformly*" [114]. He also felt that these crises were of fundamental importance in affecting human behavior and social change. As Mechanic [75] points out, Thomas made another observation that is critically important in the study of stress, namely, that the process of socialization of an individual prepares him to cope with events. Man is an active participant in his environment; indeed, perhaps the most important single factor in the development of culture is man's great learning capacity. That is, man learns to pattern his behavior in response to environmental challenges. Acclimatization to temperature and altitude are well-documented examples of the functional modification by which man increases his capability in the face of unusual environmental stress. Just as important, but less well studied, are the long-term adaptive changes which occur in human beings when they develop under particular types of environmental stress. In this process of adaptation, the individual's repertoire of coping behavior is a crucial element in understanding the ways in which people come to terms with a given stressful situation.

Finally, the theoretical contributions of Cooley and Mead round out the conceptualization of social stress presented here. Their approach, widely heeded by sociologists today, is that an individual's expectations about the behavior of others toward him, his expectations of himself, and other's expectations of him are defined in relation to his and their position or status. The total pattern of these interacting expectations influence the individual's concept of himself and the concept

[5] For a discussion of the urban ghetto as a source of stress see Reference 29.

[6] For this particular point we are indebted to David Mechanic, whose discussion of stress [75] is recommended to the reader.

others have of him, i.e., his self-identity and his public identity.

What we have attempted here is to bridge the macro-sociological theory of Durkheim and the more micro-oriented theoretical conceptions of Cooley, Thomas, Mead, and Merton. With respect to Merton's position on the blocking of means or channels to the achievement of proper goals (retreatism and ritualism), individuals may pursue alternative means or channels for reaching the same goal. That is, there are compensations, through diverse group affiliations, for those individuals whose channels to some goal may be more or less blocked. We have also suggested the important role that learning and socialization play in the process of coping with situations, using coping in Mechanic's sense:

> Coping . . . refers to the instrumental behavior and problem-solving capacities of persons in meeting life demands and goals. It involves the application of skills, techniques, and knowledge that a person has acquired [75].

Thus, there is a learning component to the matter of dealing with a situation, particularly a situation defined as stressful. These situations are shaped by the social structure, either of a community, society, or smaller system. When incongruencies develop between cultural norms and goals and the individual's capacity to behave in accord with these goals, individuals may cope and adapt in a variety of ways. In this sense, social stress has both a societal and personal component. The result of the interaction of social stress with biological processes may take a variety of possible forms, i.e., coronary heart disease, cerebrovascular disorders, essential and renal hypertension, viral infections, mental disorders, and so forth.

Efforts to Measure Social Stress

The difficulties of attempting to measure social stress are well recognized and need not be considered here at any length. In addition to objective

FIGURE 3-6 Subjective Stress Scale, Los Angeles Heart Study, 1970

STRESS QUESTIONS

INTERNAL STRESS (REACTION)	In general, I am usually tense and nervous.
	At the end of the day, I am completely exhausted mentally and physically.
EXTERNAL STRESS (EXPOSURE)	There is a great amount of nervous strain connected with my daily activities.
	My daily activities are extremely trying and stressing.

Response categories for each item were:

This describes me:

Very well	Fairly well	Not very well	Not at all

indicators of social stress it is advantageous to have some subjective assessment of stress. One such indicator is the simple instrument (Fig. 3–6) developed for use in the Los Angeles Heart Study by Reeder and his associates [15]. Its advantage is that it tells us whether or not the event or situation is perceived as stressful by the subjects. The correlation between the self-reporting of the subject and the report on the subject by a family member was at a fairly respectable level ($r = .55$). A further validation was the close association of high stress scores with the taking of tranquilizers. Results to date indicate an association with some of the risk factors in coronary heart disease. Similar results using this stress indicator have been found in a study in Holland, but it is too early to determine its effectiveness as a predictor of the disease. Clearly, the individual's assessment of the stress he is experiencing should be studied in relation to this and other diseases.

Sources of Stress and Illness: Culture Change, Situational Mobility, Life Changes and Personality

What are some of the sources of chronic social stress that may lead to illness, and to chronic disease in particular? A number of factors appear in the literature more or less consistently, including culture change, situational mobility, and personality. A brief examination of some of these sources of stress and their relationship to illness will be presented.

Culture change. Culture change such as occurs in the process of changing the economy and social structure of a locale has been implicated as producing social and psychological stress among the inhabitants. A series of studies by cultural anthropologists and other investigators has come to the general conclusion that the modernization of so-called underdeveloped countries is clearly related to an increased incidence of mental disorders [52, 55, 78]. One of the possible explanations for such a result can be drawn from our previous theoretical discussion of social stress, namely, that some individuals can cope with the stresses of change without any apparent evidence of strain or ill-health, while others will experience a variety of illnesses. Not all inhabitants of a community move at a uniform rate of speed from a traditional to a modernized cultural mode. Under such circumstances, relative deprivation is also a critical factor to be considered. Thus, differential perception, ability to cope, and relative deprivation are concepts which help us to understand the different experiences of individuals undergoing social stress in similar environments.

In their analytical review of psychosocial factors in hypertension, Henry and Cassel note that mortality from this condition is far higher in some South American cities than in others. Their data suggests a relation with the rate at which the cities are growing, a high growth rate implying more rapid social change and more accompanying social and personal stress. They state:

> Strong and repeated threatening stimuli may result from such competitive and unfavorable disordered situations. The aged frequently suffer in the competition . . . [and] will fail to achieve the goals they desire in spite of their efforts. The stimulation of the adrenergic system that they will experience may well be sustained and intense and lead to unfavorable responses . . . the repeated increases in pressure are cause and the cardiovascular disease that eventually follows is effect. . . . Thus the symptoms which bring the patient to the physician with the development of the final kidney, heart, or central nervous system breakdown may be only the last phase in a complex chain of events whose start lies buried in the early experience of the individual and his culturally determined pat-

> terns of response to an environment which is becoming increasingly dissonant . . . viscero motor and hormonal responses may take place without emotional disturbance or awareness on the part of the organism [44].

What has been said with respect to cultural change in the context of the modernizing of societies may also hold for more advanced societies. Thus, Marks's review indicates that the *processes* of urbanization are associated with higher rates of coronary heart disease [70]. In the United States, for example, it was found that in those counties undergoing rapid urbanization and industrialization there was a higher rate of mortality from coronary heart disease [108]. Thus, sharp discontinuities in social relationships, occasioned by change of whatever source, may result in social stress.

Situational mobility. Situational mobility, a concept developed by Syme, refers to personal or individual changes as distinct from societal or cultural changes. We might consider situational change as encompassing the following processes delineated by Price [85]:

1. Geographic movement
   a. Voluntary
   b. Involuntary
2. Social space change
3. Life style change
4. Goal orientation change
5. Status crystallization (status inconsistency).

Thus, situational mobility includes such social phenomena as a *change in physical space*, as in rural-to-urban migration. Whether the move is voluntary or not may have different consequences even on the various members of a family. In this context, lack of mobility could also be a critical factor. Mobility has meaning according to the expectations of the person, of significant others, and of society, and can be defined in terms of different rates of change along a set of dimensions. As Back and Pittman observe, "for each dimension, there is a standard rate of change, and we can consider stresses arising from conformity to this standard rate of change and from deviations from this standard. . . ." [5]. Clearly, more specification of the conditions that surround mobility and migration are necessary.

Physical mobility has been of considerable interest to social scientists for a variety of reasons. It has been demonstrated that mobility and migration are related to various illnesses, including cardiovascular diseases and mental disorders [101, 49]. Summarizing her review, Smith points out that migrants within a given culture have a greater frequency of cardiovascular disease than persons who are nonresidentially mobile. Intercultural mobility is also associated with disease, as we indicated earlier in this chapter.

A second type of situational mobility is *change in social space* (such as occupation, income, etc.) Changes occasioned by this type of social mobility often involve stress, the result of normative life expectancies deriving from the individual's status, on the one hand, and his personal reference groups, aspirations, and accomplishments on the other. Examples of such mobility are observed in occupational mobility from relatively low social origins or greatly increased income levels. These factors are, of course, related to the other types of situational mobility such as life style, goal orientation, and status crystallization.

A change in life style involves a change in the use of the symbols of status. Studies of changes in life style require a focus on the individual rather than on structural analysis, and consequently different types of empirical data are required; *changes in goal orientation* similarly involve quite another dimension of situational change. The study of both of these processes involves the study of role-taking by individuals in the positions at which they have newly arrived. As individuals move from position to position within the society, they encounter emotional stresses. Societal values tend to define the situations and the degree of support given to individuals at these times. Both life style and goal orientation, being individual in nature, are related to another source of social stress, namely, personality, which is discussed later in terms of these factors.

The concept of *status crystallization*, introduced by Lenski, refers to status consistency and status inconsistency [62]. A body of theory and research has developed which suggests that pronounced status inconsistencies of certain kinds tend to be a source of stress [61]. Conflicting views of the appropriateness of one's own behavior and the expectations of others resulting from status inconsistency may result in an ambiguity of role or a conflict in roles, and in efforts at achieving status equilibrium. In short, the individual with a discrepancy in rank on one or more status indicators is presumed to be under stress which, in turn, may lead to adverse effects on his physical and mental health.

A variety of researchers have employed the concept of status inconsistency to study its relationship to ill health, physical or mental. Thus, status inconsistency was one of the critical social variables examined in the study of rheumatoid arthritis by Kasl and Cobb [51]. Data from the Western Electric study by Ostfeld and Shekelle show that the greater the number of status incongruities, the greater the risk of coronary heart disease; there was an increased incidence of coronary heart disease among men with several types of status inconsistency [97].

Of particular interest to sociologists are three recent studies that indicate that the highest rates of coronary heart disease were found among men of lower-middle occupational status. Lee and Schneider [59] found that the highest rates of the disease existed among white-collar nonexecutives (foremen and clerical workers). Pell and D'Alonzo found that the highest rate of coronary heart disease existed among the lowest *salaried* groups (i.e., white-collar nonexecutives), as distinct from wage earners [82]; in a third study, Hinkle and his associates reported that "age-standardized rates for all men, regardless of education, are highest among foremen and lowest among (top level) managers and executives" [46]. Thus, these studies indicate that the lower middle-class employees, i.e., those middle-class with relatively low occupational status, appear to be at greatest risk for coronary heart disease.

As may be seen from Table 3–5, there is a generally lower rate of coronary heart disease among college men as compared to noncollege men, but the difference does not hold in all occupational categories. The noncollege "general area managers" and the college-educated foremen, who had the highest rates of heart disease were, however, a very small group; furthermore, these men were generally dissatisfied and some had psychosomatic complaints. Perhaps this is a reflection of status inconsistency. It is interesting to note that an inverse relationship of coronary heart disease to education was also observed by Rosenman and Friedman in a recent report:

> . . . the level of education was significantly associated with the rate of coronary heart disease. . . . Men of high school or less edu-

TABLE 3-5 First Events of Disabling Coronary Heart Disease Among Bell System Men Aged 30 to 59; Annual Rates per Thousand, 1963–1965*

Level	*Function*	*All men*	*Rate per 1,000* *No college*	*College*
5–7	Executives	1.85	2.46	1.65
4	General-area managers	2.85	5.14	2.07
3	Local-area managers	3.91	4.28	3.68
2	Supervisors	3.91	4.17	2.92
1	Foremen	4.52	4.53	4.68
0	Workmen	4.33	4.46	4.15

*Age standardized to U.S. population, white males, aged 30 to 59, 1965 estimate.
From L. Hinkle, Jr., L. Holland Whitney, E. W. Lehman, J. Dunn, B. Benjamin, R. King, A. Plakun, B. Flehinger, "Occupation, Education, and Coronary Heart Disease," *Science,* 161, pp. 238–246, Table 5, July 19, 1968.

cation thus had significantly higher rates than did college graduates. Annual income was not related to CHD rates [93].

Other studies in progress may provide additional evidence of the relationship of status inconsistency, as stressor, to the potential development of disease.

Life Changes and Social Stress. The concept of changes in one's life—that is, significant change, regardless of whether it is considered to be desirable, undesirable, or under the person's direct control—and its effect upon health has been examined by a number of investigators. Rahe and Holmes found that the greater an individual's life changes in a year, the higher his risk of a major change in his health in the following year [87]. These investigators found that life changes tend to cluster in certain years, in the same manner as Hinkle has described for episodes of illness [45]. As we noted earlier, a large number of psychophysiological studies indicate that situations, both naturally occurring and experimentally induced, which are perceived as threats by the individual and evoke attempts at adaptive behavior (coping), also evoke major alterations in bodily tissues, organs, and systems. (For a review of these findings see Graham and Stevenson [31]). When these situations are sustained, they tend to enhance the body's vulnerability or susceptibility to a wide spectrum of agents important in disease etiology.

The basic ideas proposed are certainly not new. For example, René Dubos discussed the phenomenon of infectious agents stimulated by environmental factors:

> There are many situations in which the microbe is a constant and ubiquitous component of the environment but causes disease only when some weakening of the patient by another factor allows infection to proceed unrestrained, at least for a while. Theories of disease must account for the surprising fact that, in any community, a large percentage of healthy and normal individuals continually harbor potentially pathogenic microbes without suffering any symptoms or lesions.... Most likely the infections will remain dormant unless brought into activity by some other intervening factor, e.g., overwork, overindulgence, an unhappy love affair, etc. [20].

Recently published experimental evidence on animals lends support to the hypothesis. In a study of viruses, Sellers indicated that unusual emotional stresses may make it easier for viruses to have access to the brain. She pointed out that the release of adrenaline and serotonin (two nerve chemicals) during social or emotional stress may facilitate the entry of viruses into the brain if they are present in the blood during the period of stress [96].

Personality factors, life styles, and stress. Although passing reference has been made to the role of personality factors in disease, it is in the context of life style as a source of social stress that we briefly consider this relationship.[7] The series of epidemiological investigations by Friedman and Rosenman may be taken as illustrative of this approach (see Figure 3–7). These investigators have been studying the role of what they refer to as "behavior pattern" in the etiology and incidence of coronary heart disease [93]. They have formulated two behavior types: Type *A* is characterized overtly by an excessive sense of time urgency, preoccupation with vocational deadlines, enhanced aggressiveness, and competi-

[7] For an extended discussion of personality factors in coronary heart disease see Caffrey [10].

FIGURE 3-7

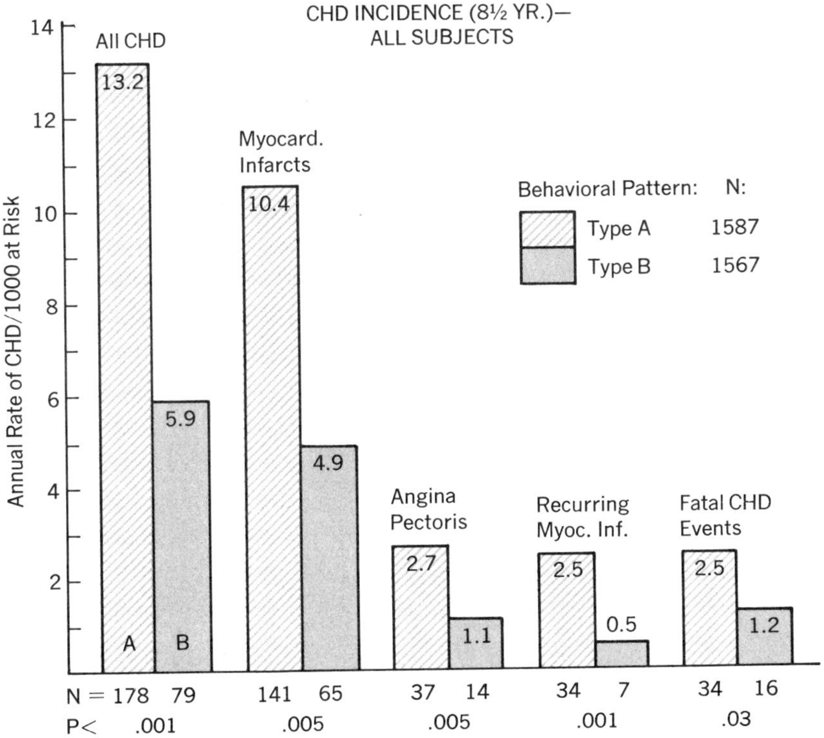

From Ray H. Rosenman et al., "The Role of the Behavior Pattern and Other Risk Factors in the Occurrence of Coronary Heart Disease in the Western Collaborative Group Study: A Nine Year Follow-Up" 1970 (unpublished).

tive drive. Persons without such characteristics are labeled Type *B*. They have found that the Type *A* behavior pattern is strongly, and independently (of other risk factors), related to risk of coronary heart disease. The Type *A* men had higher coronary heart disease rates than the men with the converse, Type *B*, behavior pattern.

The relationship of Type *A* behavior pattern to an increased rate of CHD also was observed in Caffrey's studies of Benedictine and Trappist monks [11]. Essentially, these investigators showed that there was a significantly greater proportion of Type *A* behavior in monks in the Benedictine group than in the Trappist group. Benedictine monks, it may be observed, differ from Trappists in a variety of ways: They lead more active social lives, drink alcohol, smoke cigarettes, and consume more calories and more saturated fats in their diets. Thus, the relationship of personality and life styles to social stress and disease continues to be a relevant issue for investigation, particularly with respect to the chronic disorders.

THE RECOVERY PROCESS AND REHABILITATION

When the onset of a previously undiagnosed chronic disease is rapid and quickly fatal, such as in the fatal coronary attack, the blow of sudden death to the family of the patient is profound. On the other hand, the effect on the family of long-term illness is also profound, particularly when it is realized that the illness is bound to terminate in death. When the terminal nature of an illness is well understood, the family and the patient himself are able to plan for the future. A number of decisions can be made about changes in living quarters and style of living, as well as in the economic practices of the family. Because such planning is necessary to the well-being of the family, it is important that both the family and the patient know his health situation.

The physician is the only person who can inform the family of the patient's condition and, for the most part, physicians feel that when a terminal illness is encountered, the family and patient should be made aware of it so that plans can be made. Without saying so in so many words, the physician makes the patient aware of his life expectancy, but does not destroy all hope of recovery. In certain cases, on the other hand, the sensitive physician who has gotten to know a patient and his family intimately may feel that, for the patient's peace of mind, he should not be told. In such cases, he gives the information only to other family members. (See Chapter 13 for a general discussion of physician-patient relations.)

A patient who is aware of the nature of his terminal illness may justifiably demand that the physician employ all reasonable methods of therapy at his command, even unproven ones. The patient who knows that experiments to determine new methods of therapy for the disease he suffers are in progress may justifiably feel that he should be given the opportunity to try the therapy in the hope that it will have some effect in arresting his disease. And, in situations where the therapy has been thoroughly tested on animals and seen to have very small toxic side effects, the physician may try it on the patient in tentative fashion to see whether the illness cannot be brought under control. Such experimentation on patients is often supported by grants of the Public Health Service, under the conditions just described. When the therapy has been closely screened in trials on animals, and when the unpleasant side effects are known to be unimportant in comparison with the possible therapeutic results, large-scale screening to find better therapy is always under way. From the patient's point of view, his participation in such research programs is not merely for the sake of scientific experimentation; it involves the possibility of finding a cure for a disease which is ordinarily terminal or greatly disabling and which affects him personally.

One who suffers a disease not terminal can, of course, return to his home disabled to remain unproductive and a burden on his family and community for the rest of his life. But with sympathetic help from qualified people, whatever social and physical potential remains to him can be augmented so that he will be able, if not to support himself, at least to be less of a burden on others. In the United States, a few physicians have been working many years on the problems of rehabilitation, but in comparison with the need for rehabilitation which chronic disease imposes, the number of people engaged in the field is small.

The social and psychological factors in the recovery process have only recently received the attention of investigators. Croog and his colleagues have developed a conceptual model for understanding the process of recovery from heart disease, and they provide leads for future research in this area [19]. In their model, the recovery process is considered within the framework of the individual's response to a crisis situation in his life. The variables associated with recovery are seen as elements in the response to the crisis which in various ways contribute to the eventual outcome. These include psychological response, personality factors, conceptions of disease and the sick role, physician-patient relationships and compliance with medical regimen, the family, and work and community settings. One of the interesting points discussed by these investigators is the eternal problem of obtaining valid and reliable data from sick respondents. They interviewed a number of patients three weeks after the occurrence of myocardial infarction (coronary heart disease), about their major concerns or worries. Although all the patients were still hospitalized with this life-threatening disease, virtually all maintained that their chief concerns were such practical matters as financial status, job security, and boredom. None reported the *threat of death* as a major source of worry [19]. Johnson reported similar findings in an unpublished study for the American Nurses Foundation in 1966, and Reeder's study for the Los Angeles Heart Association revealed a similar situation among a sample of patients who had suffered a coronary attack [89].

Rehabilitation requires the services of a wide variety of specialists. Medical practitioners of various sorts are needed to deal with various aspects of rehabilitation in any given case. Most useful are those specifically trained and experienced in rehabilitation, in educating unused muscles to do new things, in helping patients to use limited mental or sensory faculties, and in training patients to make adjustments to physical handicaps which have evolved in the course of the disease. In addition, social workers are needed to investigate the family and community, to see how best the patient may fit himself into the social fabric again. In all of this enterprise, sociologists can conduct valuable research into the best methods of bringing about physical and social rehabilitation, particularly to discover those milieus most favorable for successful rehabilitation. The work of Simmons and Freeman, who inquired into how the different milieus of released psychiatric patients related to their recovery, is an illustration of the kind of research which sociologists can do in the field of rehabilitation [99]. There is a profound need for sociological research on other aspects of the rehabilitative process, as well.

PREVENTION OF CHRONIC ILLNESSES

The General Hospital in Geneva, Switzerland has as its motto, "*Mieux vaut prévenir que guérir*" (better to prevent than to cure), and after a moment's reflection almost anyone would agree. The costs of illness are always best avoided: the initial and perhaps continuing pain; the pain, unpleasantness, and the side effects of much therapy; the economic costs; and the lingering problem of rehabilitation if the patient is lucky enough to be cured. Unfortunately, medical institutions throughout the world are primarily oriented towards therapy, and the training of medical personnel is similarly oriented. On the level of national and local community policy, some attention is given to prevention, but still the major preoccupations of medical personnel and the lay public, and the largest expenditures for funds, are for therapy.

In the case of the chronic diseases, the importance of prevention is particularly obvious. These are diseases the effects of which are long-term. The suffering and economic costs must be borne over many years sometimes, and the need for prevention is especially acute. As we noted earlier, some of the tools of prevention can be provided by social epidemiology. Thus, there is concrete evidence, from a number of studies on substantial populations of patients, that when individuals stop smoking their risk of lung cancer declines, and that with increases in the length of time they stop, there are corresponding decreases in their risk of that devastating disease. Similarly, there is good evidence that the use of seat belts could reduce the chronic disabilities caused by automobile accidents. The evidence is clear that a reduction in alcohol ingestion would result in reduction of deaths from cirrhosis of the liver (40,000 per year in the United States) and from automobile accidents involving drivers with high blood-alcohol titres [41].

Most practitioners would agree that if cancer at most sites can be caught in the early stages, survivorship would improve; early discovery enables the therapist to treat a localized lesion, thereby preventing the development of invasive, often fatal tumors. In the case of cancer of the cervix, the well-known Papanicalao smear examination of the characteristics of cells shed from the cervix can indicate whether a woman has cancer. This has been used in mass screenings of populations of communities. Generally, the first result of these large programs is a large increase in the number of cancers *in situ* (Stage I) over what had been observed before; the implication is that early cancers are being found in greater numbers. These can then be treated and, if the program is effective, there will be a decrease in the number of invasive cancers (Stages II-IV) in later years. This is exactly what Lundin found, as shown in (Table 3–6) [68]. Other writers have also observed this. The conclusion which can be drawn from these studies is that if women could be persuaded to undergo cytological studies at frequent intervals, the disease could be recognized in its early stages, treated, and invasive carcinoma of the cervix thereby prevented.

Similar, though more equivocal,

TABLE 3-6 OBSERVED AND EXPECTED NUMBERS OF CANCER OF CERVIX FOUND BY CYTOLOGY, BY YEAR—EXPECTED NUMBERS ARE BASED ON THOSE FOUND IN THE PERIOD BEFORE INTRODUCTION OF CYTOLOGY

	Stage			
	I		*II–IV*	
Year	*Observed*	*Expected*	*Observed*	*Expected*
1956–58	134	72.6	114	105.8
1959–62	190	102	116	150.2

From Frank E. Lundin et al., "Morbidity from Cervical Cancer: Effects of Cervical Cytology and Socio Economic Status," *J. Nat. Cancer Inst.*, 35 (1965), 1015–25.

findings obtain for cancer of the breast, the type accounting for the largest number of deaths of females from cancer. Mausner and Shimkin [73] observed that survivorship is much greater from lesions found in the early stages, but that less than half the tumors of women at their hospital were localized. Over half their patients postponed seeking care for more than one month. They see the problem as one of motivating women to seek care as soon as they recognize symptoms, or better, to persuade them to have mammography examinations at intervals frequent enough to pick up cancer before it is symptomatic and invasive.

With regard to coronary artery disease, preventive steps can also be taken. Moreover, once incipient disease is recognized and the individual has sought help, measures can be introduced to reduce the chance of a fatal attack. Thus, the American Heart Association recently published a document detailing risk factors in coronary heart disease, including: certain personality or behavior patterns, emotionally stressful situations, cigarette smoking, lack of physical activity, and dietary habits [2]. This was the first time that socioemotional stress had been officially listed as a risk factor, recognizing the efforts of social epidemiologists in recent years. These factors certainly indicate the kind of life style which would inhibit the development of coronary heart disease.

All these suggestions may involve important changes in very intimate aspects of a person's behavior patterns. Changes in dietary habits are difficult, and anyone who has tried to stop smoking knows the problems involved. It is quite possible, however, that new knowledge of the ways people can change their behavior can be furnished by sociological research. Research is just beginning in this area. Daniel Horn, a social psychologist, has studied the circumstances under which teenagers smoke, in an attempt to discover more about this problem. Other research is going on into the problem of giving up smoking once the habit has been adopted, utilizing sociological theories and findings regarding the innovation process. It is clear that a focus on this particular kind of problem can serve to help develop and test new sociological hypotheses in the areas of innovation and behavioral and attitudinal change. It is also clear that, as sociologists work more and more on the innovation process and as such knowledge is used in research into the prevention of disease, the benefits accruing to society through the reduction of death and disability from chronic disease might be profound.

REFERENCES

1. AITKEN-SWAN, JEAN AND DUGALD BAIRD, "Circumcision and Cancer of the Cervix," *British Journal of Cancer*, 19 (1965), 217–27.
2. American Heart Association, "Risk Factor and Coronary Disease: A Statement for Physicians," New York, 1968.
3. ASHER, SEGAL, AARON ANTONOVSKY AND JUDITH SHUVAL, "Israel Sibling Study," a joint project of the Harvard School of Public Health and the Israel Institute of Applied Social Research.
4. AUERBACH, OSCAR, A. T. STOUT, E. C. HAMMOND, AND L. GARFINKEL, "Changes in Bronchial Epithelium in Relation to Cigarette Smoking and in Relation to Lung Cancer." Paper presented at the Clinical Meeting of the American Medical Association, Dallas, Texas, December 4, 1959.
5. BACK, K. W. AND D. J. PITTMAN, "Dimensions of Mobility," in Mildred Kantor, ed., *Mobility and Mental Health.* Springfield, Ill.: Charles C. Thomas, Publisher, 1965, pp. 206–7.
6. BENNETT, G. C. et al., "Cardiovascular-renal Mortality in Hawaii," *American Journal of Public Health*, 52 (September, 1962), 1418.
7. BLISS, EUGENE L. AND JANET SWANZIGER, "Brain Animes and Emotional Stress," *Journal of Psychiatric Research*, 4 (December, 1966), 189–98.
8. BLUMENTHAL, I. S., "Digestive Disease as a National Problem," *Gastroenterology*, 54 (January, 1968), 86–92.
9. BORHANI, NEMAT O. AND THOMASINA SMITH BORKMAN, "Alameda County Blood Pressure Study," Berkeley, Calif.: State of California, June, 1968, p. 67.
10. CAFFREY, B., "Factors Involving Interpersonal and Psychological Characteristics: A Review of Empirical Findings," in S. L. Syme and L. G. Reeder, eds., "Social Stress and Cardiovascular Disease," *Milbank Memorial Fund Quarterly*, 45, Part 2 (April, 1967), 119–39.
11. ———, "A Multivariate Analysis of Sociopsychological Factors in Monks with Myocardial Infarctions," *American Journal of Public Health*, 60 (March, 1970), 452–58.
12. ———, "Reliability and Validity of Personality and Behavioral Measures in a Study of Coronary Heart Disease," *Journal of Chronic Diseases*, 21 (June, 1968), 191–204.
13. CARLSON, L. A., L. LEVI, AND L. ORO, "Plasma Lipids and Urinary Excretion of Catecholamines during Acute Emotional Stress in Man and Their Modifications by Nicontinic Acid," *Försvarsmedicin*, 3, supp. 2 (1967), 129–36.
14. CECIL, RUSSELL L. AND ROBERT F. LOEB, eds. *Textbook of Medicine.* 10th ed. Philadelphia: Saunders, 1965.
15. CHAPMAN, J. M., LEO G. REEDER, et al., "Relationships of Stress, Tranquilizers, and Serum Cholesterol Levels in a Sample Population under Study for Coronary Heart Disease," *American Journal of Epidemiology*, 83 (May, 1966), 537–47.
16. CHRISTIAN, JOHN J., "The Potential Role of the Adrenal Cortex as Affected by Social Rank and Population Density on Experimental Epidemics," *American Journal of Epidemiology*, 87 (March, 1968), 255–64.
17. COBB, SIDNEY, et al., "The Intrafamilial Transmission of Rheumatoid Arthritis," *Journal of Chronic Diseases*, 22 (September, 1969), entire issue.
18. COOLEY, C. H., *Human Nature and the Social Order.* New York: Charles Scribner's Sons, 1902.
19. CROOG, S. H., S. LEVINE, AND Z. LURIE, "The Heart Patient and the Recovery Process," *Social Science and Medicine*, 2 (June, 1968), 111–64.
20. DUBOS, RENE, *Mirage of Health.* New York: Harper & Row, Publishers, Inc., 1959.
21. ———, "Second Thoughts on the Germ Theory," *Scientific American*, 192 (May, 1955), 31–35.
22. DUNN, JOHN E. AND PHILIP BUELL, "Association of Cervical Cancer with Circumcision of Sexual Partner," *Journal of the National Cancer Institute*, 22 (1959), 749–64.
23. DURKHEIM, EMILE, *The Rules of Sociological Method.* New York: The Free Press, 1964.
24. EPSTEIN, FREDERICK H., ERNST P. BOAS, AND RITA SIMPSON, "The Epide-

miology of Atherosclerosis among a Random Sample of Clothing Workers of Different Ethnic Origins in New York City: I," *Journal of Chronic Diseases*, 5 (March, 1957), 300–28.

25. FERBER, BERNARD, VINCENT HANDY, PAUL GERHARDT, AND MURRAY SOLOMON, *Cancer in New York State, Exclusive of New York City: 1941–1960.* Albany: New York State Department of Health, 1962, Table 5.
26. FISHER, STANLEY H., "Psychological Factors and Heart Disease," *Circulation*, 27 (January, 1963), 113–17.
27. FRIEDMAN, MEYER, RAY H. ROSENMAN, AND VERNICE CARROLL, "Changes in the Serum Cholesterol and Blood Clotting Time in Men Subjected to Cyclic Variation of Occupational Stress," *Circulation*, 17 (May, 1958), 152–61.
28. GELLER, EDWARD, ARTHUR YUWILER, AND JAMES F. ZOLMAN, "Effects of Environmental Complexity on Constituents of Brain and Liver," *Journal of Neurochemistry*, 12 (November, 1965), 949–55.
29. GOERING, JOHN AND RODNEY M. COE, *Measurement of Socio-Environmental Stress*, The St. Louis City and County Community Laboratory, Report No. 4. Medical Care Research, St. Louis: Washington University, 1968.
30. GORDON, TAVIA, "Mortality Experience among the Japanese in the United States, Hawaii, and Japan," *Public Health Reports*, 72 (June, 1957), 543.
31. GRAHAM, D. T. AND I. STEVENSON, "Diseases as Response to Life Stress," in H. I. Lief, V. F. Lief, and N. R. Lief, eds., *The Psychological Basis of Medical Practice*. New York: Harper & Row, Publishers, Inc., 1963.
32. GRAHAM, SAXON, "Cancer of Lung Related to Smoking Behavior," *Cancer*, 21 (March, 1968), 523–30.
33. ———, "Ethnic Background and Illness in a Pennsylvania County," *Social Problems*, 4 (July, 1956), 76–82.
34. ——— AND ABRAHAM M. LILIENFELD, "Genetic Studies of Gastric Cancer in Humans: An Appraisal," *Cancer*, 11 (September, 1958), 945–58.
35. GRAHAM, SAXON AND ROBERT GIBSON, et al, "Ethnic and Religious Background in Acute Childhood Leukemia," *American Journal of Public Health*, 60 (February, 1970), 266–74.
36. GRAHAM, SAXON et al., "Variations in the Amounts of Tobacco Tar Retrieved from Selected Models of Smoking Behavior Simulated by Smoking Machine," *Cancer Research*, 23 (August, 1963), 1025–30.
37. GRAHAM, SAXON, MORTON LEVIN, AND ABRAHAM M. LILIENFELD, "The Socio-Economic Distribution of Cancer at Various Sites in Buffalo, New York: 1948–1952," *Cancer*, 13 (1960), 180 *ff*.
38. GRAHAM, SAXON et al, "Ethnic Derivation as Related to Cancer at Various Sites," *Cancer*, 16 (January, 1963), 13–27.
39. GRAHAM, SAXON AND MORTON LEVIN, "Smoking Withdrawal in the Reduction of Risk of Lung Cancer," *Cancer*, in press.
40. GROEN, J. J. et al, "The Influence of Nutrition and Ways of Life on Blood Cholesterol and the Prevalence of Hypertension and Coronary Heart Disease among Trappist and Benedictine Monks," *American Journal of Clinical Nutrition*, 10 (June, 1962), 456–70.
41. HADDON, WILLIAM AND V. A. BRADESS, "Alcohol in the Single Vehicle Fatal Accident Experience of Westchester County, New York," in William Haddon, Edward A. Suchman, and David Klein, *Accident Research*. New York: Harper & Row, Publishers, Inc., 1964.
42. HAMMOND, E. CUYLER, *Smoking in Relation to the Death Rate of One Million Men and Women*. Washington: National Cancer Institute Monograph No. 19. January, 1966.
43. ——— AND DANIEL HORN, "Smoking and Death Rates: Report on Forty-four Months of Follow-up, 187,783 Men," *Journal of the American Medical Association*, 166 (March 8, 1958), 1159–1308.
44. HENRY, JAMES P. AND JOHN C. CASSEL, "Psychosocial Factors in Essential Hypertension: Recent Epidemiologic and Animal Experimental Evidence," *American Journal of Epidemiology*, 90 (September, 1969), 171–200.
45. HINKLE, LAWRENCE E., JR. AND

Harold G. Wolff, "Ecologic Investigations of the Relationship between Illness, Life Experience and the Social Environment," *Annals of Internal Medicine*, 49 (December, 1958), 1370, 1373.
46. Hinkle, Lawrence E., Jr., et al., "Occupation, Education, and Coronary Heart Disease," *Science*, 161 (July 19, 1968), 238–46.
47. Hobbs, M. S. T., "Risk of Anencephaly in Migrant and Non-Migrant Women in the Oxford Area," *British Journal of Preventive and Social Medicine*, 23 (August, 1969), 174–78.
48. Humerfelts, Boe J. and F. Wedervang, "The Blood Pressure in a Population," *Acta Medica Scandinavica*, Suppl. 321–157, 1, 1957.
49. Kantor, Mildred, ed., *Mobility and Mental Health*. Springfield, Ill.: Charles C. Thomas, Publisher, 1965.
50. Kasanen, A. and J. Forsstram, "Social Stress and Living Habits in the Etiology of Peptic Ulcer," *Annales Medicinae Internae Fenniae*, 55 (1966), 13–22.
51. Kasl, Stanislav V. and Sidney Cobb, "Intrafamilial Transmission of Rheumatoid Arthritis: VI. Association of Rheumatoid Arthritis with Several Types of Status Inconsistency," *Journal of Chronic Diseases*, 22 (September, 1969), 259–78.
52. Kellert, S. et al., "Culture Change and Stress in Rural Peru," *Milbank Memorial Fund Quarterly*, 45 (October, 1967), 391–415.
53. Kennaway, E. L., "Racial and Social Incidence of Cancer of the Uterus," *British Journal of Cancer*, 2 (September, 1948), 177 *ff*.
54. Keys, Ancel et al., "Lessons from Serum Cholesterol Studies in Japan, Hawaii, and Los Angeles," *Annals of International Medicine*, 48 (January, 1958), 83.
55. Kiev, A., ed., *Magic, Faith and Healing: Studies in Primitive Psychiatry*. New York: The Free Press, 1964.
56. Kjelsberg, M. and J. Stamler, "Epidemiologic Studies on Cardiovascular Renal Diseases: II. Analysis of Mortality by Age-Race-Sex-Place of Residence," *Journal of Chronic Diseases*, 12 (1960), 456–63.
57. Larsen, Nils P. and Walter Bortz, "Coronary Atherosclerosis in Ethnic Groups," *Hawaii Medical Journal*, 19 (November–December, 1959), 159.
58. Leck, Ian, "Ethnic Differences in the Incidence of Malformations following Migration," *British Journal of Preventive and Social Medicine*, 23 (August, 1969), 166–73.
59. Lee, Richard E. and Ralph F. Schneider, "Hypertension and Arteriosclerosis in Executive and Nonexecutive Personnel," *Journal of the American Medical Association*, 167 (1958), 1447–50.
60. Lehman, Edward W., "Social Class and Coronary Heart Disease: A Sociological Assessment of the Medical Literature," *Journal of Chronic Diseases*, 20 (June, 1967), 381–91.
61. Lenski, G. E., "Status Consistency and Inconsistency," in Celia S. Heller, ed., *Structured Social Inequality*. London: Macmillan & Co., Ltd., 1969.
62. ———, "Status Crystallization: A Non-Vertical Dimension of Social Status," *American Sociological Review*, 19 (August, 1954), 405–13.
63. Levi, L., "Life Stress and Urinary Excretion of Adrenaline and Noradrenaline," in W. Raab, ed., *Prevention of Ischemic Heart Disease*. Springfield, Ill.: Charles C. Thomas, Publisher, 1966, 85–95.
64. ———, "Stressors, Stress Tolerance, Emotions and Performance in Relation to Catecholamine Excretion," *Försvarsmedicin*, 3, suppl. 2 (1967), 192–200.
65. ———, "Sympatho-adrenamedulary Responses to Emotional Stimuli: Methodologic, Physiologic and Pathologic Considerations," in E. Bajusz, ed., *An Introduction to Clinical Neuroendocrinology*. Basel, New York: S. Karger, 1967, pp. 78–105.
66. Levin, Morton L., L. C. Kress, and H. Goldstein, "Syphilis and Cancer: Reported Syphilis Prevalence among 7,760 Cancer Patients," *New York State Journal of Medicine*, 42 (1942), 1737 *ff*.

67. LEVIN, MORTON L., SAXON GRAHAM, ABRAHAM M. LILIENFELD, AND PAUL SHEEHE, "Nursing, Fertility, and other Factors in the Epidemiology of Cancer of the Breast." Paper presented at the meetings of the American Public Health Association, Miami, Florida, October, 1962.
68. LUNDIN, FRANK E. et al, "Morbidity from Cervical Cancer: Effects of Cervical Cytology and Socio-Economic Status," *Journal of the National Cancer Institute*, 35 (December, 1965), 1015–25.
69. MANN, G. V. et al, "Cardiovascular Disease in the Masai," *Journal of Atherosclerosis Research*, 4 (July–August, 1964), 289–312.
70. MARKS, RENEE, "A Review of Empirical Findings," in S. L. Syme and L. G. Reeder, eds., "Social Stress and Cardiovascular Disease," *Milbank Memorial Fund Quarterly*, 45 Part 2 (April, 1967), 95.
71. MARTIN, CLYDE, "Marital and Coital Factors in Cervical Cancer," *American Journal of Public Health*, 57 (May, 1967), 803–14.
72. MARTIN, W. T., "Socially Induced Stress: Some Converging Theories," *Pacific Sociological Review*, 8 (Fall, 1965), 63.
73. MAUSNER, J. S., M. B. SHIMKIN, et al., "Cancer of the Breast in a Philadelphia Hospital," *Cancer*, 23 (February, 1969), 51–64.
74. MEAD, G. H., *Mind, Self and Society*. Chicago: University of Chicago Press, 1934.
75. MECHANIC, DAVID, *Medical Sociology: A Selective View*. New York: The Free Press, 1968.
76. MERTON, ROBERT K., *Social Theory and Social Structure*. New York: The Free Press, 1957.
77. MORRIS, J. N. AND J. A. HEADY, "Social and Biological Factors in Infant Mortality: V. Mortality in Relation to the Father's Occupation, 1911–1950," *Lancet*, 268 (March 12, 1955), 556.
78. MURPHY, H. B. M., "Social Change and Mental Health," *Milbank Memorial Fund Quarterly*, 39 (July, 1961), 385–445.
79. NEEL, JAMES V., "A Study of Major Congenital Defects in Japanese Infants," *American Journal of Human Genetics*, 10 (December, 1958), 398.
80. NEWSHOLME, ARTHUR, *Story of Modern Preventive Medicine*. Baltimore: Williams & Wilkins Co., 1929.
81. PALOUCEK, FRANK P. AND J. B. GRAHAM, "Precipitating Factors in Cancer of the Cervix," *Surgical Forum of the American College of Surgeons*, 10 (1959), 740–42.
82. PELL, SIDNEY AND C. ANTHONY D'ALONZO, "Acute Myocardial Infarction in a Large Industrial Population: Report of a Six-Year Study of 1,356 Cases," *Journal of the American Medical Association*, 185 (September 4, 1963), 831–38.
83. PETERSON, JOHN E., ROBERT A. KEITH, AND ALAN A. WILCOX, "Hourly Changes in Serum Cholesterol Concentration Effects of the Anticipation of Stress," *Circulation*, 25 (May, 1962), 798–803.
84. POTT, PERCIVAL, *The Chirurgical Works of Percival Pott*. London: Hanes, W. Clarke, & R. Collins, 1775.
85. PRICE, DANIEL O., "Next Steps in Studying Mobility and Mental Health," in Mildred Kantor, ed., *Mobility and Mental Health*. Springfield, Ill.: Charles C. Thomas, Publisher, 1965, 244–46.
86. QUINLAN, C. B. et al., "Prevalence of Selected Coronary Heart Disease Risk Factors in Trappist and Benedictine Monks." Paper presented at the Conference on Cardiovascular Disease Epidemiology, American Heart Association, Atlanta, Georgia, February 4, 1968.
87. RAHE, RICHARD H., JOSEPH D. MCKEAN, JR., AND RANSOM J. ARTHUR, "A Longitudinal Study of Life: Change and Illness Patterns," *Journal of Psychosomatic Research*, 10 (May, 1967), 355–66.
88. REEDER, LEO G., "Employment Practices and the Cardiac," *Journal of Chronic Diseases*, 18 (October, 1965), 951–63.
89. ———, "The Socio-Economic Effects

of Heart Disease," Los Angeles Heart Association, unpublished, 1963.

90. ———, "The Socio-Economic Effects of Heart Disease," *Social Problems*, 4 (July, 1956), 51–54.

91. ——— AND G. A. DONOHUE, "Cardiac Employment Potential in Urban Society," *Journal of Chronic Diseases*, 8 (August, 1958), 230–43.

92. RICE, D. P., *Estimating the Cost of Illness*, U.S. Public Health Service, Health Economics Series No. 6. Washington, D.C.: Government Printing Office, May, 1966.

93. ROSENMAN, RAY H. et al., "A Predictive Study of Coronary Heart Disease: The Western Collaborative Group Study," *Journal of the American Medical Association*, 189 (July 6, 1964), 103–10.

94. SACHS, LEO AND MARIASSA BAT-MIRIAM, "The Genetics of Jewish Populations: I. Finger Print Patterns of Jewish Populations in Israel," *American Journal of Human Genetics*, 9 (June, 1957), 117–26.

95. SAUER, HERBERT I., "Epidemiology of a Cardiovascular Mortality: Geographic and Ethnic," *American Journal of Public Health*, 52 (January, 1962), 94–105.

96. SELLERS, MARGRET I., "Studies on the Entry of Viruses into the Central Nervous System of Mice via the Circulation," *Journal of Experimental Medicine*, 129 (April, 1969), 719–46.

97. SHEKELLE, R. B., A. M. OSTFIELD, AND O. PAUL, "Social Status and Incidence of Coronary Heart Disease," *Journal of Chronic Diseases*, 22 (December, 1969), 381–94.

98. SHRYOCK, RICHARD H., *The Development of Modern Medicine*. New York: Alfred A. Knopf, Inc., 1947.

99. SIMMONS, OZZIE G. AND HOWARD E. FREEMAN, "Familial Expectations and Post-Hospital Performance of Mental Patients," *Human Relations*, 7 (1959), 233 *ff*.

100. SMITH, R. L., "Recorded and Expected Mortality among the Japanese in the United States and Hawaii with Special Reference to Cancer," *Journal of the National Cancer Institute*, 17 (1956), 459–73.

101. SMITH, THOMASINA AND JOHN CASSEL, "Factors Involving Sociocultural Incongruity and Change," in S. L. Syme and L. G. Reeder, eds., "Social Stress and Cardiovascular Disease," *Milbank Memorial Fund Quarterly*, 45, Part 2 (April, 1967), 21–49.

102. STEWART, H., L. DUNHAM, J. CASPER, H. DORN, L. THOMAS, J. EDGCOMB AND A. SYMEONIDIS, "Epidemiology of Cancers of Uterine Cervix and Corpus, Breast and Ovary in Israel and New York City," *Journal of the National Cancer Institute*, 37 (July, 1966) whole issue.

103. Study Group on Smoking and Health, "Smoking and Health," *Science*, 125 (June 7, 1957), 1129–33.

104. SUSSER, M., "Causes of Peptic Ulcer: A Selective Review," *Journal of Chronic Diseases*, 20 (June, 1967), 435–56.

105. SYME, S. LEONARD, "Epidemiological Approaches to the Study of Medical Care Systems: The Need for Cross-Cultural Research." Unpublished paper, 1970.

106. ——— et al., "Cultural Mobility and the Occurrence of Coronary Heart Disease," *Journal of Health and Human Behavior*, 6 (Winter, 1965), 178–89.

107. TOOR, MORDECAI, A. KATCHALSKY, J. AGMON, AND D. ALLALOUF, "Atherosclerosis and Related Factors in Immigrants to Israel," *Circulation*, 12 (August, 1960), 265–79.

108. TYROLER, H. A. AND JOHN CASSEL, "Health Consequences of Cultural Change: II. Effect of Urbanization on Coronary Heart Mortality in Rural Residents," *Journal of Chronic Diseases*, 17 (February, 1964), 167–77.

109. U.S. Bureau of the Census, *Statistical Abstract of the United States: 1967*. Washington, D.C.: Government Printing Office, 1968.

110. U.S. National Center for Health Statistics, U.S. Public Health Service, *Vital Health Statistics: Medical Care, Health Status and Family Income*, Series 10, No. 9. Washington, D.C.: Government Printing Office, 1964.

111. U.S. President's Commission on Heart Disease, Cancer and Stroke, *Report to the President: A National Program to*

Conquer Heart Disease, Cancer and Stroke, Vol. I. Washington, D.C.: Government Printing Office, 1964–1965.

112. U.S. Public Health Service, *Economic Costs of Cardiovascular Diseases and Cancer: 1962*, Health Economics Series, No. 5. Washington, D.C.: Government Printing Office, 1965.

113. VALZELLI, L. E., S. GIACALONE, AND S. GARATTINI, "Biochemical and Pharmacological Aspects of Aggressiveness in Mice," *European Journal of Pharmacology*, 2 (November, 1967), 144–46.

114. VOLKART, E. H., ed., *Social Behavior and Personality*. New York: Social Science Research Council, 1951.

115. WELCH, B. L., "Psychophysiological Response to the Mean Level of Environmental Stimulation: A Theory of Environmental Integration," in *Symposium on Medical Aspects of Stress in the Military Climate: 1964*. Washington, D.C.: Walter Reed Army Institute of Research, 1965, pp. 39–99.

116. WINKELSTEIN, WARREN AND S. LEONARD SYME, Unpublished Statement in Research Plan of "Epidemiologic Research on Stroke," 1966.

117. WINKELSTEIN, WARREN et al., "Familial Aggregation of Blood Pressure," *Journal of the American Medical Association*, 195 (March 7, 1966), 848–50.

118. WOLF, STEWART, WILLIAM R. MCCABE, JOE YAMAMOTO, S. A. ADSELT, AND W. W. SCHOTSTAEDT, "Changes in Serum Lipids in Relation to Emotional Stress during Rigid Control of Diet and Exercise," *Circulation*, 26 (September, 1962), 379–87.

119. WYNDER, ERNEST L. AND NATHAN MANDEL, "Statistical Consideration on Circumcision and Cervical Cancer," *American Journal of Obstetrics and Gynecology*, 79 (May, 1960), 1026–30.

4

SOCIAL BIOLOGY

Bruce K. Eckland

Specialization in academia has been associated with the maintenance of fairly rigid boundaries between the social and biological sciences. There are biologists of various sorts who represent biological man; anthropologists who represent primitive man; sociologists and psychologists who represent social man; and physicians who represent ill and disabled man. But who represents man as a product of the interactions of both biological and social processes in an integrated biosocial system? What branch of science seeks to understand the reciprocal nature of these processes both in the development of the human organism during its own life cycle and in the evolution of human societies?

AN EMERGING SCIENCE: SOCIAL BIOLOGY

The traditional and sometimes artificial boundaries separating the biological and social sciences are undergoing revision. We are experiencing a convergence of interests and a synthesis of principles.

The forces accelerating this change

come from both within and outside the academic community. Scientists are discovering that to achieve further explanatory power with their own theories they must borrow the social or biological variables considered the "property" of other fields. And, perhaps equally important, the informed public, private foundations, and government seem to believe that any workable solution to today's practical social problems requires not just a multifactor approach but an approach which *integrates* the knowledge and skills of scientists from quite diverse backgrounds. Consider, for example, the magnitude of support for interdisciplinary research in mental health, population control and, now, environmental health.

Much of what is called "interdisciplinary" or "team" research unfortunately involves scientists from different fields who, although they may be working on the same problem, are carrying on their investigations quite independently of one another and without a genuine recognition or understanding of the possible interconnections of each other's work. These are marriages of convenience. On occasion, however, the research is truly interdisciplinary in character, carried on at the interfaces between the biological and social sciences. In the broadest sense, these points of convergence form the general subject matter of social biology.

Evidence of the emergence of a new field that takes as its central problem the coactions of social and biological variables is widely scattered across the scientific community. The efforts we shall describe here are certainly not representative of all that is being done, especially in the medical and health professions, but they indicate the growing support for scientists willing to bridge the gap.

Role of Russell Sage Foundation

In the mid-1960's, which brought the rapid increase of federal support for sociomedical research and training in the health field, the Russell Sage Foundation gradually reduced its support for these endeavors and began to take increasing interest in a program in social biology:

> Studies in social biology represent the largest and most advanced aspect of the expanding programs in social sciences and human biology. A number of important research investigations on the intersection of social and biological variables are underway, the deliberations of three conferences on biology and behavior held jointly by the Foundation and The Rockfeller University have been published, and grants have been made to stimulate and support the further training of persons with advanced standing in both the biological and social sciences [23].

The topics discussed at the three conferences mentioned above illustrate the kinds of "Intersections" the Foundation had in mind. The first conference in 1965, on "Neurophysiology and Emotion," focused on brain mechanisms and emotion, endocrine systems and emotion, the interaction of cognitive and autonomic nervous system variables in producing emotional states, and the effects of infantile stimulation on adult emotional reactivity [8]. The 1966 conference, called "Biology and Behavior: Genetics," discussed genetics and the study of intelligence, the genetic basis of social interaction in infrahuman species, the role of social competition in natural selection and population control, and biogenetic theories of social structure and social change [9]. The last conference, in 1967, on "Environmental Influences," dealt with early nutritional deficiencies, studies of social isolation of infrahuman species, social reinforcement and interpersonal relations, and the effects of cultural deprivation on cognitive development [10].

The Foundation has also helped to support the activities of committees in the National Research Council and the Social Science Research Council that were devoted to similar issues.

The National Research Council

Within the Division of Behavioral Sciences of the National Research Council, a new multidisciplinary Committee on the Life Sciences and Social Policy (originally called the Committee on Biological Research, Social Behavior, and Social Policy) was established in 1968. This group is concerned with the questions of social policy arising from actual and forseeable advances in biomedical research, which has implications for the organization of human societies as well as for individual behavior. Medical engineering, which the Committee sees as highly probable within the next few generations, raises possibilities of altering the genetic constitution of future human populations, organ transplantation on a large scale, human hibernation and other methods of forestalling death, and changing complexion and skin color inexpensively and effectively. The implications of such developments, if difficult to comprehend, are certainly profound.

The Committee hopes to realize the following four objectives: (1) to identify and clarify the issues and problems of social policy likely to emerge in the proximate and more remote future as a result of recent and foreseeable advances in biology, chemistry, and medicine having significant implications for social behavior; (2) to develop strategies for the conduct of research in the social and behavioral sciences, the results of which would contribute to a better understanding of the content and forms of emerging and foreseeable social policy issues and problems; (3) to stimulate interest among behavioral and social scientists in the conduct of these kinds of research on the part of governmental agencies, private foundations, and universities; (4) to determine the levels of public understanding of the social policy issues and problems necessary to their informed and sound resolution, and to recommend the means by which such public understanding could be attained.

Unfortunately, the Committee originally gave itself only three years to achieve its objectives. It will need far more time. Among other things, it must await the development of a social biology which can more clearly identify the interactions between biological and social processes. The idea that biological or medical engineering might drastically alter social structures assumes that these structures, in their "natural" state, are linked in important ways to certain biological functions. We know very little, however, about the kinds of coaction that must be involved. In order to understand the social implications of control over the genetic constitution of man, for example, we first need to know how the genetic, physiological, and social mechanism, operating jointly and interdependently, might produce a desired change. Thus, the work of the Committee of Life Sciences and Social Policy and other committees like it must eventually rely heavily upon an emerging science committed to examining such complex interrelationships.

The Social Science Research Council

In 1966, the Social Science Research Council signaled its interest in social biology by creating the Committee on Biological Bases of Social Behavior (formerly called the Committee on Genetics and Behavior). Its mandate was to foster a rapprochement between the biological and social sciences by organizing training programs and conferences and by stimulating research.

It held its first major "Conference on the Appraisal of Biological Training for Social Scientists" in February, 1969, to consider the extent to which social scientists need biological training, the availability of such training at the present time, and the current level of interest in obtaining it [18].

One outgrowth of the February conference was the formation of an *ad hoc* Committee on Social Biology. Later that year, this group sent two recommendations to its parent organization: First, it proposed holding a summer training institute in social biology for sociologists and cultural anthropologists, with lectures organized around population genetics and evolution, quantitative and developmental genetics, and physiological and behavioral ecology. Second, it proposed the formation of a field-defining group, to survey the topics which together make up the field of social biology, and to produce a report of its conclusions. This would be, if accomplished, the first collaborative effort to systematically delineate the field and develop a comprehensive definition of social biology for guidance in curriculum planning and research design.

The International Biological Program

Administered in the United States by the National Academy of Sciences, the stated objective of the International Biological Program (IBP) is to increase study and research related to biological productivity and human welfare in a changing world environment. The IBP came into being in 1964, and in the brief years that followed it has helped to organize a number of multidisciplinary teams of researchers working on the main interacting components of specific environments. While much of this research deals with large ecosystems of plant and animal life, special attention has been given to man himself—how he fits into and affects his environment, and how it affects him.

Currently, a major effort is being made by U.S. scientists in IBP to seek a rapprochement between the biological and social sciences through a set of integrated research programs in "human adaptability." As described by IBP:

> The scientific basis of human adaptability has two major components—the genetic, which sets the limit of the organism's capacity to respond, and the physiological and behavioral, which determines the range of responses available to the organism given its genetic set. At one extreme of the spectrum of inquiry that may be brought to bear on human adaptability is population genetics, and at the other extreme, environmental physiology. In between, many aspects of modern medicine and anthropology come into play.
>
> Human behavior, in contrast to the behavior of other organisms, includes a large set of cultural activities, the domain of the arts and social sciences. These establish a context, a pattern of civilization, within which the more biological attributes of human adaptability must operate. It is the limited adaptability of the latter, expressed in genetics, physiology and behavior, that are the central theme of this program [15].

Thus far, IBP's program in human adaptability has focused on vanishing cultures such as the Eskimo and the American Indian, owing to the unusual advantage of research on small populations under varying conditions of environmental extremes. A new program, however, is presently being organized to focus attention on biosocial studies of urban populations and migrant peoples.

The American Eugenics Society

Since the turn of the century, eugenic proposals have been enacted into law without scientific evidence to support them, and perhaps have served only to nurture racial prejudices [2]. The national legislation resulting in the Quota Act, state legislation on sterilization, and Hitler's prostitution of eugenics are all good examples. Most of the American public as well as the scientific community, has undoubtedly been prepared for some time to drop the word altogether from its vocabulary. It even appears that the American Eugenics Society may be preparing to do so, too.

The objectives and membership of the Society have changed radically. It no longer engages in propaganda of any kind, and its board of directors is now composed entirely of scientists from such related disciplines as population and behavioral genetics, psychology, anthropology, sociology, and demography. The Society's chief aim is to stimulate further knowledge of the biological and cultural forces affecting the structure and composition of human populations. As a means of encouraging the collaboration of biological and social scientists, the Society has held five conferences on genetics and demography since 1964.

For fifteen years, the Society has published the *Eugenics Quarterly,* a scholarly journal devoted to research in the biosocial sciences. Now published for the Society by the University of Chicago Press, the name of the journal was changed in 1969 to *Social Biology,* reflecting more accurately its scientific orientation.

In summary, there seems to be little doubt that institutionalized support for social biology is new, and growing apace. In fact, virtually all the important events related to the emergence of the field appear to have occurred within the past five years or so. Yet, social biology is still something less than an infant, and its parents are not yet wed.

It is not possible to predict what form the field will take in the future, the speed at which it will grow, or just where within the formal structure of science it will eventually reside. The need, however, for a branch of science committed to furthering our knowledge of the complex interaction of biological and social processes should be self-evident.

THE CONTENT OF THE FIELD

It may not be very useful to define *all* the possible intersections between biology and the social sciences as the proper subject matter of social biology. For one thing, if a table were designed with all the biological sciences listed in the rows and all the social sciences listed in the columns, one would find that many of the cells in the matrix would have no known entries while others had several. Moreover, to define the field so broadly at this point in time would certainly make our task unmanageable.

Thus, for quite practical reasons, we will restrict out attention to areas of primary interest to sociologists. This includes, as well, some of the boundary areas between biology and anthropology and psychology, both of which bridged the gap long ago. One of the oldest bridging disciplines, physical anthropology, appears to have made many significant advances as it has borrowed most heavily from anatomy, paleontology, and human genetics, and in recent years, has sought a new rapprochement with cultural anthropology. Along the borders of psychology, new subfields continually are emerging—behavioral genetics, psychophysiology, and psychopharmacology all being current examples.

Even having excluded many of the more elusive studies at the interfaces, the partial taxonomy which follows risks looking like a shopping list. It covers a variety of topics of varying degrees of concern to sociologists; moreover, the categories and examples are not always mutually exclusive.

In reviewing the list, the reader may well wonder just where one draws the line, and how many other areas in the future might also have to be considered within the general scope of social biology. It seems premature, however, to attempt to draw firmer boundaries. Among other things, we must await the orderly development of more realistic and adequate models of social-biological phenomena. The list, then, is a preliminary introduction to the field, with special emphasis upon the points at which sociology and biology converge:

I. Biological Factors in Individual Development and Socialization
    - Biomedical and genetic factors in human growth and development
    - Temperament and personality development
    - The stigmatization of persons who then adopt deviant roles
    - Morphology and socialization
    - Sexual dimorphism and socialization
    - Gerontology and socialization

II. Biological Factors in Social Organization and Human Evolution
    - Individual differences and social structure
    - Population genetics and evolution
    - Population genetics and social structure
    - Epidemiology and social structure
    - Human ecology and environmental health

A basic distinction will be drawn between *intra* and *inter*generational processes. Working at the boundaries their field shares with biology, behavioral scientists generally have devoted most of their attention to the intragenerational. From this perspective, the individual is viewed as a product of nature and nurture over an entire, but single, life cycle. The biological antecedents of one's nature may be genetic or, as is often the case, they may involve neurological, biochemical, and similar factors. All the topics listed in part I and some of those in part II fall into this general class.

In contrast, much less attention has been given in sociology to the intergenerational processes that link some of its core subject matter to population genetics and human evolution. These are the mechanisms that change the *genetic* structure and, in turn, the *social* structure of human populations over time. Some of these mechanisms, like assortative mating, are listed in part II, and then dealt with in greater detail in the concluding section of this chapter.

I. *Biological Factors in Individual Development and Socialization*

Most of the past battles between environmental and biological determinists were fought over the preeminence of social or biological factors in the development of individual differences in human behavior. Perhaps some of the liveliest debates are to be found in the earlier criminological literature. The sociologists' attacks against Lombrosian and neo-Lombrosian views of criminal man were so successful, in fact, that at least in this country they are given only scant attention in the most current textbooks.

Over the years, social scientists have entered into numerous other debates with medical and biological scientists over a wide range of topics. Although many of these debates are still going on, and in some quarters, new ones are just arising, the most significant trend in recent years is that the socially and biologically oriented opponents of some of the earlier disputes are beginning to seek a rapprochement, beginning to recognize that each side may have hold of some part of the truth. It is to be hoped that the distinctive feature of this new approach will be the rapid development of integrated theories which can begin to describe more precisely how particular social and biological variables are reciprocally or otherwise related.

Biomedical and Genetic Factors in Human Growth and Development. Some of the most striking, yet complicating, general findings in the scientific literature of the past decade are the variable effects of different social and biological factors at different stages of human growth and development. Even the classical Mendelian models, which were based on the notion of relatively fixed relationships between genotype and phenotype, have undergone serious revision in this respect. As most problems in behavioral genetics and related disciplines are now formulated, the particular behavior in a given individual at a particular point in time is produced by particular genes *and* by a particular environment—by the interaction, through complex biochemical and physiological mechanisms, of these two sets of factors.

The field of *mental retardation* is exemplary of this new multidisciplinary emphasis. The definition of mental retardation, in fact, has been broadened so far beyond its original scope that it now includes numerous forms of human deprivation and enlists the special expertise of many social scientists, including sociologists [19]. The recent introduction of formal research and training programs in mental health and retardation in a number of sociology departments across the country signals, we believe, rather firm commitment to this area of inquiry.

The recent scientific literature on *psychotic and autistic children* also has changed and has begun to convince some social scientists that the primary causes of these conditions may not always be parental attitudes or other family and interpersonal disturbances. There is accumulating evidence that both schizophrenia and infantile autism are basically the result of predisposing impairments of an organic, i.e., genetic, origin [22, 13]. It is, of course, clearly recognized that environment plays an etiological role, also, although the environmental modifiers, either of a social or physiological nature, are not well understood.

Despite the presence of an adequate amount of food, *malnutrition* and associated growth failure are more widespread than commonly assumed—a problem rapidly gaining attention. Various nutritional deficiencies have been identified, but the complex question of protein-carbohydrate interactions, which has not been resolved, is confounded by ethnic and socioeconomic differences [14]. Sociologists are only beginning to contribute substantially to this work.

Temperament and Personality Development. The affective, or "socio-emotional," domain of human behavior has long been a focus of the interdisciplinary research of behavioral and biological scientists. The boundaries here, as a matter of fact, are so fluid, and the research techniques often so similar, that it is sometimes difficult to tell just who the actors are—social psychologists, behavioral geneticists, or physiologists.

Largely through the efforts of experimental psychologists and behavioral geneticists, the basic components of some gene-behavior interaction related to *temperament* are in the process of being identified. Personality, while in most instances strongly modified by social experience, is not infinitely plastic. There are biological limits to its shape. Some empirical studies of the genetics of personality traits, such as dominance and introversion, show moderately strong heritability, for example [28].

Beyond the matter of genes, small-group and laboratory research on the interaction of specific environmental (social) events and individual behavior has led some physiologists and sociologists to acknowledge a distinct subdiscipline labeled *sociophysiology* [17, 25]. Much of this work deals with the responses of the autonomic nervous system to environmental stress. Cardiovascular sensitivity to changes in overt attention is an example, or the not entirely obvious proof that people of normal weight eat because they are hungry, whereas obese persons eat because they like food. The subject matter and methods used, however, do not appear to separate in any important way what psychologists call "psychophysiology" and what some sociologists call "sociophysiology," except that the latter sometimes attempt to relate emotional states to cultural patterns.

Only slightly different phenomena are the subject matter of psychopharmacology or *sociopharmacology*. In lieu of, or sometimes in conjunction with, psychogalvanometers and other instruments for measuring physiological processes, drugs are used to induce a physiological reaction under conditions of different environmental stress. Such techniques have many uses, most obviously in understanding the social-biological mechanisms involved in drug addiction. They also may, and have been, used successfully in the study of interpersonal processes in small group laboratory experiences.

The Stigmatization of Persons Who Then Adopt Deviant Roles. A dominant theme in much of the recent sociological literature on deviance involves the labeling process whereby persons possessing physical, mental, or other disabilities are stereotyped and eventually come to feel, think, and act as if the stereotype were true. In other words, the deviant role of the stigmatized person is the product of the original disabling condition and of his learning the social identity reserved for those with his disability. Until this process is clearly understood, we may never know the true extent to which some traits inherently limit what a person can do.

There is now substantial data, for example, to indicate that social deviants like *the blind* are deviant, in part, because they have been systematically rewarded for behaving in a manner that conforms to the expectations of others, and punished for behaving otherwise [24]. Obviously, a blind man *is* blind, and the role he plays is not completely arbitrary, nevertheless, a large part of the role apparently is somewhat arbitrary, or at least does not depend entirely upon the stigmatizing trait itself.

In a somewhat like manner, becoming a *drug addict* involves not only a physiological response induced by a drug, but also learning the role of the addict through the ordinary processes of socialization. This is a labeling process as well as a more-or-less individualized response to environmental stress. Sociologists, of course, have argued this point for many years. It would now appear that the most significant future advances toward an understanding of addiction will require their collaboration with biological scientists so that the social-physiological interactions that are central to the problem can be identified.

The *mentally disabled* also comprise a large class of stigmatized persons—both "sick" people and "stupid" people. Much has been written about both. Yet, except for the functionally retarded, we still know very little about the true limits of many of those who are considered stupid, who are called "inferior," who are assigned to the slowest classes in school, and who may turn out to be the victims of a self-fulfilling prophecy.

Morphology and Socialization. Within the "normal" range of human variation lie enormous differences in physical appearance. There are tall men and short men, fat men and skinny men, beautiful and ugly men. Few social scientists have taken the morphological features of human populations into account.

The classical illustration is the study of *somatotypes,* an attempt to find an association between body types, personality, and behavior. While the associations have been adequately documented—such as between mesomorphy, aggression, and delinquency—they have been dismissed by most sociologists on the grounds that it cannot be demonstrated that morphological features, in themselves, cause the behavior. Nevertheless, it would appear rather shortsighted to assume that they are not involved in the recruitment of individuals to certain types of socially defined roles.

More recently, evidence has shown that *physical attractiveness* may be as important a factor as educational attainment or class origin in the social mobility of women through marriage [6]. Yet, we know virtually nothing about the complex social and biological interaction that determines the attractiveness of women.

Sexual Dimorphism and Socialization. No human society treats men and women equally. Sex differences are a universal basis for social differentiation. Moreover, sexual dimorphism appears to have progressed further, in strictly biological terms, in man than in most other mammals. For example, except for some domesticated animals like the milking cow, only the human female maintains permanent breasts. What scientists have not yet discovered is the extent to which the observed differences between the sexes in specific behavioral and personality traits can be attributed to nature and nurture, or both. It is unlikely that the associations between *sex and temperament,* for example, are entirely bound to arbitrary cultural norms and have no biological roots, as some anthropologists would seem to have us believe; on the other hand, it is equally unlikely that any of the associations are culture-free.

A variety of yet-unexplained differences between males and females also occurs in the development of *cognitive functioning.* As a general rule, girls excel on mental tests in early childhood, but the boys catch up during adolescence. The reasons for each of these facts remain a puzzle. Of equal interest, even though the mean performance of adult males and females on tests of general intelligence is nearly the same (the tests are purposely constructed to minimize sex differences), the range of the performance of the males is much greater. This means that at some points in the tails of the distribution, there are many more exceedingly intelligent males than females (as measured by some tests), as well as more severely retarded males. What are the social-biological implications?

One of the widest gulfs between theory and research is to be found in the literature on *sexuality* and *sexual activity*, where much has been written without supporting evidence. Moreover, some sociologists have argued rather convincingly that sexual behavior in man is almost entirely socially prescribed and not the expression of any particularly potent biological drives [26]. Without adequate evidence, neither position can be uncritically accepted—the truth probably lies somewhere in between.

Gerontology and socialization. The declining health of the aged has been viewed both as a consequence of the normal deterioration of the biological organism and of a deprivation of status or, in other words, a kind of downward mobility associated with loss of control over one's own destiny. The loss of status is apparently partly due to the fact that, although elderly persons are generally aware of their changing role they nevertheless often define their rights, in terms of what their children owe them, as greater than their children themselves accept [5]. No integration of the social and biological approaches has yet been attempted.

II. *Biological Factors in Social Organization and Human Evolution*

The organizing elements of human societies, such as community, social institutions, social stratification, social roles, and the like, are generally studied by sociologists in a context so sterile and free from the contaminating influences of biological organisms that one sometimes is left with the impression that the people themselves are not actually there at all—that the only things that are real are the roles they play and the institutions they form.

The idea that "man is a product of his social environment" has been uncritically accepted by many sociologists. "All the world," some believe, "is a stage," and we are simply playing our parts with an ever-changing script. The actors themselves are quite unimportant; they bring nothing uniquely different to their roles—only what is taught them. And this, in turn, makes them quite expendable in the long run. Given the opportunity and the proper training, anyone can learn to do anything, or so some seem to believe.

Although we have overdrawn the picture, perhaps we have made the point which is that sociologists, intentionally or not, have not paid much attention to individual differences but have been interested primarily in the social contexts within which they arise. If human societies were the result of previously existing biological and social events that had no connection with each other, then there would be no reason for sociologists or other behavioral scientists to proceed as if they did. However, it can be demonstrated that there *are* connections. In the physical and cultural evolution of human societies, one form is dependent upon the other, and the end-product is something different than if matters were otherwise.

Individual Differences and Social Structure. All human groups must cope with individual differences of biological origin, and they do so in ways that are generally consistent with their central values and traditions. Highly bureaucratized and technologically advanced societies tend to emphasize rationality and progress; consequently, the allocation of individuals to economic roles tends to be based on merit or, in other words, on what people can contribute to the system. And this, in turn, ultimately depends upon each person's unique assets and liabilities.

Some positions in society confer more prestige and entail greater rewards than others essentially because the people in some positions can be replaced less easily. This is due both to the biological fact that individuals differ in their capacity to perform qualitatively different tasks, and to the social fact that invested in each individual are quantitatively different amounts of training. The efficient utilization of human resources is a key element in the organization of modern societies; it also is one of the central factors shaping the class structure and giving rise to the movement of persons of the younger generation through that structure.

The social and cultural determinants of *social stratification* in human societies have been amply studied by sociologists. Its genetic basis, however, has seldom been brought into focus. Yet, it would appear that social stratification is, in many respects, the indirect result of the biological diversity of man. We tend to forget what is insured by the nature of heredity: that no human being is born exactly like another. Individual differences alone, of course, do not produce the inequalities that form the basis of stratified societies. In the purest sense biologically, one man is simply "different" from another. But when we consider man in the context of a particular environment—one that confers either physical or social advantages to those who possess certain traits—then we refer to these differences in terms of "equality" and "inequality," or as "better" or "worse," or use the even-more-loaded labels, "superior" or "inferior." Yet, aside from the matter of stigmatization, there are numerous unanswered questions about the manner in which biologically rooted human diversity is transformed into socially valued traits.

Individual differences also bear upon the organization of *kinship systems* and *child rearing practice*. Although children tend to resemble their parents and their sibs, the genotypic differences between parent and child and between siblings are sometimes quite large. In the absence of assortative mating, the correlation of the existence in the child of highly heritable traits of the parent is only about .5, thereby permitting differences sufficiently great to cause numerous problems in parent-child relationships. This is especially the case, for example, when a parent's aspirations outrun his child's abilities or, on the other hand, when a parent is incapable of providing an appropriately stimulating environment for a potentially bright child.

Similar problems arise in the *schools*. Thrust upon our educational system is the dual responsibility of bringing all children, despite the handicaps of some, up to an acceptable level of mental and social development and, at the same time, of preparing different children, depending upon their educability, for roles that require quite diverse kinds of talent. How schools can manage to deal with the unique biogenic potential of each child and take the full range of such diversity into account is a problem within the scope of social biology.

Population Genetics and Evolution. The basic mechanisms of physical evolution are mutation, genetic drift, and natural selection. In contrast to recent rates of cultural change, physical evolution is remarkably slow. This, however, does not mean either that changes in the genetic character of human populations have been halted or that they are unimportant for understanding the structure and problems of human societies.

There are groups of scientists, particularly within the medical profession, who have expressed special concern, for example, over the increasing *relaxed selection* of potentially harmful genes [2]. New medical techniques and improved public health measures save lives, but there may be penalties in the long run. Vast numbers of people with genetic defects have been saved, enabling them to reproduce. Although the cumulative effects are largely unknown, most geneticists do not seem to believe that selection has been relaxed enough to cause alarm at the present time.

Besides migration and new mutations, gene frequencies in a population change principally as a result of *differential fertility*. Despite declining birth rates and low rates of infant mortality in Western societies, the opportunity for selection apparently has not declined as severely as previously thought. It is not average family size, *per se*, that matters so much, as variances in family size or the number of departures from the average [2]. The opportunity for selection would be approximately the same, very small, if everyone lived to have many children or if everyone had just a few. This fact has not been adequately appreciated (and seldom recognized) by either sociologists or demographers. It suggests that the opportunity for selection may be just as great, or small, today as it was before the Industrial Revolution, and probably has been highest during periods of rapid transition.

In terms of their immediate implications for human affairs, more significant than the effects of differential fertility are the effects of *assortative mating* [4]. Selective, or assortative, mating alone does not change gene frequencies, but it does change their distribution within the population. Thus, positive assortative mating for a highly heritable trait, e.g., intelligence, increases the average homozygosity of the genotype and its population variance [1]. In less technical terms, this means that assortative mating can markedly increase the parent-child and sibling correlations in almost any genotype, as well as increase the proportion of individuals in the tails of the distribution of polygenic traits. One geneticist, for example, has recently calculated that the current level of assortative mating for intelligence produces about five times as many persons with IQ's over 145 than would be found under conditions of random mating [16].

Population Genetics and Social Structure. To the extent that heredity is associated with either assortative mating or inbreeding, adults can be said to form relatively distinct breeding populations. These are statistical aggregates and must always be defined in terms of the genes or genotypes under investigation. This all simply means that, owing to some form of selective breeding, the offspring of some adults, on the average, are more likely to resemble each other with respect to a certain trait, or set of traits, than to resemble any other individual picked at random from the population.

As a result of the natural mating boundaries of man and generations of inbreeding, genes tend to be segregated. Whenever, in fact, two or more different kinds of genes appear together in the same population with more than average frequency, we can properly call the group a *racial aggregate*. This is, of course, just what the biological meaning of race implies; it also tells us why taxonomies of race are so confusing. Genes are found to combine in an almost infinite number of ways and, because both the phenotypic and genotypic correlations are seldom, if ever, perfect, we cannot speak of "fixed" or "pure" types. Only under very extraordinary circumstances, where a racial isolate has been totally segregated for many generations, could the genetic structure of a population possibly become fixed. Even this is improbable, however, since new mutations continually arise and the environment never remains stable long enough to give an identical advantage to every gene being carried in the population. In the sociological literature, however, one will nevertheless find statements to the effect that because there are no "pure" races, there can be no races at all. Or it is argued that races, if not figments of our imagination, only have something to do with physical traits, like skin or hair color, and nothing to do with behavior. On the contrary, a hereditary basis for racial differences in behavior is highly probable. In fact, it is just as probable as finding individual differences in behavior that can be attributed to some extent to heredity. Social scientists might be less alarmed by such statements if, again, they will keep in mind that we are talking here about statistical aggregates and overlapping distributions, and not fixed or pure types. Clearer thinking also will result if we remember that polygenic traits, like skin color and intelligence, are the consequence of interaction among many different combinations of genes and many patterns of environmental conditions.

In certain ways, *social classes* also can be treated as breeding populations —not just because they promote assortative mating, but perhaps mainly because mobility from one class to another sometimes depends upon the possession of heritable traits. This may be particularly true in an open society in which merit is rewarded, mobility rates are high, and education depends less directly upon social ascription and more directly upon each individual's capacity. Equality of opportunity fosters the development of a biotic or polygenic model of class structure [3]. This argument will be expanded in the concluding section of the chapter.

Epidemiology and Social Structure. The field of social epidemiology as a strategy for detecting links between biological and social phenomena is probably familiar to most general readers of this text and, since it is covered in detail in other chapters, will not be dwelt upon here. It is an area which is truly collaborative and interdisciplinary, and promises to advance our understanding of the complex social-biological processes involved in coronary heart disease, lung cancer, rheumatoid arthritis, and other chronic diseases.

Human Ecology and Environmental Health. Perhaps the broadest area of common interest among social and biological scientists lies in the general realm of human ecology, or the study of the ways in which man lives in and interacts with his environment. Historically, in sociology as well as in zoology and botany, the primary emphasis has been upon how organisms interact with each other and adapt to particular environments [11]. Every intact population comprises a set of organisms whose reaction to each other and to the habitat constitutes an integrated ecosystem. More recently, however, it has become painfully clear that the human species is as capable of acting upon as reacting to his environment.

Following traditional ecological and evolutionary approaches, the interest of some anthropologists and other scientists has shifted in recent years to the study of *biocultural adaptation.* In one of the most promising areas for collaborative research, particularly between physical and cultural anthropologists, the main goals are to examine man-environment interactions in relatively isolated and stable populations and to determine the limits of man's adaptive capacities when these populations undergo radical change. This approach may be more fruitful, in the long run, than the use of prehistoric records in reaching a better understanding of the relationships between man's biological and cultural evolution.

Regarding the sudden interest in problems of *environmental health*, it is unlikely that man's devastation of his own environment will outrun his capacities for survival. The very fact that he is able to recognize the danger is sufficient evidence that he can, as he has time and time again under other circumstances, use his unique cultural and technological heritage to combat the pollution of his skies, rivers, lakes, and oceans. Only through the control of waste products did he ever manage to live in urban environments, and only through the protective environment of a space suit has he managed to walk on the surface of a totally alien body. Neither man's rationality nor his capacity for survival should be underestimated. Nevertheless, the resources which undoubtedly will be used over the next generation to control the "ravaged" environment will provide an unusual opportunity for social and biological scientists to inspect some of the more elusive interfaces between their disciplines. Problems in environmental health clearly demonstrate that the relationship between man and his environment is a two-way process.

A SOCIAL-BIOLOGICAL THEORY OF SOCIAL MOBILITY

In the final section of this chapter we shall examine the polygenic theory of social mobility and class structure, which holds that *both* cultural and genetic approaches are required for an adequate explanation of social-class phenomena. It is not our task to quantify and test the theory with any rigor: Owing to the complexity of gene-environment intersections and the difficulty of performing transplants or similarly controlled experiments on human populations, we must rely for the moment upon inferential data and extrapolations from experiments with animals [27].

The theoretical expectations to be derived relate to some of the most fundamental issues in sociology. Its starting point is the difference in the average incidence of inheritable attributes in different social classes. Its central proposition is that these differences vary genetically in a particular population at a particular point in time.

It is quite common to find fairly high heritability of a trait between individuals and low or zero heritability of that trait between groups. This is usually because individual differences in some traits are quite large and group differences quite small, or negligible. A continuous variable like height is a good example. However, if a trait has high individual heritability *and* the movement of individuals between groups is correlated with their possession or nonpossession of that trait, then on theoretical grounds we would expect their mobility to lead to a nonrandom transfer of genes between groups. Estimating the proportion of between-group variance that may be attributed to this process, though, is often confounded by the presence of between-group environmental factors that are known to affect the presence of the trait in the same direction as the intergroup mobility. If the environmental differences between groups were reduced or were to disappear altogether, group heritability would be larger and would more closely approximate the individual heritability of the trait. Keeping these points in mind, let us turn to a comparison of the polygenic model and the traditional sociological model of social mobility, first taking up the latter.

Deprivation, or the Environmental Theory

Sociologists generally define social mobility as the movement of individuals from the social class of their family of origin to the class of their family of procreation. It is usually measured by comparing the social status of the parent and the offspring. When the social system allows little or no movement between strata, and the correlation between the father's and son's status is very high, then the strata are called "castes" instead of "classes." Most modern societies, however, are "class-like." There is a significant amount of mobility and, thus, the correlations of the status of fathers and sons tend to be only moderate. A correlation of zero could theoretically occur, but only in a completely open society—one in which it would be impossible to predict an individual's adult status on the basis of his parents'. This does not mean that the allocation of status under such conditions would occur randomly, or be left to chance, but that factors other than parental status would be the primary determinants. These would presumably be more of an individualized nature. While such mobility may be the ideal, it is not known to have ever been closely achieved. Most positions in contemporary societies are socially ascribed to some extent. Movement between classes tends to be limited by an accumulation of social and cultural advantages or disadvantages that parents confer upon their children.

Although we intend to keep the discussion simple, it may be helpful also to note that sociologists usually speak of two different kinds of deprivation or advantage. *Cultural* deprivation or advantage involves the cognitive, social, and emotional development of the child. It has to do with the transmission of behavioral traits uniquely belonging to an integrated, class-based subculture (like the "culture of poverty"). *Structural* deprivation or advantage involves differential access to the institutionalized means for achieving culturally prescribed goals, that is, the unequal distribution of educational, economic, and political opportunities (such as results from racial discrimination). Thus, environmental factors of both a cultural and structural kind are employed by behavioral scientists as the primary explanatory variables in the theory that social mobility is determined environmentally, or is the result of deprivation and advantage.

A standard schematic version of the theory is presented in Figure 4-1. The subject's phenotype *D*, which can in-

FIGURE 4-1 Standard Environment Model of Social Mobility

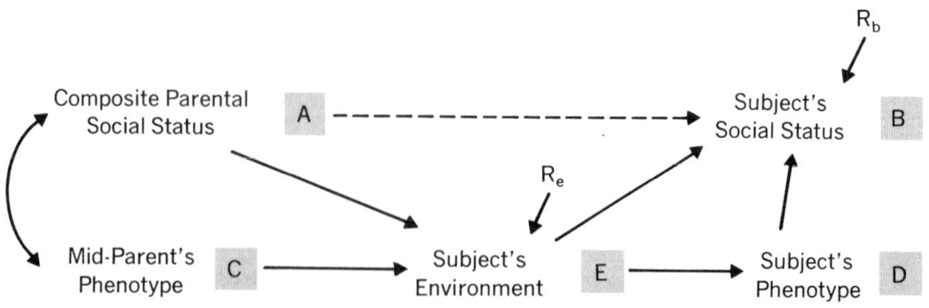

clude almost any number of personal characteristics like intelligence or motivation to achieve, is the direct result of being reared in a specific environment E which, in turn, is the product of parental influences A and C and a residual R_e which symbolizes all other possible determinants of the subject's environment that are operating independently of any social or personal attributes of the parents. The subject's social status B is the end-product of personal, parental, and other environmental factors. B also has a residual R_b which might represent factors like "forced" mobility (structural changes that occur in strata size) that lie well beyond the context of the individual's own environment.

No genetic component is recognized in the deprivation or environmental scheme. The underlying assumption is that most traits of the subject are not significantly heritable and that, if they are, the trait-relevant genotypes are randomly distributed across all classes. Any observed correlation between parental status and the subject's trait, then, is wholly a result of the kind of environment the parents are able to provide, both in the specific context of the family and in other relevant environments, like schools. Moreover, except for the confounding effect of structural or forced mobility, these same social factors are thought to completely account for the observed correlation between the parents' and subject's social status. This correlation r_{BA} has commonly been taken, in fact, as a direct measure of inequality of opportunity, or social ascription.

The Polygenic Theory

Some polygenic traits, like intelligence, are known to be highly heritable. Although the absolute magnitude of the genetic component will always remain a question (partly because it is a function of the environmental variance in the population under consideration), most of the severest critics are willing to concede that heredity is at least in some way involved in some traits. Yet, the relevant genetic factors are seldom, if ever, taken into account by social scientists, even at the theoretical level.

We have used the term "polygenic" to describe the alternative theory we are presenting for two reasons: first, because the term suggests that we are dealing with the process of natural selection, and, second, because it restricts our attention to continuous variables. Geneticists generally make a distinction, such as in the study of blood polymorphisms, between genes that appear in a population as a result of mutations and genes that appear so frequently that they cannot be explained by mutation alone but must be accounted for, at least in part, by some form of selection. Genetic markers in blood samples, for example, are said to be "polymorphic" only when their frequencies exceed the expected rate of mutation. We are interested only in genes of this kind.

We also are interested primarily in continuous variables that are typically produced by the cumulative effects of a large number of genes. These are, in fact, called "polygenes." Some genes are noncumulative and tend to have a constant expression, like sickle-cell anemia. Polygenes, on the other hand, yield more or less symmetrical and unimodal frequency distributions. Rather than discrete classes of individuals, like merely tall and short people, polygenes produce every intermediate grade, the variation being quantitative, not qualitative.

Two new terms have been introduced in Figure 4–2—the midparent's genotype (or heredity), and the subject's

FIGURE 4-2 Simplified Polygenic Model of Social Mobility

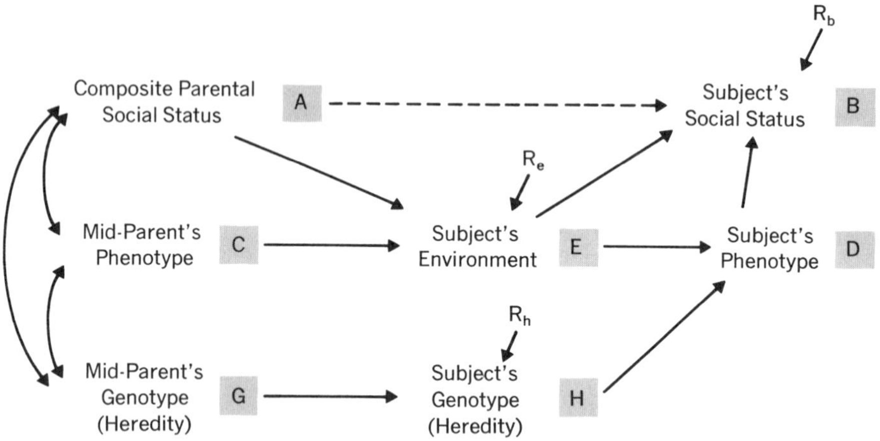

genotype. We are simply claiming that the mobility of the younger generation (or, really, the lack of it) may be due, in part, to a genetic loop that links the parent's and subject's social positions. So long as a bona fide argument can be made that the correlation r_{GA} and the paths p_{BD}, p_{DH}, and p_{HG} are all greater than zero, then the product of these paths constitutes a genetic loop which partly accounts for the observed correlation r_{BA}.

Under the quite hypothetical conditions of full equality of opportunity, only the indirect environmental loops operating either through p_{EA} or p_{EC} would be required to equal zero—a condition that eliminates all forms of deprivation arising from the family. However, the genetic loop, which operates independently of either of these two paths, is permitted, under "ideal" conditions, to remain. In fact, as usually defined, equality of opportunity *means* that individuals are allowed to achieve according to their own capabilities (and not the capabilities or incapabilities of their parents to interact with them or otherwise provide an appropriate environment). Finally, the scheme specifies that if the genetic loop has a positive entry when there are no entries in the critical environmental paths, the correlation between the parent's and the subject's social status does not disappear (as the deprivation theory requires) but retains the same value as the genetic loop.

In theory, then, social ascription due to class differences varies directly with the size of the antecedent paths that control each individual's developmental environment, but inversely with the size of the genetic loop—since the genetic and environmental paths themselves tend to be inversely related. As we said earlier, heritability always depends upon the absolute amount of variance of trait-relevant factors in the environment. This means that if concerted efforts are made to level the environmental variance, such as through upgrading the environments of children low on the socioeconomic scale, then as a general rule we should expect an increase in the proportion of variance of some traits, which could be attributed to heredity.

The Inheritance of Intelligence

Up to now we have described the polygenic model of social mobility in general terms. While there are any number of individual traits that could be used to test the model, there perhaps is only one that meets all the conditions required to complete the genetic loop. This is the phenotype, or trait, of intelligence as measured by standardized tests. For in order to close the genetic loop, *all* its paths must be significantly greater than zero, since the effects of the paths are multiplicative, not additive. Many traits have high heritability p_{DH} and high genotypic parent-child correlations p_{HG}, but only intelligence also appears to be significantly correlated with social status p_{BD}. Let us now inspect each of the three principal components in the genetic loop (in the order just listed) as a partial and preliminary test of the theory.

The heritability of intelligence, as defined by the path p_{DH}, has been shown, over a long period of time and in many different populations to be quite high. Some of the best-controlled studies have found that it may be as high as 80 percent. Reviews of this research are quite common in the literature [7]. Although all estimates of heritability have a number of serious limitations [13], the conclusion that heredity contributes substantially to intelligence and accounts for some variance is not a point in dispute.

The size of the coefficient in the next path, from the midparent's to subject's heredity p_{HG}, depends mainly upon the degree of assortative mating. (In very small populations, the degree of inbreeding might be most important.) A child receives half his genes from each parent. However, the additive genetic parent-offspring correlation actually is .5, plus one-half of the assortative mating coefficient. As we noted earlier in this chapter, the more the parents resemble each other (carry common genes), the more closely the children will resemble their parents. The long-range effect of assortative mating is to reduce the within-family variance. If, as we have suggested, intelligence is a class-linked phenomenon, then the effect of assortative mating on intelligence is, similarly, to reduce its within-class variance while increasing its between-class variance.

The strength of the genetic parent-child correlation and, thus, the entire genetic loop depends to a large extent upon the amount of assortative mating, in this case for intelligence, that occurs. Under conditions of random mating, this correlation is .5, but it would be much stronger, perhaps as high as .8, if assortative mating for intelligence is moderately high. There is some evidence that this is, in fact, true.

Societies that value individual freedom of choice in marriage and, at the same time, place most potential mates into relatively homogeneous pools of eligible people on the basis of ability are quite likely to produce a high degree of assortative mating for intelligence. In the past generation, our schools and colleges appear to have done just that. Males and females of like intelligence end up in similar educational niches—as dropouts from the same school, as college classmates, or as graduate students. Whether by choice or as a result of educational selection, assortative mating for intelligence may have even a greater bearing today upon who mates with whom than either class endogamy or residential propinquity.

The third path, p_{BD}, is perhaps the most critical for two reasons: It is the weakest link in the chain, and it is the link that connects the polygenic and social-structural components of the model. For probably the first time in the history of man, a normally distributed and highly heritable human trait is systematically being used as a primary criterion for the allocation of adult social status. To be sure, intelligence is still only moderately correlated with achievement and is not the only important factor. Both class origin and educational attainment will predict, about as well as intelligence, the positions people enter in adult life. However, a large part of the apparent effect of both these factors may actually be due to their relationship to intelligence. Although an oversimplification of the processes involved, it seems that brighter-than-average children tend to come from higher socioeconomic backgrounds; and being bright tends to get one through school and into college, and the very brightest tend to go to a more-or-less selective college that provides a passport into middle-class or upper-middle-class adult status. The educational system has become the central mechanism in the identification of talent and the allocation of status.

The genetic loop is complete. (We assume that the magnitude of the paths p_{GC} and p_{CA} in the parental generation are only slightly smaller than their counterparts p_{BD} and p_{DH} in the subject's generation.) Even though the values in some paths are quite large, they are multiplicative, so that the strength of the loop at the present time probably accounts for no more than one-third of the association between the composite status of the parents' and the subject's status. But even this estimate is based upon a number of questionable assumptions and rather crude measures of some of the values. Nevertheless, polygenic mobility no doubt does operate in the manner just described, and the strength of the genetic loop probably is sufficient to warrant closer inspection. This will become increasingly true if contemporary societies continue to operate partly on the basis of rewarding merit—a trend that, in the long run, seems inescapable.

In concluding, it might be well to note that the correlation between intelligence and adult social status p_{BD} is the link that fundamentally distinguishes the racial and class arguments regarding group differences in measured intelligence. We have shown that mobility between social classes is great and that it is not random, but based, among other things, on intelligence. In contrast, interracial migration (or interracial marriage) not only is very small, but there is no evidence that it is anything but random, at least with respect to black and white differences in intelligence. A social-biological explanation of such differences, if they exist at all, would seemingly require an entirely different approach—probably one that would include differential rates of fertility. If over a period of several generations the correlation between fertility and intelligence in one racial aggregate should differ markedly from another aggregate, such as being strongly and negatively correlated in one and positively correlated or uncorrelated in the other, then, theoretically, the two groups should be expected in time to differ significantly with respect to the trait under consideration. None but the scantiest evidence, however, has ever been presented to suggest that such a process may have occurred in respect to intelligence.

We have not ourselves introduced other selection factors, like differential fertility, into the polygenic theory of mobility, mainly to avoid complicating our presentation. Such factors, however, would have to be considered to complete the picture. Recent evidence, for example, indicates that fertility rates have been increasing among the more educated and more intelligent segments of the population and decreasing in the previously more fertile and less intelligent segments [21]. If this trend should continue, the correlation between fertility and intelligence would become positive, and possibly quite significant. For one thing, mobility rates could seriously be affected—as higher-status groups have more and generally brighter children, they may tend to fill almost all the highest positions available even in a class structure that is expanding at the top.

A Note to Medical Sociologists

Some readers may question whether the materials presented in this last section of the chapter pertain directly to problems in the sociology of medicine. It should be remembered, however, that some of the most important and basic contributions made by social scientists to medicine and the health professions have been indirect. Descriptions of gene-environment interaction may be of just this sort. The polygenic explanation of social mobility is only one example of the many facets of social biology that can and should be explored. As we stated in our introductory section, future biological and medical engineering could drastically alter the organization of human societies. One of social biology's long-range objectives should be the reduction of the basic unknown and unanticipated consequences of such developments on human affairs.

REFERENCES

1. CROW, JAMES F. AND JOSEPH FELSENSTEIN, "The Effects of Assortative Mating on the Genetic Composition of a Population," *Eugenics Quarterly*, 15 (June, 1968), 85–97.
2. DOBZHANSKY, THEODOSIUS, *Mankind Evolving*. New Haven: Yale University Press, 1962.
3. ECKLAND, BRUCE K., "Genetics and Sociology: A Reconsideration," *American Sociological Review*, 32 (April, 1967), 173–94.
4. ———, "Theories of Mate Selection," *Eugenics Quarterly*, 15 (June, 1968), 71–84.
5. ——— AND DONALD P. KENT, "Socialization and Social Structure," in National Institutes of Health, *Perspectives on Human Deprivation*. Washington, D.C.: Government Printing Office, 1969.
6. ELDER, GLEN H., JR., "Appearance and Education in Marriage Mobility," *American Sociological Review*, 34 (August, 1969), 519–33.
7. ERLENMEYER-KIMLING, L. AND LISSY F. JARVIK, "Genetics and Intelligence: A Review," *Science*, 142 (December 13, 1963), 1477–79.
8. GLASS, DAVID C., ed., *Neurophysiology and Emotion*. New York: Rockefeller University Press and Russell Sage Foundation, 1967.
9. ———, ed., *Genetics*. New York: Rockefeller University Press and Russell Sage Foundation, 1968.
10. ———, ed., *Environmental Influences*. New York: Rockefeller University Press and Russell Sage Foundation, 1968.
11. HAWLEY, AMOS H., "Human Ecology," in David L. Sills, ed., *International Encyclopedia of the Social Sciences*. New York: The Macmillan Company, 1968.
12. HESTON, LEONARD L., "The Genetics of Schizophrenia and Schizoid Disease," *Science*, 167 (January 16, 1970), 249–56.
13. HIRSCH, JERRY, "Behavior-Genetic Analysis and Its Biosocial Consequences." Paper read at the University of Illinois Conference on Contributions to Intelligence, 1969.
14. ILLSLEY, R., "The Sociological Study of Reproduction and Its Outcome," in S. A. Richardson and A. F. Guttmacher, eds., *Childbearing: Its Social and Psychological Aspects*. Baltimore: The Williams & Wilkins Company, 1967.
15. International Biological Program, *Man's Survival in a Changing World*. Washington, D.C.: National Academy of Science, Undated.
16. JENSEN, ARTHUR R., "How Much

Can We Boost IQ and Scholastic Achievement?" *Harvard Educational Review*, 39 (Winter, 1969), 1–123.

17. KAPLAN, HOWARD B., "Studies in Sociophysiology." Paper read at the Southern Sociological Society meetings, Atlanta, Georgia, 1968.
18. MCCLEARN, GERALD E., "Biology and the Social and Behavioral Sciences," *Items*, 23 (September, 1969), 33–37.
19. National Institutes of Health, *Perspectives on Human Deprivation*. Washington, D.C.: Government Printing Office, 1969.
20. OSBORN, FREDERICK, *The Future of Human Heredity*. New York: Weybright and Talley, 1968.
21. REED, E. W. AND S. C. REED, *Mental Retardation: A Family Study*. Philadelphia: W. B. Saunders Company, 1965.
22. RIMLAND, BERNARD, *Infantile Autism*. New York: Appleton-Century Crofts, 1964.
23. RUSSELL SAGE FOUNDATION, *Annual Report: 1967–68*. New York.
24. SCOTT, ROBERT A., *The Making of Blind Men*. New York: Russell Sage Foundation, 1969.
25. SHAPIRO, DAVID AND ANDREW CRIDER, "Psychophysiological Approaches in Social Psychology," in Gardner Lindzey and Elliot Aronson, eds., *The Handbook of Social Psychology*, Vol. 3. Reading, Mass.: Addison-Wesley Publishing Company, Inc., 1969.
26. SIMON, WILLIAM AND JOHN H. GAGNON, "On Psychosexual Development," in David A. Goslin, ed., *Handbook of Socialization Theory and Research*. Skokie, Ill.: Rand McNally & Company, 1969.
27. THODAY, J. M. AND J. B. GIBSON, "Environmental and Genetical Contributions to Class Difference: A Model Experiment," *Science*, 167 (February 13, 1970), 990–92.
28. THOMPSON, WILLIAM R., "Development and Biophysical Bases of Personality," in Edgar Borgatta and William Lambert, eds., *Handbook of Personality Theory and Research*. Skokie, Ill.: Rand McNally & Company, 1968.

5

SOCIAL-PSYCHOLOGICAL FACTORS IN ILLNESS

Stanley H. King

Evidence of a state of illness in the human organism is weighted heavily with biological factors, such as elevation of temperature, change in pulse beat and respiration, swelling of tissues, alteration in the composition of blood and urine, and proliferation of abnormal cells. Biological and physical factors are also important in the background and onset of illness. Bacteria and viruses, vitamins, minerals, fats and other substances in nutrition, constitutional or genetic heritage, the onslaughts of physical forces, and the ingestion of various chemical substances—these are examples of important biological and physical agents in disease and illness.

Illness, however, is not solely a biological and physical phenomenon; it is also an event that occurs in a social context and reflects the intimate association of the person with other people. Both the internal and social environments are sources of important events that affect the health of the human organism.

The relationships among physical, biological, and social-psychological factors in illness are intricate and subtle.

Although astute diagnosticians and therapists have always drawn on an intuitive understanding of the interaction of these determinants, a detailed theory has yet to be developed and substantiated. The research does, however, suggest certain patterns of interaction among the three factors. These patterns constitute the subject of this chapter.

Two different perspectives are necessary—one in which etiological, or causal, factors are the focus of interest, and one in which the patient's reactions to illness become central. The first approach concentrates on the effects of psychological and social variables on physiological processes leading to a state of illness; the second, on the effects of biological variables—as evident in illness—on psychodynamic balance and interpersonal relations.

ETIOLOGY AND THE SOCIAL ENVIRONMENT

Central to the concept of etiology is the demonstration of causes. Beginning with the experiments of the great bacteriologists of the last century, the idea of specific cause has come to be a valuable tool in diagnosing and treating diseases, especially those of infectious origin. In much of medical education and practice, the concept of specific cause is still dominant. But many of the health problems which face the modern physician cannot be explained by a specific or single cause, and the concept of multiple causation has become an important part of the theoretical framework of diagnosis. The idea of cause has thus lost some of its clarity and directness. The impact of a whole series of forces may culminate in illness, but the contribution of each variable to that process and, at times, even the mere identification of the variables themselves, can be complicated and bewildering. Medicine faces an increasing array of illnesses whose etiologies are complicated and difficult to unravel, especially the chronic and psychosomatic diseases.

When the impact of the social environment on the etiology of illness is considered, the assignment of a direct cause is often difficult, if not impossible. Causal pathways must often be inferred rather than demonstrated; in consequence, psychological and social factors are still discussed in conjectural terms rather than with certainty. With that caution in mind, let us proceed to delineate the different ways in which social-psychological variables may be associated with the onset of disease.

Of first importance are stressful situations. In these, the interaction of the individual with his interpersonal environment produces emotional reaction, conflict, and an accompanying alteration of physiological balance, often beyond the range of normal fluctuations. The end result of long-continued conflict may be irreversible tissue changes, or chronic disease. Here we are in the realm of illness which can be broadly identified as *psychosomatic*. A second class of events comprises situations in which psychological and social variables may aggravate or facilitate the action of biological or physical disease agents. These agents combine with the social situation in some manner, perhaps through an additive or a disruptive process, to bring on illness. The third category covers the results of style of life—where living arrangements, customs, and other social circumstances may result in the individual's being in a situation where he is rendered vulnerable to disease.

In studying the first of these categories, the primary interest of the research scientist is individual psychological factors, but he hopes also to make generalizations that can apply to groups of individuals. More often than not, his research technique is the clinical method. In the study of the second category, his interest lies in both individual and group factors, and he must work with adequate numbers of research subjects in various social designations. The research approach most typically used is the cross-sectional survey. In the study of the third category, he is concerned mainly with group factors, but hopes to search out their implications for the individual. This research approach, like the second, utilizes a large number of subjects, but also follows them up over a period of time.

Stress and Disease

In everyday conversation, as well as in accounts of human behavior in fiction and other kinds of literature, there are frequent observations about the relationship between strong emotions and certain types of physiological reactions. The flushed face and clenched fist of anger, a sputtering rage, eyes wide with fear, butterflies in the stomach at times of anxious anticipation, loss of energy and desire in sadness—these descriptions, and many more—are common parlance. Emotional involvement, especially when it takes the form of anger or fear, gives rise to bodily reactions that differ to a considerable degree from the normal state.

Laboratory Studies. In the last few decades the relationship between emotions and physiological change has become a matter for experimental research. Much of the early work was done by Cannon [8], whose primary interest lay in the visceral aspects of emotional expression and the excitement of the sympathetic division of the autonomic nervous system. His experiments led to a description of the "fight-flight reaction," a physiological state in which the body was mobilized, through the action of the sympathetic nervous system, either to run from danger or to stand and fight. The emotions involved were either fear or rage, and Cannon viewed the action as mediated primarily through the secretion of adrenalin by the adrenal medulla. He concluded that both fear and rage were associated with the action of adrenalin, but he recognized that the action of adrenalin could not account for all the phenomena that he observed. Subsequent to the publication of Cannon's main work, there has been a growing volume of research on the relationship between emotional states and specific bodily changes. Some representative studies should be cited.

In one project, fear and anger were found to be associated with different physiological reactivity, a finding at variance with Cannon's but explicable in large part by advances in chemical knowledge since his time. Funkenstein, King, and Drolette [16], studying healthy college students under specified conditions of stress, obtained data about their cardiovascular reactions with a ballistocardiograph. Subjects who were angry at the experimenter or the experimental situation produced ballistocardiograph tracings that were similar to those produced by an infusion of noradrenalin. On the other hand, subjects who became angry with themselves, or who said they were anxious, produced ballistocardiograph tracings that were similar to those produced by an infusion of adrenalin. Thus, anger directed outward was associated with a noradrenalin-like physiological response, while inwardly directed anger or fear was associated with an adrenalin-like response. These results were similar to those obtained by Ax [6] in specific fear- and anger-inducing experiments.

Later investigations have tended to confirm these results. Working with a human centrifuge, giving injections of mecholyl, and testing for urinary secretion of adrenalin and noradrenalin, Cohen and Silverman [9] found anxiety to be associated with the release of adrenalin and outwardly directed aggression to be associated with the release of noradrenalin. They suggest that these relationships may be due to the activation of specific hypothalamic areas, but they point out that emotional reaction and cardiovascular response is more complicated than a simple affective hypothalamic-hormonal sequence. Still, specific emotional states do seem to be associated with specific vascular responses in some manner.

Other kinds of data come from the now classic studies by Wolf and Wolff [47, 48] of Tom, the man with a gastric fistula. As a child Tom had drunk some scalding-hot clam chowder, an act which resulted in the occlusion of his esophagus and the necessity of opening an artificial fistula in his stomach and abdominal wall through which he could be fed. He was observed for extended periods of time in the laboratory, allowing a comparison of changes in gastric activity with variations in emotional state. When Tom was fearful or sad, there was a pallor of the gastric mucosa and an inhibition of gastric secretions and muscular contractions. On the other hand, when Tom seemed to be in a state of emotional conflict involving anxiety, hostility, and resentment, there was engorgement of the gastric mucosa, with accompanying hypermotility, hyperemia, and an accelerated acid secretion. If the emotional conflict was prolonged, the physiological reaction led to hemorrhages, lesions, and eventually to the formation of ulcers.

Studies of other areas of the body, including the nasal mucosa, skin, and colon, have come from the group of researchers in Wolff's laboratory [49]. Strong emotional reactions, often to symbolic threats from the environment, were clearly associated with tissue changes in these areas, even to the point of gross changes and pain, changes like ulceration or pronounced swelling.

Laboratory studies seem to have established a relationship between emotion and physiological reactivity, but as investigations continue it is evident that the relationship is complex and that the steps toward irreversible tissue changes and disease in patients cannot be demonstrated easily. Reiser [41] notes that laboratory researchers have the problem of explaining why some subjects show little or no demonstrable response to experimental procedures that evoke vigorous changes in other subjects or why some subjects will react vigorously at one time and minimally at others, to the same stimulus. Also, how can the researcher explain the exaggerated or prolonged physiological response that occurs unexpectedly? Questions about the activation of the neuroendocrine apparatus in the face of psychological conflict, and the direction and intensity that neuroendocrine response will take, continue to puzzle the investigator.

Theoretical Positions in Psychosomatic Disease. When we consider the kind of tissue change that indicates disease, clinical evidence suggests that emotional conflict appears to play an important etiological role, but the mechanisms involved are still the object of much theoretical controversy. By reviewing the major positions, we can arrive at the important issues which face those who are interested in the problems of psychosomatic disease [17, 26, 32].

Of great initial impact on the field of psychosomatic medicine was the *specificity theory*, especially as advanced by Alexander [3]. The theory is that a specific, typical, unconscious conflict results in a specific disease: In the case of peptic ulcer, for example, the conflict is the result of the individual's repressed desire to be dependent. With the unconscious conflict comes anxiety, a danger signal to the ego, which leads to the utilization of certain unconscious defense mechanisms, including regression. These emotional reactions are associated with specific sympathetic or parasympathetic innervation, affecting specific organs. The chronic tension resulting from repressed conflicts can lead to chronic overreaction in the organ. For example, a constant oversecretion of hydrochloric acid in the stomach may, in turn, produce pathological tissue changes in susceptible individuals. Alexander saw the ulcer patient as a person with a passive-dependent character structure who was blocked in some way from expressing his dependency and regressed unconsciously to an infantile oral state with increased gastric secretion.

Further contribution to the specificity theory in relation to peptic ulcer has come from Mirsky [34, 46]. He maintains that gastric activity is paralleled by the level of serum pepsinogen, which in turn is related to genetic factors. Ulcer occurs only in individuals who are born as high secretors of pepsinogen. However, the early relationship with parents is also an important factor, in terms of providing or not providing the basis for a conflict about dependency. Thus, only those individuals among the high secretors who develop such conflicts are susceptible to ulcer. Finally, there must be a stressful situation in later life which activates the dependency conflict if the susceptible individual is to develop a case of peptic ulcer. Thus the specificity theory has been extended to take into account not only a specific kind of conflict, but genetic factors and life stress situations as well.

The specificity theory has been challenged on several counts, especially with regard to the difficulty of demonstrating an identical conflict in all cases of the same disease. There is also the question of whether the same kind of conflict may be associated with several different diseases. The prediction of disease from conflict has not been too successful, although Mirsky's work indicates that such predictions might be made if variables other than the specific conflict are taken into account.

Another kind of theoretical approach might be characterized as the *regression theory*. Michaels [33] has taken the position that the somatic expression of a psychological conflict is a physiological reaction similar to that which would be found on the infantile level, especially in terms of a relatively greater reactivity to stimuli and a more marked disturbance of homeostasis. Margolin [30] adds that such infantile physiological responses were once appropriate in the person's life, but not at the adult level, so that psychosomatic disease is the expression of inappropriate response. Szasz [45] speaks of "regressive innervation," and involves the parasympathetic nervous system in psychosomatic disorder. The parasympathetic system develops earlier than the sympathetic; hence, extensive innervation of the parasympathetic system is a regressive phenomenon. He argues that the majority of diseases usually classified as psychosomatic are the result of localized, chronic, parasympathetic innervation.

The regression theory thus focuses on the defense mechanism which is brought into play by psychological conflict, emphasizing that regression has crucial physiological as well as psychological consequences. Again, however, serious questions have been raised about the validity of this theoretical approach. That excessive fluctuations in physiological response are tolerated better in infancy is open to doubt, as in the case of hypertension. At the same time, certain reactions, like ulcerative colitis, may have little or no counterpart in infancy. Finally, Mirsky's data suggest that certain people may have genetic sensitivities which do not diminish as they grow older, precluding a regressive phenomenon of a physiological nature in their cases.

A third theoretical approach, espoused by Wolff [48, 50] and his coworkers, involves a nonspecific theory of *protective adaptive response.* Disease, they submit, is the end result of the protective reactions of an organism in the face of stress resulting from symbolic threats to the total organism. Physiological reactions in an organ or tissue that were originally protective in nature may become conditioned responses to noxious psychological stimuli. Furthermore, the physiological response may in and of itself take on symbolic meanings, such as shutting out or ejecting painful situations. An individual responds to different stresses in a way that is consistent for him and that is based on his genetic equipment and the results of his prior conditioning. Wolff, who has summarized many prior studies [48], emphasizes the importance of the way that the individual himself perceives situations in which he participates, rather than the way that an objective observer might perceive them.

Data from a number of different ethnic groups are cited by Hinkle [20, 21] to show that over the course of time a small proportion of subjects have the majority of illnesses, even though they may not have experienced more objectively discernible stress. They have, however, perceived their lives as more demanding, depriving, threatening, and conflict-producing than their contemporaries. The reasons for these variations in perception, however, still are not clear.

The various theoretical approaches leave unresolved a number of issues and problems. One issue is whether specific emotional conflict leads to specific disease, or whether disease is the product of idiosyncratic response to stress in accordance with previous conditioning. The latter view is that overreactivity of tissues rests more on the individual's continuing experience; the former emphasizes relationships between emotional conflicts and biological patterns which more or less hold for all individuals. The occurrence of a particular disease is less predictable in the nonspecific theories. Hinkle's position is that the perception of the environment as "threatening" leads to a greater amount of disease of *all kinds.* The issue of specificity versus nonspecificity thus bears on the possibility of predicting who will become ill and with what disease. At present, the nonspecific approach seems to be more relevant to the question of *who* will become ill, while the specificity scheme is more relevant to the *type of illness* that will ensue.

The specific and nonspecific theories also differ in their emphasis on conscious and unconscious processes. The relevance of either theory to disease may, therefore, rest in part on the mediation of conscious and unconscious emotional processes in the central nervous system. How much this may be a matter of early conditioning, how much the use of relatively specific or diffuse neural pathways, how much a matter of developmental or genetic determination, are all critical questions that await further research. The level of consciousness, however, is an important variable for those dealing with both empirical research and the construction of theory.

There are a number of other questions to be answered, especially in reference to the specificity theory. For example, among all individuals who have a certain repressed emotional conflict, what other factors operate to produce the disease? If physiological predisposition is important, as Mirsky suggests, might the same conflict lead to a different disease in individuals with a different physiological predisposition? Also, what are the effects of social change on the development of repressed emotional conflicts? Are these effects associated with changes in the incidence of disease, as they appear to be in the shift of peptic ulcer rates among men and women? In the last century, more women than men, in the United States and Great Britain, had peptic ulcers; now the reverse is true.

A second important issue pertains to the relationship between emotional factors and other variables, especially those of a physical or biological nature. Of special interest are the cardiovascular diseases, and coronary artery disease in particular. (See Chapter 3 for a detailed discussion of social factors in coronary heart disease.) How is heart disease related to genetic factors, to diet, to exercise, and to emotional stress? The weight of the argument thus far has been on diet as the chief agent in producing high levels of cholesterol, and consequently on control of diet as one way to reduce the danger of certain kinds of heart attacks. At the same time, some investigators have found that cholesterol levels vary with emotional tension. In their study of tax accountants, Friedman, Rosenman, and Carroll [14, 15] demonstrated that severe occupational stress was associated with increases in both serum cholesterol and blood-clotting time, and that these changes could not be ascribed to variation in weight, exercise, or diet. They argue that the data on diet, cholesterol, and coronary artery disease need to be examined in the light of institutionalized occupational or other emotional stress, and that future epidemiological investigations of coronary artery disease should include control data on emotional stress.

In another study, Russek [42] presents data to show that young coronary patients, as compared with control subjects, more often showed evidence of overwork, a strong need for recognition, a sense of obligation to others, compulsiveness, unstinting effort, and an inability to recognize their own stress end-point. He recognizes that both diet and heredity are crucial variables in coronary disease in young adults, but he feels that emotional stress is also of great significance.

Unfortunately, the role of emotional factors in the etiology of disease has often been regarded as an all-or-none proposition. The research scientist either tends to ignore or discount the relevance of emotional stress, or else he ascribes to it a power that overrules relevant biological and physical data. Some interpretations of disease as symbolic manifestations of emotional conflict, for example, strain one's credulity. Research in psychosomatic illness has been moving steadily toward the point of positing an admixture of variables, and the key lies in finding a technique for handling the interaction of these variables—as in the interaction of diet, stress, exercise, and heredity in coronary artery disease. Most or all of the psychosomatic diseases probably can only be understood in terms of a compounded etiology, and the relationships among the factors leading to the onset of disease will be an issue for some time to come.

Two final points should be made

about the relationship between emotional factors and other variables. First, data are needed, especially in epidemiological studies, which can best be supplied by the sociologist. Although there is a uniqueness to each individual's perception of his environment, there are perceptions of social events which all members of the group share. The sociologist can point up those areas of stress which are structured by the social order, or those situations which involve conflict, and these can become strategic areas for research. A case in point would be the analysis of an organization and the impingement of the organization on individuals within it, such as Argyris [4, 5] has made. Also, the study of cholesterol by Friedman, Rosenman, and Carrol [15] shows how important social events can affect individuals. In sum, sociological data can make a basic contribution to the definition of the relevant variables in psychosomatic illness.

Our second point concerns a serious difficulty in research design. Most of the data which have been gathered about psychosomatic illness have come "after the fact," and background variables—especially early experiences—must be filtered through the screen of subsequent experience. In some situations, the charge can be made that the psychological data may be explicable as part of the reaction to the disease itself. Coronary artery disease is a case in point. Mordkoff and Parsons [35] comment that in many patients with this disease there is a resulting disturbance characterized by depression, anxiety, increased hostility, and concern over failure. Under these conditions, the recall of prior events or emotional states could easily be distorted. Prospective studies are therefore crucial in the gathering of data on which etiological conclusions can be based. The report by Ostfield et al. [36] is an example of what must become numerous large-scale longitudinal studies of coronary heart disease and other diseases in which emotional factors may play a causal role.

Psychosocial Factors as Facilitators of Illness

Basic to an understanding of the secondary effects of psychological or social data in precipitating illness is the distinction between necessary and sufficient cause. Some factor, which can be labeled the *necessary cause*, must be present for disease or illness to occur, but its presence alone is not sufficient to produce disease. Other factors, one or more, must coincide with the necessary cause and provide the sufficient conditions for the disease. These other factors are called *sufficient causes*. In certain situations the necessary cause may be a bacterium or virus without which the disease could not develop. However, the body's resistance may be such that, until some alteration occurs in homeostasis, the bacterium or virus will not be able to multiply and produce the clinical manifestations of illness. Sufficient causes, often psychological or social as well as physical, can provide the impetus for that alteration in homeostasis. Dubos [11] cites *herpes simplex*, more commonly known as fever blisters or cold sores, as an example. The herpetic blisters are due to the effects of a virus, usually acquired early in life and thereafter constantly present in the body of the infected individual. Disease is produced, however, only when certain conditions upset the chemical balance of the body—overexposure to ultraviolet light in the form of sunshine, menstruation, emotional stress, or infection with the common cold. The herpes virus would be, in this situation, the necessary cause (since the blisters would not occur without its presence), while the other factors—physical, biological, or emotional—provide the sufficient conditions under which the disease will occur.

There is some evidence to suggest that tuberculosis can occur in response to the social environment and psychological stress. In a study of patients in Seattle, Holmes and his associates [22] found a number of factors in the backgrounds or life situations of the patients which appeared to be relevant to the onset of the disease. For example, data that related to the life experiences of each patient were plotted for a twelve-year period preceding hospitalization. In the majority of the patients' lives there had been a gradual increase of experiences which were perceived by the individual as significant and stressful, and these culminated in a crisis during the two-year period prior to hospitalization. From psychiatric studies of patients in the same sanitarium, the authors noted that in general the patients were poorly equipped to deal effectively with the realities of social relationships, especially when these were full of tension.

In a related study, Hawkins [19] considered all the newly detected cases of tuberculosis in Seattle within a given year in relation to census tract data. The city was divided into four rather distinct socioeconomic residential areas, from the city center with its skid row, through working class and middle class, and out to the area of the well-to-do. Tuberculosis rates per 100,000 population were then computed for each of the four areas, keeping separate the variables of age, sex, and race. As ecologists would predict, the highest rates occurred in the center of the city. However, when rates in the four areas were considered by race, the white rate was highest in the center-city area, but the nonwhite rate was highest in the outer, well-to-do, area. In other words, rates for whites and nonwhites were inversely proportional to the degree to which their ethnic members were dominant in the area.

These data are mainly suggestive, but they do indicate the possibility that psychological and social factors play some part in the onset of tuberculosis. Dubos has noted that the tubercle bacillus can be found in a great many people who do not show clinical manifestations of the disease; hence the bacillus itself, though necessary, may not be sufficient to cause the disease. The stresses arising from interpersonal relationships and social demand may, in some people who carry the bacillus, be sufficient for the disease to occur.

Again, the matter of pathway or mechanism becomes important. Holmes and his co-workers [22] suggest that endogenous adrenocortical hormones influence resistance to tuberculosis and that the secretion of these hormones can be altered by chronic psychological stress caused by threats from the environment. The mechanism, however, still awaits solid demonstration.

These two examples, *herpes simplex* and tuberculosis, are only illustrative of the proposition that psychological and social variables can act as facilitators of illness. Some of the degenerative diseases of the older years may also be facilitated by the emotional upheavals of retirement or rapidly changing social conditions. At the moment, clinical hunches are more numerous than controlled studies. However, the interaction between psychological and social variables, as sufficient causes, and biological or physical variables, as necessary causes, is receiving a steadily increasing amount of research attention.

The Social Milieu and Illness

The culture in which an individual lives includes customs and traditions, values, patterns of interaction between classes of people, methods of trade and subsistence, and techniques for bringing both positive and negative sanctions on the members of the culture. If we think of culture as both the direct and indirect social milieu surrounding the individual, then we can posit a number of cultural factors in illness. For example, in some of the underdeveloped countries with warm climates, an agricultural, low-subsistence economy keeps many individuals in close contact with farm animals, especially cows, and perpetuates the ecological relationships between flies, animals, humus, and people. Under these conditions fly-borne diseases can flourish. The relationship becomes difficult to change if tradition and a sense of psychological security are bound up with a close physical association with animals. In this instance, the social and psychological variables in the milieu place the individual in a position where he is vulnerable to disease or injury from any number of other factors.

Of special interest is the effect of the social milieu on nutrition, particularly in terms of the limitation of available foods by the nature of the climate or soil, by the economy of the society, or by the customs of the social group. Jelliffe [23] cites the limitation of food by both economy and customs in rural West Bengal as producing diseases of protein malnutrition, especially kwashiorkor. In a culture where the available protein foods are restricted, some which could theoretically be utilized are proscribed by custom, either completely or at important stages in the early development of the child. Under these circumstances, the children are especially vulnerable to diseases caused by nutritional deficiency.

Cultural taboos can also be important indirect factors in illness. An individual may be prevented, by these taboos, from getting the proper information about avoiding illness. Control of syphilis and gonorrhea, for example, depends in part on adequate knowledge about their transmission, the use of contraceptives to prevent their transmission, adequate case finding of infected individuals, and prompt treatment of infected persons to prevent infection of others. Thus the cultural taboos against public discussion of sexual matters, including venereal disease, can prevent adequate public health campaigns. As was pointed out in Chapter 3, an intensive educational campaign during World War II did break thorugh the cultural taboos, and control of venereal disease was facilitated.

Social change, and the consequent disruption of established cultural patterns, may bring about many conditions that are conducive to illness. Change in economic position often means changes in nutritional patterns, but not necessarily for the better. New occupational hazards may be introduced. Shifts in behavioral patterns among family members may take away the sources of advice for prevention or treatment of illness, or may place intolerable strain on the physical and emotional capacities of parents and children. The current change in patterns of sexual activity, particularly among the young, and the difficulties in communication between generations, are at least responsible for the alarming reversal in venereal-disease rates and difficulties in control which currently face public health authorities. The drastic social changes occurring in many parts of the world today are having a significant effect on health and illness, a point which is considered again in Chapter 15.

ILLNESS AS A PSYCHOSOCIAL PHENOMENON

Illness is a universal phenomenon. Occurring in all societies, it forces the temporary disruption, to varying degrees, of regular patterns of social interaction and responsibilities. Fulfillment of normal tasks by the sick person is often impossible. At times the regular obligations of the patient's family cannot be carried out. Job, home, and community, the major locations of social roles, are all affected in one way or another by illness. At the same time, psychological balance is also threatened. Anxiety can be aroused, often deep and abiding anxiety, and depression may occur. Patterns of emotional response may emerge that are not characteristic of mature adult behavior, for illness provides an opportunity for many "childish" responses. Yet, because it is an experience of strong emotional significance, illness can be the impetus for the expression of great courage, love, and faith. As a social and psychological event illness is rarely uneventful, usually stressful, and occasionally devastating.

The Sick Role

Considering the ubiquitous nature of illness and its potentially disruptive effects, all societies need to have certain general expectations that define the obligations of the sick person and of those who interact with him. Thus the sickness may be contained, the disruptive effect reduced, and steps taken to restore social functioning. These general expectations can best be understood through the concept of the "sick role." As Mechanic has pointed out [31], this concept is like an ideal type, a framework for viewing behavior. The individual acts, of the sick person or others, only approximate the ideal type. Thus, there will be variations according to the individual, the conditions, and the social context. However, as a way of gaining perspective on the social properties of illness and of accounting for the uniformities in the behavior of ill persons in a given society, the concept of a sick role is useful.

Parson's Conception of the Sick Role. Parsons [37, 38] has defined the demands and expectations of the sick role in Western societies, particularly the United States, as follows: There is a disturbance of the capacity of the individual to perform ordinary tasks or roles in his social group, an incapacity which is "not his fault," not an act of conscious decision. Furthermore, the incapacity must be reversed by some kind of therapeutic process, natural or manmade. The ill person is more or less exempted from his normal obligations, the exemption varying in accordance with the nature and degree of his illness. Even a common cold carries with it some legitimate exemptions from social obligations. However, although being ill and being exempted from responsibilities is a legitimate state, in a social sense, this legitimacy is only partial and conditional. Illness is basically undesirable, socially speaking, and the person who is in the sick role has an obligation to try to get well and to cooperate with other people in that effort. Both the ill person and those responsible for his welfare have an obligation to seek technically competent help for the therapeutic process. In our society the principal source of such help is organized medicine.

The sick role, therefore, involves two rights and two duties. The rights are exemptions from normal social responsibilities and the recognition that the ill person is not to blame for his state. The obligations are a desire to get well and to seek technically competent help to achieve that end. As we shall see in a moment, these rights and obligations can conflict with deep-seated personality traits and cause strain in certain kinds of social groups.

The undesirable aspect of illness, in the social sense, is that illness is a form of deviance. Parsons differentiates between deviance that has a normative focus and that which has a situational focus, the former including immorality and crime. Within a situational focus, deviance involves an inability to meet commitments or to utilize one's capacities for performance. One might say that illness is therefore a kind of alienation in American society, alienation from a set of expectations that puts particular stress upon independent achievement. The passivity and dependence of the ill also characterize behavior which is counter to the activism of American society. Not only is the individual unable to perform his everyday tasks and roles, but he also cannot measure up to some of the values of his society.

Because it is a socially disruptive or deviant factor, illness cannot be allowed to spread, bacteriologically or motivationally. Thus, as we said earlier, the sick role is legitimate only in a conditional sense, meaning that the deviancy of the role must be recognized by the patient and his family, and that steps must be taken to get well, to move back into the "healthy role." When the sick person is a patient in a hospital or is in bed at home, he is permitted to indulge his dependency under strictly regulated conditions, the proviso being that sickness should only be a temporary state and that he should do everything he can to get well.

More Recent Conceptions. Parsons' formulation has been of great use to medical sociologists, but there is a tendency to regard it as unimodal. Only recently have studies been undertaken which reveal that social status affects the process of defining who is to be regarded as sick. This growing theoretical sophistication is reflected in Gordon's study [18]. In essence, he found that the poorer or more uncertain the prognosis, the greater the tendency to define someone as sick. Beyond that, however, there was an inverse relationship between socioeconomic status and the importance of physical incapacity as a factor in defining someone as sick. Upper socioeconomic groups used a wider range of conditions for the definition of sickness; lower socioeconomic groups were more likely to limit the conditions to some kind of physical incapacity. However, there were no differences among the socioeconomic groups regarding the way a sick person should be treated once he had been placed in that role.

Gordon also found evidence for a condition which he called *impaired role*. In the sick role the prognosis is likely to be serious and uncertain, and there is a consistent tendency to treat the sick person as dependent. In the impaired role, health is impaired but the prognosis is not serious, and there is a tendency to encourage the ill person to fulfill his personal and social responsibilities even though he is also encouraged to seek medical care.

The sick role is also a useful concept in analyzing certain reactions of institutions or societies. Mechanic [31] has listed a number of these. In time of war, admission to the sick role may become more stringent, especially in the army under combat conditions. The needs of the combat unit take precedence over individual needs, except when the individual soldier is incapacitated. Moreover, experience in recent wars has shown that when a soldier goes back to a base hospital, thus reinforcing his sick role, it is more difficult to get him ready for combat again than if his sick role is minimized by keeping him near the front lines.

In a wider sense, Field [12] describes how the Russians limited admission to the sick role during the early decades of the new society in order to keep more workers in the factories. Production took precedence over individual persons. In this case, as in the above, the physician had the responsibility of determining admission to the sick role, and thus was under pressure from both the social institution and the individual who tried to manipulate the system to his own advantage.

In our society the doctor is often asked to certify illness or justify a person's inability to comply with social demands. Exemption from military service is a current example, the attempt being to extend certain aspects of the sick role to areas that are pretty much unrelated to health or, in Gordon's sense, to make an impaired role into a sick role. Akin to this is the differentiation often made between "ill" and "bad," as in the attempt to define alcoholism as a disease rather than immoral behavior. Psychiatric practice is becoming more and more the ground where such differentiations are made. Changes in laws and court procedures, and the controversy surrounding these, are consequences. Mechanic points out, however, that labeling a person "sick" can have quite negative social consequences, especially in the psychiatric sphere. It is all too easy to use psychiatric labels for political purposes or to solve a sticky interpersonal or social situation by defining a person as emotionally ill, and acting accordingly.

The conflict between social expectations and the individual centers on the secondary gain which can accrue from the sick role. Being dependent may gratify a childlike need to be taken care of, to the point where symptoms may persist beyond reasonable limits, the patient may be reluctant to leave the hospital, or malingering may occur. Dependency may also offer an outlet for the gratification of aggressive needs through control over others. This may be short-range control, through demands for special foods, or long-range, through demands for job changes or special living arrangements. In a functional sense, the person occupying the sick role is abusing his rights to be taken care of by extending them into areas which are not immediate to the illness; thus, he is abrogating his responsibility to try to get well. Almost invariably, the ensuing social strains are wearing.

A further complication of the dependency of the sick is the conflict which may result when a patient has a strong need for autonomy and independence. For such people the enforced dependency may be very threatening. Some become sarcastic and disagreeable, thereby fighting the system which threatens them. Others may disregard medical advice or control, like the coronary patient who continues to lead a strenuous life against the recommendation of his physician. When the conflict is that serious, the threat of dependency may be felt to be even greater than the threat of death.

Assuming the Sick Role

Under certain circumstances, the movement to the sick role is a fairly clear-cut decision. In traumatic injury of serious proportions, or with the sudden occurrence of severe symptoms when none existed before, like sharp abdominal or chest pain, or blackouts, most individuals quickly seek medical aid. These conditions, however, do not constitute the great bulk of medical practice. Even surgeons see and treat a great many patients whose physical symptoms have existed for some time.

The decision to seek medical help, to legitimate the sick role both personally and socially, is one that has only recently come under systematic scrutiny by social scientists and physicians. The evidence thus far obtained suggests that the process of defining oneself as sick often involves social and psychological factors as much as physical ones. The recent studies of Zola [51, 52] and Stoeckle [43, 44] illustrate this relatively new and fascinating area of research into illness.

Zola interviewed newly admitted outpatients of the clinics of the Massachusetts General Hospital, selecting patients from Italian, Irish, and Anglo-Saxon Protestant groups. The interviews took place before the patient was seen by the doctor. Two major results emerged. Most of the patients had had symptoms for some time before they decided to consult a physician. The reactions to the symptoms and the reasons for finally coming to the clinic varied among the three ethnic groups to a statistically significant degree. Zola argues that a person accommodates himself to a set of symptoms, and that some break in that accommodation leads to the decision to seek medical care. This may not come when the patient is physically sickest. In other words, he found that the physical symptoms alone were not sufficient to force the decision. Some patients experienced an interpersonal crisis or an interference with social or personal relations. These were most often the Italian patients. Another deciding factor was what Zola calls "sanctioning"—one person takes the responsibility to seek aid for someone else, a husband for a wife, for example. This was most often true among the Irish. The Anglo-Saxons most often made the decision because their symptoms interfered in some way with work or physical functioning. Zola sums this up as follows:

> For our patients the symptoms were "really" there, but their perception differed considerably. There *is* a sense in which they sought help because they could not stand it any longer. But what they could not stand was more likely to be a situation or a perceived implication of a symptom rather than any worsening of the symptom *per se* [52].

Stoeckle and Davidson [43, 44] have argued that the concept of crisis, in a psychological or social sense, helps us to understand the process of deciding to get medical help, and that the physician who treats the patient needs to pay as much attention to the crisis and the interpersonal "triggers" as he does to the physical symptoms. To the patient, the former may be just as important as the latter.

Illness and the Concept of Self

Illness, once admitted, poses a series of threats, not the least of which may be death. Although the illness may be one that will improve without help, or a condition that can be treated successfully by modern medicine, thoughts of death may be introduced, even though fleetingly. The more serious or ambiguous the illness, the more likely that death will be on the patient's mind at some point. Reduced functioning can also be viewed as a threat, temporary in many cases but more lasting in others, as in the coronary patient. Reduced functioning involves a sense of loss, of incompleteness; if long-continued, it will necessitate a shift in the conception an individual has of himself and his body. Of a different nature is the threat induced by the change in customary routines and relationships, reflected in a decrease of function within the family or job. Social homeostasis, as well as biological homeostasis, is disturbed in illness.

When there is threat, anxiety is aroused and ego mechanisms are brought into play in order to control and minimize the anxiety. Chief among these seems to be emotional regression, a slipping back to the kinds of reactions that are more indicative of childhood than of mature adulthood [10, 29]. In this regression the ill person may manifest a number of different kinds of behavior. One is egocentricity, a concern about himself and his problem that pushes other interests to the periphery of attention. He wants to talk about *his* illness and *his* pain, not illness or pain in the abstract. A visitor's recital of former operations is of little interest to him, and he may impatiently shift the conversation back to his own case. His illness is the center of his world.

There may be an exaggerated concern with trifling matters that relate to the self, such as having others attend to his wants, provide services, often do errands that would ordinarily be of little concern to him. The extreme is the sickroom despot: dominant, intolerant, and infuriating to doctor, nurse, and family. The caricature is the husband who is home in bed with a cold, running his wife ragged with his demands for service and his whims of every sort. In most cases, however, we do have a person who perceives the situation around him more subjectively than he usually would.

Egocentricity and constriction of interests may be due in part to the physiological effects of illness, to a narrowing of the perceptual range which is associated with fever, altered blood composition, or other factors. In part, the exemption from normal responsibilities contributes to the constriction: The amount of sensory input—especially of symbolic material—is reduced, and therefore a variety of interests is no longer stimulated. In part, the cause of the constriction may be that the organism is fighting disease and injury; by excluding thoughts of other matters, energy can be concentrated on the process of getting well. Whatever the cause, an avid baseball fan may be quite unconcerned that his team is languishing in the cellar, a manufacturer undismayed by a threatened strike in his plant, a professor oblivious to the fact that there is no one to take his classes. Clearly, it is unwise to ask such sick persons to make decisions or expect them to help with matters outside the sick room.

As part of the regression, there may be an exaggerated emotional reactivity. Many patients cry more easily, or lose their tempers, but of especial significance is the increased need for help, attention, and affection [24]. The prescription of TLC—tender, loving care—so often heard in nursing circles is a prime need of many patients. Its absence can be a source of bitter complaints about members of the patient's family or the hospital personnel [1, 2, 7, 13, 27]. On the other hand, most patients are grateful for attentions from friends and family, for personal consideration by nurses or doctors, for actions small or large that symbolically indicate affection. Many of these patients would not feel so strong a need for affection-indicating actions were they well and leading a normal life.

There is still another kind of behavior that is related to the regression process, behavior which involves some subtle shifts in the perception of people in the environment. In particular, physicians and nurses are subject to this shift, but if the ill person is hospitalized, other kinds of people may also be involved. Putting the shift in terms of role, medical care personnel may be invested, on an unconscious level, with role characteristics of family members, particularly of mother and father [10]. Because the physician has great and perhaps ultimate responsibility for the patient, because he seems all-wise and all-powerful, his relationship to the patient may be perceived by the latter much like that of father to child. Patterns of behavior which characterized the father-child relationship may, therefore, be projected into dealings with the doctor, whether these be patterns of submission, rebellion, or dogged stubbornness. The nurse may be invested with characteristics of the mother's role, so that she becomes what one anthropologist, LaBarre, has called the "id mother" [28]. Thus the patient may perceive the nurse as comforting, protecting, supporting, as meeting his needs for help, and as giving him security in his state of dependence. As with perceptions of the doctor, both conscious and unconscious manifestations of the perception may be present. The intensity and instability of emotional reaction can lead the patient to expressions of sincere appreciation at one point and, at other times, of rage and frustration. If she accepts the emotional reactivity of the patient for what it is and does not allow herself to become disturbed, the nurse can be a more powerful force in speeding the patient's physical and psychological recovery.

The Sick Person and His Family

Since the nuclear family is the crucial social unit in our present society, there are potential stresses inherent in the relationship between the ill person and his family, stresses which are not likely to be as severe in an extended family. Parsons and Fox [39] argue that the great increase of hospital facilities in our society is attributable not only to technological advances but also to the vulnerabilities of the small family in sickness. They feel that the emotional intensity of our family relationships allows little room for absorbing shock. They also suggest that most American families find it difficult to maintain a good balance between the supportive and dependent aspects of sickness, on the one hand, and the disciplinary aspects of treatment, on the other. These stresses can be minimized if the seriously ill person is treated outside the family, particularly in the hospital. The reluctance of physicians to treat serious illness elsewhere than in the hospital, even when necessary care could be given at home, may stem in part from an intuition that the ensuing strain would be a factor to contend with in treatment. Parsons and Fox's interpretation is made from strictly a functional point of view, in the sociological sense. It is difficult to test, but has marked heuristic value.

A useful framework for analyzing the problem of the relationship between the ill person and his family is that of role allocation and its meaning within the family. Particularly relevant is the way in which allocation and its meaning may vary in families from different social classes and ethnic groups. Work, authority or decision making, and emotional support or affection are the areas that will make the point clear.

Work, or "the job," affects family life differently throughout the class structure [25]. In the upper-middle class a career, especially in the business world, is likely to dominate. Family life is built around the exigencies of the career. Interference with work for an extended period of time or at certain crucial points may disrupt the career. Frequent illness, long-term illness, or illness at a specific point in time may, therefore, jeopardize chances of advancement. The sickness of the husband or wife may affect the man's career, either by taking the husband out of the career line temporarily or by reducing his wife's support of his career-oriented activities. In the working class, a job does not play such a central place in the family; it is viewed largely as a means of obtaining the material things of life, rather than as an end in itself. Illness is not likely to affect seniority and, if there is a company insurance plan, the financial burden may not be overwhelming. This is not to say that illness in a working-class family is not disruptive but that its effect, in terms of roles, is subtly different.

Families also vary in the division of authority and responsibility for decisions, a factor often affected by ethnic background and traditional family structure. When the decision-making process is shared by husband and wife, the illness of one will not seriously affect that process. Second or third-generation urban American families frequently have this kind of division of responsibility. If, however, decisions are usually made by the husband and his authority is not questioned, difficulties can arise when he becomes ill. The wife may not have the training to make decisions or may be reluctant to do so. When other male members of the extended family are not present to take over the authority, she may become very anxious and find it difficult not to communicate the anxiety to her ill partner. In some rural families, in Spanish-American families, or in first-generation families with a patriarchical organization, the husband's illness can pose a serious threat to the effective functioning of the family unit.

Finally, the question of emotional support can be viewed in terms of allocation among family members. Frequently the wife-mother is called upon to assume the greatest share of support-giving activities, especially if the husband's energies are directed toward a career. When she becomes ill the affective fabric of the family may be strained. Perhaps this is not a serious problem in most families, because her illness may be short or adjustments of function can be made by other family members, but it is a potential threat.

Reaction to illness is in part an individual psychological phenomenon based on adjustment to the anxiety induced by fear of death, mutilation, or reduced functioning. In the last analysis each person must face these anxieties on his own, for although others can help him, the core of his psychological world is himself. The reaction to illness is, at the same time, a social phenomenon, affecting the pattern of relationships between the ill person and others close to him, particularly his family. The demands and expectations that go with social roles are disrupted by illness, not only for the ill person, but also for those with whom he has reciprocal relationships. Individual and social reactions to illness do not exist apart from each other, even though they have been separated here for analytical purposes, and a full understanding of the implications of illness must consider both the idiosyncrasies of the individual and the milieu in which he lives.

REFERENCES

1. ABDELLAH, F. G. AND E. LEVINE, "Developing a Measure of Patient and Personnel Satisfaction with Nursing Care," *Nursing Research*, 5 (February, 1957), 100–108.
2. ———, "Polling Patients and Personnel," *Hospitals*, 31 (November 1, 1957; December 1, 1957), 44–48, 53–57.
3. ALEXANDER, FRANZ, *Psychosomatic Medicine*. New York: W. W. Norton & Company, Inc., 1950.
4. ARGYRIS, CHRIS, *Diagnosing Human Relations in Organizations: A Case Study of a Hospital*. New Haven: Labor and Management Center, Yale University, 1956.
5. ———, *Personality and Organization: The Conflict Between System and the Individual*. New York: Harper & Row, Publishers, Inc., 1957.
6. AX, A. F., "The Physiological Differentiation between Fear and Anger in Humans," *Psychosomatic Medicine*, 15 (1953), 433–42.

7. Berg, R. H., "A Report on Hospitals," *Look*, February 3, 1959, 15–19.
8. Cannon, Walter B., *The Wisdom of the Body*. New York: W. W. Norton & Company, Inc., 1932.
9. Cohen, S. I. and A. J. Silverman, "Psychophysiological Investigations of Vascular Response Variability," *Journal of Psychosomatic Research*, 3 (1959), 185–210.
10. Dichter, Ernest, "A Psychological Study of the Hospital-Patient Relationship" series: "What the Patient Really Wants from the Hospital" *Modern Hospital*, 83, September 1954, pp. 51–54, 136; "The Patient's Greatest Need is Security" *Modern Hospital*, 83, October 1954, pp. 56–58, 134; "How "Secure" is Your Hospital?" *Modern Hospital*, 83, November 1954, pp. 61–63; "How to Make Your Hospital 'Secure' " *Modern Hospital*, 83, December 1954, pp. 69–73; "What the Community Thinks of the Hospital", *Modern Hospital*, 84, January 1955, pp. 74–77.
11. Dubos, Rene, "The Gold Headed Cane in the Laboratory," in National Institutes of Health, *Annual Lectures*. Washington, D.C.: Government Printing Office, 1953, pp. 89–102.
12. Field, Mark, *Doctor and Patient in Soviet Russia*. Cambridge: Harvard University Press.
13. Freidson, Eliot and Jacob J. Feldman, *The Public Looks at Hospitals*, Health Information Foundation Research Series, No. 4, New York, 1958.
14. Friedman, M. and R. H. Rosenman, "Association of Specific Overt Behavior Pattern with Blood and Cardiovascular Findings," *Journal of the American Medical Association*, 169 (March 21, 1959), 1286–96.
15. ——— and V. Carrol, "Changes in the Serum Cholesterol and Blood Clotting Time in Men Subjected to Cyclic Variation of Occupational Stress," *Circulation*, 17 (May, 1958), 852–61.
16. Funkenstein, Daniel H., Stanley H. King, and Margaret Drolette, *Mastery of Stress*. Cambridge: Harvard University Press, 1957.
17. Gitelson, M., "A Critique of Current Concepts in Psychosomatic Medicine," *Bulletin of the Menninger Clinic*, 23 (1959), 165–78.
18. Gordon, Gerald, *Role Theory and Illness*. New Haven, Conn.: College and University Press, 1966.
19. Hawkins, N. G. and T. H. Holmes, "Environmental Considerations in Tuberculosis: Ecologic Factors in Tuberculosis Morbidity," in *Transactions of the National Tuberculosis Association*, 50, 1954, 233–38. National Tuberculosis Association, New York.
20. Hinkle, L. E., "Ecological Observations on the Relation of Physical Illness, Mental Illness, and the Social Environment," Psychosomatic Medicine, 23 (July–August, 1961), 289–97.
21. ——— et al., "An Investigation of the Relation between Life Experience, Personality Characteristics, and General Susceptibility to Illness," *Psychosomatic Medicine*, 20 (July–August, 1958), 278–95.
22. Holmes, T. H. et al., "Psychosocial and Psychophysiologic Studies of Tuberculosis," *Psychosomatic Medicine*, 19 (March–April, 1957), 134–43.
23. Jelliffe, D. B., "Social Culture and Nutrition," *Pediatrics*, 20 (July, 1957), 128–38.
24. Joseph, A., "Physician and Patient," *Applied Anthropology*, 1 (1942), 1–6.
25. Kahl, Joseph A., *The American Class Structure*. New York: Holt, Rinehart & Winston, Inc., 1953.
26. Kaplan, H. I. and H. S. Kaplan, "Current Theoretical Concepts in Psychosomatic Medicine," *American Journal of Psychiatry*, 115 (June, 1959), 1091–96.
27. Koos, E. L., " 'Metropolis': What City People Think of their Medical Services," *American Journal of Public Health*, 45 (December, 1955), 1551–57.
28. LaBarre, W., "The Patient and His Families," in *Casework Papers 1958*. New York: Family Service Association of America, 1958, pp. 61–71.
29. Lederer, H. D., "How the Sick View Their World," *Journal of Social Issues*, 8 (1952), 4–16.
30. Margolin, S. G., "Genetic and Dynamic Psychophysiological Determinants of Pathophysiological Processes," in

F. Deutsch, ed., *The Psychosomatic Concept in Psychoanalysis.* New York: International Universities Press, Inc., 1953.
31. MECHANIC, DAVID, *Medical Sociology.* New York: The Free Press, 1968.
32. MENDELSON, M., S. HIRSCH, AND C. S. WEBBER, "A Critical Examination of Some Recent Theoretical Models in Psychosomatic Medicine," *Psychosomatic Medicine*, 18 (October, 1956), 363–73.
33. MICHAELS, J. J., "A Psychiatric Adventure in Comparative Pathophysiology of the Infant and Adult with some Theoretical Suggestions in regard to Regression in Somatic Visceral Functions," *Journal of Nervous and Mental Diseases*, 100 (1944), 49–63.
34. MIRSKY, I. A., "Psychoanalysis and the Biological Sciences," in F. Alexander and H. Ross, eds., *Twenty Years of Psychoanalysis.* New York: W. W. Norton & Company, Inc., 1953.
35. MORDKOFF, A. M. AND O. A. PARSONS, "The Coronary Personality: A Critique," *Psychosomatic Medicine*, 29 (1967), 1–14.
36. OSTFIELD, A. M., B. Z. LOBOVITS, R. B. SHEKELLE, AND O. PAUL, "A Prospective Study of the Relationship between Personality and Coronary Heart Disease," *Journal of Chronic Diseases*, 17 (1964), 265–76.
37. PARSONS, TALCOTT, *The Social System.* New York: The Free Press, 1951.
38. ———, "Definitions of Health and Illness in the Light of American Values and Social Structure," in E. Gartly Jaco, ed., *Patients, Physicians, and Illness.* New York: The Free Press, 1958, pp. 165–87.
39. ——— AND R. FOX, "Illness, Therapy, and the Modern Urban American Family," *Journal of Social Issues*, 8 (1952), 31–44.
40. REEDER, L. G., "The Socioeconomic Effects of Heart Disease," *Social Problems*, 4 (July, 1956), 367–71.
41. REISER, MORTON F., "Reflections on Interpretation of Psychophysiologic Experiments," *Psychosomatic Medicine*, 23 (September–October, 1961), 430–39.
42. RUSSEK, H. I., "Role of Heredity, Diet, and Emotional Stress in Coronary Heart Disease," *Journal of the American Medical Association*, 171 (October 3, 1959), 503–508.
43. STOECKLE, J. D. AND G. E. DAVIDSON, "The Use of 'Crisis' as an Orientation for the Study of Patients in a Medical Clinic," *Journal of Medical Education*, 37: 6 (June, 1962), Part I.
44. STOECKLE, J. D., I. K. ZOLA, AND G. E. DAVIDSON, "On Going to See the Doctor: The Contributions of the Patient to the Decision to Seek Medical Aid," *Journal of Chronic Diseases*, 16 (September, 1963), 975–89.
45. SZASZ, T. S., "Psychoanalysis and the Autonomic Nervous System," *Psychoanalytic Review*, 39 (1952), 115–51.
46. WEINER, H., M. THALER, M. F. REISER, AND I. A. MIRSKY, "Etiology of Duodenal Ulcer: I. Relation of Specific Psychological Characteristics to Rate of Gastric Secretion (Serum Pepsinogen)," *Psychosomatic Medicine*, 19 (January–February, 1957), 1–10.
47. WOLF, S. AND H. G. WOLFF, "Evidence on the Genesis of Peptic Ulcer in Man," *Journal of the American Medical Association*, 120 (October 31, 1942), 670–75.
48. WOLFF, H. G., "Changes in the Vulnerability of Tissue: An Aspect of Man's Response to Threat, in National Institutes of Health, *Annual Lectures.* Washington, D.C.: Government Printing Office, 1953, pp. 38–71.
49. ———, "Protective Reaction Patterns and Disease," *Annals of Internal Medicine*, 27 (1947), 944–69.
50. ———, *Stress and Disease.* Springfield, Ill.: Charles C Thomas, Publisher, 1953.
51. ZOLA, I. K., "Culture and Symptoms: An Analysis of Patients' Presenting Complaints," *American Sociological Review*, 31 (October, 1966), 615–30.
52. ———, "Pathways to the Doctor: From Person to Patient," Resource Paper for the 1st International Conference on Social Science and Medicine, Aberdeen, Scotland, Sept. 4–6, 1968 (mimeographed).

6

THE "ADDICTIVE" DISORDERS AS SOCIOENVIRONMENTAL HEALTH PROBLEMS

Edward A. Suchman

The health of man is rooted in his environment. Environmental conditions affect the growth and development of etiological agents of disease and the exposure and resistance of man as the susceptible host. In recent years, since the relatively successful conquest of the communicable diseases and the rapid growth in importance of the chronic degenerative diseases, increased attention has been focused on the social as well as the physical aspects of man's environment. How man lives has become as important as where he lives.

SOCIOENVIRONMENTAL FACTORS IN HEALTH

Socioenvironmental factors determine how man lives; thus these factors are intimately related to an individual's exposure and susceptibility to disease. His group memberships, his family structure, his work and his recreation all influence where he lives, what he eats, and how he sleeps and exercises, and these in turn determine his physical and mental state of health. Socioenvironmental factors, furthermore, advance or impede the progress of an illness after its onset; they are largely responsible for an individual's awareness of and interpretation of symptoms, his arrangements for medical care, and his behavior as a patient.

On a much broader level, changes in the physical environment, brought about by modified social conditions, may effect subsequent changes in a community's state of health. The development of cities and suburbs, the shifts in demographic composition of the population, and the changes in customs and morals, have had a marked impact on the levels of health of community members and on the quality and quantity of medical care which they receive.

There is a complex interplay between socioenvironmental factors, social problems, health conditions, and public-health programs. Each may lead to the other in myriad ways. For example, poor housing (a physical condition) may lead to the growth of slums (a social problem), which in turn increases exposure to tuberculosis (a health condition), which then requires the development of a preventive and therapeutic measure (a public health program). On the other hand, certain public health problems, such as venereal disease, become social problems as they impinge upon the value structure of the community. Moralistic attitudes may interfere with scientific analysis; both the diagnosis and treatment of the health problem often become areas of conflict between medical and lay forces [77].

The interaction between health problems and social values underlies much of the current controversy in the field of the so-called "addictive" disorders. Socioenvironmental forces have created a class of sociomedical pathology, such as alcoholism and narcotics addiction, which must be viewed as both social and medical problems. This interrelationship is a reciprocal one. On the one hand, a social problem such as juvenile delinquency may lead to a medical problem, e.g., narcotics addiction; on the other hand, narcotics addiction may lead to juvenile delinquency.

In actuality, the social and health aspects of the problems considered in this chapter cannot be clearly isolated from each other. Certain social and health problems are so closely related that the value system of a society will do much to determine their definition and the types of corrective actions that can be taken. This premise underlies much of the current controversy in the field of addictive disorders.

THE ADDICTIVE DISORDERS

An addiction is primarily a man-made illness which has its roots in socioenvironmental conditions. The addiction is a behavioral disorder which may lead to an organic condition harmful to the individual's health and society's welfare. The motivating factors frequently are embedded in the psychological needs of the individual, but his exposure to and use of the addictive substances is largely determined by his social environment. Clausen views drug use as a manifestation of the social disorganization of slum environments [22]. Elsewhere [21], Clausen offers a sociological analysis of the use of drugs.

The judicious use of most addictive substances is beneficial to man; abused, they create serious medical and social problems. Their capacity to make man forget his physical and mental aches and pains is the source of both their strength and danger. Inhibiting as they do the individual's control over his own actions, their use—or at least their overuse—becomes subject to moral judgment. Their uncontrolled use is apt to evoke social condemnation rather than sympathy, and to result in legal punishment rather than medical care.

Currently, the most important of these addictive substances is alcohol; next in importance are the narcotizing drugs such as heroin, morphine, cocaine, and opium. In recent years, marijuana, barbiturates, amphetamines, and a whole new array of tranquilizers and hallucinogens have taken their place alongside the natural drugs as relievers of physical pain and mental distress—and enslavers of all those who cannot regulate their dependency upon them.

Historically, man has always sought respite from the trials and tribulations of daily life in certain drugs, herbs, and potions which have the capacity of relieving tension and anxiety and transforming reality. In many societies these drugs have attained acceptance and even approval. Their use is often associated with ceremonial occasions, and various rituals have developed to govern when and how they are to be taken. Why, then, do they constitute an important social and public-health problem today?

The answer to this question lies in the tremendous influence of public opinion in defining the legitimate concerns of medicine and public health. A health condition typically becomes a public-health problem when a society or an important segment of its members develops the necessary concern to demand remedial medical action. It is only in recent years that alcoholism and drug addiction have gained prominence as public-health problems—but the basis for concern is still to be found not so much in the medical as in the social consequences of these disorders. Although alcohol and narcotics can have detrimental effects upon the physical health of the individual, it is their effect upon his social behavior which alarms society and elicits a demand for legal and public-health action.

There is no universally accepted definition of "addiction." Medically, the term is largely restricted to those substances which produce a physiological dependence. The body develops a physical need for the drug in order to function normally, and withholding the drug produces withdrawal sickness, an abstinence syndrome of definite physical and mental symptoms. Thus, there is a distinction between habit-forming substances such as tobacco and coffee, which create a psychological dependency, and addictive drugs such as the opiate derivatives which result in a true physical dependency.

While this distinction has pharmacological significance, it is not of major importance for understanding the type of sociomedical problem created by the development of a dependency, either psychological or physical, upon such substances as alcohol or narcotics. We will therefore accept as our definition of addiction "any behavioral disorder resulting from the repetitive use of and subsequent craving for some particular substance." Thus, alcohol may not create a true physical dependence, but it does produce a behavioral disorder based upon an uncontrollable need, which results in a sociomedical problem of major proportions.

The general view is that the processes of addiction involve a combination of: (1) psychological need, which makes the host susceptible to the promise of relief through use of the addictive substance; (2) social pressure and support from a subgroup of addicted individuals; and (3) environmental conditions which make the addictive substance and the means for its use available. The process itself, once initiated, becomes self-reinforcing. The temporary relief from stress may make the act itself rewarding, and a psychological dependence is built up in which the individual forsakes other means of alleviating his tensions and anxieties.

In the case of some narcotics, an actual physiological dependence may be created—that is, the body needs the addictive substance. Unsuccessful experiences with abstinence, accompanied by painful withdrawal symptoms, create the self-image of one hopelessly "hooked," and the self-definition as an addict. Rejection by the larger society and segregation with others like himself may lead to the development of subgroup values and customs which further reinforce the addictive pattern and the development of deviant, antisocial behavior. The addictive process indeed is a vicious chain of events which requires a concentrated attack at many different points and from many different approaches. The currently high rate of recidivism of both alcoholics and narcotic addicts bears witness to the inadequacy of traditional forms of medical treatment.

In the last decade, a relatively new form of drug use has entered the scene. These are the so-called "soft" drugs, such as marijuana, the amphetamines, barbiturates, and hallucinogens [26]. The use of these drugs is largely associated with the desire for new experiences or "kicks," rather than with escape from painful living conditions. As such, they have become the symbol of a rebellious youth culture; users tend to be concentrated among young people, including the middle and upper classes. The smoking of marijuana, especially among students, has grown so rapidly in the past five years as to rank today as one of the foremost problems of drug use. As described by President Nixon:

> Several million college students have at least experimented with marijuana, hashish, LSD, amphetamines or barbiturates. . . . It is doubtful that an American parent can send a son or daughter to college today without exposing the young man or woman to drug abuse. Parents must also be concerned about the availability and use of such drugs in our high schools and junior high schools [79].

ALCOHOLISM

It is necessary to distinguish between the social use of alcohol and chronic alcoholism. As a form of social behavior, drinking is deeply rooted in the folkways and mores of Western society [68]. As a means of escape from tension and anxiety, drinking may satisfy some of the psychological needs of the individual, and many people consume alcoholic beverages without developing a dependency upon them. The temporary effects of alcohol create many social problems—social drinking is a major cause of automobile and pedestrian accidents [70]—but as a habit-forming substance with deleterious effects upon organic structure and function, alcohol also creates a major medical problem.

Definition and Description of Alcoholism

As defined by the World Health Organization, alcoholism is "a chronic illness that manifests itself as a disorder of behavior. It is characterized by the repeated usage of alcoholic beverages to an extent that exceeds customary dietary use or compliance with social customs of the community and that interferes with the drinker's health or his economic or social functioning" [30]. According to the American Medical Association, alcoholism refers to "those excessive drinkers, whose dependence on alcohol has attained such a degree that it shows a noticeable disturbance or interference with their bodily or mental health, their interpersonal relations, and their satisfactory social and economic functioning."

From these definitions it is apparent that alcoholism, as an individual and public health problem, is largely determined by personal circumstances and public reaction rather than by an objective medical symptomatology and diagnosis. The World Health Organization makes a further distinction, between two types of regular drinkers —the "habitual symptomatic excessive drinkers" and the "addictive drinkers." The habitual, symptomatic, excessive drinker places greatest emphasis on the duration of drinking bouts rather than on their intensity. His drinking is planned to enable him to maintain a limited level of effect from alcohol for as long a time as possible. The addictive drinker, on the other hand, seeks to attain a maximum degree of intoxication in as short a time as possible. He seems to have an impulsive drive to raise the level of concentration of alcohol in the blood as quickly as possible.

These are apparently only two of the many different patterns that alcoholism may assume. Jellinek has recently hypothesized five different patterns, representing different stages of alcoholism [41]. The American Public Health Association describes the following five "drinking states": (1) nondrinkers; (2) social drinkers; (3) episodic-excessive drinkers; (4) progressive-excessive drinkers; and (5) chronic alcoholics [24]. This individual variation makes it extremely difficult to diagnose alcoholism except in the most advanced stages, and furthermore necessitates an individualistic therapeutic approach to each patient.

Recently, a highly significant new focus of interest, upon social and "problem drinking," rather than on alcoholism, has developed [62]. This approach does not attempt to define or identify alcoholism as a disease, but instead examines the frequency, circumstances, and consequences of drinking practices [61]. As defined by the Cooperative Commission on the Study of Alcoholism, "The term 'alcohol problem' . . . refers . . . to any drinking behavior that is defined or experienced as a problem" [1]. The emphasis is upon the social and economic difficulties created by the individual's drinking patterns, rather than on the physiological or medical effects. It is recognized that a sizable proportion of individuals drink alcohol (about 70 percent, of whom 40 percent are regular drinkers), but that most of these have no "drinking problems" [14, 53]. Etiological studies and treatment programs attempt to determine the causes of variations in drinking patterns and their attendant problems and to develop preventive and rehabilitative programs based upon the social functioning of the individual, even as a drinker, rather than to bring about medical cures for alcoholism [6]. This approach is particularly relevant to drinking among youth—a problem which is receiving increasing attention [5, 75].

The Extent and Distribution of Alcoholism

Statistics concerning the extent and distribution of alcoholism are not very reliable. The prevalence and incidence of a disease is measured in terms of morbidity and mortality statistics, but because of the social stigma attached to alcoholism, an unknown number of cases remain hidden. Many physicians are reluctant to report alcoholism as a cause of death; chronic alcoholics are frequently institutionalized without being reported; and in many other cases private physicians, clinics, and hospitals refuse to accept alcoholics for treatment [76]. Most existing statistics come from arrests for drunkenness or various admissions to mental hospitals, which are inherently selective and biased. A true count of alcoholism would require specially designed field studies of total populations, an extremely difficult task [37].

Granted these shortcomings, it has been estimated that there are about five million problem drinkers in the United States, and alcoholism is commonly regarded as the fourth most important public health problem [27]. The rate of alcoholism varies—Nevada and California are in first and second place, respectively, and Alabama is in last place. Rates in urban areas exceed rural ones. Among the larger cities, San Francisco ranks first, followed by Boston and Los Angeles, in that order. Of the five million problem drinkers, one million are considered chronic alcoholics. This represents a prevalence rate of 2.4 percent for the total population. Cases are largely concentrated among males twenty years of age and older. Mulford found that, contrary to popular belief, the proportion of the population that drinks tends to increase with income, occupational level, and education [53].

According to Keller and Efron, the rate of alcoholism in the United States showed an increase of 44 percent between 1940 and 1953. This increase was larger among women than men, greatest in New England, and smallest in the Pacific region. The authors suggest, however, that the "increases" may be an artifact of improved diagnosis and more complete reporting [43].

Using a formula based on the relationship of cirrhosis of the liver and the occurrence of identifiable mental or physical sequelae to excessive consumption, the World Health Organization places the United States first, with an alcoholism rate—with and without complications—of 4,390 per 100,000 adults. The United States is followed by France with a rate of 2,850 per 100,000; Italy is lowest with a rate of only 500 per 100,000. In general, the rates of alcoholism are estimated to be lowest in the Mediterranean countries and in China, and highest in Northeast Europe [29].

Alcoholism kills more people in France than in all the other major Western industrialized countries put together. Per 100,000 population, the French death rate from alcoholism was 12, compared with 1.4 in the United States and 0.1 in England and Wales. In the death rate from cirrhosis, France led with 34.2; followed by Portugal, 30.4; Chile, 29.8; Austria, 26.9; Italy, 22.9; and West Germany, 22.5 [85].

Bales discusses the influence of drinking customs on the rate of alcoholism [7]. In general, the Jews and Italians appear to have an exceptionally low rate of alcoholism; the Irish, a high rate. The low alcoholism rate among the Jews and Italians may stem from their use of alcohol as a mealtime beverage or as part of solemn ceremonial occasions [69].

The frequency of chronic alcoholism is also found to vary with sex and age. It is more prevalent among males between 35 and 55 years of age. The ratio of male to female alcoholics in the United States is about 5 to 1; in Great Britain, 2 to 1; and in Scandinavia,

23 to 1. These differences underscore the socioenvironmental basis of this disease, since they probably arise from the differing status of women in these countries. Little is known about the female drinker, although in general she arouses more concern and social disapproval than the man. Gelber offers several interesting suggestions for research on women drinkers [34].

Social Factors in the Etiology of Alcoholism

Alcoholism has often been referred to as a symptom rather than a disease in itself. Excessive drinking may be regarded as the outward manifestation of some underlying social or psychological condition which creates the need for alcohol—e.g., the need to escape from feelings of inadequacy, insecurity, anxiety, or depression. A combination of psychological need and social custom underlies the development of this form of addictive behavior.

According to Fox, alcoholics may be grouped into three categories:

1. Situational drinkers who . . . . turn to drink to see them through difficult situations. These situational drinkers may or may not be able to return to controlled drinking.
2. Secondary addicts who find that after years of steady drinking they can no longer resume controlled drinking.
3. Primary addicts who are basically maladjusted and use alcohol to help them meet their daily social and psychological problems [33].

Several investigators have proposed a single type of alcoholic personality —an individual whose psychological makeup predisposes him to alcohol [51].

Nevertheless, although many alcoholics do exhibit such traits as anxiety and compulsiveness, there are many others who do not. There are also many individuals who possess these same traits, who do not become addicted. At the present time there does not seem to be sufficient evidence to warrant the identification of any single personality type as especially prone to alcoholism.

Plaut offers the following model for understanding the etiological factors in the making of a problem drinker:

An individual who (1) responds to beverage alcohol in a certain way, perhaps physiologically determined, by experiencing intense relief and relaxation, and who (2) has certain personality characteristics, such as difficulty in dealing with and overcoming depression, frustration, and anxiety, and who (3) is a member of a culture in which there is both pressure to drink and culturally induced guilt and confusion regarding what kinds of drinking behavior are appropriate, is more likely to develop trouble than will most other persons [61].

The Consequences of Alcoholism

The personal, social, and economic costs of excessive use of alcohol run high. The personal disintegration that accompanies chronic alcoholism destroys not only the drinker but also entangles almost all other individuals close to him. It has been estimated that there are some ten million wives, husbands, parents, or children in the United States who must live with the alcoholic and who suffer from his disordered behavior. Alcoholism is a major concomitant of divorce. The social costs of alcoholism include the expense of maintaining a large number of community facilities—police, courts, prisons, welfare agencies, hospital and medical-care facilities, family and domestic-relations organizations—which expend a large share of their resources in dealing with alcoholics or the people affected by them.

The National Council on Alcoholism points out that 70 percent of the compulsive alcoholics are employed. Economically, the costs of alcohol to industry in terms of their absenteeism, decreased productivity, hospitalization and medical expenses, accidents, and turnover have been estimated in the billions of dollars. These costs do not include the indirect effects, inefficiency due to hangovers and the negative effect on the morale of other workers [25]. Alcohol has also been implicated as a major cause of automobile accidents [38].

Social Factors in the Control of Alcoholism

The prevention, treatment, and control of alcoholism may be approached from three points of view: medical, psychological, and social. Medically, the problem involves the care of the chronic alcoholic, especially during periods of acute alcoholism. Many private physicians are still reluctant to take alcoholics as patients, and some public hospitals continue to refuse to admit patients classified as alcoholics [75]. Their reluctance is understandable in view of the extremely low rate of cures; nevertheless, most alcoholics require physical rehabilitation before they can start the long, hard road back—and medical care is an essential part of the therapeutic process.

One form of emotional support and guidance comes from an organization known as Alcoholics Anonymous. Composed of alcoholics who attempt to help each other, this organization apparently has one of the best records for cures. Organized in 1935, it now has more than 10,000 groups in the United States alone, and more than 300,000 members [80].

In addition to medical, psychiatric, and social approaches to the treatment of alcoholism, there is a broader public health approach which stresses community responsibility [24, 63]. More and more, voluntary and public social agencies are establishing community programs for the care and rehabilitation of alcoholics, and less reliance is being placed upon prisons and mental hospitals. Communities are beginning to provide shelters where alcoholics can stay while receiving care, out-patient clinics for treatment, counseling and guidance centers, rehabilitation services, and follow-up care by public-health nurses. In addition to these increased community services, which no longer condemn the alcoholic to a skid-row existence, public-health educational programs are being introduced into schools and throughout the community.

Public health education about alcoholism is particularly sensitive to the underlying conflict between viewing alcoholism as a medical condition and public morality. There are many who believe that open discussion, especially in the public schools, only increases curiosity and undermines the resistance of the listeners. Such conflict between objective medical care and the subjective value system of a society is a major characteristic of these so-called "social" diseases. Rather than discuss the condition openly, large segments of society would choose to suffer the disease. And even when education and discussion are permitted, the emphasis is usually upon abstinence rather than upon recognition of the discrepancy between public behavior and public morality. Thus, health education about alcoholism in public schools usually advocates total abstinence—despite the fact that a large majority of all adults drink.

Impinging as these diseases do upon public morality, legislative and judicial measures are apt to be invoked in an attempt to deal with them. A large number of all arrests are for drunkenness (Kruse [46] estimates 40 percent). The ill-fated Eighteenth Amendment prohibited the manufacture, sale, or use of alcoholic beverages. The Cooperative Commission on the Study of Alcoholism found the traditional approach by the courts, police, and prisons to the handling of drunkenness "inhuman as well as ineffective." They recommended that "Public drunkenness should be approached as a medical-social rather than as a legal-criminal problem" [62]. The report of President Johnson's Crime Commission recommended elimination of all public-drunkenness laws.

DRUG ADDICTION

The second major addictive disorder today is the use of drugs, especially narcotics [55, 82]. Like alcoholism, drug addiction may be viewed as a symptom of an underlying behavioral disorder rather than as a disease in its own right, although the personality problem of the alcoholic may be quite different from that of the narcotic addict. Alcohol tends to make a person aggressive, while most narcotics usually produce a desire to get away from it all. The user of drugs, perhaps because of their more dramatic physiological effects, suffers from even more seething social condemnation than the user of alcohol, however. Hanlon characterizes the current medical attitude as follows: "Alcoholism is to tuberculosis as narcotic addiction is to leprosy" [39].

Definition and Description of Drug Addiction

Drug addiction, like alcoholism, represents a compulsive need on the part of the addicted individual, but it proceeds more rapidly and the signs of addiction are more clear-cut. Contrary to popular opinion, however, not all users of drugs are addicts. Chein points out that there are more-or-less-regular users of narcotics and that individuals differ greatly in their susceptibility to dependence. True addiction, he argues, goes beyond dependence, involving the development of a "craving" for the drug [16].

The World Health Organization distinguishes between drug addiction and drug habituation, a condition marked by a desire but not a compulsion to use drugs and the absence of any physical dependence upon the drug. As defined by the World Health Organization, drug addiction is "a state of periodic or chronic intoxication produced by the repeated consumption of a drug (natural or synthetic)" [20]. The characteristics of drug addiction include: an overpowering desire or need to continue taking the drug and to obtain it by any means, a tendency to increase the dose, a psychological and eventually a physical dependence upon the drug, withdrawal sickness or syndrome upon abstinence, and a detrimental effect upon the individual and society.

This last characteristic makes drug addiction a serious public health problem. The unregulated sale of addictive drugs is illegal. It has been estimated that a narcotics addict requires a minimum of ten to twenty dollars a day to secure the drugs he needs. To obtain the money, he often must turn to crime [64]. Zimmering found that almost all the young male drug addicts at Bellevue Hospital engaged in crime when they needed money for drugs [87].

As with most addictive behavior, one may hypothesize stages of addiction rather than an all-or-none diagnosis. Chein has developed a nine-point scale of severity of narcotics involvement based upon a combination of tolerance, dependency, and craving. At one end of the scale are those who use drugs occasionally and sporadically, while at the other end are those with a craving for the drug, a history of dependence, and a conviction that they are permanently "hooked" [18]. This self-image of addiction, reinforced by social "labeling" [10] and the expectation and fear of withdrawal symptoms, are basic forces in the continuation of addictive behavior [48].

Various narcotics produce characteristic effects. Cocaine, for instance, acts as a stimulant and produces a feeling of elation; morphine, on the other hand, acts as a depressant, producing feelings of ease and contentment. The use of heroin results in tolerance (the need for increased doses) and physical dependence; the use of marijuana and cocaine does not. The kind of drug used by an addict will depend upon such factors as geographical location, socioeconomic status, sex and personality, and the price and availability of the drug [58]. The most commonly used narcotic is heroin [51].

The Extent and Distribution of Drug Addiction

It is even more difficult to obtain valid data on the incidence and prevalence of drug addiction than on alcoholism. The data we have are drawn largely from criminal records. In a message to Congress on July 14, 1969, President Nixon said that it was estimated that hundreds of thousands of Americans had become narcotics addicts. He described the drug-abuse problem as a "serious national threat," cited "as the primary cause of the enormous increase in street crimes over the last decade" [79]. New York City alone is believed to account for more than half the known cases of addiction, and these addicts are reported as accounting for half the crime in New York County—the estimated annual there, from stolen property, being $250,000,000. The California State Bureau of Criminal Statistics, in 1960, listed 19,243 arrests for narcotic offenses, of which more than two-thirds occurred in Los Angeles County. These arrests accounted for more than one-third of all adult arrests in 1960 [15].

There is some evidence that narcotics addiction in such metropolitan centers as New York City, Chicago, and Los Angeles has been on the increase in the last decade. It is concentrated in the socially disorganized sections of the cities, especially among Negroes and Puerto Ricans and among young people [16]. As Clausen points out:

> The areas of highest rates of drug use tend to be inhabited by the most disadvantaged minority groups and by the least successful or most deviant members of other population groups. These are the areas with the highest rates of adult crime, the highest rates of prostitution and illegitimacy, the highest prevalence of infant mortality and of tuberculosis, the highest proportion of broken families and of non-family living arrangements [21].

Ausubel also suggests that "the disproportionate number of addicts who originate in the lower class can undoubtedly be attributed to the greater availability of drugs in slum areas" [4].

The characteristic pattern of drug addiction appears to have undergone a change since World War II. Before 1940, drug addicts were older, a higher proportion were women, and they were less concentrated among nonwhite groups. The explanation for this shift may lie in a change from the use of drugs as physical pain-killers to their use for "kicks." Unlike alcohol, narcotics addiction is a behavioral disorder of youth. There is now a large concentration of cases in the 15–25 year old group, 30 percent of whom become addicted before their twentieth year. Addiction among boys is almost ten times as great as it is among girls [13]. In certain deviant groups, such as juvenile gangs in New York City, the taking of narcotics appears to have achieved a certain amount of acceptability and even approval [31]; however, a study of working-class groups in 1966 revealed an increasing change from "hard" (addictive) to "soft" (nonaddictive) drugs, a result of increased knowledge about the bad effects of hard drugs and of stricter legal controls [44].

Social Factors in the Etiology of Drug Addiction

The causes of narcotics addiction are probably similar to those of alcoholism. There is a need to escape from reality, from oneself, and from one's group. Like alcoholics, narcotic addicts tend to be immature, anxious, maladjusted, and dominated by feelings of inadequacy and insecurity [85]. As summarized by Feldman, "In near unanimity, investigators have described the drug user as maladjusted, hostile, immature, dependent, manipulative, narcissistic—or any number of other reprehensible traits that place the blame for drug experimentation on the personality weaknesses of the individual user" [31]. His own analysis emphasizes "the life-style of the action-seeking youth in the slums"—the "stand-up cat" ideology as a major causal factor.

Of particular interest are the factors underlying the choice of the narcotic to which the user becomes addicted. Studies have shown that drug use is largely a socially acquired pattern of behavior. Almost all addicts first learn about drugs through association with someone who is already using them. A study of marijuana in Chicago places greatest importance upon the social experience, as opposed to psychological predisposition, as the initiating force in drug addiction [9].

Alksne reports that social pressure was the major reason given by a majority of addicts for trying a drug [2]. A California study of 19,243 arrests for narcotic offenses in 1960 concluded that "most youths are probably enticed, or at least given their first opportunity for using narcotics, by someone on a more personal level . . . [a] girl friend or buddy, for example" [15]. In many cases an addict will become a "pusher" in order to secure the funds for his own supply of narcotics. Winick talks about the "life cycle of addiction" [83], while Alksne, Lieberman, and Brill describe "the process through which an individual moves in and out of an 'addiction system' i.e., a way of life built around compulsive use of narcotics" [1].

The importance of personal association among drug addicts has led some sociologists to posit the presence of an addict subculture. As summarized by Ray:

> The social world of addiction contains a loose system of organizational and cultural elements, including a special language or argot, certain artifacts, a commodity market and pricing system, a system of stratification, and ethical codes. The addict's commitment to these values gives him a status and an identity [66].

These addict subgroups develop strong interpersonal bonds, similar images of appropriate and acceptable narcotic behavior, a language and rituals of their own, and feelings of rejecting and being rejected by society [17]. They are usually found in high-delinquency areas, belong to delinquent groups, and have a history marked by deviant and antisocial behavior. The members of these groups often have strong allegiances to each other and to the norms of the subgroup at the same time that they reject the values of the larger society.

This point of view is developed in great detail by Cloward and Ohlin as a theory of delinquent behavior. In a discussion of pressures leading to "retreatist" subcultures, they place great stress upon the patterns of association that are built up in socially deviant subgroups. In relations to drug addiction, they claim:

> The drug user, in other words, must be understood not only in terms of his personality and the social structure, which creates a readiness to engage in drug use, but also in terms of the new patterns of association and values to which he is exposed as he seeks access to drugs. The more the individual is caught in this web of association, the more likely that he will persist in drug use, for he has become incorporated in a subculture that exerts control over his behavior [23].

In describing the "drug users'" world, Chein stresses the urban slum in which they live, their inadequate home life, the initiation into and continued use of drugs as part of ordinary social relationships, and their generally hopeless and futile future [16].

Social Factors in Control of Drug Addiction

The confusion as to whether drug addiction is a legal or a medical problem underlies much of the current effort at control. In fact, the addict who wishes to break the habit must often turn himself over to the courts in order to secure treatment. A report by the Joint Committee of the American Bar Association and the American Medical Association on Drug Addiction strongly recommends that drug addiction be viewed as a disease and not a crime, and that the current laws be revised to abolish prison terms for addicts, to allow qualified doctors to dispense narcotics, and to establish experimental outpatient clinics for the care of addicts. This Committee pointed to the success of these measures in other countries, such as Britain, where narcotics addiction is claimed to be practically nonexistent [42]. Lindesmith found that very few drug addicts in Britain were imprisoned for any kind of offense. He also points out that under the British system, "there is little or no economic incentive to spread the habit to others" [47]. Schur's analysis of drug addiction under British policy also offers much support for a medically oriented, rather than a legal, approach to the control of drug addiction [71]. Kolb believes that addicts who return to use of drugs after treatment should be allowed to have maintenance doses under medical supervision. Treated in this way, he feels that chronic addicts "would work, support themselves, and create no public problem" [45]. This point of view is opposed by the World Health Organization which argues that "the maintenance of drug addiction is not treatment" [19].

The controversy over legal-versus-medical responsibility for the drug addict is complicated by the fact that the currently prescribed medical treatment is ineffective. It calls for detoxification and rehabilitation. The U.S. Public Health Service maintains hospitals where addicts may undergo six months of treatment and rehabilitation, but the number of hospital beds available for detoxification in local hospitals is sadly deficient. Furthermore, like the alcoholic, the drug addict makes a poor patient. He is apt to be uncooperative, deceitful and troublesome; in addition, he constitutes a potential source of difficulty for the doctor with Federal and State law-enforcement officers.

Detoxification can be achieved quite easily, but the recidivism rate is extremely high. In a study of addicts who had been discharged at least six months from Lexington Hospital, Pescor found only 13.5 per cent still abstinent [60]. In 1955, at Lexington Hospital, out of 3,724 admissions, two-thirds were readmissions. Alksne and his associates, in a study of former patients of Riverside Hospital in New York, found a similarly low proportion of abstainers [2]. A study of the cycle of abstinence and relapse among heroin addicts placed particular emphasis upon the addict's self-image during periods of abstinence and relapse.

> ... the abstainer's social expectations during a period when he is off drugs are frequently not gratified. Here again, socially disjunctive experiences bring about a questioning of the value of an abstainer identity and promote reflections in which addict and non-addict identities and relationships are compared. The abstainer's realignment of his values with those of the world of addiction results in the redefinition of self as an addict and has as a consequence the actions necessary to relapse [66].

The high rate of relapse is attributed largely to the continued association of the patient with addicts after detoxification. The "cured" addict returns to the same addict subculture from whence he came and quickly reverts to his former pattern of drug use. The hospitalization experience itself may even serve to reinforce his old beliefs and values, through close association with other addicts, and provide knowledge of new contacts. Lindesmith found that addicts are more likely to relapse unintentionally, by "playing around" with drugs again, than to resume their addiction deliberately. He found that attitudes developed during addiction, such as the belief that drugs are good for every ailment, and the rejection of moral taboos, predispose the former addict to revert to the use of drugs [48].

Wikler raises a crucial question concerning the evaluation of a "cure" in narcotics addiction. He notes that the abstinence rate of Lexington patients (about 20 percent) compares quite favorably with the recovery rate from certain chronic diseases, like diabetes mellitus or pulmonary tuberculosis [81]. However, the diabetic's return to hospital care is not viewed with the same disapproval and condemnation that is focused on the narcotic addict. Winick proposes that the term "cure" be used with caution in cases of drug addiction. Instead he suggests terms like "successful treatment" and "total abstinence" [83].

The high rate of recidivism underscores the need to couple detoxification with physical and psychological rehabilitation and to attempt to change the environment to which the "cured" addict returns. Most important is a change in the community's attitude toward the former addict. As of now, the addict returning to the community is likely to find himself treated as an exconvict, for whom there are few employment possibilities. This negative public attitude may only drive him back all the more quickly into the addict subgroup, with an even more confirmed antisocial attitude. From a social point of view, the narcotic addict, like the delinquent, is largely the product of his environment, and until environmental conditions conducive to the development of such forms of deviant behavior are changed, little progress will be made in meeting the narcotics problem [59].

Two other problems related to the prevention and control of drug addiction are of general social significance. The first concerns the degree of voluntary control to be permitted the addict in seeking a cure; the second relates to the efficacy of public education to the dangers of addiction. Both these problems contain dilemmas. By definition, the addict cannot control his need for alcohol or drugs. How, then, can he be expected voluntarily to enforce the rigorous routine involved in breaking a habit which has such deep psychological roots? Yet everything we know about psychotherapy and personality change indicates the necessity of having the patient's voluntary cooperation.

The dilemma in regard to education about alcohol and drugs involves the classical problem of dispensing information about a vice which contains certain attractive elements, without creating even more sinners. Given an underlying need in many individuals for the kind of relief from anxiety and tension offered by alcohol and drugs, perhaps it is best not to talk about the existence of these forms of escape [3]. But how, then, are susceptible individuals to be warned against a danger which they may well stumble upon by themselves?

These two dilemmas underlie much of the heated controversy over the prevention and control of the addictive disorders, as well as certain other so-called "social" diseases, such as venereal disease. In the United States, treatment for alcoholism is generally voluntary, but narcotics addiction is considered a crime and the addict is often subjected to compulsory detoxification. The reputed success of Alcoholics Anonymous and the failure of compulsory hospitalization to cure narcotics addiction argues in favor of the voluntary approach. As Chein maintains:

> Every experience we've had shows that the addict would not be cured under any compulsion. Part of an optimum therapeutic program is to give the addict a chance to fail. He will begin to realize that he is truly ill and not simply caught by unfortunate circumstances. You cannot give psychotherapy to a person who does not think there is anything wrong with him [56].

The problem is that most alcoholics and drug addicts are not interested in treatment and will not volunteer. The World Health Organization recommends some form of legal compulsion because "Most addicts require some degree of coercion, preferably civil commitment for medical treatment, to force them to desist from what is to them often a pleasurable experience" [19]. Pescor's comparison of voluntary and involuntary cures among addicts at Lexington Hospital showed that the average longest period of abstinence for expatients was 2.2 years after voluntary cure and 1.8 years after involuntary cure. He concludes that voluntary cures are generally more effective than enforced cures [37]. But Lexington records indicate that many voluntary patients sign themselves out long before the completion of their treatment. Perhaps one answer to this dilemma would be the voluntary decision by the addict to subject himself to an enforced course of treatment.

MARIJUANA

While the use of marijuana (cannabis) has been widespread throughout the world for centuries, and the number of users was estimated at 200 million in 1966, mostly in Africa and Asia [50], this hallucinogen is a relative newcomer on the drug scene in the United States. The heated controversy concerning its control dramatically illustrates many of the social, medical, and legal issues that we have already discussed in regard to alcohol and narcotics. Medically, marijuana does not produce physical dependence or tolerance and cannot, therefore, be classified as an addictive drug [49]. Psychologically, however, it can become habit-forming and, socially, it is generally regarded as harmful to the individual and the community. Most important, legally, the possession or sale of marijuana is a criminal offense subject to severe penalties [28]. Thus we observe once more the intricate relationship between social, medical, and legal problems [11].

The Prevalence of Marijuana Use

Little is known about the frequency of marijuana use in the United States, although it is generally assumed to be high and on the increase [36]. Major social concern is focused upon the adolescent population, especially high-school and college students, but estimates of their use vary widely. A survey of students at over fifty colleges and universities by Goldstein [35] found that 15 percent of the students had tried drugs, mainly marijuana, while a Gallup Poll of 426 college campuses reports only 6 percent as having smoked marijuana [67]. Various college surveys estimate the use of marijuana at 33 percent at the University of California at Los Angeles, 25 percent at Harvard, 21 per cent at University of California at Santa Barbara, 20 percent at Yale, 15 per cent at Princeton, and 14 percent at the California Institute of Technology. As reported by the National Institute of Mental Health, surveys of high-school and college students show that approximately 20 percent have some experience with marijuana [57]. These figures, however, refer to any exposure to marijuana and by no means represent habitual use.

In an extensive review of the literature, Murphy [54] found that studies of heavy marijuana users in North Africa, India, and the United States describe them as being predominantly males, under 35, from lower-income groups, and with evidence of neurotic or psychopathic histories. Earlier studies in the United States also described marijuana use as a lower-class, slum phenomenon [49], and probably a large part of public concern today stems from the spread of this form of drug use to high schools and colleges. There can be little doubt that the smoking of marijuana is rapidly becoming part of the college scene today. While the introduction of "pot" may have been part of the "hippie" culture originally, in recent years it has been spreading rapidly among conventional college and high-school students [73].

Social Factors Associated with the Use of Marijuana

The use of marijuana and other hallucinogenic and consciousness-expanding or psychedelic drugs (e.g., LSD) is largely a phenomenon among the young [12, 39]. These drugs have come to occupy a central position in the "happening" scene [74]. In a study of a representative sample of students at the University of California at Santa Barbara, the author found that the more the student adhered to a "hang loose" ethic (nonconformist, antiestablishment, rebellious), the more likely he was to smoke marijuana. We posited the following sequence, based on our findings:

> Adherence to the "hang-loose" ethic is more likely to occur among certain predisposed personality types (i.e., rebellious, cynical) and in certain social sub-groups (i.e., males, non-religious); such adherence is likely to lead to favorable attitude toward smoking marijuana both for its "high" effects and its symbolism of rebellion against authority; this favorable attitude will be supported by other students who also embrace the "hang-loose" ethic and engage in similar overt and covert expressions of rejection of the established order. Finally, given this climate of opinion and behavior, the smoking of marijuana becomes almost a "natural" act for many students far removed from the public's current efforts to define it either as a legal or a health problem [78].

Becker [9] stresses the role of social

pressure and support in the initiation of a marijuana user. Unlike narcotics use, smoking marijuana is predominantly a social act, usually engaged in as a catalyst to, and enhancer of, other social experiences—to help one get "turned on." Violent or aggressive behavior is rare. There is little scientific evidence to support the accusation that marijuana leads to crime or to the desire for stronger drugs [72]. The President's Crime Commission concluded that, "the most reasonable hypothesis here is that some people who are predisposed to marijuana are also predisposed to heroin use" [65].

While valid evidence of the effects of marijuana, especially its long-term use, is lacking, it would appear reasonable to argue that a great deal depends upon who uses it, how often, and under what conditions. Among delinquent gangs, it is quite probable that early use of marijuana may be followed by heroin and may be associated with crime—as would the use of any drug, including alcohol. However, among college students, where marijuana use would be largely an occasional thing and where delinquency and crime are not a problem, there seems little reason to associate smoking marijuana with either heroin or crime.

Social Control of Marijuana

At present, the control of marijuana is strictly a legal matter. The law itself is severe, but enforcement is haphazard and subject to constant controversy. There is strong sentiment for liberalizing the laws against marijuana or abolishing them completely. The feeling is that, until smoking marijuana can be proven to have harmful medical or social effects, attaching strict penalties to its use is more an act of vengeance than justice. Simmons links this controversy with broader social issues; "It (the marijuana issue) seems to be the pivot around which far deeper conflicts and confrontations are raging —oldsters versus youngsters, hippies versus straight society, administered morality versus personal freedom" [73].

The social use of marijuana can perhaps best be compared to the social use of alcohol. One cannot deny, as we have seen, that there are problem drinkers for whom alcohol has had very harmful consequences. There can be little question that the use of marijuana could be subject to similar abuse. The question, it seems to us, is one of adequate regulation and control, rather than prohibition, combined with education about these drugs and positive learning experiences, rather than suppression. In any case, this discussion once again illustrates the close relationship between health and social problems that has been the central theme of this analysis of the addictive disorders.

FUTURE PROSPECTS FOR THE ADDICTIVE DISORDERS

The punitive treatment of addicts is slowly giving way to a more therapeutic approach. The medical profession is beginning to accept responsibility for the care of addicts, and the field of public health is seeking methods of prevention and rehabilitation. Local hospitals are setting aside beds for the treatment of alcoholics and drug addicts. Public health agencies are expanding their efforts to increase public understanding of the problem, to secure the cooperation of the addicted individual, and to provide community facilities for detoxification and rehabilitation.

But the ultimate success of any effort to meet the problem of the addictive disorders must rest with society itself. Public attitudes toward the addict must change. The stigma of weakness and depravity must be removed. A therapeutic approach must be substituted for punishment. The community must continue to fight to remove or ameliorate the socioenvironmental conditions which expose the individual to addictive influences and to provide the needed rehabilitative measures to help the cured addict make a fresh start.

Treatment and Rehabilitation Programs

A major need in the field of addictive disorders today is for action programs which help to keep the cured alcoholic or narcotic addict from returning to the use of the addictive substance. The basis of his addiction rests largely upon his inability to find some other less harmful substitute to satisfy his craving for the kind of reaction afforded by the addictive substance. Thus, the basic ingredient of any effective program must be the provision of a continuing source of substitute support which enables the ex-addict to meet his craving without returning to the use of drugs. There is probably no real cure for the addictive disorders, just as no cure exists for many chronic diseases—there is only a slow rehabilitative process which involves continuous support and a changed way of life. Perhaps this is the major reason why single-shot approaches to the control of addiction show such discouragingly high rates of recidivism. The former addict will relapse after any single "cure," unless he is provided with some kind of ongoing support.

There are a number of forms such "after-cure" programs can take; the local neighborhood "club" for ex-addicts; the halfway house which serves as a supervised residence; the sheltered workshop which offers employment in a supportive environment; and the work and training camp which moves the ex-addict from his old environment into a therapeutic community. These programs combine a supportive therapeutic environment with realistic help in vocational guidance, housing, family counseling, and recreation. Coordination and integration are, however, badly needed.

Needed Research on Addictive Disorders

Much remains to be learned about the addictive disorders. Relatively little research has been done on their etiology, prevention, treatment, and control. The physiological process whereby these substances induce addiction, as well as the system of effecting detoxification and withdrawal from addiction are fairly well known. What is not yet known is how to keep cured addicts from relapsing, how to free them of the underlying psychological and social forces which compel them to seek an escape into the make-believe world of drug-induced dreams and fantasies.

Very little is known at present about the epidemiology of these disorders. Current data on the incidence, prevalence, and distribution of addiction in the total population are woefully inadequate. Which groups are particularly susceptible? What personal characteristics distinguish high-risk from low-risk groups? Why do some geographical areas show such high addiction rates while in others the problem is practically nonexistent?

New methods of dealing with the addiction problem must be developed and evaluated. Physicians and hospitals must replace police and prisons. Such methods as out-patient clinics, short-term hospitalization, training and work camps, and rehabilitation centers must be utilized. Such problems as the use of voluntary or compulsory treatment methods, group psychotherapy, social work with the families of addicts, and the use of public health nurses in aftercare must be explored. Better public health education programs are required, both to increase the knowledge of the temptations and the dangers of addiction and to change the public's attitude toward the addict.

Finally, a new attitude is needed toward the social uses of alcohol and marijuana. The vast majority of users of these substances do so in moderation, with full awareness of the risks involved and with due regard for the problems inherent in their abuse. Such use should constitute neither a medical nor a legal problem. To label them as "sick" or "criminals" and to subject them to discriminative action is more an emotional expression of personal and social vindictiveness than an objective and realistic appraisal of the situation. Learning to use such substances properly may well be an important aspect of their control.

Rooted as they are in the social and psychological forces in the individual's environment, the addictive disorders are a new type of health problem which cannot be understood or managed in traditional terms—of infectious agents or degenerative processes. They are a new class of behavioral disorders which require a redefinition of etiological and therapeutic concepts and a reformulation of prevention and treatment programs. The task of building an effective approach to this increasingly important public health problem is a real challenge to the newly developed field of social medicine.

REFERENCES

1. ALKSNE, HAROLD, L. LIEBERMAN, AND L. BRILL, "A Conceptual Model of the Life Cycle of Addiction," *The International Journal of the Addictions*, 2 (Fall, 1967), 221.
2. ALKSNE, HAROLD, S. PATRICK, R. TRUSSELL, AND J. ELINSON, "A Follow-up Study of Treated Adolescent Narcotic Users." Mimeographed, 1960.
3. ANSLINGER, HARRY J., "Drug Addicts," *Journal of the American Medical Association*, 144 (1950), 333.
4. AUSUBEL, DAVID P., *Drug Addiction: Physiological, Psychological and Sociological Aspects*. New York: Random House, Inc., 1958, p. 64.
5. BACON, M. AND M. B. JONES, *Teen-age Drinking*. New York: Thomas Y. Crowell Company, 1968.
6. BAILEY, M., P. HABERMAN, AND H. ALKSNE, "The Epidemiology of Alcoholism in an Urban Residential Area," *Quarterly Journal of Studies on Alcohol*, 26 (March, 1965), 19–40.
7. BALES, ROBERT F., "Cultural Differences in Rates of Alcoholism," *Quarterly Journal of Studies on Alcohol*, 6 (March, 1946), 480–99.
8. ———, "The Therapeutic Role of Alcoholics Anonymous as Seen by a Sociologist," *Quarterly Journal of Studies on Alcohol*, 5 (September, 1944), 267–78.
9. BECKER, HOWARD S., "Becoming a Marijuana User," *American Journal of Sociology*, 59 (November, 1953), 235–42.
10. ———, *Outsiders*. New York: The Free Press, 1963, p. 133.
11. BLOOMQUIST, EDWARD R., *Marijuana*. Beverly Hills, Calif.: Glencoe Press, 1969.
12. BLUMER, HERBERT, *The World of Youthful Drug Use*. Berkeley: School of Criminology, University of California, 1967.
13. Bureau of Narcotics, U.S. Treasury Department, *Traffic in Opium and Other Dangerous Drugs*. Washington, D.C.: Government Printing Office, issued annually.
14. CAHALAN, DONALD AND IRA CISIN, "American Drinking Practices: I. Extent of Drinking by Population Subgroups," *Quarterly Journal of Studies in Alcoholism*, 29 (1968), 130–51.
15. California State Bureau of Criminal Statistics, *Annual Report: 1961*.
16. CHEIN, ISADOR, "The Status of Sociological and Social Psychological Knowl-

edge concerning Narcotics," in Robert B. Livingston, ed., *Narcotic Drug Addiction Problems.* Washington, D.C.: Government Printing Office, n.d., pp. 146–58.

17. ——— AND EVA ROSENFELD, "Juvenile Narcotics Use," *Law and Contemporary Problems,* 22 (Winter, 1957), 52–68.

18. CHEIN, ISADOR, D. GERARD, R. LEE, AND E. ROSENFELD, *The Road to H.* New York: Basic Books, Inc., Publishers, 1964.

19. *Chronicle of the World Health Organization,* "Treatment and Care of Drug Addicts," 11 (October, 1957), 323.

20. ———, "Drug Addiction or Drug Habituation," 11 (May, 1957), 165.

21. JOHN A. CLAUSEN, "Social Patterns, Personality and Adolescent Drug Use," in Alexander Leighton, J. Clausen and R. Wilson, eds., *Explorations in Social Psychiatry.* New York: Basic Books, Inc., Publishers, 1957, pp. 230–77.

22. ———, "Drug Addiction," in Robert K. Merton and Robert A. Nisbet, eds., *Contemporary Social Problems.* New York: Harcourt, Brace & World, Inc., 1961.

23. CLOWARD, RICHARD A. AND LLOYD E. OHLIN, *Delinquency and Opportunity: A Theory of Delinquent Gangs.* New York: The Free Press, 1960.

24. CROSS, JAY N., *Guide to the Community Control of Alcoholism.* New York: American Public Health Association, 1968.

25. DANA, A. H., "Problem Drinking in Industry," *Research Reports in Social Science* (Florida State University, Institute for Social Research), Vol. 6 (1963), No. 1.

26. DEBOLD, RICHARD C. AND RUSSELL C. LEAF, eds., *LSD, Man and Society.* Middletown, Conn.: Wesleyan University Press, 1967.

27. EFRON, V. AND M. KELLER, *Selected Statistical Tables on the Consumption of Alcohol, 1850–1962 and on Alcoholism, 1930–1960.* New Brunswick, N.J.: Rutgers Center of Alcohol Studies, 1963.

28. ELDRIDGE, WILLIAM B., *Narcotics and the Law.* Chicago: American Bar Foundation, 1962.

29. Expert Committee on Mental Health, Alcoholism Subcommittee, World Health Organization, *Medical Report Series* (Geneva), No. 42 (1951).

30. ———, *Medical Report Series* (Geneva), No. 48 (August, 1952).

31. FELDMAN, HARVEY W., "Ideological Supports to Becoming and Remaining a Heroin Addict," *Journal of Health and Social Behavior,* 9 (June, 1968), 131.

32. FINESTONE, HAROLD, "Cats, Kicks and Color," *Social Problems,* 5 (July, 1957), 3–13.

33. FOX, R., "Treatment of Alcoholism," in H. M. Heimwitch, ed., *Alcoholism: Basic Aspects and Treatment.* Washington, D.C.: American Association for the Advancement of Science, 1957, pp. 164–65.

34. GELBER, IDA, *Alcoholism in New York City.* New York: New York City Department of Health, 1960.

35. GOLDSTEIN, RICHARD, *1 in 7: Drugs on Campus.* New York: Walker and Co., 1966.

36. GOODE, ERICH, ed., *Marijuana.* New York: Atherton Press, 1969.

37. GORDON, JOHN, "Treatment of Alcoholism," *New York State Journal of Medicine,* 58 (June, 1958), 1011–18.

38. HADDON, WILLIAM, "Alcohol and Highway Accidents," in J. D. Harvard, ed., *Alcohol and Road Traffic.* London: British Medical Association, 1963.

39. HANLON, JOHN J., *Principles of Public Health Administration.* St. Louis: The C. V. Mosby Co., 1960, p. 581.

40. HARMS, ERNEST, ed., *Drug Addiction in Youth.* Oxford: Pergamon Press, 1965.

41. JELLINEK, E. M., *The Disease Concept of Alcoholism.* New Haven: Hillhouse Press, 1960.

42. Joint Committee of the American Bar Association and the American Medical Association, *Drug Addiction: Crime or Disease?* Bloomington: Indiana University Press, 1961.

43. KELLER, MARK AND VERA EFRON, "The Prevalence of Alcoholism," *Quar-*

terly Journal of Studies on Alcohol, 16 (December, 1955), 619–44.

44. KLEIN, JULIUS AND DEREK L. PHILIPS, "From Hard to Soft Drugs: Temporal and Substantive Changes in Drug Usage among Gangs in a Working Class Community,"" *Journal of Health and Social Behavior*, 9 (June, 1968), 139–45.

45. KOLB, LAWRENCE, "Narcotic Addiction: An Interview," *Spectrum* 5 (March, 1957), 136.

46. KRUSE, HARRY D., *Problem Drinking and Alcoholism*. New York: The New York State Interdepartmental Health Resources Board, 1957.

47. LINDESMITH, ALFRED, "The British System of Narcotics Control," *Law and Contemporary Problems*, 22 (Winter, 1957), 138–54.

48. ———, *Opiate Addiction*. Bloomington, Ind.: Principia Press, 1957.

49. Mayor's Committee on Marihuana, "The Marihuana Problem in the City of New York," in David Solomon, ed., *The Marihuana Papers*. Indianapolis: The Bobbs–Merrill Company, Inc., 1966, pp. 233–360. For an excellent analysis of this report see David Arnold, "The Meaning of the LaGuardia Report," in Jerry Simmons, ed., *Marihuana: Myths and Realities* (North Hollywood, Calif.: Brandon House, 1967), pp. 111–35.

50. McGLOTHLIN, WILLIAM H., "Cannabis: A Reference," in David Solomon, ed., *The Marihuana Papers*. Indianapolis: The Bobbs–Merrill Company, Inc., 1966, p. 402.

51. MEYER, ALAN S., *Social and Psychological Factors in Opiate Addiction*. New York: Bureau of Applied Social Research, Columbia University, 1952.

52. MONIQUE, S. J., "The Alcoholic," *Alcohol Hygiene*, 3 (March, 1957), 5–10.

53. MULFORD, H. A., "Drinking and Deviant Behavior: U.S.A., 1963," *Quarterly Journal of Studies on Alcohol*, 25 (1964), 634–50.

54. MURPHY, H. B. M., "The Cannabis Habit: A Review of Recent Psychiatric Literature," *Bulletin on Narcotics*, 15 (1963), 15–23.

55. National Clearinghouse for Mental Health Information, *Bibliography on Drug Dependence and Abuse: 1928–1966*. Washington, D.C.: Public Health Service, n.d. A comprehensive, 258-page bibliography.

56. *New York Herald Tribune*, March 12, 1960.

57. *New York Times*, March 7, 1968, p. 26.

58. O'DONNELL, JOHN A. AND JOHN C. BALL, *Narcotic Addiction*. New York: Harper & Row, Publishers, Inc., 1966.

59. PATRICK, SHERMAN W., *The "Score": A Survey of New York City's Narcotics Program*. Unpublished thesis, New York University, 1962.

60. PESCOR, MICHAEL J., "Follow-up Study of Treated Narcotic Drug Addicts," *Public Health Reports*, Suppl. No. 170 (1943), pp. 1–18.

61. PITTMAN, D. J. AND C. E. SNYDER, eds., *Society, Culture, and Drinking Patterns*. New York: John Wiley & Sons, Inc., 1962.

62. PLAUT, THOMAS F., *Alcohol Problems: A Report to the Nation*. New York: Oxford University Press, 1967.

63. ———, *Some Major Issues in Developing Community Services for Persons with Drinking Problems*. Washington, D.C.: National Clearinghouse for Mental Health Information, Public Health Service, 1966.

64. President's Commission on Law Enforcement and Administration of Justice, *Task Force Report: Narcotics and Drug Abuse*. Washington, D.C.: Government Printing Office, 1967.

65. ———, *The Challenge of Crime in a Free Society*. Washington, D.C.: Government Printing Office, 1967, pp. 211–31.

66. RAY, MARSH B., "The Cycle of Abstinence and Relapse among Heroin Addicts," *Social Problems*, 9 (Fall, 1961), 132–40.

67. *Reader's Digest*, November, 1967.

68. RILEY, JOHN W. AND C. S. MARDEN, "The Social Patterns of Alcohol Drinking," *Quarterly Journal of Studies on Alcohol*, 8 (September, 1947), 265–73.

69. Room, Robin, "Cultural Contingencies of Alcoholism," *Journal of Health and Social Behavior*, 9 (June, 1968), 99–113.
70. Schmidt, W. S. and R. G. Smart, "Alcoholics, Drinking and Traffic Accidents," *Quarterly Journal of Studies on Alcohol*, 20 (September, 1959), 631–44.
71. Schur, Edwin M., "Drug Addiction under British Policy," *Social Problems*, 9 (Fall, 1961), 156–66.
72. Simmons, Jerry L., "Marihuana: A Checklist of Facts," in *idem*, ed., *Marihuana: Myths and Realities.* North Hollywood, Calif.: Brandon House, 1967, pp. 227–36.
73. ———, "The Current Marihuana Scene," in *idem*, ed., *Marihuana: Myths and Realities.* North Hollywood, Calif.: Brandon House, 1967, pp. 7–23.
74. ——— and Barry Winograd, *It's Happening: A Portrait of the Youth Scene Today.* Santa Barbara, Calif.: Marc-Laird Publications, 1966.
75. Straus, Robert, "Medical Practice and the Alcoholic," *Annals of the American Academy of Political and Social Science*, 315 (June, 1958), 117–24. The entire issue of this journal is devoted to the topic, "Alcoholism in the United States."
76. ——— and Selden D. Bacon, *Drinking in College.* New Haven: Yale University Press, 1953.
77. Suchman, Edward A., *Sociology and the Field of Public Health.* New York: Russell Sage Foundation, 1963.
78. ———, "The 'Hang-loose' Ethic and the Spirit of Drug Use," *Journal of Health and Social Behavior*, 9 (June, 1968), 153–54. This entire issue is devoted to recreational drug use.
79. *The Cincinnati Enquirer*, July 15, 1969, p. 1.
80. Trice, Harrison M., "Alcoholics Anonymous," *Annals of the American Academy of Political and Social Science*, 315 (January, 1958), 108–16. This entire issue is entitled "Understanding Alcoholism."
81. Wikler, Abraham, "Clinical Aspects of Diagnosis and Treatment of Addictions," *Bulletin of the Menninger Clinic*, 15 (September, 1951), 157–66.
82. Wilner, Daniel M. and Gene G. Kassebaum, eds., *Narcotics.* New York: McGraw Hill Book Company, 1965.
83. Winick, Charles, "Narcotics Addiction and Its Treatment," *Law and Contemporary Problems*, 22 (Winter, 1957), 31. This entire issue is devoted to a symposium on narcotics.
84. ———, "The Life Cycle of the Narcotic Addict and of Addiction," *U.N. Bulletin on Narcotics*, 16 (1964), 22–32.
85. World Health Organization Survey, as reported in the *New York Times*, April 13, 1969, p. 72.
86. Yost, O. R., *The Bane of Drug Addiction.* New York: The Macmillan Company, 1954.
87. Zimmering, Paul, J. Toolan, R. Safrin, and S. Wortis, "Heroin Addiction in Adolescent Boys," *Journal of Nervous and Mental Diseases*, 114 (1951), 19–34.

7

THE SOCIOLOGY OF MENTAL DISORDER

John A. Clausen

It has been suggested that the concepts of health and disease may be extended beyond the province of somatic processes and into the realm of social behavior (see Chapter 5). The biological organism is also a behaving person, and behavior may be viewed in terms of whether it is normal, deviant or, in some sense, pathological. Because standards for assessing deviance or behavioral pathology are formulated by the particular society in which one lives, the problem of specifying the nature and content of mental disorder is greatly complicated.

THE NATURE AND EXTENT OF MENTAL DISORDER

Mental disorder is primarily manifested in behavior. It may be associated with a variety of physical symptoms or with no physical symptoms whatsoever. There are some social scientists [64] who agree with Szasz [71] that the whole concept of mental illness is a myth, and that the great majority of persons said to be suffering from "mental illness" or "mental disease" might be more appropriately said to be suffering from severe "problems of living." Others, myself included, would say that what we call "mental disorder" consists of a variety of behavior and mental or emotional states—some reflecting the psychological influence of organic disease or genetic constitution, some constituting reactions to intense psychological stress, some representing inadequate or maladaptive personal strategies, and some constituting deviant modes of behaving, thinking, and feeling that are common to members of particular subcultures. Almost everyone would agree that certain of these conditions are illnesses. Some social scientists would, however, be reluctant to use the term "illness" when talking about maladaptive personal strategies, and almost all would definitely rule out subcultural deviance.

Mental disorder exists in all societies, but the guises in which it presents itself may vary. Even more variable are the concepts which, in different societies and at different times, characterize mental illness and the ways in which the mentally ill are treated [27, 59]. In Biblical times the mentally ill were seen as "possessed of an unclean spirit" or a devil; in Colonial days they might be burned as witches; and in some societies they have been regarded as soothsayers. In contemporary America, mental disorder is likely to result in a person's seeking treatment from or being brought to the attention of mental health professionals, particularly psychiatrists. When legal considerations are at stake, it is the medical profession that determines whether one is to be labeled "insane" or not; the concept of insanity is, however, a legal concept, not a medical one. Nevertheless, until recently it was on the basis of a legal determination of insanity that most persons came into treatment for severe mental illness in the United States. As we shall see, this situation has changed markedly in the past two decades.

It will be apparent that the terms "mental disorder" and "mental illness" have even broader connotations than the term "physical illness." There is, unfortunately, a tendency to set one off against the other and to assume a dualism of body and mind. But mind is not to be conceptualized as "nonbody." As was made clear in Chapter 5, emotions and thought processes are functions of a behaving organism; "mind" may be regarded as a symbolic incorporation and integration of experience that serves to direct and regulate the organism's reactions to its environment.

THE MAJOR TYPES OF MENTAL DISORDER

There have been many systems for classifying mental disorders, none of which is wholly satisfactory. For diseases other than mental disorders, most developed nations have long followed the nomenclature of the International Classification of Diseases. For mental disorders, however, it was not until 1968 that the standard nomenclature used in the United States was brought into agreement with the International Classification of Diseases [3]; the purposes and problems of psychiatric classification and a wide range of research bearing upon such problems and alternative ways of dealing with them are discussed in Reference No. 29.

Even with the revised nomenclature, there are still major differences in diagnostic practice and in criteria for deciding between alternative diagnoses, not only among psychiatrists in different countries but even among various schools of psychiatry in the United States. Ideally, a system of classification should be based upon adequate theories of the nature of the disease or disorder, and should deal with such features as etiology, pathological processes, course, and outcome. For only a few disorders do adequate theories exist, however; therefore, even the recently revised nomenclature, which is based very largely on symptomatology, leaves much to be desired. Nevertheless, it incorporates both the best clinical knowledge and such research evidence as has been amassed about various classes of disorder. Research on the distribution of mental illness, the effect of treatment, and the expected long-term outcomes requires reliable methods of classification and valid means of making distinctions between subcategories of disorder. Such investigations are likely in turn to contribute to the improvement of classification schemes [29]. Regarding gross categories and aspects of mental disorder, there is now substantial agreement among psychiatrists (although there is much less agreement in diagnosing individual cases).

The Psychoses

The most severe disorders, those that account for a high proportion of persons in mental hospitals, are the psychoses. These are the conditions that most often lead to the label "insanity." The psychoses entail such severe impairment of mental functioning as to interfere seriously with the individual's capacity to meet the ordinary demands of life. Delusions and, more rarely, hallucinations, may distort perceptions. There may be pronounced swings of mood or extreme agitation and anxiety. Often, however, psychotic episodes may be sufficiently infrequent and of such short duration that the individual may function in relatively undemanding roles with reasonable success for years. Even the acutely psychotic person may retain the capacity to function more or less normally, at least part of the time, in some social roles. In general, the behavior manifested by a psychotic person is a product not only of the underlying psychological disorder but the general personality of the individual and the way that others have responded to his difficulties. Symptoms are also culturally patterned [45]. This enormously complicates both diagnosis and treatment. The influence of cultural norms and situational contexts is one reason for the unreliability of routine psychiatric diagnoses.

Psychoses are of two general types: those that result from, or are at least associated with, *organic damage* to the brain (senile dementia, alcoholic psychoses, psychoses due to syphilis of the central nervous system, and so forth) and those for which no specific organic cause has yet been found (schizophrenic, manic-depressive, and involutional psychoses). The latter are known as the *functional psychoses* and account for a very high proportion of the younger patients in mental hospitals.

The functional psychoses. The most serious of all mental disorders, from the standpoint of frequency, duration, and degree of impairment of function, is *schizophrenia*. This disease or class of diseases (there is much disagreement on the point) is most frequent among young adults, though it may occur at any age level. Originally called "dementia praecox" (psychosis of adolescence) because so many cases occur in late adolescence, schizophrenia usually entails a profound degree of psychological withdrawal from others, coupled with a variety of distortions and derangements of thought processes, such as delusions and bizarre thoughts. The "split personality" of the schizophrenic refers to the divorcing of emotional and cognitive processes. Thus, the emotional state of the schizophrenic will very often seem inappropriate to his thought processes and the situations in which he finds himself.

Occurring most often in middle age are the severe depressive states which tend to characterize both manic-depressive and involutional psychoses. The classic *manic-depressive* type alternates between periods of manic excitement with extreme euphoria and periods of utter despair and depression. The manic phases are now much more rare than the depressive. This type of psychosis tends to be recurrent, with periods of remission in which the patient is free of symptoms for months or years at a time. *Involutional melancholia* is often difficult to distinguish from manic-depressive reaction but tends more often to be found in somewhat older patients, since, as the name implies, the symptoms are thought to be related to the involution or decline of sexual functions.

Organic Brain Syndromes. Most important in this category are the mental diseases of old age, *senile dementia* and psychosis with *cerebral arteriosclerosis.* Such disorders produce a variety of symptoms—confusion, suspiciousness, lack of concern for the amenities, loss of control of bodily functions—which make the older person difficult to care for in the small urban household. Although such disorders are associated with organic damage to the brain, the symptomatology also seems to depend upon personality attributes and psychological stresses [38].

Other organic brain syndromes are psychotic reactions stemming from syphilis (paresis), those resulting from chronic alcoholism, and those which are a product of continued trauma to the brain—such as may be received by professional boxers. All these types of mental illness tend to occur much more frequently among males than among females, simply because of the more frequent exposure of males to the etiologically relevant agents or situations.

The Psychoneuroses

Psychoneurotic reactions are disturbances in the functioning of personalities. They do involve "dis-ease," for the chief characteristic of such disorders is intense anxiety. The anxiety may be consciously felt and directly expressed, or unconsciously felt and expresed by various indirect defense mechanisms. The symptoms of the neurosis depend on the way that the person has learned to handle his anxiety. Common forms are the diffuse and uncontrolled *anxiety reaction,* the symbolically focused *phobic reaction* (specific fears), the organically expressed *conversion reaction* (paralysis, tics, and the like), *obsessive-compulsive reactions* in which there is a persistence of unwanted ideas or repetitive impulses to perform irrational acts, and *depressive reactions* in which feelings of guilt are usually involved.

Psychoneuroses were a major reason for rejection of men for Selective Service during World War II and are a major reason for absenteeism and ineffective performance in industry and the occupational sphere generally. They impair the functioning of a very high proportion of the population to some degree and at one time or another. But most psychoneurosis goes untreated, perhaps because it less often involves the acute disruption of life patterns that is found in psychosis.

Psychosomatic Disorders

Somewhat akin to the psychoneuroses are those disorders that manifest themselves in physiological malfunction without apparent organic cause. (The relationships between emotional states and physiological function have been discussed in Chapter 5.) Almost everyone reacts to emotional stress—at least occasionally—with transitory physical discomfort. This may take the form of a headache, an attack of diarrhea, a skin rash, or some other relatively mild symptom. But in some persons the symptoms may be so intense as to thereaten life itself, as in ulcerative colitis, severe asthma, or anorexia nervosa (loss of appetite, often coupled with vomiting). Although psychiatrists are deeply involved in research and treatment relating to such disorders, the fact that the symptomatology is somatic removes these illnesses from the realm generally regarded as mental illness.

THE PREVALENCE OF MENTAL ILLNESS

How widespread is mental illness? The answer depends, of course, on our definition of "mental illness." We might rephrase the question as What degree of mental disorder or upset is serious enough to lead us to count a person "mentally ill" for purposes of health statistics? But even this question is hard to answer. Anyone suffering from a psychosis or a severe psychoneurosis would clearly qualify, but what about occasional emotional upsets that come with stress and fatigue and that might be equated with a bad head cold as a source of discomfort and impairment of function? Almost everyone suffers such upsets at some time, but unless they become frequent or of severe intensity, few people seek psychiatric care for such episodes. Most of us would not apply the term "mental disorder" to such symptoms or episodes; although the current psychiatric nomenclature provides categories for their classification (for example, "transient situational disturbances" and "social maladjustments without manifest psychiatric disorder"), they are clearly distinguished from severe or chronic disorders.

Until after World War II, the amount of mental illness in the United States was commonly equated with the number of persons in hospitals for mental patients—and in the 1940's there were just about as many patients in our mental hospitals, on any given day, as in all hospitals for the treatment of patients with other forms of illness. (Statistics on mental health patients and facilities in the United States are compiled annually by the Biometry Branch, National Institutes of Mental Health. See [32] and [51].) At that time, the mental hospitals constituted our primary—and almost our only—resource for the treatment of mental illness. A person recognized as having a mental disorder of some severity was very likely to be hospitalized, unless he could afford private psychiatric care. On January 1, 1948, there were roughly 600,000 persons in the public mental hospitals of the United States, and another 10,000 in private mental hospitals [51]. At that time there were less than 450 clinics providing outpatient psychiatric care, and roughly half of these concentrated on the treatment of children with behavior problems. Clinics did not then systematically report on their patient loads, but it is doubtful that as many as 50,000 adult patients were treated in clinics other than those of the Veterans Administration.

In 1968, at any given time, there were substantially fewer patients in the mental hospitals of the United States than there had been in 1948—nearly 150,000 less—despite an increase in population of roughly 40,000,000. But, during 1968, it is estimated that nearly 1,500,000 persons were served by outpatient psychiatric clinics. These changing statistics on treated mental illness indicate one major difficulty in ascertaining how much mental illness exists within the population. If we take hospital statistics as an indication of how much severe mental illness there is, we might be inclined to infer that there has been a marked decrease in the past twenty years. On the other hand, clinic statistics might suggest an alarming increase in less severe mental illness. Neither inference would be warranted. In these twenty years there has been a substantial change in modes of treatment and in the allocation of resources for dealing with mental illness. A higher proportion of the population now receives occasional psychiatric care without ever being hospitalized. Moreover, while the number of patients in hospitals on any given day is much less than it was twenty years ago, the number of persons who spend *some* time in a mental hospital has actually increased along with the general population increase. What accounts for the smaller number of patients on any given day is a markedly shorter duration of hospitalization of the average patient. Patients are somewhat more likely to return to the hospital after having been discharged, but the net effect is nevertheless a marked decrease in total time spent in the hospital.

Moreover, many persons suffering from mental illness never see a psychiatrist. Unlike the physically ill, the mentally ill may be unaware of the nature of their difficulties and therefore quite unwilling to seek treatment or help. Almost all neurotic patients, and most psychotics, are frequently aware of being unhappy or upset, but this awareness does not impel them toward medical treatment. Therefore, the number of patients under treatment does not give an accurate estimate of the over-all amount of mental illness in the United States or any other nation or society.

Much effort and ingenuity has gone into attempts to measure the extent of symptoms and impairment resulting from untreated mental disorder. A discussion of the technical problems entailed in such measurement, beyond the scope of the present chapter, is to be found in a number of recent works [13, 66, 75]. Psychiatric examination of a cross-section of the population is simply not feasible, both because of costs and because many people would be unwilling to submit to an examination. And psychological tests and measures of personality, though useful for a rough screening of the population, do not permit an accurate assessment of the individual's ability to function in diverse situations and roles, nor do they permit accurate diagnostic classification.

In the past decade, several major studies have attempted to measure the prevalence of mental illness through the use of interviews with a cross-section of adults in the community, inquiring into their physical health, worries and emotional tensions, relationships with other persons, and other aspects of daily living that would afford information on symptoms and resulting impairment [35, 68]. The interviews are then abstracted and rated by psychiatrists. This approach leads to estimates that roughly 20 to 25 percent of the population suffer or have suffered from significant symptomatology, and that less than a fifth of the population are completely symptom-free. While much useful information has been derived from such surveys, as we shall see shortly, the concept of mental disorder that underlies them is quite different from that used by our psychiatric services. An adequate understanding of the amount and nature of mental disorder in any population requires, then, that one examine the interrelationships among the various indices of psychiatric disability and treated mental illness in that population.

THE SOCIAL EPIDEMIOLOGY OF MENTAL DISORDER

The importance of epidemiological investigations in providing clues about the relationship of social factors to chronic illness has been discussed in Chapter 3. Epidemiological studies have also been undertaken in the field of mental disorder; these examine variations in the rates of hospitalization or of symptomatology in different population groups. Such studies have, however, revealed more about differences in life patterns and the ways in which persons with emotional problems came to attention or treatment than they have revealed about etiological factors. Before examining some of the most salient findings of such studies, we might note the nature of the process of becoming a mental patient.

Stages of Becoming a Patient

Psychosis seldom develops overnight. Studies of the antecedents of hospitalization have found that in most instances there has been a period of months or even years during which the patient has been nervous, upset, moody, or beset by a variety of somatic complaints. Even when more extreme signs of emotional disorder, such as delusions, hallucination, or bizarre behavior, are present, however, the families of the patient frequently interpret these simply as signs of "upsetness" or strain [9]. For many, the realization that mental illness is entailed comes only when some crisis requires that the ill member be restrained or attended to in a manner outside the family's usual repertoire of responses. For long periods, the family may try to protect the ill member or placate him, never realizing that he is ill and needs treatment. Very often, the stresses entailed in trying to live with a mentally ill person will engender mutual hostility and recriminations.

The psychotic person tends to see the problem not in himself but in those around him or in circumstances over which he has no control. He may deny any implication that he is ill or needs help. This denial may be massive and unremitting, or it may alternate with periods of willingness to consider the need for help. Whether the psychotic comes into treatment voluntarily or is committed to a mental hospital by legal action will depend in large part on the kind of treatment facilities available and on the extent to which persuasive communication can be established at some point in the process.

If professional resources for dealing with mental illness are not available, it appears that there is frequently a mobilization of family and friends to deal with the crisis in whatever way the culture defines as appropriate. Reports of psychotic episodes witnessed by anthropologists suggest that there are frequently ritualized ways of redefining the nature of the dilemma confronting the disturbed person, and that hostility and tension may be sufficiently dissolved by these modes of response to permit a reintegration of the individual into stable relationships.

Even where treatment facilities are most fully developed, they are used very differently by different segments of the population. Hollingshead and Redlich [26], studying all persons under psychiatric treatment in New Haven during a given year, found that upper-status patients came into treatment largely as a result of the urging of family and friends, while lower-status patients came into treatment largely because of the reactions of the police or social agencies. Self-referrals are much more frequent among better-educated persons, largely because of their more favorable view of psychiatry.

The kinds of treatment given to a patient, as well as its duration, depend to a significant degree on the social status of the patient and the way he is presented to the treatment agency. Response to the patient often seems to be as much determined by his social characteristics as by the diagnosis he receives. Indeed, diagnosis may itself be influenced by social characteristics. This makes it difficult to compare rates of mental disorder among various population groups, even when the same services are theoretically available to them, and it makes extremely problematic any cross-national or cross-cultural comparisons. One must always ask whether observed variations reflect true differences in the prevalence and incidence of mental illness, or merely differences in social and cultural patterns for dealing with mental illness.

SOCIAL AND CULTURAL FACTORS IN MENTAL ILLNESS

Do some patterns of social organization or cultural emphasis cause more mental illness than others? Is mental illness generally on the rise in modern urban society? We are constantly reminded of the stresses and frustrations imposed upon man in an urban, industrial society, and one might anticipate an increase in the amount of mental illness as a consequence. Insofar as psychosis is concerned, there is no conclusive evidence of any increase and, indeed, there is a good deal of evidence against it. A study of the records of jails and almshouses in Massachusetts more than a century ago suggests that, except for the aged, at least as many people were incarcerated for mental illness then as were hospitalized at the time of peak utilization of mental hospitals [22]. Rates of admission to mental hospitals are in general somewhat lower in rural areas than in large cities, but the difference tends to disappear when one takes into account the differences in available facilities. Moreover, surveys of levels of symptomatology do not suggest any lower levels in rural areas than in cities [8].

Persons who move around a great deal tend to have higher rates of mental illness, but this statement can as readily be turned around: Persons who have mental illness tend to have interpersonal difficulties and to move around a great deal [8]. There is, however, some evidence that migrants living among populations who speak a different language are somewhat more likely to develop paranoid symptomatology—that is, to become suspicious and perhaps delusional—as a consequence of the uncertainties that they experience in relationship with the dominant population group [34].

Differences between the sexes seem largely to reflect cultural definitions of sex roles. Hospitalization of males occurs somewhat more often at the younger ages, but may simply reflect more frequent manifestations of aggression, leading to police arrest, or a low level of social tolerance of males who are unable to meet the social expectation of regular employment. A number of studies suggest that markedly symptomatic women are somewhat more likely to be cared for at home than men with the same level of symptomatology.

Although cultural features markedly color the symptomatology of mental illness and provide diverse roles for the mentally ill, there is no conclusive evidence that cultures differ greatly in rates of psychosis [5, 48]. Murphy has suggested that some cultures impose upon their members lines of action which are seemingly at variance, or unachievable, or confusingly mapped out, and that these impose stresses that may result in increased mental illness [46], but the available data are not adequate to prove the point. Rates of neurosis and personality disorders appear to vary much more than rates of psychosis within different cultural groups, but since the great bulk of such disorders remain untreated in all societies, the inference is based upon impressions and psychological inventories.

The existence of marked differences in rates of hospitalization for mental illness among the social classes has made social status the most intensively studied correlate of mental disorder. The sharpest differences are noted among schizophrenic patients. In New Haven, for eaxmple, Hollingshead and Redlich found that the number of persons under treatment for schizophrenia on any given day was eight times as high in the lowest of five social strata as in the upper two strata [26].

In large part, the higher prevalence of schizophrenia in the lower social stratum reflects the longer duration of hospitalization of schizophrenics from this population. At any given time, for this reason alone, there will be more lower-status persons in hospitals or otherwise under treatment. But it also appears that persons whose social status is lowest are more likely to develop schizophrenia [30, 43, 61]. In general, while there is considerable intergenerational mobility from class to class, with a net upward movement as a result of increases in the average level of education and the higher proportion of white-collar jobs in the occupational structure, persons who become schizophrenic are less likely to move upward, and somewhat more likely to move downward, in the social hierarchy [72]. It is not clear whether the higher prevalence and incidence of schizophrenia at the lower status levels is largely due to the drift into this stratum of persons with a genetic vulnerability to schizophrenia, or whether it also reflects the greater stresses and personal devaluation encountered at the lowest status levels. There is now overwhelming evidence of a genetic component in schizophrenia, but there is reason to believe that overt manifestation of the disorder depends on an interaction between experiential and genetic components [60].

When psychological inventories or psychiatrically evaluated interviews are used as a basis for assessing symptom patterns in the general population, there is no question but that lower-status persons have far more symptoms and are more often impaired by them. A major contribution of the Midtown Manhattan study [68] and the Sterling County study [35] is that they make abundantly clear the discrepancy between the distribution of symptoms and treated mental illness. Outpatient treatment of neuroses is, in most communities, far more common among the middle class than the working class, both because of the cost of treatment and the more favorable attitude toward psychiatry among the middle class. In the working class, far more people "live with" their symptoms than seek professional help. Members of the lower stratum of the working class are subject to the greatest degree of job uncertainty, disorganized community contexts, and a variety of other stressful life circumstances. Moreover, at any given level of external stress, they appear to manifest a greater degree of personal distress, perhaps because their resources for coping with life's problems are much less adequate [33].

Many neurotic, personality, and behavior disorders appear to have their roots in early family life. In recent years psychoanalytic formulations have been buttressed by a large body of research on socialization which attests to the fact that social-role learning and patterns of communication within the family are as important as psychosexual development in influencing the personalities of family members. Some of the most intensive research on family dynamics has come from studies of the families of schizophrenic patients [8, 38, 44, 60]. Parental intrusiveness, conflicting messages at different levels of communication, the breakdown of intergenerational boundaries, and other deviant family patterns are extremely frequent in families containing a schizophrenic child. But whether the patterns are the cause of the schizophrenia, a reflection of genetically transmitted pathology shared by parent and child, or primarily a response to a schizophrenic child is not at all clear, except that there is unequivocally some measure of genetic involvement [60].

PROFESSIONAL RESOURCES FOR DEALING WITH MENTAL DISORDER

Because severe mental disorder constitutes a threat to stable social relationships and often entails long periods of incapacitation, mental illness has been more a matter of governmental concern than other forms of illness. Each state in the United States has enacted laws that specify the circumstances and the procedure by which a person may be declared insane and therefore deprived of his liberty [57]. All states have long provided hospitals for the long-term care of the mentally ill, and now all states support outpatient services as well. Many general hospitals (nearly 1,300 in 1967) now provide beds for psychiatric patients, and an increasing number of communities have day-care and night-treatment programs for mental patients who do not require the full round of institutional care.

State and county mental hospitals are the most costly and heavily staffed of our mental-health facilities. To serve the needs of the roughly 400,000 patients in the public mental hospitals of the United States in 1968, over 200,000 full-time staff members were employed. Only a small fraction of the staffs of mental hospitals are professionals, however. More than half the total consists of nursing assistants or attendants, who provide the bulk of direct care for hospitalized mental patients; another fourth are maintenance personnel concerned entirely with the operation of the physical plant. Psychiatrists and psychiatric residents constitute less than 2 percent of the full-time staff of the hospital, other staff physicians constitute an additional 1 percent, and registered professional nurses roughly 5 percent [51]. Thus it is apparent that the mental hospital, even though far better staffed than in the past, is not equipped to deliver very intensive medical or professional nursing care to the patient population.

As we have observed, there has been a great increase in the provision of outpatient psychiatric services, through *community mental-health clinics*. In 1968 there were 2,300 such clinics in the United States, more than five times the number twenty years earlier. The mental-health clinic is most often a team operation, involving a psychiatrist who serves as director and chief therapist, one or more social workers who conduct intake interviews and provide therapy to less-disturbed patients and to family members, and a clinical psychologist or psychometrician who does diagnostic testing and occasionally conducts research. To a much greater extent than ever before, community clinics are now treating adults with severe emotional problems, combining drug therapy with various forms of group and individual psychotherapy to maintain the patient in the community. As we noted earlier, nearly 1,500,000 persons received diagnostic services or treatment at mental health clinics in 1968, slightly less than two-thirds of whom were 18 years of age or older.

In addition to the hospitals and the clinics, there are the many *community agencies* which provide services to individuals and to families. These may offer specific mental health services—as of many private physicians, school guidance personnel, marriage counselors in social agencies, or clergymen trained in pastoral counseling—or they may serve to direct persons with emotional difficulties to appropriate diagnostic or treatment services [56].

Relatively few of the most highly trained psychiatrists are engaged in treating persons suffering from severe mental disorder. The private practice of psychiatry is vastly more rewarding financially than service in a mental hospital. Intensive psychotherapy with neurotic patients still claims a large part of the time of many psychiatrists in private practice, though more than hitherto now have part-time affiliations with clinics that treat seriously impaired individuals.

Before commenting further on recent developments in the care of patients, we shall turn to a closer look at the functioning of the mental hospital and some of the problems entailed in hospitalization for mental illness.

THE MENTAL HOSPITAL

Our large, prison-like mental hospitals are a heritage of nineteenth-century thinking. They were a response both to humanistic arguments against the jailing of mental patients and to the desire to deal cheaply and efficiently with madmen and misfits by locking them up in relatively isolated institutions where they could be maintained on bare subsistence. Despite the laudable humanistic intentions of some who campaigned for a system of state hospitals, on the whole such hospitals represented a substantial setback in standards of patient care, in comparison with the better asylums and rest homes of the early-nineteenth century [11, 27].

For the patient who is committed to a mental hospital, or who enters voluntarily after he has been threatened with commitment, admission to the mental hospital is often a shattering experience. He may feel betrayed, or at least abandoned, by his family and friends. He may be aware of his aggressive impulses and anxious lest they get out of check (in which case hospitalization and even restraint may be reassuring), but he is also aware of the devaluation of an adult who cannot control his impulses. To go to a mental hospital still conjures up images of being regarded as a "raving maniac," though probably less than it did a decade or two ago. At very least, it constitutes an acknowledgement that one is not able to manage his own affairs. The nature of mental disorder makes it extremely difficult for the newly hospitalized person to take the view that he is simply someone presenting himself for a form of medical treatment. Nor do most of his peers in the community take such a view [10, 11, 52, 67], although the greater utilization of outpatient services as an alternative to hospitalization and the great improvements in the care of mental patients in the past twenty years have probably diminished somewhat the stigmatization of mental patients in general.

Entrance into the mental hospital usually entails giving up both one's freedom of movement and control over one's affairs. Particularly in large public institutions, patients are regimented and "processed" with little regard for their personal feelings or sense of identity. Goffman has characterized the larger mental hospital as a "total" institution, sharing many attributes with prisons, monasteries and concentration camps, all settings in which the individual is an inmate twenty-fours a day [21]. The newly admitted patient seldom receives any introduction to staff or to other patients or any orientation to the regimes and expectations to which he will be subject in the mental hospital. His personal belongings and the trappings which serve to symbolize his identity are often taken from him. He is subject to the rules of the institution, often arbitrarily imposed according to the whims of its least-trained personnel. Under these circumstances, the dominant motivation of the patient is to get out, which entails learning to control or at least conceal certain impulses and to present the kind of demeanor which will lead to release.

Social Structure and Interaction in the Mental Hospital

The cost of maintaining and staffing mental hospitals is a major item in the annual budget of most states. There are constant pressures to hold such costs to a minimum, and so, when governments economize, they frequently do so at the expense of their mental health programs. Salaries for all categories of mental hospital staff tend to be substantially below those for comparable jobs in the larger community. The attendants and nursing aides who make up the great bulk of the staff tend to come from the ranks of the unskilled and poorly educated. There is a tremendous gap in cultural level and social status between the medical staff and the attendant staff. The "mobility-blocked" nature of roles in the mental hospital, coupled with the impossible span of professional control designated by the formal organizational structure and the difference between the goals and conceptions about mental illness held by the medical staff and the attendant staff, gives rise to an informal organizational system quite at variance with the formal system [4, 14, 21].

Although supervision of the wards and all decisions relating to the patients' care and release from the hospital are the responsibilities of the medical personnel, the limited number of physicians available in most public hospitals precludes any substantial amount of contact between the doctor and the patients. The doctors, and even the graduate nurses, must spend much of their time maintaining records and handling problems of patient disposition. In consequence, in many hospitals it is the attendants who control the operations of the wards, largely by their control over the access of patients to the physicians and of the physicians to information about patients. One of the most significant influences for more adequate mental hospital care has been the increased attention in recent years to the recruitment, training, and supervision of the attendant staffs [74].

The situation confronting patients and staff is most dismal in large public hospitals, but problems in this basic relationship are by no means confined to such hospitals. Even in the best private and teaching hospitals, staff members tend to respond to patients in a stereotyped way. In psychoanalytically oriented hospitals, for example, the patient's simplest requests, arising out of the needs of daily life, may be analyzed for hidden meanings rather than being accepted as legitimate statements of need [69]. The patients and the various categories of staff have very different expectations of each other, and misunderstandings frequently lead to mutual avoidance and withdrawal from communication [7]. The provision of a therapeutic milieu is fraught with difficulties. The organization must cope with the diverse needs of patients (many of which have nothing to do with their being ill or disturbed), with the staff's anxieties that inevitably derive from working with disturbed persons, and with the tasks of preparing the patients to return as active participants in community life and resume roles for which the hospital has no counterparts [54].

The care of the mentally ill entails many uncertainties. There is little solid evidence of the effectiveness of most therapies. In consequence, ideologies tend to substitute for solid knowledge, providing a measure of assurance and justification for particular therapeutic efforts but also often obsuring from those who hold the ideologies most strongly the gross inadequacies of many hospital programs [70].

The Changing Patterns of Care of Patients

As we noted earlier, the number of persons hospitalized for mental illness on any given day has been declining for more than fifteen years, despite a large increase in the population. This decline, we recall, reflects a shorter duration of hospitalization of those who enter a mental hospital, rather than a decrease in the number of persons hospitalized in the course of a year. There are several reasons for the decline. Increased federal support of mental health services, and especially of research, has created an awareness of the dangers of long-term hospitalization, which has led to increases in staffing of hospitals and more training of nonprofessional staff members.

The introduction of the tranquilizing drugs in the early 1950's had a spectacular impact. These drugs do not cure mental illness, but they greatly lessen the manifest anxiety and agitation of most patients. By reducing the amount of "acting out" by patients, the tranquilizers had their most outstanding effect on the atmosphere of large, poorly staffed public mental hospitals. Physical care of patients was markedly facilitated, since far less time had to be spent dealing with assualts, incontinence, and other unpleasant and disruptive behavior. Patients were apparently able to communicate their needs and their strengths more adequately to the staff. Professional staffs were, in turn, more willing to try returning the patient to the community in a relatively short period.

Prior to 1950, admission to a public mental hospital with a diagnosis of schizophrenia was almost a guarantee that the individual would be locked up for at least a year. Many patients were retained for decades, partly because most psychiatrists believed that schizophrenia was incurable. Such a belief tended to be a self-fulfilling prophecy, for incarceration in a locked ward, with almost no professional attention and no opportunity to exercise personal responsibility, could hardly prepare a person for a return to normal life. Hence the public fear of the mental hospital, which still persists in large measure, was soundly based.

Now, however, many persons diagnosed as schizophrenic are hospitalized and returned to their normal social roles in the community within one to three months. Hospitalization may, indeed, not even be necessary when outpatient care and drug therapy are available. For example, Passamanick and his associates [49] carried out a carefully controlled study in which persons who had been admitted to a mental hospital with a diagnosis of schizophrenia were examined and then (after eliminating those who appeared potentially suicidal or homicidal) assigned randomly to one of three groups. Members of two of the groups were sent back at once from the hospital to their homes, where they received weekly visits from a public health nurse. Members of one of these groups were prescribed tranquilizers, while members of the other group were given placebos (inert pills). Neither the nurses nor the patients knew who was receiving drugs and who was receiving placebos. The third group of patients remained in the hospital and received standard care. Three-fourths of the patients receiving drug therapy in the community, and a third of those receiving placebos, were able to remain in the community throughout the period of study (which ranged from six to thirty months, depending on when the patient initially entered the hospital).

The possibility of maintaining severely disturbed patients in the community through the use of drugs and outpatient services is not, however, without cost to the family. Careful studies comparing the problems of families of hospitalized patients and those of patients who are retained at home reveal that hospital care more often alleviates both anxiety and financial problems, as Jacqueline Grad shows in her thoughtful discussion of the problem [23]. A recognition of the often disastrous consequences of long-term hospitalization is thus not an argument against the hospitalization of a patient whose behavior is tearing his family apart. Nor can short visits by relatively untrained staff, coupled with the heavy use of drugs, resolve the difficulties of most persons diagnosed as schizophrenic.

At times, as when tension within the family is great and is contributing to the patient's intense stress, hospitalization may provide a respite for patient and family and permit the working out of more satisfactory arrangements. This appears to be true not only when a patient has responsibilities as spouse or parent, but also when older persons are living with their children. A brief stay in a mental hospital, coupled with situational planning and a measure of counseling, can give both patient and family an opportunity for the relaxation of tension and a restructuring of the future.

Return from the Mental Hospital

The return of the patient from the mental hospital to the community is a tremendously important symbolic transition for patient and family, but it does not usually represent a return of the patient to full functioning. Depending on the nature of the illness and the length of hospitalization, the patient may still manifest various symptoms of illness, or at least display uncertainty and anxiety. In most state hospital systems, the patient will be returned home for trial visits or for indefinite periods for up to one year before being formally discharged. If there are periods of regression into more acute stages, the patient can be returned to the hospital without going through additional legal commitment.

Until recently, there was little continuity between the care provided in the mental hospital and the services available to patients and their families in the community. State hospitals had few links with community facilities, largely because they were separately funded and operated. With the marked expansion of community facilities in the 1950's and 1960's and with the development of community mental health centers in the 1960's, closer coordination is being achieved. More states now have halfway houses in which relatively long-term hospital patients may live while working out their transition back to normal life in the community. Many more have provisions for continuing outpatient services.

In general, there are substantial differences in the performance of a patient who has experienced many years of hospitalization and that of the person who was hospitalized for a brief period of acute distress. Quite apart from the psychologically devastating effects which many years in the chronic ward of a mental hospital have on him, the patient is in need of resocialization and acceptance if he is to build up an image of himself as an adequate member of society. After a long interval, the patient's family roles are likely to have been redistributed: He cannot easily fit into the old patterns of expectations, for they have disappeared [10]. Wives who have had to take over the role of breadwinner for the family and who have become accustomed to other responsibilities and freedoms are often reluctant to yield them to the returned husband. Husbands who have worked out new regimes after the hospitalization of their wives may be unwilling to go back to former arrangements. On the other hand, parents who have in the past carried full responsibility for the dependent child are more often willing to accept a reversion to this role and are more tightly bound by prevailing mores to make a home for the child, whatever his age or condition [42].

A number of studies have investigated the relationship between the patient's ability to function in the community and the characteristics of the setting to which he returns. Release from the hospital often depends in part on pressure exerted by family members to have the patient back or, conversely, on their reluctance or even refusal to accept him. Rejection is not common, however, when patients have been hospitalized a relatively short time. Once the patient is returned, the expectations of those with whom he lives become an important factor in influencing his remaining in the community. For example, in a study of a cross-section of male psychotics released from mental hospitals in the Boston area, Freeman and Simmons found a marked difference between the work performance and social participation of adult patients living in parental homes and those in conjugal settings [19]. More than three-fifths of the former patients in conjugal settings were rated high in both work performance and social participation, as against less than one-fifth of those in parental families. Very few of the patients who returned to and remained at home with their wives were rated low in performance. It also appeared that low performance more often resulted in rehospitalization in the conjugal family while being tolerated to a much greater degree in the parental family. A subsequent study [20] by the same investigators revealed that, in general, patients who returned to parental homes performed at lower levels than those who returned to their conjugal families. The former group was *not,* however, more successful in remaining in the community, even though those who did remain were more problematic. While there were still some differences in the degree of tolerance of deviance, it appeared that in both groups the manifestation of bizarre symptoms was most decisive in leading to the patient's return to the hospital.

In a study of chronic schizophrenic patients discharged from mental hospitals near London, Brown and his associates made somewhat similar findings [6]. Patients returned from the hospital to parental homes or to live with siblings were, in this instance, somewhat more likely to remain in the community than those who returned to live with their wives. Most successful of all, among these chronic patients, were those who arranged to live in lodgings where they could avoid intimate contact with others. For these patients, all of whom had been hospitalized for at least two years, it appeared that the possibility of remaining in the community was maximized when family pressures and obligations were minimal. It should be remembered, nevertheless, that return to full participation in the community is most often accomplished by currently married patients and least often accomplished by patients who had never attained this hallmark of adult status.

GOVERNMENTAL POLICY AND RECENT DEVELOPMENTS

Outpatient clinics developed rapidly in the United States after the passage of the National Mental Health Act of 1946. So did research on mental illness, which had previously received no federal support. Federal leadership spurred many of the states to improve their hospital systems and to fund their mental-health services far more adequately. Nevertheless, until the mid-1950's, when hospital populations began to decline, progress was hardly visible.

Ten to twenty years ago, the most promising efforts to deal with mental disorder through the development of comprehensive mental health programs were to be found in Great Britain and the countries of Northwestern Europe. Far fewer patients in Great Britain were being forcibly committed to mental hospitals, far more wards of mental hospitals were unlocked, and quite clearly patients responded favorably to such circumstances. Despite the reservations of some American psychiatrists (who believed that American patients had basically different orientations than British patients), a few hospitals in the United States began to unlock many of their wards. Here, too, patients responded favorably. The past decade has seen much wider use of unlocked wards.

In 1955 the Congress appropriated a substantial sum for a thorough nationwide analysis of the human aspects and the economics of mental illness. To carry out this analysis, a Joint Commission on Mental Health and Illness was established cooperatively by a number of professional organizations. It resulted in a series of reports, of which the final summary statement [1] became a point of departure for subsequent governmental policy. At the urging of President Kennedy, Congress enacted the Community Mental Health Centers Act of 1963, which authorized large appropriations for financing up to two-thirds of the costs of community mental health centers. Subsequent legislation authorized grants to assist in the staffing of such centers. Thus the federal government has played a preeminent role in furthering the development of more adequate mental health services.

Despite great gains, we are still far from meeting the mental health needs of very large sectors of the population. Thirty years ago, Kingsley Davis pointed out the middle-class bias of the mental health movement in the United States [12]. In the past three decades, study after study has attested to our failure to understand the needs of lower-status persons faced with mental disorder or with severe problems of living. Large segments of American psychiatry are at least aware of the problem now, yet few psychiatrists are adequately trained to deal with many of the issues that confront them when they seek to develop services to meet community needs [41]. Indeed, few are able to assess such needs adequately. Much that is currently being written about "community psychiatry" is unrealistic if not naïve. Too often psychiatrists claim jurdisdiction over problems that they are not fully competent to deal with, although this is not to suggest that the psychiatrist's role in society should be limited to treatment of the mentally ill. Increasingly, psychiatrists are contributing much-needed perspectives to social planning and educational programs. Mental health problems are frequently intertwined with other health problems and with general conditions of life. As a consequence, issues arise both as to the allocation of resources and the most effective auspices for tackling the underlying sources of difficulty. These issues will probably not be resolved until alternative plans have been tried out under various auspices. There are a number of hopeful developments, especially in programs that do not separate mental health from the rest of health care and that involve the local population in the planning and operation of the program.

Perhaps the greatest promise for the future is in the further development of a broadly based social psychiatry. Long-term systematic study of the distribution and correlates of mental illness can serve in the design of more realistic, flexible treatment programs aimed at meeting the needs of specific population groups. Then intensive study in a variety of communities will be needed to maximize the effectiveness of such programs. Certain of the severe disorders that are frequently encountered now will probably yield eventually to drug therapy or other biological interventions (just as paresis yielded to penicillin and psychosis with pellagra disappeared with the administration of vitamins). Even so, it is scarcely to be doubted that a wide variety of mental health problems, closely associated with other life problems, will remain. We shall still need more adequate knowledge of the ways in which distressed persons can best be recognized, given assistance, and reincorporated into full social participation.

REFERENCES

1. *Action for Mental Health: Final Report of the Joint Commission on Mental Health.* New York: Basic Books, Inc., Publishers, 1961.
2. ALBEE, GEORGE W., *Mental Health Manpower Trends.* New York: Basic Books, Inc., Publishers, 1959.
3. American Psychiatric Association, *Diagnostic and Statistical Manual of Mental Disorders* (2nd ed.). Washington, D.C.: American Psychiatric Association, 1968.
4. BELKNAP, IVAN, *Human Problems of a State Mental Hospital.* New York: McGraw-Hill Book Company, 1956.
5. BENEDICT, PAUL R. AND IRVING JACKS, "Mental Illness in Primitive Societies," *Psychiatry*, 17 (November, 1954), 377–90.
6. BROWN, GEORGE W., "Experiences of Discharged Chronic Schizophrenic Patients in Various Types of Living Group," *The Milbank Memorial Fund Quarterly*, 37 (April, 1959), 105–31.
7. CAUDILL, WILLIAM, *The Mental Hospital as a Small Society.* Cambridge, Mass.: Harvard University Press, 1958.
8. *Causes of Mental Disorders: A Review of Epidemiological Knowledge.* New York: Milbank Memorial Fund, 1961.
9. CLAUSEN, JOHN A., *Sociology and the Field of Mental Health.* New York: Russell Sage Foundation, 1956.
10. ——— AND MARIAN R. YARROW, eds., "The Impact of Mental Illness on the Family," *Journal of Social Issues*, 11 (1955), 3–67.
11. CUMMING, ELAINE AND JOHN CUMMING, *Closed Ranks.* Cambridge, Mass.: Harvard University Press, 1957.

12. Davis, Kingsley, "Mental Hygiene and the Class Structure," *Psychiatry*, 1 (February, 1938), 55–65.
13. Dohrenwend, Bruce P. and Barbara Snell Dohrenwend, *Social Status and Psychological Disorder: A Causal Inquiry.* New York: John Wiley & Sons, Inc., 1969.
14. Dunham, H. Warren and S. Kirson Weinberg, *The Culture of the State Mental Hospital.* Detroit: Wayne State University Press, 1960.
15. Eaton, Joseph W. and Robert J. Weil, *Culture and Mental Disorders.* New York: The Free Press, 1955.
16. *Encyclopedia of Mental Health.* New York: Franklin Watts, 1963.
17. Faris, Robert E. L. and H. Warren Dunham, *Mental Disorders in Urban Areas.* Chicago: University of Chicago Press, 1939.
18. Freeman, Howard E. and Ozzie G. Simmons, "Feeling of Stigma Among Relatives of Former Mental Patients," *Social Problems*, 8 (Spring, 1961), 312–21.
19. ———, "Mental Patients in the Community: Family Settings and Performance Levels," *American Sociological Review*, 23 (April, 1958), 147–54.
20. ———, *The Mental Patient Comes Home.* New York: John Wiley & Sons, Inc., 1963.
21. Goffman, Erving, *Asylums.* Garden City, N.Y.: Doubleday & Company, Inc., 1961.
22. Goldhamer, Herbert and Andrew Marshall, *Psychosis and Civilization.* New York: The Free Press, 1953.
23. Grad, Jacqueline, "A Two Year Follow-Up" in Richard H. Williams and Lucy D. Ozarin (eds.), *Community Mental Health: An International Perspective.* San Francisco: Jossey–Bass, 1968, pp. 429–54.
24. Gurin, Gerald, Joseph Veroff, and Sheila Feld, *Americans View Their Mental Health.* New York: Basic Books, Inc., Publishers, 1953.
25. Hammer, Muriel, "Influence of Small Social Networks as Factors in Mental Hospital Admission," *Human Organization*, 22 (Winter, 1964), 243–51.
26. Hollingshead, August B. and Frederick C. Redlich, *Social Class and Mental Illness.* New York: John Wiley Sons, Inc., 1958.
27. Jones, Kathleen, *Lunacy, Law and Conscience: 1744–1845.* New York: Humanities Press, 1955.
28. Jones, Maxwell, *The Therapeutic Community.* New York: Basic Books, Inc., Publishers, 1953.
29. Katz, Martin M., Jonathan O. Cole, and Walter E. Barton, eds., *The Role and Methodology of Classification in Psychiatry and Psychopathology.* Chevy Chase, Md.: U.S. Department of Health, Education, and Welfare, 1968.
30. Kohn, Melvin L., "Social Class and Schizophrenia: A Critical Review," in *The Transmission of Schizophrenia*, ed. David Rosenthal and Seymour S. Kety. London: Pergamon Press, 1968.
31. ——— and John A. Clausen, "Social Isolation and Schizophrenia," *American Sociological Review*, 20 (June, 1955), 265–73.
32. Kramer, Morton, "Epidemiology, Biostatistics, and Mental Health Planning," in *Psychiatric Epidemiology and Mental Health Planning*, Psychiatric Research Report No. 22, American Psychiatric Association. Washington, D.C., 1967.
33. Langner, Thomas S. and Stanley T. Michael, *Life Stress and Mental Health.* New York: The Free Press, 1963.
34. Leighton, Alexander H., John A. Clausen, and Robert N. Wilson, eds., *Explorations in Social Psychiatry.* New York: Basic Books, Inc., Publishers, 1957.
35. Leighton, Dorothea C. et al., *The Character of Danger: Psychiatric Symptoms in Selected Communities.* New York: Basic Books, Inc., Publishers, 1963.
36. Lemert, Edwin M., "Paranoia and the Dynamics of Exclusion," *Sociometry*, 25 (March, 1962), 3–20.
37. Lennard, Henry L. and Arnold Bernstein, *The Anatomy of Psychotherapy.* New York: Columbia University Press, 1960.

38. Lidz, Theodore, Stephen Fleck, and Alice R. Cornelison, *Schizophrenia and the Family*. New York: International Universities Press, Inc., 1965.
39. Lowenthal, Marjorie F., Paul L. Berkman et al., *Aging and Mental Disorder in San Francisco: A Social Psychiatric Study*. San Francisco: Jossey-Bass, Inc., 1967.
40. Malzberg, Benjamin and Everett S. Lee, *Migration and Mental Disease*. New York: Social Science Research Council, 1956.
41. Mechanic, David, *Mental Health and Social Policy*. Englewood Cliffs, N.J.: Prentice-Hall, 1969.
42. Mills, Enid, *Living with Mental Illness*. London: Routledge & Kegan Paul, Ltd., 1962.
43. Mishler, Elliot G. and Norman A. Scotch, "Sociocultural Factors in the Epidemiology of Schizophrenia: A Review," *Psychiatry*, 26 (1963), 315–51.
44. Mishler, Elliot G. and Nancy E. Waxler, *Interaction in Families: An Experimental Study of Family Processes and Schizophrenia*. New York: John Wiley & Sons, Inc., 1968.
45. Murphy, H. B. M. et al., "A Cross-cultural Survey of Schizophrenic Symptomatology," *International Journal of Social Psychiatry*, 9 (1963), 237–49.
46. ———, "Sociocultural Factors in Schizophrenia: A Compromise Theory" in Joseph Zubin and F. A. Freyhan (eds.), *Social Psychiatry*. New York: Grune and Stratton, 1968, pp. 74–92.
47. Nunnally, Jum C., *Popular Conceptions of Mental Health*. New York: Holt, Rinehart & Winston, Inc., 1961.
48. Opler, Marvin K., *Culture and Social Psychiatry*. New York: Atherton Press, 1967.
49. Pasamanick, Benjamin, ed., *Epidemiology of Mental Disorder*. Washington, D.C.: American Association for the Advancement of Science, 1959.
50. Pasamanick, Benjamin, Frank Scarpetti, and Simon Dinitz, *Schizophrenics in the Community: An Experimental Study in the Prevention of Hospitalization*. New York: Appleton-Century-Crofts, 1967.
51. *Patients in Mental Institutions: 1967*. Washington, D.C.: Government Printing Office, 1969. Published annually in several parts.
52. Philips, Derek L., "Rejection: A Possible Consequence of Seeking Help for Mental Disorders," *American Sociological Review*, 28 (December, 1963), 963–73.
53. Phillips, Leslie, *Human Adaptation and Its Failures*. New York: Academic Press, Inc., 1968.
54. Rapoport, Robert N., *Community as Doctor*. London: Tavistock Publications, 1960.
55. *Report of the Royal Commission on the Law Relating to Mental Illness and Mental Deficiency*. London: Her Majesty's Stationery Office, 1957.
56. Robinson, Reginald, David F. DeMarche, and Mildred K. Wagle, *Community Resources in Mental Health*. New York: Basic Books, Inc., Publishers, 1960.
57. Roemer, Ruth, "Mental Health Legislation Affecting Patient Care," *American Journal of Public Health*, 52 (April, 1962), 592–99.
58. Rogler, Lloyd H. and August B. Hollingshead, *Trapped: Families and Schizophrenia*. New York: John Wiley, & Sons, Inc., 1965.
59. Rosen, George, *Madness in Society: Chapters in the Historical Sociology of Mental Illness*. Chicago: University of Chicago Press, 1968.
60. Rosenthal, David and Seymour S. Kety, eds., *The Transmission of Schizophrenia*. London: Pergamon Press, 1968.
61. Rushing, William A., "Two Patterns in the Relationship between Social Class and Mental Hospitalization," *American Sociological Review*, 34 (August, 1969), 533–42.
62. Sampson, Harold, Sheldon L. Messinger, and Robert D. Towne, *Schizophrenic Women: Studies in Marital Crisis*. New York: Atherton Press, 1964.
63. Sarbin, Theodore R., *Studies in Behavior Pathology*. New York: Holt, Rinehart & Winston, Inc., 1961.
64. Scheff, Thomas J., *Being Mentally Ill: A Sociological Theory*. Chicago:

Aldine Publishing Company, 1966.

65. ——— "The Societal Reaction to Deviance: Ascriptive Elements in the Psychiatric Screening of Mental Patients in a Midwestern State," *Social Problems*, 11 (Spring, 1964), 401–13.

66. SELLS, SAUL, *The Definition and Measurement of Mental Health*. Washington, D.C.: Government Printing Office, 1969.

67. SPITZER, STEPHEN P. AND NORMAN K. DENZIN, *The Mental Patient: Studies in the Sociology of Deviance*. New York: McGraw-Hill Book Company, 1968.

68. SROLE, LEO et al., *Mental Health in the Metropolis*. New York: McGraw-Hill Book Company, 1962.

69. STANTON, ALFRED H. AND MORRIS S. SCHWARTZ, *The Mental Hospital*. New York: Basic Books, Inc., Publishers, 1954.

70. STRAUSS, ANSELM et al., *Psychiatric Ideologies and Institutions*. New York: The Free Press, 1964.

71. SZASZ, THOMAS S., *The Myth of Mental Illness*. New York: Hoeber-Harper, 1961.

72. TURNER, R. J. AND M. O. WAGENFELD, "Occupational Mobility and Schizophrenia: An Assessment of the Social Causation and Social Selection Hypotheses," *American Sociological Review*, 32 (September, 1968), 104–13.

73. WEINBERG, S. KIRSON, ed., *The Sociology of Mental Disorders: Analyses and Readings in Psychiatric Sociology*. Chicago: Aldine Publishing Company, 1967.

74. U.S. Public Health Service, *The Psychiatric Aide in State Mental Hospitals*, Publication No. 1286. Washington, D.C.: Government Printing Office, 1965.

75. ZUBIN, JOSEPH, ed., *Field Studies in the Mental Disorders*. New York: Grune & Stratton, Inc., 1961.

76. ——— AND FRITZ A. FREHAN, eds., *Social Psychiatry*. New York: Grune & Stratton, Inc., 1968.

part two

PRACTITIONERS, PATIENTS, AND MEDICAL SETTINGS

8

MEDICAL EDUCATION

Howard S. Becker, Blanche Geer, and Stephen J. Miller

A medical career requires long years of training and study. In 1963, some 8,500 students entered eighty-one medical schools to begin four years of undergraduate medical training. Since then the number of students entering medical schools each year has increased, and new medical schools have been established. Today more than 11,000 students begin training every year at 107 medical schools in the United States.

Sociologists have conducted numerous studies of medical education. Medical schools are ideal laboratories for the study of such sociological problems as the structure of complex institutions, the socialization of adults, and group organization. Though sociologists do not agree completely about the purpose of such research, they have produced a body of findings, hypotheses, and insights of interest to medical educators as well as sociologists.

Medical educators worry more now than in the past about the training they provide their students: They worry about the kinds of physicians being turned out; they have begun to experiment with new methods of selection; they try new teaching methods; and they redesign their curricula. The viewpoint and findings of sociological research may help them to deal with the problems of medical education and effect changes in the educational process.

RECRUITMENT

Medical students tend to be recruited from the higher socioeconomic groups in our society. More than half of those graduating in 1960 had fathers who were professionals, proprietors, or managers [31]. On the other hand, a substantial minority had fathers in white-collar, manual, or farm work. In the period from 1900 to 1950, recruitment was increasingly democratized, and progressively increasing proportions of physicians came from lower ranks in the social structure [1]. Their proportion will continue to increase as medical schools actively search among minorities for students that can be recruited to medicine.

The process of recruitment into medicine—the choice of a medical career and progressive commitment to it—appears to vary greatly. Many doctors come from families where the father or a close relative is a practicing physician. In these cases, the process described by Oswald Hall probably is crucial:

> ... one can see why doctors tend to be recruited from the families of professional workers. The latter possess the mechanisms for generating and nurturing the medical ambition. Only the members of a profession can translate the public protestations of the profession into the vernacular of useful advice.... In most cases family or friends played a significant role by envisaging the career line and reinforcing the efforts of the recruit. They accomplished the latter by giving encouragement, helping establish the appropriate routines, arranging the necessary privacy, discouraging anomalous behavior, and defining the day-to-day rewards [16].

Other students have no such advantages. They make their decision to enter medicine somewhat later. We know little about the processes involved, about the way ambitions are generated and nurtured without parental help [30]; and cf. Chapter 9 of this work, on the recruitment of nurses. We know more about the processes by which students choose particular careers in medicine. The medical school curriculum provides opportunities for medical specialists to recruit colleagues and successors by using the students' time to create favorable impressions of their particular specialties [5].

THE EFFECTS OF MEDICAL EDUCATION

Much of the research done by sociologists on medical education has concerned itself with the consequences of medical education for the student. How does he change over the four years? In what ways does his experience in school affect him? In what ways has it left him untouched? How will his experience in school affect his practice as a doctor?

A medical education, first of all and most obviously, gives the student the rudiments of medical knowledge and technique. He learns the signs and symptoms of many diseases. He learns how to take a medical history from a patient and how to perform a physical examination. He learns to order laboratory tests and to interpret their results. He acquires the skill of arriving at a diagnosis by deductive reasoning. He learns the various methods of treatment available for the conditions he diagnoses.

The efficiency of the modern medical school in inculcating information is attested by the students' success in passing national board examinations and state licensing examinations. Yet the acquisition of knowledge, the most obvious effect of medical education, may not be lasting. Peterson et al., in a study of general practitioners in North Carolina, found only a very slight relationship between the rank the doctor held in his medical school graduating class and the quality of his practice. Doctors who had ranked high in their graduating classes were only a little more likely to perform a complete physical examination than those who had ranked poorly. Those who ranked in the top 30 percent of their graduating classes were likely to practice in a more knowledgeable way but "the difference is not striking, and the range of performance even among the top group of students was wide." Furthermore, even this slight difference disappears among doctors who have been out of school more than a few years. The relationship between rank in graduating class and quality of practice appeared only among men between 28 and 35, who had just begun to practice, and disappeared completely among those over 35 [29]. What one learns in school, then, may not be as important as the conditions under which one practices afterward: If patients and colleagues do not expect a doctor to maintain a high level of medical knowledge, he may quickly lose it.

Sociologists, in fact, have concerned themselves less with the learning of specific medical facts and techniques than with the more generalized effects of medical education. In particular, they have studied the medical student's acquisition of the values of the medical profession. They assume that the institutional system of medicine, if it is to perform effectively the necessary function of maintaining the level of health in the society, must operate on the basis of such values, for example, as affective neutrality and universalism. If this is the case, physicians (who occupy the key positions in the institutional system) must internalize these values. The medical school prepares doctors for their institutional roles by inculcating them.

Fox has argued that medical students acquire important values characteristic of the medical profession through the influence of their day-to-day experience in the medical school [14]. For instance, she suggests that students develop a tolerance for uncertainty, a characteristic point of view the practicing physician must have if he is to perform successfully. Similarly, she finds that students develop the ability to live up to the norm of detached concerns: They learn how to be interested in a patient without becoming emotionally involved.

A study at the University of Kansas medical school concluded that students acquired at least the knowledge of certain basic medical values—two of which were likely to be important parts of the culture of medicine: clinical experience and medical responsibility. Clinical experience is experience gained from actual medical practice, as opposed to that acquired from laboratory research or reading books and articles. Medical responsibility is the responsibility of the doctor for the welfare of his patient; it is the responsibility he has for the damage he may do to a patient if he performs badly and, conversely, for the good he can do if he performs properly [4]. It may not be as correct to say that students acquired "the values of experience and responsibility" as to say that they learned to think in the terms suggested by these phrases, that they acquired the attitudes associated with these phrases. While we do not know how long they continue to think in these terms, the evidence showed that they tended to organize their own views of their medical future in these terms. They made choices among kinds of internships on the basis, for instance, of how much responsibility each kind allowed them to exercise. Similarly, they use the notion of medical responsibility in assessing the desirability of possible specialties and organizational settings for practice or further training [4].

Further research is needed to discover the extent to which practicing physicians base their actions on the values of experience and responsibility, and into situations in medical practice in which such values are or are not maintained. The value placed on experience and responsibility, however, persists during subsequent stages of medical education. Interns, for example, use perspectives associated with experience and responsibility as a rationale for "learning by doing," the prevailing principle of graduate medical education [27].

Lay people, physicians, and sociologists alike have taken the view that one major effect of a medical education is to make the medical student more cynical and less idealistic. This view rests for the most part on the common observation that medical students lose interest in patients as people and come to regard them as mere embodiments of disease entities. Students appear to become callous in the face of death and human suffering. Eron, for instance, found that medical students tended to score higher on a "Cynicism" scale and lower on a "Humanitarian" scale as they moved through the four years of school [13]. Similarly, Christie and Merton report that, on a scale which measures "Machiavellianism," seniors from several medical schools score higher than college students, business executives, or Washington lobbyists [9]. Nathanson, comparing interviews of freshmen and senior medical students, concludes that freshmen are oriented to the interests of the patient and think of the relationship among colleagues as potentially subversive, while seniors stress the need for preserving the solidarity and protecting the interests of the professional group [28].

Nathanson, however, puts the matter of idealism and cynicism in a different light. She concludes, on the basis of her interview data, that students' conceptions of the doctor's role become more specific and less stereotyped as they go through school [26]. The findings of the Kansas study suggest that the apparent cynicism of the medical student is actually a consequence of the greater specificity of his views [4]. His attitudes are specific to his role as student. He tends to ignore death and human suffering because, being a student and not a practicing physician, he is not in a position to do anything about either. He tends to regard patients as objects from which he can learn. In the second place, students' ideas become much more specifically medical. When they enter school, they have only the ordinary lay notions about medicine. Many of these are unrealistic and would not serve as a practical guide to a physician's activity. For instance, as both the Nathanson and Kansas studies show, medical students enter school desiring to "help" people, but with no technical understanding of how to do it. As they go through medical school they discover specific things that ought to be done. In short, while students may (from the layman's point of view) acquire a cynical veneer during the four years of medical school, they also acquire specific notions of how to put into effect the underlying idealism with which they entered medical school, and they propose to do it when they do become practicing physicians [3, 6].

Another effect of medical education is a growing tendency of the student as he moves through school to develop a professional self-image—to take on the identity of a doctor. Huntington showed that the proportion of students who thought of themselves primarily as doctors rather than students increased regularly, from 31 percent in the first year to 83 percent at the end of the fourth year. She also showed that the student's tendency to think of himself primarily as a doctor is related to the kind of person he is dealing with. Students do not think the faculty define them as doctors, and in dealing with faculty they do not think of themselves as doctors. On the other hand, they think patients do define them as doctors, and 31 percent of them view themselves accordingly [19]. (We should note that these students are from Western Reserve, a school in which students have close and continuing contact with patients from the beginning of the first year.)

Similarly, Nathanson found that freshmen do not think of themselves as doctors, but that seniors finally become satisfied that their image of themselves as doctors is accepted by others. However, students complain about not being recognized as doctors by their teachers during the third year, particularly about not being given sufficient responsibility for patients, something they regarded as an essential component of the doctor's role [28].

A final question which has provoked much research concerns the effect medical school has on the career choices made by the graduating student. Does it affect his decision to go into general practice or to specialize? Does it affect his choice of a specialty?

Several studies indicate that medical school causes students to shift their preference from a general to a specialized practice. However, this simple statement masks a complex process. A number of students apparently enter medical school definitely intending to specialize, and in the main they do not change their minds. Another group definitely intends to go into general practice, and a few of these are likely to change their minds and decide that they would prefer to specialize. A sizable number of students enter medical school not knowing for sure what they want to do: It is this undecided group that accounts for the rise in the number of students who intend to specialize. The same is also true of interns, who can enter practice or choose among the specialties. Many who do not choose to enter practice may not know what else they want to do until as late as the end of the first year of a residency [27]. In short, the educational experience affects mainly those who have made no firm career plans, pushing them in the direction of particular specialties [4, 11, 15, 17, 21, 23].

If medical education affects the career plans of those who are undecided, what accounts for the choices of those who have already made their minds up when they enter school? The answer appears to be related to the student's social background. Students who come from low income families, who come from rural areas, who have had greater financial difficulty in getting through school, tend to prefer general practice, and the more well-to-do prefer to specialize [11]. This is undoubtedly accounted for by the fact that specialization requires a considerably longer period of training, during which the student makes very little money. Only those whose family background permits them to feel they can afford this extra period of low income are likely to choose specialization. New research will be needed to determine the choices of the Afro-Americans and Spanish-Americans who are being admitted in increasing numbers to medical schools. Will they, for example, choose to specialize or, like whites of comparable economic backgrounds, prefer general practice?

Why do the undecided (and a few of those who have decided early on general practice) eventually choose to specialize? Evidence from several studies indicates that students come to believe the body of knowledge necessary to perform adequately in general practice is too extensive to acquire in the relatively short time they spend in medical school and internship [4, 14, 23, 27]. In fact, many doubt that anyone can properly master all the knowledge necessary. Therefore, they may decide to practice in a limited field.

The effect of the medical school experience on a student's choice of specialty seems to be indirect. Most students change their choice of specialty while they are in school. In one study, only one-fifth of the students consistently chose the same field through all four years of school. However, many of them shifted back and forth and ended up choosing the one they had started with [30].

In short, it appears that medical school does not operate to produce a firm choice of a specialty. But it does have an effect. The Kansas study found that, while students did not make firm choices of specialties, they acquired relatively stable criteria for choosing among specialties. Students varied—both among themselves and in the course of time—in the importance they attached to different criteria. They also varied a great deal in how they assessed various specialties in relation to these criteria. They might disagree among themselves as to whether a particular specialty was interesting, provided an adequate income, and so on [4].

The Kansas study found that idealistic criteria, such as the intrinsic medical interest of a field and the ability to help patients, ranked very high, while wages and hours were seldom considered [4]. This finding is supported by the results of a survey of a national sample of American medical students. Cahalan, Collette, and Hilmer [6] report that the reasons most often given by medical students for preferring a specialty were: (1) the intellectual challenge and learning opportunity provided by the specialty—33 percent; (2) the attractiveness of the subject matter or aims of the specialty—24 percent; (3) the certainty of benefits to patients—18 percent; (4) the comprehensiveness of the specialty—16 percent; and (5) a preference for dealing with the type of patients to be treated —14 percent. Beale and Kriesberg, analyzing other data from the same survey, report that while the number of students who think that income and hours of work are important tends to rise during the years in medical school, sizable majorities in each school year say that having the opportunity to know their patients well and meeting particularly challenging diagnostic problems will be most important in their choices of a specialty [3].

The increase in medical knowledge has fostered the growth of medical specialties. More and more students, however, are apparently concerned with the health of communities or populations rather than with the treatment of individuals with special problems or diseases [25]. The increasing number of students with this apparent concern has caused medical schools to evaluate their curricula with regard to their relevance to health and the community. Future research will determine the effect of changes in curriculum on students' knowldege of the relationship between health, demographic characteristics, and socioeconomic conditions of populations. But entering students are apparently interested in practicing medicine of the more general sort, and medical schools are experimenting with curriculum revisions that would provide relevant training. The changes can be expected to provide an alternative to specialization and, thereby, reduce the number of students available for recruitment by the traditional specialties of medicine.

To sum up, the effects of medical school are not clear-cut or easy to discern. Students learn medical facts and acquire a knowledge of medical techniques. They acquire a working understanding of certain basic medical values, such as clinical experience and medical responsibility. They become less generally idealistic, in a lay sense, and more specifically idealistic in medical terms. They begin to think about possible modes of practice and choose among these, developing criteria on which to base their choices from their experience in the medical school.

One thing is certain: they never develop exactly as the faculty would wish them to. Medical educators are always uneasy, wishing they could do something to give their students more knowledge, better values, and more worthwhile perspectives on medical practice. To understand why students learn some things and do not learn others, we must understand the nature of the student's experience in medical school: the situation he faces, the resources he has to deal with them, and the solutions he eventually finds for the problems his situation poses.

THE MEDICAL SCHOOL AND THE HOSPITAL ENVIRONMENT

We should say at the outset that this discussion is largely based on a report of the Kansas study [4]. Although we think the school typical of most medical schools at present, there are certain variations in curriculum and emphasis. In a few schools even freshmen see patients; in others, students get little clinical experience. Several schools involve students heavily in research, and in others the standard four-year program has recently been combined with undergraduate studies. These variations in curriculum may well produce different patterns of experience for students from that given here, but until extensive research has been done, the effects will remain undetermined.

The environment freshmen encounter when they enter medical school is more academic than medical. Though more schools are involving clinicians in the teaching of preclinical subjects, the students taking courses in the preclinical sciences (anatomy, biochemistry, physiology, and the like) are taught by the Ph.D.'s whose career interests lie in the research of their disciplines rather than in medical practice. The student is further separated from the faculty because the large class is taught as a unit in which all students do the same work at the same time. It is a familiar environment—the same round of lectures, laboratories, reading, and examinations the student has known throughout his years in school and college.

The emphasis upon the academic, and particularly upon examinations, catches the typical freshman unprepared. He seldom, if ever, sees clinical personnel or patients. He does not expect to begin treating patients right away and knows there will be courses and tests, but he expects medical school to be different from college, where much of his work seemed to have little direct bearing on his personal goals. In medical school, he thinks, everything will have practical application. He enters medical school convinced that medicine is the best of all professions and he is highly motivated to learn everything the school can teach about what one must know in order to practice medicine [4].

The freshmen's values lead them to work seventy to eighty hours a week in the early months of medical school, but they find that no matter how hard they work, they cannot learn everything. Faced with an apparently insoluble problem, they enter a period of doubt and confusion, marked by increasing discussions with fellow students about the best way to study. The difficulty of the first examinations upset many students accustomed to good grades in college. Eventually, the freshmen agree that the best thing to do is to stop trying to learn everything and to decide, instead, which things are most important and concentrate on them [4].

At first students are divided on what criterion to use in selecting what is important. Some choose the things they think will be important when they begin practice, others decide the most important thing is to pass examinations. Many students question the relevance of required courses and examinations, but most try to find out what the faculty wants them to know. They study only the things that are likely to appear on examinations. Their level of effort remains high, but they direct their efforts toward finding the most economical ways of learning; nearly all members of the class cooperate in sharing information derived from faculty "tips" and files of old examinations [4]. Thus, students find a collective solution to their common pressing problem: that there is more to learn than they have time for.

In many ways, the students' collective attitudes and the student culture these comprise run counter to faculty wishes. The freshmen work very hard —and the faculty appreciates this— but they solve the problem of having too much to learn by directing their efforts toward finding out "what the faculty wants" and studying the things that will be on examinations—a solution far from satisfactory to the teacher who wants students to think for themselves and work up to their own capacities. Freshmen often reject faculty efforts to get them to adopt critical attitudes toward textbooks; they seldom (from the faculty point of view) take enough interest in theory and research. While there is disagreement among first-year faculty members on the proper direction of student effort, most of them find the freshmen too pragmatic and fact-bound [4].

In the clinical years, the student faces additional problems, arising from his new situation as part of the hospital environment. Academic studies now share importance with his new role as an apprentice who learns by doing many of the things his teacher does. Under the supervision of staff physicians and residents, the student takes histories from patients, performs physical examinations, undertakes therapeutic procedures, and makes his own differential diagnoses. He must still deal with the faculty as teachers and examiners, but he now has the additional problem of working closely with fellow students in the small groups in which they are assigned to ward duties on the various hospital services, and of carrying forward his learning in the hierarchical organization of the hospital where many others precede him in access to his chief source of learning, the patient [4, 27].

Clinical faculty members are practicing physicians with many duties besides that of teaching medical students. They also teach and supervise the work of resident physicians and interns, and they also have medical responsibility for patients and administrative responsibilities on their wards. This means that the medical student is now at the bottom of the ladder, outranked in experience, responsibility, and access to the faculty by a hierarchy of other learners. The student has the further handicap that, of all these categories of learners, he is the only one without legal authority to practice medicine.

The very high status of his physician-teachers, his own lowly place in the hospital hierarchy, and the introduction of patients as a chief source of learning provide the student with many new problems. Most of his examinations are now oral; he also has frequent examination-like encounters at a patient's bedside or in the hall during rounds, when the faculty quizzes him on the diagnosis and progress of a patient he has been assigned.

This is a very personal style of teaching, without the privacy of the examination paper. A student may be humiliated before fellow students and make a bad impression on the faculty if he gives a wrong answer. Since a staff physician may ask whatever he wishes—unconstrained, as he would be in the formal teaching situation, by the subject matter already covered in the course—students regard the faculty as unpredictable and capricious. The textbook is no longer good authority; it is outweighed by the staff physician's many years of clinical experience. Students feel it necessary to make a good impression and are careful to give high priority to learning and doing the things they think will please the faculty [4]. This often, in a clinical setting, conflicts with the high priority that interns and residents give to the patients' care [27].

The clinical faculty, itself more varied, is even more varied in its demands upon students. The staff does not approve of the student's efforts to please with the "right" answer. It worries when students shirk certain duties and restrict their production on group assignments. It does not see why students spend so much effort and time in pursuit of clinical experience and medical responsibility. On the contrary, staff members wish students would learn material for its own sake, not theirs. They want students to carry out all assignments responsibly. They want them to realize that medical school is only the first step in a life-long medical education, that there will be more than enough opportunities to get experience and exercise responsibility after school. They cannot understand the students' exclusive interest in common diseases and their failure to take advantage of the opportunities afforded by the medical center to see rare cases seldom encountered in practice [4, 27].

The direction of the students' efforts therefore often diverges from the faculty's wishes. In view of the student's subordinate position, his high motivation to learn, which continues throughout four years of school, his respect—even awe—of the faculty, and his earnest efforts to please, how can we account for this divergence? For in spite of their desire to do what the faculty wants, in pursuing their notion of learning what they think they will need to practice medicine students exercise a great deal of autonomy.

The fact that students are assigned

to a hospital during the clinical years makes it necessary for them to develop ways of dealing with each other and with other hospital personnel. Students expect one another to do a fair share of the work. They reach collective agreements on the amount of work each will do, and they set norms in situations where a limitation of work will not reduce the amount of learning they think necessary [4]. Interns, with whom the students must work, also develop a common viewpoint to guide their actions. The hospital as a learning environment requires that students and interns define the situation, set goals for themselves, and evolve a rationale for the level and direction of their effort [27].

The students are introduced to their work as they come face-to-face with the problems and duties of their jobs. They value clinical experience with patients highly, and they strive to get it in every way they can. They want to have first-hand experience with what is described in their texts. During their time on the wards and in clinics they pursue their superiors (particularly residents) to get information from them —practical tips on diagnosis and treatment, often referred to as "pearls." Although a great deal of work is delegated to students at this time, they are not empowered to exercise much discretion; they are supervised by and must defer to interns and residents. Students must, therefore, reach some agreement with interns, who also value clinical experience highly. This relationship between interns and students is characteristic of environments in which fledgling physicians at varying levels of education are being trained.

The relationship between interns and students is an example of "social exchange." There are numerous exchange relationships in which students, interns, and residents are involved because the hospital has service, rather than teaching, as its primary purpose. The relationship is discussed in the study of Harvard teaching at the Boston City Hospital [27].

THE FACULTY AND STUDENT AUTONOMY

Across the country, medical faculties complain about the results of their work and search for ways to do better. It may be true that teaching has not yet reached the status of an exact science; yet it seems clear that some faculty complaints about difficulties in teaching are more related to the development of student culture than to the state of the teaching arts. Several aspects of the organization of medical school faculties and their beliefs prevent them from using their power to make the students do what they want —that is, a medical faculty could have a much more powerful impact on student culture than it ordinarily does.

One very important condition limiting the action a medical faculty can take is the real lack of consensus among its members. Medical educators will agree on very general propositions, such as that students need to be trained at least to the extent that they will not endanger human life when they enter practice. But beyond these very general and somewhat vague propositions, faculties exhibit little agreement about what should be done in the day-to-day operation of a medical school. The current experimentation with curriculum at many schools illustrates the lack of agreement about what a medical school should be. Teachers do not agree on the best methods of teaching; some are in favor of "spoon-feeding," others prefer a method that maximizes the amount of independent thinking a student must do [4]. Nor do teachers agree on medical matters; they are apt, for instance, to disagree on the kind of treatment appropriate for a given disease (the differences between practitioners of internal medicine and surgery in this respect are striking). They differ also on the importance of the social and psychological aspects of illness and medical care [7]. It would not be unfair to say that the working consensus of the faculty is minimal, best represented by the schedule of the curriculum, which allocates a specific number of hours to each discipline or specialty. We do not mean, however, that everybody is happy with this allocation; rather, they are resigned or adjusted to it. A study of a national sample of clinical faculty members provides interesting data on this point. Most of the clinicians, asked their opinion of the basic science curriculum of the first two years, did not recommend any change at all—although there has subsequently been a great deal of change in the basic science curriculum. Such changes as were recommended, however, were directly tied to the specific interests of different departments. For instance, internists and psychiatrists wanted to allot less time to anatomy, which is of relatively little interest to them, but surgeons, who use anatomy every day, wanted no change in this. Similarly, psychiatrists wanted to allot more time to the behavioral sciences and surgeons did not [22].

A second fact which allows students freedom to develop their own views about their work in medical school is the autonomy of the several departments within the school. If departments were relatively weak, a determined administration could make extensive changes in the way school is carried on, and the students' behavior might then be quite different. But it is common knowledge that medical school departments have a great deal of autonomy, as do the hospitals in which graduate medical education is provided. Their independence may stem from the fact that the teaching of the departments (in the clinical years) is so closely interwoven with the care of patients. Few departments will allow any change to be made in the way they handle patients simply for pedagogical reasons. They say that the welfare of the patient comes first and that they will not change; and they do not.

In fact, this means that each department is likely to go its own way. Together, they present the students with a variety of viewpoints on many major problems, both of medicine and of medical education. There is much talk now about the integration of medical knowledge, and about teaching integrated courses, but it is very likely that the autonomy of disciplines and departments will continue to be such that what integration is done will have to be done by the student himself because the faculty cannot agree. There has been almost no study of the political arrangement within medical institutions, such as between hospitals and medical schools—a very important area for future research in medical education.

Another reason faculty members do not take action to produce better results than they now feel they achieve is that there are various external constraints on their behavior. One, for example, is that the members of a clinical faculty typically practice medicine themselves. This means that a certain amount of their time must be devoted to matters that have nothing to do with students, but have instead to do with their own practices and the care of their patients. It may be that the degree to which this factor affects teaching is related to the financial arrangements of the school with its faculty. Research is needed to determine whether, for instance, a staff that is on full-time salary pays more attention to its teaching duties and gives more time and attention to students than one that makes a considerable proportion of its incomes from patients' fees.

Other constraints are imposed by the various organizations within medicine and medical education that set standards for schools to live up to. For instance, an organization may base its judgment on the performance of a school's students on the National Board of Medical Examiners tests given at the end of the sophomore and senior years. The school need not require its students to take the exams, but most do. The faculty members, though they may realize that such instruments as the national board examinations are not perfect, also recognize that their own performance may be judged by the scores their students make. Thus, they may feel that they cannot make changes in curriculum and teaching methods, lest they jeopardize their students' scores. A basic science department might wish to institute a radically new method of teaching, but be inhibited by the knowledge that the examination will be written by people who hold different views. The pressure for standardization of educational practice which comes from national organizations of one kind or another can effectively keep a faculty from instituting changes that might help it achieve its teaching goals and reduce the autonomy of the students which interferes with those goals.

Another circumstance that interferes with any attempt by the faculty to redirect the level and direction of the students' effort is its unfamiliarity with the conditions of private practice. Most students in American medical schools intend to go into private practice; on the other hand, it is increasingly true that medical school teachers have never been in the private practice of medicine. (Of course, there are some schools in which the majority of teachers spend most of their time in private practice.) Moreover, many students intend to be general practitioners, while those teachers who are physicians have rarely been in general practice. Students may discount much of what a faculty member says because they feel that he has not had the experience of practice [18]. For instance, a surgeon may tell students that they should never attempt, as general practitioners, to remove an appendix, while the students may often feel, rightly or wrongly, that as general practitioners they may sometimes have to perform an appendectomy. They feel that the faculty member probably does not understand the circumstances (for instance, of small town practice) which might create such a necessity.

Many medical teachers probably recognize that they do not exactly know what a private practitioner might need to know, and this may account for some of their uncertainty about curriculum. They may recognize that no student can learn everything that all the faculty, taken together, knows but, lacking knowledge of the conditions under which students will practice, they do not have any way of determining just what the student most needs to learn. In fact, the conditions of practice vary so greatly that there would be great difficulty in organizing a curriculum to provide the optimum training for each kind of practitioner. Some students will end up practicing alone in small isolated towns; others will be partners of older and more experienced men; still others will be members of a community clinic staff, with colleagues who are well-trained specialists. Some students will be able to send difficult cases to medical centers that are conveniently located nearby, others will have to handle them themselves. Finally, the situation of the general practitioner is changing rapidly, and it is difficult to foresee what new variations will arise in years to come.

Another major obstacle to faculty action directed toward changing the way students work in medical school is the existence of what we may call "inhibiting ideologies." These are sets of beliefs, held by faculties, which make it seem to them unlikely that their schemes will work or that they know enough to devise good schemes for change. One of these ideologies we have already touched on, namely, the belief that the conditions under which students will practice are such that the faculty probably cannot know what most needs to be taught.

Another ideology that inhibits faculty action is the belief that students are not as good as they used to be or that a particular school does not recruit the best available students. This belief is widespread among medical educators, particularly now that more and more members of minorities are being admitted. It is a fact that the number of applicants for admission to medical school has dropped in the very recent past [20]. Medical educators tend to think that the larger the number of students from among whom they can select their freshmen class, the more likely they are to get very good students; consequently, when the number of applicants drops, faculties around the country believe that they are not getting as good students as when they had a greater selection. They may then draw the conclusion that it is really impossible to expect any better or increased academic work of the students because they are not capable of delivering it. They may decide that the students, being less "selected," are incapable of doing any better, and that any scheme for change is doomed before it starts by the students' limitations.

Another inhibiting ideology takes cognizance of the fact that most medical students are now married. Faculty members believe that the obligations the student assumes with marriage drain the time and interest he might otherwise apply to his medical studies. If he were not married he might stay in the hospital longer, read in the library, work in the laboratory, or see and examine his patients. Generally, they are probably inclined to think student marriage a bad thing. But they recognize that the trend toward early marriage is a national one, and realize that if they restricted the student body to unmarried people they would have an even smaller number of applicants to choose from. Accepting the fact of student marriage, they do not feel free to force the students to spend too much time away from their families, and are thus inhibited by their own humane instincts from doing things that might get the students to spend more time at the hospital.

In short, members of medical faculties are prevented in a number of ways from attempting to make major changes in the way the schools operate. Many of these factors inhibiting change are deeply rooted in the structure of the medical profession and of medical education. They cannot be changed without prolonged political effort, for in many cases there are quite divergent interests involved. It is our impression that much of the talk about change in medical education consists of a search for *panaceas*: schemes which will cause great changes in all the places where change is desired without in any way hurting anyone's interests or causing any basic change in the operating structure that now exists. It is false hope to think that such panaceas exist. Many studies of college teaching have shown that a change in the style of grading, or the integration of two courses that formerly were separate, does not change the way students work [26]. In any institution, one can make big changes only by making big changes. This is a truism about social organization, but one that is often overlooked.

On the other hand, panaceas do work, in another sense. The effect of a panacea probably is to provide a ritualized way of dealing with dissatisfaction (for instance, the dissatisfaction an idealistic medical faculty feels with its work) without at the same time disturbing a somewhat fragile consensus (such as the agreement a faculty has achieved on how to run a medical school). The panacea seems to be something that could be done, something "practical," and therefore gives the faculty the feeling that it is at least trying to do something about its problems; but it does not affect anything enough to hurt anyone and cause trouble.

Much research is needed on the forces promoting and obstructing change. We need to know about the political structure of medical schools. Who has power? Who influences the working consensus on which the school operates? We also need to know more about the external constraints on faculty members as they try to deal with their problem. Finally, we need to know a great deal about the beliefs with which a faculty approaches its job. What things do they think possible? What things impossible? Why do they think some things possible and others not? Questions of this sort have not yet been asked by sociologists, but they are relevant to medical education.

REFERENCES

1. Adams, Stuart, "Trends in Occupational Origins of Physicians," *American Sociological Review*, 18 (August, 1953), 404–9.
2. Back, Kurt W., Robert E. Coker, Jr., Thomas G. Donnelly, and Bernard S. Phillips, "Public Health as a Career in Medicine: Secondary Choice within a Profession," *American Sociological Review*, 23 (October, 1958), 533–41.
3. Beale, Lathrop V. and Louis Kriesberg, "Career-Relevant Values in Medical Students: A Research Note," *Journal of the American Medical Association*, 171 (November 14, 1959), 1447–48.
4. Becker, Howard S., Blanche Geer, Everett C. Hughes, and Anselm L. Strauss, *Boys in White: Student Culture in Medical School*. Chicago: University of Chicago Press, 1961.
5. Bucher, Rue and Anselm Strauss, "Professions in Process," *American Journal of Sociology*, 46 (January, 1961), pp. 325–34.
6. Cahalan, Don, Patricia Collette, and Norman A. Hilmar, "Career Interests and Expectations of U.S. Medical Students," *Journal of Medical Education*, 32 (August, 1957), 557–63.
7. Caplovitz, David, "Value-Orientations of Medical Students and Faculty Members." Paper read at the meeting of the American Sociological Society, Washington, D.C., August, 1957.
8. ———, "Student-Faculty Relations in Medical School: A Study of Professional Socialization." Unpublished Ph.D. dissertation, Columbia University, 1960.
9. Christie, Richard and Robert K. Merton, "Procedures for the Sociological Study of the Values Climate of Medical Schools," *Journal of Medical Education*, 33, Part II (October, 1958), 125–53.
10. Coker, Robert E., Jr., Kurt W. Back, Thomas G. Donnelly, Norman Miller, and Bernard S. Phillips, "Public Health as Viewed by the Medical Student," *American Journal of Public Health*, 49 (May, 1959), 601–9.
11. Coker, Robert E., Jr., Norman Miller, Kurt W. Back, and Thomas Donnelly, "The Medical Student; Specialization and General Practice." Paper read at the 105th annual session of the Medical Society of the State of North Carolina, 1959.
12. Coker, Robert E., Jr., Norman Miller, Kurt W. Back, Lloyd H.

STRICKLAND, AND THOMAS G. DONNELLY, "Patterns of Influence: Medical School Faculty Members and the Values and Specialty Interests of Medical Students." Paper read at the annual Meeting of the Association of American Medical Colleges, 1959.
13. ERON, LEONARD D., "Effect of Medical Education on Medical Students," *Journal of Medical Education*, 10 (October, 1955), 559–66.
14. FOX, RENEE C., "Training for Uncertainty," in Robert K. Merton, George G. Reader, and Patricia L. Kendall, eds., *The Student-Physician*. Cambridge, Mass.: Harvard University Press, 1957, pp. 207–41.
15. GLASER, WILLIAM A., "Internship Appointments of Medical Students," *Administrative Science Quarterly*, 4 (December, 1959), 337–56.
16. HALL, OSWALD, "The Stages of a Medical Career," *American Journal of Sociology*, 53 (March, 1948), 327–36.
17. HAMMOND, KENNETH R., FRED KERN, et al., *Teaching Comprehensive Medical Care: A Psychological Study of a Change in Medical Education*. Cambridge, Mass.: Harvard University Press, 1959.
18. HUGHES, EVERETT C., "Stress and Strain in Professional Education," *Harvard Educational Review*, 29 (Fall, 1959), 319–29.
19. HUNTINGTON, MARY JEAN, "The Development of a Professional Self-Image," in Robert K. Merton, George G. Reader, and Patricia L. Kendall, eds., *The Student-Physician*. Cambridge, Mass.: Harvard University Press, 1957, pp. 179–87.
20. HUTCHINS, EDWIN D. AND HELEN HOFER GEE, "The Study of Applicants: 1959–60," *Journal of Medical Education*, 36 (April, 1961), 289–304.
21. KANDEL, DENISE BYSTRYN, WILLIAM A. GLASER, AND JANE EMERY, "Changes in Career: Expectations of Medical Students." Paper read at the annual meeting of the American Sociological Society, 1958.
22. KENDALL, PATRICIA L., "Clinical Teachers' Use of the Basic Science Curriculum," *Journal of Medical Education*, 35 (February, 1960), 148–57.
23. ——— AND HANAN C. SELVIN, "Tendencies toward Specialization in Medical Training," in Robert K. Merton, George G. Reader, and Patricia L. Kendall, eds., *The Student-Physician*. Cambridge, Mass.: Harvard University Press, 1957, pp. 153–74.
24. LEVINE, GENE. N. AND NATALIE ROGOFF, with the assistance of David Caplovitz, "Diversities and Role Conceptions: Some Opinions of Clinical Faculty Members at Cornell Medical College." Unpublished document from the Bureau of Applied Social Research, Columbia University, November, 1955.
25. LEWIS, CHARLES E., "Students, Social Change, and Community Health," *Archives of Environmental Health*, 18 (January, 1969), pp. 67–72.
26. MCKEACHIE, W. J., "Procedures and Techniques of Teaching: A Survey of Experimental Studies," in Nevitt Sanford, ed., *The American College*. New York: John Wiley & Sons, Inc., 1962, pp. 312–64.
27. MILLER, STEPHEN J., *Prescription for Leadership: Training for the Medical Elite*. Chicago: Aldine Publishing Company, 1970.
28. NATHANSON, CONSTANCE A., "Learning the Doctor's Role: A Study of First and Fourth Year Medical Students." Unpublished M.A. thesis, University of Chicago, 1958.
29. PETERSON, OSLER L. et al., "An Analytical Study of North Carolina General Practice: 1953–54," *Journal of Medical Education*, 31, Part II (December, 1956).
30. ROGOFF, NATALIE, "The Decision to Study Medicine," in Robert K. Merton, George G. Reader, and Patricia L. Kendall, eds., The *Student-Physician*. Cambridge, Mass.: Harvard University Press, 1957, pp. 109–29.
31. SCHUMACHER, CHARLES F., "The 1960 Medical School Graduate: His Biographical History," *Journal of Medical Education*, 36 (May, 1961), 398–406.

9

NURSING: CHURNING FOR CHANGE?

Hans O. Mauksch

During recent years, possibly no other occupation has been the object of as much study and analysis as nursing. The literature includes the work of members of the occupation itself [12, 29, 35, 77, 80], of social scientists [11, 19, 37, 40, 56], and of members of other health professions whose interest has ranged from inquiry to polemics [18, 33, 62, 64].

In this chapter we will emphasize social change as a perspective for the occupation's current state of strain and unrest; thus, we will select evidence of innovation and mobilization.[1] We will utilize several theoretical and practical frames of reference for an analysis of nursing without exhaustively exploring any one. In our selection of content we

[1] The author wishes to express his gratitude to his wife, Ingeborg G. Mauksch, R.N., Ph.D., who served generously as resource and critic in the preparation of this chapter. This essay does not bear her name as coauthor because the conclusions and implications are entirely the responsibility of the author. Thanks are also due to Mrs. Susanne Dougherty, Miss Chris Marshall, and Miss Linda Maasch.

sought those phenomena which can serve as portents of trends and which can help us to understand the direction, impetus, and obstacles of an occupation in the process of social change.

First we will discuss some historical antecedents of the place of nursing among today's health occupations. A brief summary of nursing manpower will provide background information. Then, after having examined educational choices, we will look at the individual in nursing from career selection through socialization into the profession. This will be followed by a discussion of the organizational arrangements of the nurse's work, and of her role and functions. Viewing the individual, the interaction processes within the profession, and the conditions of the social structure as interdependent though distinctly separate vantage points, we will seek to examine the implications of these facets of social existence for the current status of nursing.

ANTECEDENTS

Not unlike medicine, the roots of nursing grew in a variety of different soils. The antecedents of the modern functionary who cares for those who are ill include the servant hired to perform tasks which illness prevents the sick person from performing himself. It simultaneously included those who, as an obligation stemming from wealth and status, believed that charitable attention to the poor and the sick was a proper activity for nobility. The soil of Christian beliefs gave rise to the idea of the sanctity of caring for those in need; indeed, the religious tradition in nursing is possibly the one which, from its very inception to the current day, has remained a significant force. It is associated not only with the spiritual quality of serving, but also with the sacred aura of the healing process itself—that is, the very act of nursing, like that of medicine, is linked to the cultural tradition of invoking spiritual and magical resources in response to malady. The fourth major early tributary to the flow of modern nursing must be accorded to the military. Though less constant an influence than the other three roots of nursing, it has been influential during major wars. The military root of nursing has been particularly identified with the Crimean War [23], and its contribution can be observed throughout history, right up to the major impact of World War II on the history of modern nursing.

During the eighteenth century, and the first half of the nineteenth, nursing was performed as a supportive activity distinct from the medical concern with the cure of disease. Those who nursed —particularly religious sisters—even sometimes counteracted what they considered morally improper aspects of medical activities, such as by refusing to expose an infant's behind, notwithstanding the physician's request for cleansing or care activities.

It was during the middle of the nineteenth century that the sproutings of the various roots of nursing began to affect each other on a major scale, and that historical events determined which of these were to be more influential on the future course of the occupation. The impetus for change sprang partly from a response to the social composition of nursing. Although, particularly in England, there was a tradition for young women from better families to join nursing, the major changes occurred largely as a reaction to the large number of women recruited to do nursing tasks who were coming from the lowest socioeconomic stratum. They were reported to be "uneducated, untrained and slovenly." Though this manpower situation can be traced back to the Crusades, the reaction to it in the nineteenth century was a turning point in the development of nursing [27].

Attempts to establish standards for nursing and to organize the delivery of nursing care into an institutionally responsible system are primarily associated with Florence Nightingale and her activities in the Crimean War. Thus, the establishment of nursing as a collectively organized, institutional resource is linked to its military root. This period also witnessed the addition of two further strands which were to play major roles in the future of nursing. The war and other social changes at mid-century brought the nurse into close association with the physician. This gave him control and jurisdiction over nursing activities—not only over actions which aided in the cure of the patient, but also over those which involved his comfort, sanitary needs, and all other conditions associated with his bedridden status. The other strand made its appearance in the organization of nursing as an institutional system, which gave rise to "the matron," thereby introducing formal management into the edifice of nursing—the "matron" being the managerial nurse who functioned as administrator of the institution and as chief of nursing [27].

An examination of the historical antecedents of nursing would not be complete without looking beyond historical events to nursing's symbolic heritage. In Western culture those who care for the sick are identified with labels which are primarily profoundly female. The term "sister" is applied not only to the religious functionary, but in many European languages generically identifies the nurse. In the English language, "nursing" implies the essence of the mother's relationship to her offspring. This link to female role images has persisted throughout history, even though males have been involved in the performance of nursing tasks since the Crusades, both in religious and secular contexts. Actually, a large proportion of nursing services in the United States during the early part of the nineteenth century was performed by males.

Yet, the history of nursing is inextricably interwoven with the history of women. The selection of nurses, their relationships, and the images they evoke can be fruitfully examined by linking them to the past. The quasi-innate qualities which always were perceived to be the attributes of the mother represent images which influence the fate of nursing education to this day. The natural tendency of a mother to care for her family without having formal boundaries to her area of competence as well as her tendency to manage her home, underlie the expectations still held today about the appropriate role of the nurse.

In linking these historical antecedents to modern nursing in the United States, one must consider the influences of the different cultural contexts on nursing as its historical momentum shifted from Europe to the United States around the beginning of the twentieth century. The relative stability of the social structure of European societies, and of the organization of the European hospitals, was less favorable to further changes toward the professionalization of nursing than were conditions in the United States. The generally more open society here, the new approaches to the division of labor, and the emerging American belief in the value of education affected the moves of those who spoke for nursing. The common human game of balancing the values of the past and the promises of the future yielded a less change-oriented climate in Europe than developed in American society. Furthermore, the growth of management as a characteristic of American institutions, and the transfer of administrative responsibility to special functionaries, laid the groundwork for American nursing's involvement in a tug-of-war between partnership with medicine and identification with hospital management. Actually, the management of the American hospital has gone through roughly three overlapping periods. In the initial era, the nurse assumed responsibility for institutional management. Then the physician took over, and in many hospitals management is still firmly in medical hands. The emergence of the professional hospital administrator, including the early appearance of the "lay manager," is the latest of these three phases.

Closely linked to the strands which make up the history of nursing are the processes which gave rise to the various forms of nursing education. Some of the earliest forms of training, primarily apprenticeships, existed in the religious orders. In the United States, formal training as a prerequisite for performing nursing tasks did not become a prevailing pattern until the last quarter of the nineteenth century. The first schools of "professional nursing," so called, were opened in 1873.

The institutionalization of educational prerequisites for nursing was closely linked to attempts to formalize the job of the nurse, and is again associated with Miss Nightingale. Just as the second half of the nineteenth century saw the linking of nursing into the paramedical orbit, so did this early form of nursing education emphasize what was essentially obedience training. The impetus towards nursing education was largely a secular process. Despite their earlier beginnings, religious orders, in subsequent years, tended to be conservative rather than progressive educational forces. Historical precedent contributed to the placement of nursing education under the control of those who managed hospital services, initially the matrons, and in the twentieth century, the hospital administrators.

The development of nursing as an organized occupation has to be linked to the emergence of collective, representative bodies. The first national organizations devoted to the promulgation of the interest of nursing in the United States occurred at the turn of the last century. By the 1940s these developments had given rise to six major organizations which, in some of their concerns and activities, overlapped and conflicted. In response to this increasingly complicated situation a "structure study" was initiated at the Biennial Convention in 1952 [7a]. This study never resulted in a published document, but it proved to be the formal turning point in the public representation of nursing, for its recommendations resulted in the restructuring of the five national organizations into three. One of these—the American Nurses Association—has become the professional organization and the official representative of nursing. Another, the National League for Nursing, was given a difficult and, as history has since shown, an incompatible set of purposes. Its membership was to include individual nurses, members of other health-oriented professions, and citizens who share a concern for the nursing needs of society. In addition, the National League for Nursing provides membership to nursing agencies as well as to individuals, since this association was also charged with representing institutions devoted to nursing education and nursing practice. In this role, the League was charged with the accreditation of education and, in some instances, of service programs in nursing.

An examination of the antecedents of modern nursing would not be complete without calling attention to a fairly recent development which has had a profound impact on the questions which nursing is forced to face today. As a result of the scarcity of manpower during World War II, and in response to an increased need and to the postwar economy, categories of personnel which became ancillary to nursing emerged. The practical nurse, the nurse's aide, and the nursing assistant were among those who, although born in response to wartime requirements, remained and proliferated as a permanent fixture on the nursing-care scene. This development closed the circle of historically developed pressures on nursing. Placed in the position where pressure from above is competitively exerted by medicine and management, exposed to the demands of patients who view nursing as the gateway to all patient care services, nursing now also faces the pressure from below from people who want a larger slice of the pie.

In many ways the history of nursing is the emergence of an occupation which has, in the relatively recent past, moved far toward acquiring the institutional characteristics of an organized occupation. Throughout, the strands which make up its history can be linked to the issues which confront nursing today.

NURSING MANPOWER

In 1969 there were approximately 680,000 practicing registered nurses, of whom 187,000 were engaged in part-time work—a mean ratio of 338 nurses per 100,000 population.[2] Contrary to the impression held by the general public, this ratio has been on the increase during the last fifty years: In 1954, it was only 251 per 100,000. These figures, however, do not represent the entire, potential nursing force, for a significant number of nurses are not engaged in the practice of their occupation. According to *Facts About Nursing* [2], there were 909,131 nurses registered in the United States during 1969—which means that close to one-third of those who maintained their registration were not employed in nursing. This is obviously partly due to the female composition of the profession, even though sex may not be the sole determining factor. By contrast, one study has shown that 90 percent of female physicians in the United States continue to be actively engaged in the practice of medicine, despite the advent of marriage and motherhood [71].

The norms of the social class to which physicians and nurses respectively belong may partly account for these different perceptions of the woman's proclivity to work after marriage. The profile of husbands of female physicians and female nurses may also show a difference in orientation towards the working woman. The differential economic reward of the two professions is certainly crucial. Yet, the commitment, satisfaction, and sense of worth ideally associated with nursing, when blocked in actual experience may, in fact, operate as a negative force and may be manifested in disenchantment, frustration, and the desire to get away from the hospital [8, 15, 65].

These manpower considerations have to be borne in mind as we pursue our discussion, since the future of current

[2] Unless otherwise indicated, the statistics in this section are from References [2] and [4].

trends, the proposals for change by nursing leaders, and the power and resources which can be mustered will depend on the cohesiveness and commitment of those who practice. The permeability of the membrane which defines nursing is probably not unrelated to the ability of its membership to close ranks and to choose goals within nursing despite the beckoning of home, service to medicine, management, and safe retreat into noninvolving routine.

One indication of the problems faced by those who identify with changes in nursing comes from the participation of American nurses in their national associations. In 1969, the American Nurses Association reported 203,909 members, roughly one-third of all actively engaged registered nurses. This level of involvement in membership ought to give much concern to those who view nursing as a profession. The National League of Nursing which, by virtue of its objectives, tends to appeal primarily to educators and nurses in leadership positions, reported in 1969 only 21,157 individual members. The League also has 1,826 agency members, primarily schools of nursing. These data assume particular importance, in light of the high degree of institutionalization of nursing education and the high proportion of institutional employment of nurses. The combination of the ecology of nursing manpower and the rigidity of the employing institutions provides a risky setting for a drive toward professional autonomy, academic orientation, and militant demands for control over conditions of practice. The author is concerned that these institutional strains in nursing, rather than foreshadowing the upward mobility of an entire occupation, may in fact mark the historical moment of institutional cell division and the straining of the internal universe of language, purpose, and presentation beyond the point of structural tolerance.

ENTRY ROUTES INTO NURSING

If one were to look for one aspect of nursing which best reflects the current state of this occupation—its stresses, its confusion, its groping, and its hopes —one must look at the currently available routes for becoming a nurse. Various ways, requiring different amounts of educational involvement, are available. It is possible to become a registered nurse via a four-year baccalaureate program, a two-year Associate of Arts program, or by attending a three-year, diploma-granting, hospital-based school. And, for all practical purposes, the graduates of all of these diverse programs—with greatly different investments of time, effort, money, and presumably intellect—end up being mutually substitutable, at least in most of their first jobs.

The three-year, hospital-based diploma school was by far the major source of nursing manpower until recent years. In 1968, it still enrolled 53 percent of all students in schools of nursing, although this represented a considerable, steady drop from 1959, when diploma schools accounted for 81 percent of all nursing students. In order to understand nursing today, one has to comprehend the nature of these programs, which were administratively and philosophically controlled by hospital management and profoundly influenced by medical opinion. They overtly and covertly set the stage for the perceptions, expectations, and definitions of the nurse's role which are the targets of attack by those in nursing who seek to bring about changes.

Typically, the three-year hospital school combined education with a considerable admixture of apprenticeship. This is not to say that among the roughly 900 diploma programs in the late 1950s there were not many which had developed curricula and faculty capable of educational excellence. During the 1940s, nursing consultants of the U.S. Public Health Service gave 147 such schools—but only 13 percent of all diploma programs—a ratng of good or excellent [10]. The point made here goes beyond the quality of the classroom content. The diploma school taught the nurse subordination to institutional goals and needs; it ritualized status subordination to the physician, stressing it beyond the necessary functional dependence of nursing tasks upon medical initiative.

The three-year diploma program sanctioned and institutionalized what turned out to be one of the most difficult problems for nursing: Hospital control meant that the nursing student, and therefore the nurse, could be used any place, any time, to do whatever needed to be done. The aura of the generalist of ascribed rather than achieved competence, was deeply ingrained in the image of nursing, not only as seen by the other professions and the public but, indeed, as seen by nursing itself.

Unlike the graduate of any other educational institution, but in keeping with the traditions of apprenticeship, the graduate of the diploma program is expected to be an experienced, competent practitioner on the day of graduation. Indeed, such is normally the case, in view of the student's share of the heavy burden of servicing the hospital which the school of nursing traditionally performs for its host institution. During the last fifteen years, however, persistent efforts on the part of nursing educators, nursing leaders, and the national nursing organizations have resulted in great reductions in the amount of service expected from diploma students. These reductions in service have in turn rendered the diploma programs financial burdens for the hospital; nevertheless, its spokesmen—notably hospital administrators—collectively and individually continue to fight to "save the diploma schools."

The two avenues to nursing in the ascendancy are the four-year college baccalaureate and the community college, two-year Associate of Arts degree. The latter avenue, which essentially originated in the early 1950s [57, 36], has had a dramatic, albeit controversial, growth. The choice of the community college for the Associate of Arts degree program evoked vocational rather than professional symbolisms at a time when the battle for the label "professional" was being fought with more heat than light. The introduction of the two-year program made the claim that all RNs were covered by the umbrella of professional status an increasingly difficult one to defend.

The dissension within nursing about these programs was intensified by choosing the term "technical nurse" for the graduate of the two-year program. This choice was unfortunate, partly because of its divisive impact and partly because the term "technical," in its proper meaning, does not seem to describe accurately the actual task expectations and role performances of these practitioners. The technical task is characterized by a predictable and patterned means-end relationship involving maximally efficient use of means. While it clearly applies to some nursing tasks, it is deprecated by all levels in nursing as a portrait of the nursing function *per se*. If a way had to be found to distinguish the vocational product from the professionally oriented college graduate, the model of the "craft" might have been a more fortunate selection.

Notwithstanding the mixed reception initially accorded the Associate-degree programs in nursing, their growth has been remarkable. While there were only 57 programs in 1960, there were 390 in 1965. The acceptance of their graduates has by now been generally achieved. Actually, the lumping together of positions and expectations of all RN's, regardless of educational origin, has frequently placed the graduates of two-year programs into the same career lines as those from other programs. For example, they have been placed early into head-nurse positions, for which they are clearly even less prepared than the graduates of other basic programs.

While the Associate degree program is a recent phenomenon, the academically based baccalaureate program in nursing had its beginning in the first decades of this century. (The first collegiate nursing course, offered at Teachers College, Columbia University, in 1899, emphasized preparation of nursing administrators.) Even in the early days of baccalaureate education, there were some who argued that all practicing nurses should be the products of a college-based program [1, 9, 10, 69]. Others saw the university programs as functioning primarily as the training ground for teachers and leaders, an orientation which seems to have prevailed and which became particularly influential in determining the flavor and curricula of the emerging graduate programs. A large proportion of the Master's programs in nursing developed curricula in which nursing practice was secondary, overshadowed by the preparation of teachers or administrators.

It is interesting to compare the baccalaureate programs in nursing with other undergraduate programs leading to professionally oriented degrees. Some of these curricula, notably engineering, place priority on the preparation of the future practioner. Except for a gesture toward liberal studies, the curriculum is primarily governed by vocational requirements. The undergraduate curricula in education, although there is considerable variance, generally seek to mix occupational preparation and a liberal-arts education. Nursing has opted for this model. Although no data can be cited, it is suggested here that this mix is more strainfully experienced by the nursing student than by the major in education. The social distance between the nursing faculty and the arts and sciences faculty, and the all-embracing demands of acquiring the role of nurse may be part of the problem. Questions of relevance, continuity, and integration of the undergraduate nursing curriculum have not yet given rise to overt student protests, but the seeds of discontent have been observed [20].

The number of baccalaureate programs has also increased significantly. From 172 in 1960, the number of these programs rose to 254 in 1969. While they doubled, and the Associate programs mentioned above increased sixfold, diploma programs during the same period decreased, from 908 in 1960 to 695 in 1969.

In this shifting picture of the three major routes to becoming a nurse, the arguments about their relative merit have frequently included references to the need for more nurses and the danger of choking off manpower supply by closing the diploma school. These arguments need to be discussed on two levels. From the point of view of sheer numbers, it is noteworthy that the enrollment of students in all RN programs rose from 123,861 in 1962 to 145,588 in 1968. This represents approximately a doubling of baccalaureate students, who increased from 23,656, in 1962, to 40,341, in 1968. The 4,927 Associate-degree students in

1962 grew to 27,471 in 1968. Diploma enrollment dropped from 95,278 to 77,776.

The important question, from the point of view of manpower recruitment, is not merely one of sheer numbers but of change in the nature of the candidate pool. There is some evidence that baccalaureate programs have succeeded in attracting some students who would not otherwise have considered nursing as an occupation. Conversely, it is not certain whether the reduction in diploma programs closes the road for certain potential candidates who want nursing but will not choose an academically based program—perhaps more a sociopsychological process of role perception and self-perception than a matter of academic capability and intellect. Rigorous research on the symbolic components of the various educational routes is unfortunately absent. The goal of nursing, which is to reach the broadest possible spectrum of possible candidates, may have been approximated by the coexistence of the Associate degree program and the baccalaureate program, at least as far as academic capability is concerned. The effect of a changing image on recruitment will need to be watched as the diploma program recedes and, with it, the promise of an opportunity for immediate involvement in direct patient care. This question needs to be raised even though the community college programs do offer early patient contact and are cheaper and shorter, also.

One other commonly held notion should receive comment. Students entering university programs in nursing are not academically less successful or able than those who pursue graduate professional education. It is not uncommon to find at least comparable achievement scores among nursing and medical students. The difference between these career choices is thus not necessarily based on intellect, but rather has to be sought in factors involving motivation, self-perception, the images of nursing, and social origins [73].

THE PEOPLE WHO MAKE UP NURSING

The many studies devoted to the examination of the human raw material which is recruited and initiated into nursing have included studies of personality characteristics, of subjective role images, of social background, and of the motivation and aspirations of the novices. Examining these data in the context of social change in nursing, one must regret that only rarely is attention paid to the relationship between the characteristics and behavior of the occupational collectivity and the attributes of its individual members.

It would seem that the link between the whole and its members is particularly significant in the case of nursing, since the strongly developed public image of nursing is likely to favor greater homogeneity than might be true of occupations involving more diffuse symbols. Furthermore, the embattled position of nursing among other health occupations might tend to reinforce certain incipient characteristics of its members since diversity among novices or peers is likely to be discouraged in the cause of a common defense.

Beginning with the late 1930s, a variety of investigators sought to apply various personality tests to nursing groups [7, 21, 34, 59, 76]. Depending on the theoretical basis of the studies and the instrument used, the results varied considerably. Yet, when one groups the results of these studies with those which investigated primarily the self-image and role-oriented tendencies of nurses [3, 30, 46, 55], a pattern of findings emerge which can provide a sketchy, but suggestive, allusion to some of the forces affecting the occupation's current dilemmas and trends.

On the level of conscious and expressed motivation, those who seek to enter nursing express a strong desire to serve their patients, to be needed, and to be engaged in a one-to-one helping relationship. Almost as frequent as patient-oriented interest is the expressed desire to serve the physician. To expect to work for and with the physician is, to be sure, a realistic anticipation, but it is also a profoundly felt motivating force. This attribute of nurses has implications for the current drive in nursing for professional autonomy and for colleagueship with the physician, Genevieve Meyer found that nurses tend to be attracted to relationships with either patients or physicians, and prefer these by far to close contact with their peers [54]. This finding, if valid, serves as background information for our own subsequent discussion of the emerging cohesiveness in nursing, the development of an occupational identity, and the current struggle which frequently forces the individual nurse to make a choice between her allegiance to her own occupation and to others, such as medicine or administration in the employing institution. Furthermore, the actual conditions of nurse deployment tend to mitigate against the development of formal or informal working groups, since they tend to be dispersed throughout the institution and have more contacts with others in the hospital than with scarce fellow RN's.

The motivational dynamics exist within the context of the obvious appeal which nursing cannot help but have for the young female. Few occupations combine, simultaneously, what Ginzberg et al. refer to as "function pleasure" and "symbolic status attraction" [26]. The glamour of the uniform and the apparent importance of the nurse is combined with a wide variety of dramatic and feasible tasks. The ready link between the nursing image and the nurturant symbolisms of the mother role adds to the seductive appeal of nursing as an occupational choice.

A study conducted by this author found evidence of these tendencies among those who chose nursing [46]. The study included a sample of high-school students who were planning to enter nursing, a group of nursing students, and nurses actively engaged in various facets of their occupation for a number of years. Common, almost identical patterns emerged. Significantly more than a comparison group of female college students, the entire group of nurses seemed to desire nurturant and affiliative relationships, and they also sought a succorant environment. These strongly evident needs to help, and for close relationships, were accompanied by the consistent finding that they also sought to avoid individual risks and blame-producing situations, and that they preferred the safety of the institutionally established social order and of specific task demands. Another finding in this study was that the subjects universally perceived the typical nurse to be considerably more restrained in all needs than they perceived themselves to be. The impression of nursing as an occupation which combines the opportunity to exert control over certain segments of the outside world with the capability of imposing control on oneself has also been suggested by other authors [3, 30].

Although the findings reported in the preceding paragraph are based on a nursing population identified with the diploma-school environment, they have implications for the current scene, partly because today's nursing population still counts large numbers from this tradition and partly because whatever changes the baccalaureate program may have caused, it will still have to exist within the context of these forces.

The data on the social background of nurses suggests that, even though there has been an expanded base of recruitment during recent years, nursing has largely drawn on the lower-middle-class for its manpower. Furthermore, nursing is not uncommonly viewed as a road to social mobility [41, 49]. There is also an apparently consistent correlation between a choice of nursing and the Christian model of service and the woman's role. The exceedingly small number of Jews in nursing is noteworthy; it is partly attributable to the different role of the Jewish mother, and partly to the high concentration of Jews in cities. Until recently, nurses seem to have been recruited primarily from smaller towns and communities at the fringes of metropolitan areas. Croog, Caudill, and Blumen have found that religious identity also was a factor differentiating nursing aspirants in Japan [17].

All these factors set the stage for an occupational group which is not likely to be characterized by assertiveness, risk-taking, and personal autonomy, and the socialization process further tends to reinforce these tendencies. It can be said of all professional curricula that they impose attitudinal constellations, as well as role expectations, upon the novice. The imposition is likely to be more forceful in professional training programs which involve the novice in direct participation in work with his elders. It is likely to be particularly effective when the institutional arrangement of socialization resembles what Goffman calls "total" institutions [28]. Thus, medicine, the military, the convent, and nursing, involve socializing conditions which imply maximum control. One of the stresses in the baccalaureate programs in nursing is the transition from the liberal arts environment to the world of nursing, usually occurring in the junior year. These early tribulations, the "stripping process" [28] associated with these institutions, is interpreted by future physicians and officers as ritual hazing, leading to future power. To nurses it seems a window on future reality.

The socializing process in nursing includes two sets of messages: First, it involves the revelation to the novice that her role models—the teachers as well as the practitioners—do not control the conditions of their practice. Moreover, the gap between classroom-taught ideals and hospital-based reality derives not merely from the typical adjustments to routinization and proficiency, but from institutionally imposed obstacles and pressures. The second message associated with becoming a nurse involves the transfer of personal qualities, attitudes, and demeanor to the occupational role, making them subject to occupational norms and rewards or punishments. For those in uniform, dress, manners, speech, and expression of beliefs cease to be personal rights [47]. This reduction of the private, personal domain has diminished markedly in nursing during the past fifteen years, particularly in the academically based schools, but its traces still affect the current scene.

If it is true that one can project onto the behavior of a collectivity the findings obtained about its individual members, we might select several themes which seem to characterize nurses and then examine them as they relate to social movement and change. The most positive force for change exhibited by nurses is the pervasive and apparently profoundly felt need to engage in affiliative and nurturant relationships as the core of occupational behavior. If this motivation is successfully harnessed in the process of socialization, education, and the development of an occupational identity, it can provide the momentum for its fulfillment. If, on the other hand, these motivational forces are suppressed or subverted, it could account for disenchantment, disengagement, or perfunctory participation.

The apparent tendency of prospective nurses to seek social conditions which are structured and safe can be a conservative force. It can, however, also assure convergent behavior once a sufficiently all-embracing structure has been established, whether it is one devoted to the *status quo* or the accomplishment of new goals. Possibly, the most significant aggregate consequence of individual findings lies in the observation that the perception of nursing seems to be closely linked with the traditionally perceived female role. This perception creates a woman who serves sacrificially, who supports and protects a dominant male, and who identifies her successes as a nurse with her successes as a woman. This picture is manifestly one in transition, and is clearly not as applicable to the leader, the spokesman, the agent of change in nursing. Yet, even among these there are probably fewer sympathizers with the kind of woman projected by the Woman's Liberation Movement than there might be in other predominantly female occupations, such as social work. The striving for colleagueship with the physician, which we shall discuss subsequently, represents a process which needs to be examined as a movement linked to changes in the self-image of new and currently active nurses.

THE SETTING IN WHICH NURSES WORK

Approximately two-thirds of all employed registered nurses work in hospitals or similar institutions. The remainder are distributed among public health agencies, schools, industries, community agencies, and doctors' offices. The private-duty nurse has almost disappeared: In 1966, there were only 57,193, less than 10 percent [2]. Regrettably, only a few studies have explored the structural variations in the nurse's work in extra-hospital settings.

These settings provide different degrees of autonomy, different relationships to the physician, and different definitions of nursing tasks. The public health nurse, the school nurse, and sometimes the industrial nurse, function independently much of the time, with only episodic and intermittent links with the physician who determines the policy and treatment. In many instances, particularly in sparsely populated regions, the public health nurse functions almost on her own, serving the health care system as the intake agent who responds directly to the needs or decides when intervention of a physician is appropriate.

The office nurse is usually in the opposite situation, in that she is likely to be continuously at the beck and call of the physician, who directs most of her activities. In this setting the nurse's opportunities for displaying her professional judgment are minimal. Yet, even this structurally and contractually most dependent nursing role includes a variety of real situations containing clues to change and examples of the flexibility of the negotiated results of physician-nurse accommodations.

While the data on nursing outside the hospital are scarce, the literature on the place of nurses within the hospital is abundant [14, 24, 48]. In this section we shall examine only the structural arrangements of the position of the nurse in the hospital. We shall observe the implications of these arrangements for the work processes and analyze them within the framework of relevant historical antecedents.

The concept which is most useful to an understanding of the nurse's position in the hospital was probably first stated by Harvey Smith [75]. The nurse's conditions of employment and the convergence of the architectural and administrative organization of the hospital place her in the position of manager of the hospital's territorial and operational subdivision, the patient care unit. This role is linked to a pattern of management organization peculiar to hospitals—that is, notwithstanding the increased professionalization of the hospital administrator, his management of the hospital has been confined to its topmost echelons. The nurse, serving as his de facto delegate in the administrative process, is a dilettante as a manager no matter how competent she may be as a nurse. Along with this delegated authority for administration, we find that the head nurse is also the deputy of the authority of medicine—imposing cure-oriented activities on behalf of patients and representing the physician vis-à-vis other hospital services.

The management process is linked to the bureaucratic organization of the hospital and exhibits all of its attributes—such as fixed positions, job descriptions, and prescribed channels of communications. The cure process places the nurse (primarily the head nurse, but also the staff nurse) into direct contact with the multitude of physicians who maintain their own relationships with a vast number of patients. In the implementation of cure the nurse serves as a performer of tasks, as a link to other resources in various parts of the hospital. But she also acts as representative for the frequently absent physician and as integrator of the highly diversified, increasingly segmented components of the many activities which affect the patient. Thus, the nurse suffers ambiguity of status as she plays the role of a bureaucratically placed employee or alternately wears the mantle of the physician's deputy.

This description of the structural arrangements of the nurse's work is at variance with Eliot Freidson's, whose otherwise superb analysis depicts the nurse as exclusively "paramedical," i.e., only moved by the initiative of the physician [24]. The discrepancy between these views is emphasized because it illustrates the existence of differing perspectives which allow us to define identical situations in different ways. Freidson's description is all too frequently the physician's view of the situation.

The organizational vehicle of nursing is typically a department of nursing service, which tends to be the largest department in the hospital. The director of this department is frequently accorded the title of Assistant Hospital Administrator. This is a de jure recognition of her place in the chain of managerial functions that link the hospital administrator to the head nurse, the manager of the hospital's subsystems. The nursing service department comprises a supervisory cadre and staff which is allocated to the various patient care units. Its personnel includes registered nurses, practical nurses, nurses' aides, nursing assistants, and clerks. Its organizational flavor is hierarchial, oriented toward meeting specific job and task descriptions. This highly formalized and structured context favors expeditious routinization and mechanization of tasks. It is not a climate which encourages individual experimentation or the diversification of roles. Predictably, the introduction of the new, clinically oriented nurse practitioners to this setting causes stresses, uncertainties, and a sense of organizational disruption. Her orientation toward a self-determined nursing response to patients' needs and her challenge of delegated technical tasks threatens the very foundations of the nursing hierarchy.

That the nurse is placed at the juncture of medical and administrative flow of demands suggests that the system may be overloaded. Since medical orders are determined by the patients' needs as perceived by individual physicians, and since they need not consider the limited number of nurses available, their demands on the nursing force frequently exceed the available supply of manpower. Many of the medical tasks performed by nurses, and a considerable proportion of their administrative tasks, must be recorded or reported in written form. In a bureaucratic environment, tasks which thus become officially accountable tend to squeeze out activities which rest only within the individual performer's jurisdiction and judgment. The traditional hierarchy of prestige, which has placed a high value on such delegated technical activities as the passing of medicines, is in direct conflict with the priorities inherent in the concepts identified with the clinical nurse specialist. This new type of nurse seeks to determine and respond to those aspects of patient care which are not necessarily therapeutic procedures nor hotel services, but rather arise from an assessment of the nursing needs of each patient and his family.

If we link these conditions to the antecedents of modern nursing and to the history of other health occupations, we can observe several revealing processes. One of these can be described as a shift, from independence through dependence to a search for autonomy within interdependence. As we observed earlier, the early pattern of nursing, which was unrelated to medicine, gave way to the complete subordination of all nursing tasks to the physician. Although we have seen dramatic changes in this respect in the last decade, the policies in many hospitals to this day make it the sole prerogative of the physician to determine whether patients can have their hair washed, the extent of their recuperative exercises, and the scope of the information they receive. Today's pressures are for a reexamination and realignment of the jurisdictional domains among the health professions. When should nurses be able to make decisions? To what are the domains of their expertise? What restraints on communications—such as the patient's temperature, plans for his treatment, or the name of the drug he is receiving—are legitimate either as medical prerogative or as requirement of medical management decision? Which plans should be made jointly? Although national nursing organizations speak of distinguishing between "independent" and "dependent" functions, the development of any autonomy in the day-to-day work setting is slow, at best, and still largely nonexistent.

The second trend worth observing is the historical parade of tasks of patient care from occupation to occupation, from job category to job category. This picture is complicated by the coexisting movement of traditional tasks, and by the fitting into the functional arena of a plethora of continuously emerging new activities. Time was when diagnostic and therapeutic activities were few in number. Only physicians took temperatures; later, only they took blood pressures and administered treatments. Nurses washed the floors, made the beds, cooked, and performed all supportive services, since there was no one else. As new tasks emerged, and as patient care institutions became more complex, new functionaries were added to the scene. The game of "pass the task down the line" began. Low-prestige activities, and those which were repetitious, were transferred down the ladder. Tasks which required increased specialization as new areas of technology were discovered or identified were moved laterally to new occupations.

Medicine discards whatever it does not wish to do itself, always downward. Nursing has become the turntable from which vertical or horizontal shifts take place. Tasks traveled either downward, to ancillary nursing categories, or laterally, outside of nursing into new occupations. Some of these, from the point of view of hospital prestige, are "out and down," others are "out" but not "down," competing for status and prestige with nursing. The momentum of this process has presented nursing with a double dilemma. On one hand, the generalist, managerial image of nursing has created a situation in which nursing has transferred many activities to other occupations and departments, but without losing a sense of obligation for them and still feeling fundamentally responsible for their performance. Nursing appears to have maintained a sense of responsibility for all the components and flow of patient care even though they have eluded its organizational and jurisdictional boundaries [48]. This condition of responsibility without power is intensified by the physician who, after having written or given an order, expects nursing to see that it gets done no matter who does it.

If we look at the nurse's work from the point of view of process and interaction, we are reminded of the concept of "negotiated order" [79]. The content of nursing activities is not sharply outlined, and it contains many grey areas. The borders of the nursing domain—up, down, and sideways—vary from hospital to hospital, from geographic region to geographic region; they vary even within the different patient care units of one hospital. In some hospitals nurses perform such highly technical medical tasks as defibrilliation and venipuncture. In others, they may not add fluids to intravenous feedings. In some hospitals nurses exercise vast judgment about the range of the patient's activity and treatment; in others, decisions by nurses are rarely tolerated. Regional customs, medical traditions, manpower resources, and the history of the specific institution are all factors which need to be examined to understand these variations in the nursing reality. This ethnographic variety of what constitutes the nurse's domain, which should have attracted the interest of sociologists or anthropologists, has at best received descriptive attention.

The nature of the patient care institution profoundly influences the interaction between medicine and nursing. Functional requirements affect relationships. Chronic disease institutions and hospitals devoted to rehabilitation, for example, are likely to favor an expansion of the nursing domain. The informal climate of the small-town hospital favors minimal differentiation, not only between physicians but also between medicine and nursing. Increased bureaucratization of large-scale hospitals, with its resultant emphasis on rigid job descriptions and committee-born compromises, tends to be reflected in circumscribed definitions of the nurse's work. The university medical center, in which the medical presence is much more pervasive because of the special space and time required for medical education and research, tends all too easily to push nursing aside, thereby minimizing its capability to negotiate and to reoccupy its place when the doctor is gone [42].

An altogether different perspective on the organizational setting of the nurse's work emerges when the normative criteria of patient care and patient needs are invoked. The assumption that the physician's viewpoint, his concerns and priorities, are identical with the requirements of patient care is subject to challenge and should be studied. While this topic begs for exhaustive, independent treatment, it bears on our concern by suggesting two kinds of questions: Are there important areas of objective or subjective patient care needs which would or could be met by nurses if their time and effort were not totally preempted by externally imposed medically or managerially oriented activities? Is the formal arrangement for utilizing nursing manpower wasteful of skills when those who are presumably closest to the patient are linked to functions which they do not control?

The second group of questions suggested by a patient care oriented approach is concerned with the optimal division of labor, competence, and jurisdiction. Are all areas which are currently under medical control best situated in the physician's domain? Is there a difference between the initiation of a service and the control over the way it is rendered? Is nursing (and incidently, also clinical nutrition, social work, and other fields) hampered by the fact that the delivery of the services in which they are expert is substantively controlled by those who, though they ought to set objectives, could not possibly be experts in all phases of delivery? [60]. The formal structure of the nurse's work is not merely affected by the bureaucratic arrangements of the institution, but also by a formal system of jurisdictional allocations. Both these systems appear to be strained by the winds of change.

INTERACTION: NURSE AND PHYSICIAN

The relationships between the incumbents of an occupational role and those of other functionally linked occupations are affected by the human characteristics of the members of this occupation as well as by the formal structure of their conditions of work. Symbols, cultural values, and attitudes are also influential. Yet, the processes of interaction are separable from formal organization and from intrapersonal dynamics. Though interdependent, these components of social life need not be consistent. Within the overall process of social change, one should not assume that changes in the formal, rule-oriented domain inevitably modify attitudes, or vice versa. Changes in the symbolic inner life of a group, also, need not be immediately reflected in its interaction with the outside world. Whether on the cultural, political, or occupational scene, social change does not occur at an even pace. Any of these factors—the inner life, the formal framework, or the flow of attitudes—can be leading or lagging in the process.

So it is in nursing. It is suggested here that the inner life of nursing is in the process of uneven, yet significant, motion. By contrast, the pattern of deploying nurses, at least in the hospital, has shown very little inclination toward change. At the same time, the tenor of the national dialogue between nursing and other health professions has changed.

Interaction is governed by the dramaturgy of the social context within which relationships take place. Nursing interacts with others on a variety of such stages, each with its own content, flavor, and cast of characters. The stage on which patient care takes place, the administrative conference room, and the national scene provide material for three very different vignettes of the contact of nursing with others. "Offstage"—the social scene—and "backstage"—where nurses are not within listening range—represent additional and very different perspectives.

The predominant climate on the patient care unit is that of an unquestioned hierarchial arrangement [16]. Communications flow primarily downward, and the nurse is perceived and treated by the physician as the receiver and the presumably unquestionably obedient implementor of medical directives. Yet even this simple picture is not complete. Somewhat as in the authoritarian climate of the army, considerable leeway is given to the trusted soldier who conforms to the overt rituals of disciplined obedience. Day-to-day physician-nurse contacts are full of delicate and mutually understood games in which the nurse imposes her wishes while pretending to stay within the framework of "Yes, Doctor" [78]. Somewhat reminiscent of the senior officer in the army who expects the master sergeant to "make a soldier" out of the new lieutenant, an important aspect of the reality in the nurse-physician relationship can be observed in the annual cycle of the hazing game between nursing and the "house staff." During the first few weeks after their arrival on July 1, interns are subjected to a "socializing experience" by nursing, usually with the quiet yet open acquiesence of the senior medical staff. By the middle of the year, the tables turn and "rank exerts its privileges."

Fundamentally, the relationship between the physician and the nurse on the stage of the work environment is characterized by a peculiar mixture of subordination, informal trust, and discontinuity of responsibility. It is characteristic of this relationship that orders are "turned over" to nursing, thereby freeing the physician of continued responsibility; this converts him from the superordinate who gave orders into the client who expects to receive services. Thus, the inadequate process of task prescription will not protect the nurse from blame or recrimination, for the relationship of trust is primarily downward. The physician expects the nurse to compensate for his shortcomings and cover up his mistakes. The nurse cannot expect similar treatment; on the contrary, she may even be expected to acknowledge a shared mistake as her own.

Active participation of nursing in the planning of the care of the patient tends to occur in some settings, but is by no means the typical pattern. In response to a questionnaire from the American Medical Association, less than 10 percent of a sample of physicians indicated that they ever bothered to look at nurses' notes [41a]. This is partly due to the ritualistic quality of the peculiar document called the patient's chart, which in its design reflects the status structure of the hospital rather than the process of patient care. Nevertheless, the observer who leaves the patient care unit and participates in a policy-level conference in the hospital will be impressed with the changes in interaction and the differences in the symbolisms which govern the parts played by the physicians and nurses when they meet on this stage. The normative pressure for acknowledging changes in status is more readily visible in settings in which the climate is one of negotiation rather than the conduct of business-as-usual. Gestures towards "professional status," towards nursing autonomy, as well as ritualistic appeals to a variety of changing symbols in the style of relationship characterize these performances around the green table.

It is appropriate here to suggest the comparison between the nurse and the

Negro from the point of view of the social psychology of minority group status. Myrdal has already suggested interesting comparisons between the status of the Negro and that of the woman [58]. The nurse, in her interaction with the physician—at least within the work environment—suggests what might be the last vestigial remains of the nineteenth-century relationship between the sexes. In other ways she can fruitfully be compared with the Negro in American society. Reminiscent of the stereotyped views held about Blacks, physicians, when interviewed, will claim that the best characteristics of the nurse are her innate, biologically determined qualities; that she is happiest when working for the physician; and that he, the physician, understands her best and loves her most. This, of course, does not include the "uppity nurses" who, many physicians interestingly believe, are primarily stirred up by outsiders (sociologists?). An important aspect of this parallel is that in the work setting, the relationship of the physician is frequently one to the category "nurse" rather than to an individual co-worker. This perception is similar to inter-caste relationships.

In examining the interaction between the physician and the nurse one cannot overlook the sexual nexus, whether myth or reality. The definition of the nurse as a sexual target is one of the most severe obstacles to colleague-like, professional, and intellectual relations. A truly militant mobilization of nursing towards professional relationships with physicians might require a deliberate, collective elimination of physicians as recipients of extramarital sexual favors. It should be added that there is a difference between sexual partnerships which are based on basically personal contacts and those which stem from status claims (in addition to the basic male-female status consequence). Though dating between physicians and nurses is not always, or even typically, status exploitation, the social definition prevails and thus distorts other modes of interaction [74].

On the third stage, the national scene, there have been a number of formal attempts during recent years to explore and improve the relationships between the physician and the nurse [52]. These conferences were useful and important; however, they remain gestures in the groping and exploring which characterize the relationship between the professions. Similarly, hospital administrators, either within the orbit of the American Hospital Association or as members of the National League for Nursing, have gone through a decade of probing changes in the relationship with nursing without giving up much control or many management prerogatives.

Not unlike the changes in language, attitudes, and gestures used in respect to other minority groups, the dynamics of the current stirring in the physician-nurse relationship are governed by mixed motivations. Genuine reconsiderations of traditional norms, as well as of the implications of changed conditions of knowledge and technology, are mixed with political and cultural considerations in creating the fashions which govern the changes in the labels given to minority groups. None of the relationships observed on any one of the stages is either a completely true or false picture of the interaction network between medicine and nursing. The same physician who barks not-to-be-questioned demands at the nurse in the patient care area may be completely sincere when, in a conference on professional affairs, he assures the nurses present that they deserve more autonomy and dignity. Furthermore, neither of these communications may be consistent with the "offstage" expression of a flippant attitude shared—somewhat off the record—with a few of his medical colleagues.

One of the most remarkable characteristics of research in the health care setting is the coexistence of phenomena which suggest opposite conclusions. In the midst of a picture of generally rigid restraints, there have been a significant number of focal points of change and experimentation in recent years. In some instances this has resulted in an exploration of the relationship between the two professions [5, 6, 63]. In other instances, the development of respect and cooperation between leaders in both professions has made experimental changes possible. For example, the experimental approach to patient care organization and unit management at the University of Florida Medical Center was profoundly influenced by the cooperation of Dean Dorothy Smith of the School of Nursing and Dr. Sam Martin, then Dean of the School of Medicine [45, 53]. In other situations, these explorations were the background for experimental approaches to an expanded role of the nurse [13, 44].

CHANGING ROLE MODELS

The play of forces which move an occupation and motivate its members is, in a way, cast as choices between the role options legitimated by the occupation's norms. The college professor navigates between teaching and research, with the possibility of administration lurking as a deprecated, yet upwardly mobile alternative. Physicians choose between private practice, institutional practice, public health, or academic medicine. Moreover, within any of these fields the physician can choose among alternatives leading to financial success, professional eminence, or institutional power. In each occupation the historical moment, the specific scene, and certain situational circumstances tend to favor some options over others.

Early in this chapter the antecedents of nursing were identified with the emergence of the major role models which have influenced nursing behavior, nursing relationships, and nursing images. These have been variously characterized by social scientists. Sam Schulman's classic distinction between the "mother-surrogate" and the "healer" remains a valid dichotomization: The early, nurture-oriented tradition of supportive ministering to the sick is contrasted with the later inclusion of nursing into the paramedical orbit [70]. To these two models, symbolizing substantive role-orientations, needs to be added, as this author has suggested elsewhere, a third competing option [48]. The management model is a genuine, bureaucratically imposed, third alternative to both supportive patient care and the sensory and motor extension of the medical act.

A very different approach to nursing roles, which provides fewer alternatives, emphasizes the essence of the meaning of nursing. Early discussions by Devereux and Weiner [22], Johnson and Martin [39], and Thorner [81] are antecedents to the recent, sophisticated, and suggestive treatment by the Simpsons [73]. These approaches—rather than implying a choice of alternative roles—suggest that the female composition, the recruitment base, and the structural constraints provide a nearly inescapable role path.

The essay by Simpson and Simpson makes reference to another set of role options which was formulated in one of the earliest, conceptually sophisticated studies of nursing. Habenstein and Christ distinguished between the utilizer, the traditionalizer, and the professionalizer [32]. While these models do not entirely correspond with the ones discussed here, they do offer an important way of distinguishing and analyzing alternatives in the current scene.

The traditionalizer finds the legitimation for her nursing role in either the sacred or the secular truths of the past. Whether it is Christian charity and service or the natural endowment of the female as mother, the traditionalizer feels commitment to a personal role, to a function, and to her patients. Yet, she is fundamentally local [31].

The utilizer is primarily engaged in the economic exchange of performing a job for wages received. Several interpreters of Habenstein and Christ's trichotomy have identified the utilizer with poor nursing. Although such a correlation may exist, it is by no means an inevitable one. The conscientious performance of a responsibility that is felt to be primarily a contractual job obligation is entirely possible. The question of whether ideological orientations are in fact essential to quality performance is one to which sociologists have yet to address themselves.

The professionalizer is oriented towards the norm, status, and collective ideals of the occupation. She worked for "change," even before the term was being used, and looked toward the future attainment of desirable conditions for nursing. Although the direction of change and the priority of battle may vary among professionalizers, they all claim a cosmopolitan, professional role and strive for control over content, conditions, and conduct.

These constructs have been introduced to facilitate the discussion of the current scene. On the one hand, the tug of history is taking place between the old role options and the new ones. On the other hand, as is often the case in periods of innovation, battle lines are being drawn among the proponents of the various new role alternatives.

Numerically, the preponderance of practicing nurses remain in traditional settings and still accommodate themselves to prevailing role demands. This should not blind the observer to the increasing strain which is felt by the new generation of nurses and to the questions that are being asked. Obviously this is particularly true in the collegiate setting [61], but it is by no means confined to the baccalaureate nurse. The increasing militancy of nurses in the economic sphere is not confined to wages and working conditions, but typically involves questions of control over domains of nursing practice [50, 38].

Among the new voices there are some who argue that one of the roles available to the nurse must be management, and that it must be embraced more deliberately and with greater expertise [43]. This option is seen as a direct means of gaining and maintaining the power to assure and to protect desirable conditions for nursing. Management is also seen as a continuing career ladder.

The more frequently debated experimentations in new role models are identified with the two concepts of "the nurse-clinician" [25, 45] and "the expanded role of the nurse." The first of these was proposed by Frances Reiter [66]. The concept of the nurse-clinician represents a translation of a rather traditional domain of nursing into a repertory of intellectually based, autonomously performed, and interprofessionally planned nursing functions. The nurse-clinician participates in the diagnostic process, in the planning of patient care, and in the selection of resources. She serves as a resource and guide to the bedside nurse but, according to her proponents, does not assume supervisory functions. These new functionaries have often had a difficult time gaining acceptance from the occupants of traditional nursing positions and from practicing physicians; yet, in some instances, even without such support, they have been able to earn respect and make an impact. The author, for example, recently had the opportunity to observe a nurse who functioned in a pediatric department as a nurse clinician, essentially without sponsorship. She succeeded in assuming heretofore-never-performed nursing functions for severely ill children, and she gained acceptance as a resource from some of the nurses and staff physicians. With one physician, she coauthored an article. Since her recent move to another city, even some of those who initially opposed her have requested that she be replaced with a nurse who could function in a similar way.

The experimentations with the "expanded role of the nurse" are not as easily described in a way that applies to all of them. While the nurse-clinician is building her strength in the core area of nursing, "expansion" means a testing of the frontiers of the nursing turf. It frequently involves placing the nurse into positions where she has the primary contact with the patient, thus functioning as gatekeeper, as channeling agent, and—most importantly—as the direct and primary resource of those who seek entry into the health care system. Whether this occurs in an out-patient department [44] or whether it involves the pediatric service [13], the nurse assumes the full responsibility for taking care of patients and completely plans their care, unless she judges that the physician's involvement is advisable. After some initial hesitation, patients have generally expressed satisfaction with these experiments; however, they have upset traditionally oriented nurses and physicians.

Some of these experiments have been undertaken as academic innovations [67, 68]. Others have emerged from new ideas translated immediately into programs. Some of these, such as the pediatric nurse associate, have caused mixed reactions, raising questions whether "expansion" in this instance did not mean "abandonment" [72]. The entire concept of the expansion of the nurse's role is fraught with a mixture of risk and opportunity. Particularly in nursing, an occupation whose boundaries have sometimes seemed to have the rigidity of an amoeba, the degree to which the nurse's identity can be stretched must be a crucial question.

Experimentation with the nurse's role is also affected by external pressures. Medicine, which feels the need to pass on some of its routine or easily taught functions, has projected the concept of the physician's assistant. In some instances, as at Duke University, this idea may give rise to a functionary who is wholly within the medical sphere, and not a substitute for the nurse. However, there are those who seek to make this physician's assistant essentially a substitute for nursing. Others have sought to present the role of physician's assistant as a "promotion" for nurses.

Whether the churning that is taking place in nursing will have consequences will partly depend on the capability of nursing to develop legitimated leaders and to close ranks. In another way—which ought to intrigue the sociologist—the future of nursing will be linked to the scientific, logistic, and political feasibility of organizing experimental approaches to manpower use, to role performance, and to organizational arrangements. Rigorous experimentation with sociological variables has, for obvious reasons, lagged behind that of the physical and biological sciences. In its groping, nursing may succeed in establishing the conditions for a laboratory for the sociology of work.

REFERENCES

1. AMERICAN NURSES' ASSOCIATION, "Education for Nursing," *American Journal of Nursing*, 65 (December, 1965), 106 ff.
2. ———, *Facts about Nursing: A Statistical Summary*. New York, 1969.
3. ARGYRIS, CHRIS, *Diagnosing Human Relations in Organizations: A Case Study of a Hospital*, Studies in Organizational Behavior, No. 2. New Haven, Conn.: Yale Labor and Management Center, 1956.
4. "At Press Time," *American Journal of Nursing*, 70 (April, 1970), 687–688.
5. BATES, BARBARA, "Doctor and Nurse: Changing Roles and Relations," *New England Journal of Medicine*, 283 (July, 1970), 129–34.
6. ——— AND SUE KERN, "Doctor-Nurse Teamwork: What Helps? What Hinders?" *American Journal of Nursing*, 67 (October, 1967), 2066–71.
7. BEAVER, ALMA PERRY, "Personality Factors in Choice of Nursing," *Journal of Applied Psychology*, 37 (October, 1953), 374–79.

7a. "Biennial Highlights," *American Journal of Nursing*, 52 (July, 1952), 824–27.

8. BRACKETT, MARY E. AND EMMA SPANEY, "What Nurses Like and Dislike about their Jobs," *Modern Hospital*, 89 (December, 1957), 53–58.
9. BRIDGEMAN, MARGARET, *Collegiate Education for Nursing*. New York: Russell Sage Foundation, 1953.
10. BROWN, ESTHER LUCILE, *Nursing for the Future: A Report Prepared for the National Nursing Council*. New York: Russell Sage Foundation, 1948.
11. ———, *Professional Role in Institutional Nursing*. Part I of *Nursing Reconsidered: A Study of Change*. Philadelphia: J. B. Lippincott Co., 1970.
12. CHAYER, MARY ELLA, *Nursing in Modern Society*. New York: G. P. Putnam's Sons, 1947.
13. CONNELLY, JOHN P., et al., "The Physician and the Nurse: Their Interprofessional Work in Office and Hospital Ambulatory Settings," *New England Journal of Medicine*, 275 (October, 1966), 765–69.
14. CORWIN, RONALD G., "The Professional Employee: A Study of Conflict in Nursing Roles," *American Journal of Sociology*, 66 (May, 1961), 604–15.
15. ———, MARVIN J. TAVES, AND J. EUGENE HAAS, "Professional Disillusionment," *Nursing Research*, 10 (Summer, 1961), 141–44.
16. COSER, ROSE LAUB, "Authority and Decision Making in a Hospital: A Comparative Analysis," *American Sociological Review*, 23 (February, 1958), 56–63.
17. CROOG, SYDNEY H., WILLIAM CAUDILL, AND JEAN L. BLUMEN, "Career Decisions of Student Nurses in Japan," *Journal of Nursing Education*, 5 (January, 1966), 3–6, 20–21, 23–27.
18. CROSBY, EDWIN L., "Coordination or Fragmentation," *Nursing Outlook*, 11 (January, 1963), 42–43.
19. DAVIS, FRED, ed., *The Nursing Profession: Five Sociological Essays*. New York: John Wiley & Sons, 1969.
20. ——— AND VIRGINIA L. OLESEN, "Initiation into a Women's Profession: Identity Problems in the Status Transition from Coed to Student Nurse," *Sociometry*, 26 (March, 1963), 89–101.
21. DE LORA, JACK R. AND DOROTHY V. MOSES, "Specialty Preferences and Characteristics of Nursing Students in Baccalaureate Programs," *Nursing Research*, 18 (March–April, 1969), 137–44.
22. DEVEREUX, GEORGE AND FLORENCE R. WEINER, "The Occupational Status of Nurses," *American Sociological Review*, 15 (October, 1950), 624–34.
23. DOCK, LAVINIA L. AND ISABEL M.

Stewart, *A Short History of Nursing.* New York: G. P. Putnam's Sons, 1938, pp. 58 ff.

24. Freidson, Eliot, *Profession of Medicine.* New York: Dodd, Mead & Co., 1970.

25. Georgopoulos, Basil S. and Luther Christman, "The Clinical Nurse Specialist: A Role Model," *American Journal of Nursing,* 70 (May, 1970), 1030–39.

26. Ginzberg, Eli, Sol W. Ginzberg, Sidney Axelrad, and John L. Herma, *Occupational Choice: An Approach to a General Theory.* New York: Columbia University Press, 1951.

27. Glaser, William A., "Nursing Leadership and Policy: Some Cross-National Comparisons," in Fred Davis, ed., *The Nursing Profession: Five Sociological Essays.* New York: John Wiley & Sons, 1966, p. 4.

28. Goffman, Erving, *Asylums: Essays on the Social Situation of Mental Patients and Other Inmates.* Garden City, N.Y.: Anchor Books, Doubleday & Company, Inc., 1961, pp. 1–124, "On the Characteristics of Total Institutions."

29. Goldmark, Josephine, *Nursing and Nursing Education in the United States.* New York: The Macmillan Company, 1923.

30. Goldsen, Rose K., "Factors Associated with the Selection of a Career in Nursing." Paper read at the 52nd Annual Meeting of the American Sociological Society, Washington, D.C., August 28, 1957.

31. Gouldner, Alvin W., "Cosmopolitans and Locals: Toward an Analysis of Latent Social Roles I," *Administrative Science Quarterly,* 2 (December, 1957), 281–306.

32. Habenstein, Robert W. and Edwin A. Christ, *Professionalizer, Traditionalizer, and Utilizer.* Columbia, Mo.: University of Missouri, 1963.

33. Hale, Thomas, "Clichés of Nursing Education," *New England Journal of Medicine,* 278 (April, 1968), 879–86.

34. Healy, Irene and Walter R. Borg, "Personality Characteristics of Nursing School Students and Graduate Nurses," *Journal of Applied Psychology,* 35 (August, 1951), 275–80.

35. Henderson, "The Nature of Nursing," *American Journal of Nursing,* 64 (August, 1964), 62–68.

36. Hiatt, Wilma, "Associate Degree Nursing Programs in California," *American Journal of Nursing,* 61 (October, (1961), 93–95.

37. Hughes, Everett C., Helen MacGill Hughes, and Irwin Deutscher, *Twenty Thousand Nurses Tell Their Story.* Philadelphia: J. B. Lippincott Co., 1958.

38. Jacox, Ada K., "Who Defines and Controls Nursing Practice?" *American Journal of Nursing,* 69 (May, 1969), 977–82.

39. Johnson, Miriam M. and Harry W. Martin, "A Sociological Analysis of the Nurses' Role," *American Journal of Nursing,* 58 (March, 1958), 373–77.

40. Katz, Fred, "Nurses," in Amitai Etzioni, ed., *The Semi-Professions and Their Organization: Teachers, Nurses, Social Workers.* New York: The Free Press, 1969.

41. Kitchell, Myrtle E., "A Study of the Relationship of Certain Socio-Economic Factors to the Choice of Educational Institution and Program of First Year Students in Nursing in the North Central Region." Unpublished Ph.D. dissertation, Department of Education, University of Minnesota, June, 1955.

41a. Oral communication from Dr. Donald D. Kozoll, Medical Director, Northeast Community Hospitals, Chicago, Illinois.

42. Kramer, Marlene, "Collegiate Graduate Nurses in Medical Center Hospitals: Mutual Challenge or Duel," *Nursing Research,* 18 (May–June, 1969), 196–210.

43. Lambertsen, Eleanore C., "Toward a Clearer Definition of the Nurse's Function," *Hospitals: Journal of the American Hospital Association,* 35 (July, 1961), 51–54, 96.

44. Lewis, Charles E. and Barbara Resnik, "Nurse Clinics and Progressive Ambulatory Patient Care," *New England Journal of Medicine,* 277 (December, 1967), 1236–41.

45. LOOMIS, MAXINE E., "The Clinical Specialist as a Change Agent," *Nursing Forum*, 7 (1968), 136–45.
46. MARTIN, SAMUEL P., "Medical Staff Agrees: Unit Plan Is Good for Patient," *Modern Hospital*, 99 (August, 1962), 76–77.
47. MAUKSCH, HANS O., "The Nurse: A Study in Role Perception." Unpublished Ph.D. dissertation, Department of Sociology, University of Chicago, 1960.
48. ———, "Becoming a Nurse: A Selective View," *Annals of the American Academy of Political and Social Science: Medicine and Society*, 346 (March, 1963), 88–98.
49. ———, "The Organizational Context of Nursing Practice," in Fred Davis, ed., *The Nursing Profession: Five Sociological Essays*. New York: John Wiley & Sons, Inc., 1969.
50. MAUKSCH, INGEBORG G., "The Background of Students Selecting Two Large Metropolitan Schools of Nursing." Unpublished Master's thesis, Committee on Nursing Education, University of Chicago, 1957.
51. ———, "Collective Reaction to Occupational Grievances: A Case Study of Nurse Involvement in a Collective Bargaining Endeavor." Unpublished Ph.D. dissertation, Department of Education, University of Chicago, 1969.
52. ———, *A Socio-Occupational Profile of the University of Missouri at Columbia School of Nursing's Graduates (1951–1969) and Their Assessment of the Program*. Columbia, Mo.: School of Nursing, 1970.
53. *Medical and Nursing Practice in a Changing World*. Proceedings of the First National Conference for Professional Nurses and Physicians, sponsored by the American Nurses' Association and the American Medical Association, Williamsburg, Va., February 13–15, 1964.
54. MERCANDANTE, LUCILLE T., "The Functions and Benefits of the Unit Manager," *Hospital Progress*, 47 (January, 1966), 114–17.
55. MERTON, ROBERT K., "The Search for Professional Status," *American Journal of Nursing*, 60 (May, 1960), 662–64.
56. MEYER, GENEVIEVE ROGGE, *Tenderness and Technique: Nursing Values in Transition*, Monograph Series No. 6. Los Angeles, Calif.: Institute of Industrial Relations, University of California, 1960.
57. ——— AND MABEL JOHNSON HOFFMAN, "Nurses' Inner Values and Their Behavior at Work," *Nursing Research*, 13 (Summer, 1964), 244–49.
58. MONTAG, MILDRED AND LASSAR G. GOTKIN, *Community College Education for Nursing: An Experiment for Technical Education for Nursing*. New York: McGraw-Hill Book Company, 1959.
59. MYRDAL, GUNNAR, *An American Dilemma*. New York: Harper & Row, Publishers, Inc., 1944, Appendix V.
60. NAVRAN, LESLIE AND JAMES C. STAUFFACHER, "A Comparative Analysis of the Personality Structure of Psychiatric and Nonpsychiatric Nurses," *Nursing Research*, 7 (June, 1958), 64–67.
61. NORRIS, KATHERINE, "Direct Access to the Patient?" *American Journal of Nursing*, 70 (June, 1970), 1006–10.
62. OLESEN, VIRGINIA L. AND ELVI W. WHITTAKER, *The Silent Dialogue: A Study in the Social Psychology of Professional Socialization*. San Francisco: Jossey–Bass, Inc., 1968.
63. PELLEGRINO, EDMUND D., "The Changing Role of the Professional Nurse in the Hospital," *Hospitals: Journal of the American Hospital Association*, 35 (December, 1961), 56, 59–60, 62.
64. ———, "The Physician and the Nurse," *Annals of Internal Medicine*, 64 (May, 1966), 1140–45.
65. PRATT, HENRY, "The Doctor's View of the Changing Nurse-Physician Relationship," *Journal of Medical Education*, 40 (August, 1965), 767–71.
66. REINKEMEYER, SISTER AGNES M., "It Won't Be Hospital Nursing!" *American Journal of Nursing*, 68 (September, 1968), 1936–40.
67. REITER, FRANCES, "The Nurse-Clinician," *American Journal of Nursing*, 66 (February, 1966), 274 ff.
68. SCHLOTFELDT, ROZELLA M. AND JANNETTA MACPHAIL, "An Experiment in

Nursing: Rationale and Characteristics," *American Journal of Nursing*, 69 (May, 1969), 1018–23.
69. ———, "Experiment in Nursing: Implementing Planned Change," *American Journal of Nursing*, 69 (July, 1969), 1475–80.
70. Schryver, Grace F., *A History of the Illinois Training School*. Chicago: Illinois Training School for Nurses, 1930.
71. Schulman, Sam, "Basic Functional Roles in Nursing: Mother Surrogate and Healer," in E. Gartly Jaco, ed., *Patients, Physicians and Illness*. New York: The Free Press, 1958, pp. 528–37.
72. Shapiro, Carol et al., "Careers of Women Physicians: A Survey of Graduates from Seven Medical Schools 1945–1951," *Journal of Medical Education*, 43 (October, 1968), 1033–40.
73. Silver, Henry K. and Loretta Ford, "The Pediatric Nurse Practitioner at Colorado," *American Journal of Nursing*, 67 (July, 1967), 1443–44.
74. Simpson, Richard L. and Ida H. Simpson, "Women and Bureaucracy in the Semi-Professions," in Amitai Etzioni, ed., *The Semi-Professions and Their Organization: Teachers, Nurses, Social Workers*. New York: The Free Press, 1969, pp. 202 ff.
75. Skipper, James K., Jr. and Gilbert Nass, "Dating Behavior: A Framework for Analysis and an Illustration," *Journal of Marriage and the Family*, 28 (November, 1966), 412–20.
76. Smith, Harvey Liss, "Two Lines of Authority Are One Too Many," *Modern Hospital*, 84 (March, 1955), 59–64.
77. Smith, Jeanne E., "Personality Structure in Beginning Nursing Students: A Factor Analytic Study," *Nursing Research*, 17 (March–April, 1968), 140–45.
78. Staaff, Astrid, "Conditions of Work and Employment of Nurses," *International Nursing Review*, 6 (October, 1959), 18–24.
79. Stein, Leonard, "Thc Doctor-Nurse Game," *American Journal of Nursing*, 69 (January, 1968), 101–05.
80. Strauss, Anselm et al., "The Hospital as a Negotiated Order," in Eliot Freidson, ed., *The Hospital in Modern Society*. New York: The Free Press, 1963.
81. Tauber, Lenore, M., "Scanning the Future," *Nursing Outlook*, 5 (June, 1957), 369–70.
82. Thorner, I., "Nursing: The Functional Significance of an Institutional Pattern," *American Sociological Review*, 20 (October, 1955), 531–38.

10

THE NATURE AND ORGANIZATION OF DENTAL PRACTICE

Wesley O. Young and Lawrence Smith, Jr.

INTRODUCTION

The nature of a health profession is largely determined by the social and economic characteristics of the population it serves and the health problems that are of major concern. Preventive medicine and curative medicine have virtually eliminated the major communicable diseases and have made major strides in the control of chronic disease and disability. The saving and prolongation of life, medicine's most critical concern, has been largely achieved. Society can now be concerned with ways to assure that its members can work at full capacity toward the fulfillment of meaningful and purposeful living. Under these circumstances, it is not surprising that dentistry—concerned in developed countries primarily with comfort and appearance—should become a major health service. And, in fact, dentists now make up the second largest group of primary, direct service, health practitioners in the nation. Despite the relatively circumscribed part of the body for which they assume major responsibility, there is roughly one dentist in practice for every two and one-half physicians [34].

Because dentistry shares with medicine a concern for the total health of the individual and because of the parallel historical development of the two professions, they share many common characteristics. These similarities will be alluded to briefly, but the main task of this chapter is to identify areas in which there are significant differences in practice. These differences are due to the historical development of the two professions, the nature of dental disease, the characteristics of clinical practice, and the type of individual who enters the dental profession.

THE HISTORICAL SETTING

The history of dentistry begins in ancient times [4]. Although modern man suffers an unusually high attack of dental disease (more than 95 percent experiencing dental decay, for example), peoples of the remote past also experienced the pain and disability resulting from diseases of the teeth and supporting structures. The development of dentistry was slow, but there is evidence that throughout the centuries there were those—usually priests or physicians—who were looked upon as having special skills in treating the oral cavity.

The era of modern dentistry began in the seventeenth and eighteenth centuries in Europe and is often identified with the distinguished career of Pierre Fauchard (1678–1761) of Paris. And European concepts of dentistry were early introduced into colonial America. (The best-known practitioner there was probably Paul Revere of Boston, who combined this service with a variety of other skills including silversmithing, horseback riding, and communications. The most illustrious patient was George Washington, who suffered oral discomfort most of his adult life and endured a series of ill-fitting dentures, which probably explains the rather grim and close-mouthed portraits painted during the years of his maturity). Before the nineteenth century settlers in the colonies, and later the states, sought what care was available from dentists of varying competence who had only trained as apprentices under established practitioners.

In the United States the modern profession took shape less than 150 years ago. The first dental school, the Baltimore College of Dental Surgery, was founded; the first national dental periodical in the world, the *American Journal of Dental Science*, began publication; and the first national dental society, the American Society of Dental Surgeons, was organized—all within the period from 1839 to 1840 [26]. It is significant that the first dental school was organized because the medical profession in the Baltimore area declined a request that dental subjects be included in the curriculum of the medical school. This was one of several factors which helped to establish a significant characteristic of dentistry in America—that it was to be an autonomous profession. Although the development of dentistry as a health service has paralleled that of medicine, the profession has remained independent, and as it has grown and matured during the past century, it has become increasingly jealous of and proud of its own destiny. This is in contrast to the history of the profession in Europe, which was characterized by conflict between those trained as dentists and those who were physicians but who, because of additional training in clinical dentistry, elected to practice dentistry. In fact, one of the major crises that faced international dentistry in the early 1900's was the conflict between the "dentists" and the "stomatologists" (as those with medical training referred to themselves) within the Fédération Dentaire Internationale [21].

Today, even in European countries which have separate educational systems to prepare dental practitioners, dentistry is much more closely tied to medicine than in the United States. In England, for example, dentists desiring advanced training are examined and certified by the Royal College of Surgeons—not by a specialty body controlled by the dental profession.

With other health professions, dentistry shares protection from the competition of untrained individuals by a dual control over those who are admitted to practice—through professional school accreditation and through laws which regulate the practice of the profession under powers granted to state licensing bodies. The latter, although technically agencies of state government, are composed of dentists; they effectively transform the opinion and judgment of the profession into statutes and regulations. The first state laws to regulate practice were passed by Kentucky in 1867 and by New York and Ohio in 1868 [26].

Dental education followed a stormy course during its first century. The earliest schools had to struggle against the opposition of dentists who had been trained as preceptors and against a lack of support from physicians, most of whom held dentistry in low esteem. These obstacles were overcome, however, when dental schools (along with the early medical schools) were recognized as a source of potential profit by entrepreneurs of the period. As a result, dental schools, both good and bad, proliferated, resulting in the establishment of as many as 150 (which lasted for varying periods of time) prior to 1920 [19]. Operating a professional school for profit seems a quaint anachronism in this generation, but it was an important factor in permitting the rapid growth of an infant profession. This quick growth is dramatically illustrated by the fact that the number of persons served by each dentist dropped steadily and rapidly over a seventy-year period, from 5,500 in 1860 to about 1,700 in 1930—this, despite a burgeoning of the total population to be served [43].

Efforts of the American Dental Association to upgrade the standards of professional education during the 1920's were guided and reinforced by the publication, in 1926, of a survey of dental education. It was financed by the Carnegie Foundation (which had supported the Flexner survey of medical education about twenty years previously) and conducted by William Gies. As a result of these efforts, many schools of doubtful caliber were closed, and the number of schools dropped drastically. Those that remained were university-affiliated and able to meet the new standards. The Depression further reduced the educational capacity of the nation by limiting the number of students who could afford to attend professional school. By 1935, only thirty-nine schools remained, and fewer dentists were being graduated than were lost to the profession through death and retirement [19].

The developments of the 1920's and 1930's, therefore, had a major impact on the profession. Educational standards were increased and made relatively uniform, clinical teaching was raised to a high level, the foundations were established for a sound biologic preparation (a trend which would come to fruition in the forties and fifties), and the basis for a scientific health profession was established. At the same time, unfortunately, the relative supply of dentists was reduced so that the number of persons served by each dentist rose steadily from 1930 on. Thus was created the shortage of manpower which was to plague the profession in the 1960's and threatens to reach crisis proportions in the 1970's.

To a certain extent, the shortages of dentists and the increased load of patients has already affected the nature of dental practice. Patients find it more difficult to obtain appointments and must travel greater distances to seek care, particularly in rural areas and in areas of urban poverty. When they arrive at a dental office, they are likely to find that they spend less time with their dentist and that there is small likelihood that a personal relationship can be developed. These trends may be expected to be intensified in the next two decades.

CHARACTERISTICS OF DENTAL DISEASE

Dental diseases are nearly universal in their attack. Dental caries, the most prevelant disorder of the early years of life, frequently begins soon after the deciduous teeth erupt into the mouth at two or three years of age. The number of carious lesions increases dramatically with age, and few have failed to experience an attack by late adolescence or young adulthood. Diseases of the soft tissues that support the teeth (periodontal disease or pyorrhea) begin in young adult life and affect almost everyone by middle life. They represent, in fact, the major cause of tooth loss after the age of forty [5].

Malocclusions and congenital malformations are found in a significant number of children and adults, and in many cases become severe handicaps unless properly treated. Treatment requires complex, long-term professional service, sometimes coordinated with the efforts of medical specialists, speech therapists, etc. Cancerous lesions in or near the oral cavity occur frequently enough to constitute a serious health problem.

The high rate of attack of dental diseases is complicated by their irreversible nature and compounded by the frequency with which they are neglected by the patient. Once under way, most dental diseases can be checked only by expensive and time-consuming professional treatment—treatment that primarily must be rendered by the dentist himself. Healing seldom occurs spontaneously, and rarely can it be accomplished solely by advice and prescription or through the efforts of auxiliary personnel.

It is generally assumed by dentists that to detect disease early, patients should be examined every six to eight months. Yet, only 40 percent of the population goes to the dentist in any one year, and it is estimated that only about 20 percent seeks care on a routine, preventive basis [20, 24]. As a result, need for treatment accumulates, and as disease progresses unchecked, it becomes increasingly complex and difficult to treat. In any one population or group of patients, therefore, the need for treatment is a combined function of the continued increment of new disease and the backlog of needs that have accumulated and have been complicated by neglect. The backlog of unmet treatment needs has already reached staggering proportions in the American population.

The nature of dental disease has had an important impact on practice. First, the accumulation of treatment needs compounds pressure on the practitioner to increase his productivity and see more patients, as a greater number of people seek more professional service. The pressure to provide more care for more people is also encouraging the profession to examine the practicability of delegating to trained auxiliaries some duties that are now reserved to the dentist. Because the results of a high rate of disease attack are apparent in the mouths of most of his patients, the conscientious dentist has a daily motivation to emphasize prevention. The results of the accumulation of defects caused by neglect are also readily apparent, so a parallel commitment is encouraged—a commitment to motivate patients to seek professional service regularly and frequently on a preventive, maintenance basis.

Most dental diseases are not acute or viewed as hazardous by the patient. Acute oral infections were once a serious problem, but they occur infrequently and, since the advent of antibiotic therapy, can be readily controlled. Although life-threatening, oral cancer is often not identified by the patient in its early stages; also it occurs with relative infrequency. The chronic nature of most dental diseases makes educating and motivating patients to seek regular care a difficult task and encourages neglect and the postponement of professional services. This characteristic of the diseases often creates a wide dichotomy between the patient's perceived need for care and that of the dentist.

CHARACTERISTICS OF THE PRACTITIONER

Very little information is available for creating a description of the practitioner of dentistry. Almost nothing is known about such factors as personality characteristics, attitudes toward practice of the profession, or relations with patients. The best information about the graduate dentist comes from data that have been gathered about the future members of the profession—the student dentists—and the process by which they achieve professional status.

The Student Dentist

The student entering dental school can be characterized as a highly motivated, upwardly mobile individual. According to Warner, he can generally be categorized in the lower-middle to upper-middle socioeconomic class [42]. His father is often a college graduate, usually employed in a professional or managerial occupation [30, 31]. His mother is also college educated and, in many instances, has a higher level of education than does his father. Adequate family income is a prerequisite for most dental students, since the cost of acquiring a dental education is high. For example, the four-year tuition ranges from an average of $5,400 in state schools for residents of the state to $9,700 in private schools [12]. In addition, the student must pay for his room, board, and other living expenses, plus sizable expenditures for dental instruments—amounting to as much as $2,000 in the first year. Throughout the remaining three years of schooling, he will accumulate an additional $2,000 to $3,000 worth of professional equipment, most, but not all, of which will be used in his future private practice. Students from families with limited incomes can and do attend dental school, but it is a difficult undertaking, requiring unusually high motivation and a willingness (and ability) to borrow from $6,000 to $10,000. This problem has been eased somewhat by the availability from the federal government of loans with low interest rates and extended terms of payment. Recently, however, the amount of money available for these loans, inadequate to begin with, has been cut roughly in half—creating additional hardships for professional students.

The dental student is scientifically and pragmatically oriented. Characteristically, he is strongly concerned with detail and, to some degree, compulsive toward it [23]. His pre-dental school (undergraduate collegiate) education reflects a strong interest in the physical and biological sciences and little interest in speculative and abstract subjects [27, 31]. Some dental students have had only three years of undergraduate work, but more than 60 percent of first-year students begin their professional education after completing four years of college [12].

Pathways to Dentistry. There are several pathways by which a dental student selects his professional commitment [33, 36]. A major influence is the presence of a dentist in the student's immediate family, notably a father, brother, or uncle. The career choice is often reinforced through other contacts with dentists—contacts obtained through a sustained, positive relationship with the family dentist, for example. Many times the choice of dentistry is influenced by a general interest in the sciences—notably the biological sciences. It is also through the medium of basic science courses that the prospective dental student "tests" his aptitude for and his involvement with a future career in the life sciences. The decision to select a dental career does not necessarily emanate from a thwarted admission to medical school or an unsuccessful matriculation there. Less than a fourth of entering dental students have applied to medical schools as a "first choice." However, two-thirds of such students list medicine as an alternative career choice in the event of nonacceptance to a dental school [36]. A study of applicants by More indicated that the "top" dental school applicant has credentials for acceptance in "most any" medical school [30, 31]. Undoubtedly there are exceptions, but the concept of dental students being "frustrated medical students" has been definitely dispelled [38]. And other professional careers are often considered by the dental student—mainly engineering, law, and academic or research positions in one of the basic sciences [30, 31].

A recent study of student motivations to dentistry by Sherlock and Cohen confirms the works of others, but ingeniously describes the choice pattern as one of "minimax." The minimax strategy guides the individual to choose an occupation having minimum difficulty of access along with maximum rewards. The minimax hierarchy of six occupations, as perceived by a California dental student sample, was dentistry, law, medicine, teaching in a university, business, and accounting, reflecting a belief that access to dentistry was less difficult but gave rewards comparably high with medicine. When the sample was asked to list a maximax occupational choice, i.e., a choice which considers both rewards and difficulty of access, the order was medicine, dentistry, law, university teaching, accounting, and business. These data suggest that pre-dental students often entertained both the "minimax" and "maximax" strategems in their pursuit of career choices but favored dentistry as their "minimax" choice because it combined high rewards with an easier access than medicine [39].

There are, of course, several reasons for choosing dentistry as a career. The prospective student may be initially motivated by humanistic or altruistic concerns or by a desire for individual autonomy, high financial rewards, the prestige associated with the high social status of dentists, and pleasure gained from manual achievement. Thus, there appears to be a mixture of intrinsic and extrinsic rewards.

More's study of dental students reports a consistently high concern for human service as a factor in career orientation [31]. Unlike the study by Becker and others [1], which depicted a change in the value orientation of medical students from humanism to cynicism, More's data state that humanistic concerns held by the freshman dental student remain as a viable and significant orientation after four years of dental education. What has shifted in terms of a professional "world view" is the desire for prestige and a preoccupation with manual skill [31]. However, data in a recent, yet-to-be published study by Sherlock and Morris [40], on the professionalization of 242 dental students, compellingly suggest a contradiction to earlier known findings. The authors noted that high cynicism scores occurred in 10 percent of first-year students but that by the time these students reached their fourth year, 30 percent had high cynicism scores. A further change in value orientation was noted in the decline in "ethicalness" over the course of a student's dental education. (High ethical scores were attained by 64 percent of freshmen students at the commencement of their studies, while later, as seniors, only 25 percent scored highly.

Because of the marked difference in their educational experiences, it should be easier for students of dentistry to maintain an orientation to human service during their basic professional training than for students of medicine. Medical students have almost no contact with patients in their first two years of school, and in the later years their contact is largely limited to periodic observations of the care being rendered by the faculty and house staff. Furthermore, medical students know they will have to serve a one- or two-year internship before facing the sobering demands of complete responsibility for the management of patients.

Most dental students, on the other hand, have some patient contact during their first two years, and all provide relatively comprehensive care, under faculty supervision, of patients assigned them during their last two years. Furthermore, the majority of dental students will enter practice after graduation (either private practice or in the armed forces) and are aware that they will have independent responsibility for patient care relatively soon. It should be easier, therefore, for dental students to maintain a motivation for human service.

The fact that the student may retain an orientation to service during his professional training does not mean that he will function as a "starry-eyed idealist" during his subsequent professional career. In the first place, his motivations, from the beginning, have included desires for financial rewards and prestige. Furthermore, increasing maturity, the assumption of family responsibilities, and exposure to a largely commercial middle-class world would lead one to expect some tempering of initial idealism and the reinforcement of the desire for financial gain. Additionally, realization of the end of his dental education—the extended period in which gratification was necessarily deferred—and the subsequent necessity to repay educational loans or "make up for lost time," etc., may be salient factors in the young dentist's early identification with and participation in the "establishment."

The Nature of Professionalization. Conceptually, professionalization is akin to adult socialization. In this usage, *socialization* is viewed as the process by which people "selectively acquire the values and attitudes, the interests, skills, and knowledge—in short, the culture—current in the groups of which they are, or seek to become a member." In regard to the professional student, Merton suggests that socialization "refers to the processes through which he develops his professional self, with its characteristic values, attitudes, knowledge, and skills which govern his behavior in a wide variety of professional (and extra-professional) situations" [28].

The professionalization process occurs through exposure to and participation in dental education. Formally, it is a rigorous and attention-consuming curriculum. The early courses emphasize the basic sciences and make professional identification difficult, although dental schools are attempting to assure early patient contact to ease the transition from laboratory to the clinic. Instruction is generally dogmatic, with limited speculative content. The later courses, on the other hand, are mainly clinical in substance, and serve to aid identification with the dental profession.

Presumably, between the first and fourth years of dental school, the student is confronted by the "formal" professionalization process. His instructors are, with the exception of some in basic science courses, men who have also completed a dental education. Therefore, he is exposed to a number of dentist-role-models, and their interaction with the student affords him the opportunity to identify with "genuine" dentists—members of his chosen profession.

It is important to note that the dental student-faculty relationship is analogous to the apprentice-journeyman dyad, since the inculcation of professional skills is affected largely by on-the-job training, frequently on a one-to-one basis. This fact is especially true throughout early and later clinical courses and experiences. Hence, information transfer and the acquisition of skills occur in a structured manner through the intense contacts with men (dentists) with whom the dental student aspires to identify. Additionally, dental students can expect their instructors' understanding of their plight, i.e., their anxieties, frustrations, feelings of stress, etc., since they know the instructor was once a student and, therefore, has "gone through all this himself."

There exists an informal aspect of dental professionalization, which is independent of the rigorous didactic conglomeration of coursework and clinics. It exists in the dental school milieu; there is a quasi-ubiquitous nature of dentistry which reinforces the student's role and reminds him of his identity. He wears a white laboratory coat, and in his early years of dental school, may be addressed by some kind hearted faculty members as "Doctor." In his clinic contacts with patients, even as early as in the second year, he is addressed as "Dr. Brown", "Smith", or whatever, and when calling patients, he may say "This is Dr. Brown calling."

He is encouraged to join the student professional organization (Student American Dental Association), which encourages professional and social interaction on both a formal and an informal level. He is encouraged to read and subscribe to dental journals and to attend professional meetings and extramural dental lectures given in the dental school and elsewhere. His social interaction is often with classmates, and his wife may be encouraged to participate in the SADA auxiliary or dental school "widows" clubs, to prepare herself for her future as a dentist's wife.

Social Sensitivity. The process of professionalization of dental students apparently has been successful in creating members of a viable and vigorous profession. One evidence is the extremely high membership of practicing dentists in their professional organization—the American Dental Association. Eighty-seven percent of the eligible dentists in the United States are members of this Association; this contrasts with 47 percent membership of those eligible for the American Bar Association and 68 percent for the American Medical Association [2]. The significance of the high membership figures is heightened by the fact that only minor financial or personal advantages accrue because a dentist belongs to the Association. The dentist does not ordinarily need hospital affiliation and, otherwise, membership is not a prerequisite to the practice of his profession. (Such advantages as do accrue personally relate to organized programs for group insurance and benefits provided to the professional in terms of the acquisition of scientific knowledge and the advancement of the profession.) The American Dental Association is the largest organization of dentists in the world and is generally recognized to be the most active, influential, and best organized of the dental associations.

It is clear that most dentists in practice follow a code of behavior and a set of social and ethical values that conform, on the surface, to the norms demonstrated by the professional schools. Among many leaders of the profession, however, there has been deep discontent with the product of dental education of the past several decades. It has been felt that the technical excellence achieved by dentists in America and their grounding in the biological sciences have not been accompanied by the development of socially aware individuals who function at optimum levels, either in relation to the patients they treat or to the community in which they practice. In a paper presented about a decade ago—one that had a major influence in developing trends in dental education—Blackerby summarized this view of practicing dentists:

> I am motivated by a strong conviction that the social aspects of dentistry are now seriously neglected in the typical dental student's education, and by a sincere desire to find ways of correcting this basic deficiency in the methods of preparing dentists for their role in society.
>
> The dearth of research on the social attitudes and performances of dentists and dental students makes it impossible to support adequately the widely held opinion, which I share, that dentists generally are relatively lacking in social consciousness and that this attitude may be traced directly to a weakness in their professional education and to the professional isolation that characterizes the dental practitioner [3].

The concern expressed by Dr. Blackerby was not an isolated phenomenon. His paper carried the title "Why Not A Department of Social Dentistry?" and suggested the need for curricular and organizational changes in dental schools to correct the deficiencies identified in dental education. The response from the profession was surprisingly rapid, and within the relatively brief period of three years, several dental schools organized instructional departments along the lines that had been suggested. Today, some thirty-five schools have departments of "community and preventive dentistry" (the generic name used to include courses given under a variety of titles in different schools), and the number is increasing [13].

CHARACTERISTICS OF DENTAL PRACTICE

Physical Setting

The ability to practice medicine solely with the resources of the individual practitioner (largely contained in a black bag) became obsolete with the passing of the horse and buggy. Today, the ability of the physician to utilize his professional skills is largely dependent on the availability of facilities and resources provided by the community. Laboratory and radiographic facilities; surgical suites; complex therapeutic devices such as cobalt units and intensive care units; and a wide variety of paramedical personnel represent a major investment in health care in almost every community. The availability of these resources determines, to a large extent, the nature of medical practice in the community and the number and type (general practitioners and specialists) of practitioners that can be attracted to serve the area.

The distribution of dentists, on the other hand, does not reflect the availability of community health facilities but primarily the personal choice of the practitioners. The dentist ordinarily is completely self-contained and depends on almost no outside resources, either from other practitioners or from the community. One reason for this is that the most expensive items of equipment, such as the dental chair and "unit" (the major equipment usually located next to the dental chair), are in almost constant use by the dentist himself, so there is no opportunity to share them with other health practitioners. And the balance of the dentist's instrumentation is relatively inexpensive and does not create a demand for a facility in the community where these can be shared with others. Because the dentist cannot share community-financed facilities with other practitioners, the initial cost of entering practice is significant. It was estimated that in 1969 the cost of establishing a dental practice (over and above rent and other ongoing costs) ranged from $12,000 to $22,000 [18]. This is probably considerably higher than for other health practitioners entering practice.

Organizational Structure

The overwhelming majority of dentists (seven out of ten) practice alone in their own offices [6]. This is true despite the fact that the advantages of some type of cooperative effort have been extolled by leaders of the profession for many years. This is probably because those who choose dentistry are a self-selected group who enter the occupation because it offers an opportunity to be "one's own boss." Dental school faculty members report that their students comment frequently that they wish to be independent. The concept of "independence" apparently implies freedom not only from a "boss" but also from the constraints inherent in an association with professional peers or the complex organizational structure and management problems involved in a multidentist office. The typical dental students and dental practitioner is not an "organization man." And this initial bent is fortified by the fact that the student and young practitioner are ordinarily exposed to only one model of practitioner—the man in independent solo practice. Even should the student develop an interest in alternative methods of practice organization, dental school teaches him little about these alternatives which would prepare him to organize or participate in unorthodox methods of delivering dental care.

Actually, dental practices are organized in an infinite variety of ways

—matching the variety of individuals who enter practice. For the purposes of clarity, however, they may be divided into three basic types: independent solo practice (including associateships), solo with facility sharing, and partnership-group practice.

Independent solo practice reflects the unfettered personal judgment and preference of an individual practitioner. At the minimum level, such a practice may involve one practitioner working completely alone, utilizing one dental operating room, a waiting room, and a small laboratory-darkroom. In this case, he carries out his professional treatment, prepares filling materials, fabricates prosthetic appliances, answers the telephone, cleans up after each patient, and maintains whatever records he feels are necessary. His own efforts may be supplemented slightly by a person—perhaps his wife or a high school girl—who comes in for a few hours a day. Archaic as they may appear, practices such as this still exist. (In 1967, 7 percent of the dentists in private practice reported that they had no employees.) A more common pattern is for the dentist to have at least two dental operating rooms and to employ one, one and a half, or two dental assistants. (A 1967 survey of dentists indicated that 22 percent had only one assistant, 8.6 percent had one full-time and one part-time assistant or receptionist, and 11 percent had two full-time assistants or receptionists [8].) The professional tasks of the dentist may be supplemented by the skills of a dental hygienist, currently the only auxiliary in dentistry professionally trained and licensed to perform clinical procedures in the mouth. Her responsibilities usually include patient education, radiographic, and clinical examinations, and oral prophylaxis (cleaning the teeth), which is the basic requirement for the control of periodontal disease. In 1967, about 12 percent of the dentists employed a dental hygienist on a full-time basis, and an equal number employed a part-time hygienist.

A few dentists (probably not more than 2 or 3 percent) have gone further in refining the organization of solo practice to achieve maximum productivity [7, 8]. Their practices utilize as many as four or five rooms equipped to treat patients and employ as many as five auxiliaries. In such cases the auxiliaries will often include a full- or part-time dental laboratory technician, who fabricates complete and partial dentures, crowns, and fixed bridges under the professional supervision of the dentist.

Older dentists, or those with unusually large practices, sometimes invite a younger man to join them as an "associate," a euphemistic term used to describe the employment of a dentist on a salary, a percentage of the employed dentist's gross income, or a combination of these. The practice and the patients are those of the senior dentist, and it may be assumed that the characteristic of the services rendered reflect his training, experience, and preferences. For this reason, the small group of dentists who fall in the associate category (3.5 percent) can be considered as participating in an extension of independent solo practice [6].

The second organizational pattern is that of facility sharing. Again, a wide variation exists. There are offices in which all equipment and physical facilities and even auxiliary personnel are shared by two or more dentists who still maintain their individual practices. Each practice collects its own income, but costs of the shared facilities are paid jointly on a pre-agreed basis. A more common pattern is to share only a limited part of the physical facilities, such as the waiting room, laboratory, and radiographic equipment. Regardless of the extent to which costs are shared, even this small departure from complete independence has not proved to be significantly popular, since only eight out of a hundred dentists in private practice in 1967 reported that they participated in arrangements of this type [6].

The most radical departure from tradition is the full partnership, or group practice. There have been a variety of definitions of *group practice,* but Sarner has pointed out that the crucial characteristic of this method of organization is that income, as well as facilities and expenses, is shared by the participants [37]. For several decades professional leaders have viewed group practice as the desirable pattern for the future. Some have said that it would be more professionally rewarding to the dentist, since he could concentrate primarily on providing those services he felt most competent to perform and could share the remainder with his associates. Others have pointed to the potentialities of more efficient and effective use of auxiliaries, leading to an increase in income, a lowering of fees, or both. Some who have been concerned with the quality of care have felt that having dentists associated with each other would reinforce professional standards and performance.

Despite its seeming advantages, group practice has not developed rapidly. About 1.6 percent of the dentists practicing in 1952 had such an arrangement. This increased only to 2.6 percent in 1958, and nine years later, the percentage had risen to 4.6 [6, 25]. Although the complete sharing of dental practice has not become a significant trend in dentistry, it has earned an established position. Given the steady (if small) growth over the past two decades and the pressure for increased productivity from the profession, there is reason to believe that full partnerships and other forms of group practice may become an important organizational pattern for dental practice in the near future.

Comprehensive Care and Specialty Practice

One of the major problems that has plagued medicine in recent decades has been the proliferation of specialties. This trend has been viewed by many observers as leading to a fragmentation of services, resulting in an emphasis on sporadic, episodic care of the patient. A number of leaders in the medical profession have sought ways to bring about a return to one primary physician (the so-called family physician) who could provide continuing, recurrent, preventive, and family-centered medicine.

Because of the chronic and recurring nature of dental disease, the profession has been forced since the beginning to emphasize continuing, recurring preventive care rather than episodic treatment. (As has been noted, the ideal of the dentist may not necessarily parallel that of the patient, who may choose to seek only episodic care for emergencies and pain.) This characteristic of dental practice has been reinforced by the relatively slow development of dental specialties. Out of roughly 120,000 dentists in the United States in 1969, less than 10 percent were recognized as specialists [11]. The oldest and most clearly defined of the specialties is that of orthodontics (with 4,000 practitioners), which is concerned with the treatment of malformation of the mouth and teeth. This service is rarely performed by the general practitioner of dentistry because, traditionally, dental schools have given limited instruction in the special techniques used in this field. The only other areas not generally shared with the general practitioner are very small—oral pathology with fifty diplomates and dental public health with sixty-five diplomates.

In other areas of practice, the most common pattern is for the general dentist to perform the routine procedures and refer to specialists only those of unusual severity or complexity. Even the second oldest and largest specialty, oral surgery (2,200 practitioners), largely shares its area of clinical competence with the general practitioner. Although no definitive data are available, informed observations suggest that dentists limiting their practices to oral surgery probably do not perform more than half the surgical procedures done in most communities. The other clinical specialties (with figures in parentheses representing the number of practitioners) are endodontics (400), which is concerned with the health of the pulp or nerve; pedodontics (1,000), which is essentially the general practice of dentistry for children; periodontology (850), which is concerned with the treatment of periodontal disease and other lesions of the soft tissue of the mouth; and prosthetics (600), which is the art of replacing teeth and other missing oral structures.

Development of a Practice

In chapter 14 Freidson refers to the "colleague network" that both provides constraints on the developing practice of the physician and/or facilitates promotion and advancement. Because the general practice of dentistry is not related to an organizational framework, such as a hospital, such constraints in relation to patient referral and access to resources are virtually nonexistent. (The colleague network may be said to exist for those who wish to become active in professional associations, but this activity is unrelated to patient treatment and is a very optional form of professional activity.)

Little is known about the factors involved in patients' selecting a particular dentist. Experience suggests that it is a rather random procedure related to (1) the need to find a new dentist; (2) visibility of a particular dentist's existence through casual questioning of friends or through seeing a professional sign in the neighborhood; or (3) looking through the telephone directory to find a dentist in the area. The final input appears to be any chance opportunities of finding individuals who have gone to the particular dentist who is being considered.

Obviously, the dentist-selection process begins with a perceived need for dental care. This may either be because of the culturally imposed sanction that teeth are important and should receive routine professional treatment, or it may rise out of symptoms identified by the patient. The perceived need for care must be coupled with the need to find a dentist, since experience suggests that only infrequently do people voluntarily terminate an association with a dentist. A certain continuing loyalty would be expected in the dentist-patient relationship, since the initial choice implied a certain degree of confidence in the dentist. To terminate such a relationship without external reasons (such as moving to a new community) would require the patient to admit that he had been in error in his initial choice. The stability of the relationship with a dentist is strongly reinforced by the very common practice in dentistry of maintaining systems by which patients are periodically notified by the office that it is time to return for reexamination. This characteristic of dental practice is, of course, dictated by the recurring nature of dental diseases and the need for continuing periodic professional care.

The young dentist entering practice is therefore largely dependent on being selected by individuals who have severed their previous relationship with a dentist because of an unfortunate experience or, more likely, have recently moved into the area. The average new practitioner may attract a very few referrals from physicians, school personnel, or even older dentists whose schedules are heavily committed. On the whole, however, he depends upon attracting the attention of prospective patients. Within the context of a profession that does not tolerate advertising or other obvious methods of doing this, it is commonly thought that a choice of location in which the office will be visible is important in attracting patients. Also desirable is a location in which there are a high proportion of mobile people who may be looking for a new dentist-patient relationship. For this reason, there has been a marked trend toward locating in the shopping centers of newly developed suburban areas.

It is difficult to generalize as to the attitude of mature individuals toward a young dentist. A fifty-year-old may view a twenty-three-year-old as lacking in judgment and experience. On the contrary, however, he may feel that because the twenty-three-year-old is a new graduate, he will have more access than an older dentist to the latest technological advances. But the relationship between the new graduate and the mature patient is often complicated by the fact that the young dentist is advocating and attempting to perform advanced procedures not utilized by the patient's previous dentist. In this case, he faces the difficult task of attempting to gain the patient's confidence by explaining the reasons for his treatment without directly, or by implication, criticizing the professional behavior of the patient's previous practitioner.

In a considerable number of cases, the new dentist's practice contains a large proportion of children. This is partly because some established dentists decline to treat children and partly because patients sometimes maintain a personal loyalty to their dentist but are willing to take their children to another dentist to receive care. Probably for these reasons, and also because those of the same age are most comfortable with each other, there is at least limited evidence that the age of a dentist's patients tends to be related to his own age. A young dentist usually has a relatively young practice [22, 29]. As he becomes middle-aged, a considerable number of his patients are in the same category, and as he ages he has an aging practice.

Unlike some phases of medicine that are primarily intellectual and consultative in nature, providing dental care requires considerable physical exertion and meticuluous attention to detail. For this reason, many dentists feel that the physical strain of practice is a limiting factor on long-term productivity. Data on practice characteristics tend to confirm this judgment. On the average, the dentist obtains full productivity within five to ten years after entering practice. He is maximally productive during his forties, but patient visits and income drop off thereafter, a reduction which is particularly rapid after the age of 59 [9, 25].

Continued Competence

In chapter 14 Freidson points out, "Medicine is practiced in privacy. Work in the other established professions is carried on publicly—in the court, the church and the lecture hall—as often as in the office. . . ." Because dentistry is not related to the hospital, it is an even more private service. Only rarely will a dentist's work be seen by any other person trained in one of the health fields. Only a very small portion of dentists ever perform technical procedures in the presence of another dentist. There are few opportunities to share professional experiences, and these are limited almost exclusively to dental meetings, which have grave drawbacks as an effective method of transmitting information. Because of the lack of these outside contacts, the continued competence of the dentist is almost exclusively his own responsibility. Technically speaking, there are professional grievance committees in many dental societies, and state boards of dental examiners are supposed to be responsible for insuring that licensed practitioners offer a quality service. In actual practice, however, the almost complete lack of opportunities for dentists to view the work of their colleagues means that these channels are rarely utilized.

It is not surprising, then, that along with the many dentists who are rendering a conscientious service to meet the health needs of their patients there are those who are incompetent or at least not motivated to provide high standards of care. This situation has naturally been of concern to the profession. To combat it, it is felt that the first step should be to increase the degree to which dentists utilize formal continuation courses to update their professional skills. It is difficult to determine the extent to which members of the profession are currently participating in short, formal postprofessional courses. However, it is estimated that somewhere around 10 percent engage in continuing education during the course of a year.[1]

Concern about maintenance of quality has increased in recent years, with the growth of third-party payment programs, either through private groups, such as unions, or through governmental programs, such as those under Title 18 and Title 19 of the Social Security amendments. Not surprisingly, those concerned with expending large sums of money to obtain professional services feel it necessary to obtain some assurance that the services they are paying for have been, in fact, rendered and rendered with at least a minimum level of quality. Several dental service corporations (professionally sponsored nonprofit insurance corporations such as the well-known Blue Cross–Blue Shield) are now offering dental insurance, with provisions for periodic audit of records and for professional examination of a sample of patients having received treatment. In several states consideration is being given to amending practice acts to require periodically a certain minimum number of hours of continuing education in order to remain licensed. One large metropolitan state has made a similar requirement for dentists' receiving payments under the Medicaid provisions of Title 19 of the Social Security Amendments of 1965.

Organization of the Profession

With only two exceptions (students and dentists serving in the armed forces), a dentist may not join the

[1] During 1967–68 there were 24,829 enrollments for continuing education courses in dental schools, and those who participated in such study during 1967 took an average of 2.5 courses per man [10, 12]. This would indicate that fewer than 10,000 men participated in continuation courses during that year. In contrast, about half the dentists responding to a mail questionnaire in 1967 claimed that they had enrolled in a continuing education course in a dental school or hospital [10]. This figure appears unreasonably high and may be due to overresponse by the younger segment of the profession or confusion between formal continuation education and attendance at dental society meetings.

American Dental Association directly. Instead he applies to a local society (for a group of counties or a large city) for membership. If accepted at this level, he is automatically made a member of the state dental association and, in turn, the American Dental Association. In general, the membership requirements include graduation from an accredited dental school, licensure to practice dentistry in the area, and a record free from conduct considered unethical by the profession. The ultimate judgment is often made by a membership committee or a board of censors. In recent years this arrangement has created problems because the national group strongly supports integration of the profession to enforce equality of treatment of dentists of different races at the local level where membership is determined. Progress has been made, but the number of black dentists who have been admitted to membership has been low in some states. As a result, there has been a continued need for the existence of the National Dental Association, composed primarily of nonwhite dentists. A stated objective of both the National Dental Association and the American Dental Association is complete integration of the profession.

As noted earlier, membership in the American Dental Association brings certain individual fringe benefits such as group insurance plans and the availability of health education materials and other aids. However, the professional organization serves its membership—and indirectly the welfare of the public—primarily in three important roles. The professional association is the fundamental mechanism for information transfer and exchange within the profession. This is conducted mainly through scientific meetings held at the local, state, and national levels, and through a number of professional and scientific journals. The second role is establishing standards in a variety of areas. One of the most important is the accreditation of professional schools for dentists, dental hygienists, dental assistants, and dental technicians. Indirectly, educational standards are also reinforced informally through the influence of the Association on state examining boards. Standards are also established for materials, drugs, and devices used by dentists in practice and, in a few instances, for products offered for sale to the public. Panels of experts act on behalf of the Association in evaluating and setting standards for educational offerings, drugs, and products related to oral health.

Another major, although less easily identifiable, function is the development of a consensus among the profession on important social issues and the transmittal of this consensus to governmental agencies and others concerned with establishing social policy. To be effective in influencing public policy, a profession must speak with a relatively unified voice. A unity of opinion can be developed only by a dialogue involving conflicting and converging views. Such a dialogue is necessary to establish a statement of policy to guide the officers and staff of the Association. In complex social issues, however, there is a more important latent function—that of alerting and educating the profession to changes in society and the demands that society is making on the health professions.

National Leadership. There is essentially no evidence to define the social and political orientation of practicing dentists, but there is no reason to believe that they differ markedly from their counterparts in the community, such as the physician, the attorney, or the small businessman. Experience suggests that they largely share the innate conservatism and reluctance to accept rapid change that is common among middle-class members of the Establishment.

At the national level, however, dentistry has had strong leaders who have been sensitive to changing social demands. In the 1961, "Report of the President," for example, Patton warned the timid that: "The greatest danger . . . is not the invasion of health fields by the government, but, rather the loss of leadership by the health professions" [35]. Hillenbrand, who occupied the key position of Executive Director of the American Dental Association for nearly twenty-three years, frequently emphasized the necessity for open channels of communication between government and the health professions and a rational exploration of ways of improving the methods of delivering health care. So, when the stock phrase "socialized medicine" was aimed at new federal programs, he observed that catch phrases should not be used to dismiss health proposals without full or fair hearings. On the other hand, when government programs appeared ill-conceived he was quick to question whether the suggested approach was "an instrument that had evolved through experience or one that was being imposed out of prejudice." When rightwing extremists attempted to influence the profession, he lashed out at their performance in stinging terms: "Their flight from the realities of the nineteenth century, to say nothing of the twentieth; their pathologic fear of any change in the status quo; their use of the evil tactics of subversion, distortion, and untruth to gain their private ends, and their sneering contempt for the democratic process make these groups a clear and present danger" [2].

Whatever the reason, organized dentistry has adopted a posture of enlightened leadership in national policy that, to some, may appear surprising in a major professional organization. In 1948, for example, the House of Delegates affirmed that "dental care should be available to all regardless of income or geographic location as rapidly as resources will permit"[14]. From about the same time, the Association has supported the use of federal funds for the construction of educational and research facilities [16]. It was largely through the efforts of the Association that a National Institute of Dental Research was created. In the mid-fifties, a concerted effort was made to obtain funds earmarked for dental health programs in state health departments. In recent years the major emphasis has been on encouraging more adequate support for dental education in order to increase the number of dentists, and on programs to increase the productivity of dentists, including experimentation with expanding the functions of auxiliary personnel [17].

The most dramatic legislative program has been a National Dental Plan for Children, which calls for federal authorization and funding for the gradual implementation of a program to provide dental care for all children, with payment for care for the indigent and the medically indigent being met from tax funds [41]. Authorizing legislation for pilot projects of this nature have been passed by Congress, but despite vigorous efforts, the Association has been unable to secure appropriation of the necessary funds to implement the proposal [15].

THE PROFESSION FACES THE FUTURE

In the last century and a half dentistry in the United States has grown to a position of maturity and strength. It commands respect and admiration throughout the world. Independent of other health professions, it is a valued partner in team efforts to provide comprehensive health services. The successes of the profession, however, have resulted in grave problems which will plague it, and the public, in the closing decades of the twentieth century. Dentistry is now accepted as a basic health service, and health care has come to be viewed as a right that should be available to all—not a privilege reserved for the affluent. The delivery of the service required by these two commitments of public policy will require ingenuity and flexibility of a high order.

The profession must increase its numbers, learn how to increase productivity by new uses of auxiliaries, develop methods of controlling both cost and quality, and adapt to serve the needs of segments of the population having special health and social needs. If these efforts are successful, both the profession and the public will benefit.

REFERENCES

1. BECKER, H. et al., *Boys in White: Student Culture in Medical School.* Chicago: University of Chicago Press, 1961.
2. BISHOP, ERIC, "Harold Hillenbrand, D.D.S., Executive Director Emeritus, American Dental Association," *Journal of the American Dental Association*, 80 (January, 1970), 58–68.
3. BLACKERBY, P. E., "Why Not a Department of Social Dentistry?" *Journal of Dental Education*, 24 (September, 1960), 197–200.
4. BREMNER, M. D. K., *The Story of Dentistry*, 3rd ed. Brooklyn, N.Y.: Dental Items of Interest, 1954.
5. Bureau of Economic Research and Statistics, American Dental Association, "Survey of Needs for Dental Care, II: Dental Needs According to Age and Sex of Patients," *Journal of the American Dental Association*, 46 (February, 1953), 200–211.
6. ———, "The 1968 Survey of Dental Practice, II: Income of Dentist by Location, Age, and Other Factors," *Journal of the American Dental Association*, 78 (February, 1969), 342–46.
7. ———, "The 1968 Survey of Dental Practice, III: Income of Dentist by Type of Practice, Personnel Employed, and Other Factors," 78 (April, 1969), 803–5.
8. ———, "The 1968 Survey of Dental Practice, V: Auxiliary Personnel," *Journal of the American Dental Association*, 78 (June, 1969), 1355–59.
9. ———, "The 1968 Survey of Dental Practice, VII: Number of Patients and Patient Visits," *Journal of the American Dental Association*, 7 (August, 1969), 378–80.
10. ———, "The 1968 Survey of Dental Practice, X: Some Aspects of the Dentist's Professional Development," *Journal of the American Dental Association*, 79 (October, 1969), 918–22.
11. Bureau of Processing Services, American Dental Association, *1969 American Dental Directory.* Chicago: American Dental Association, 1969.
12. Council on Dental Education, American Dental Association, *Annual Report on Dental Education, 1968–69, Part 1.* Chicago: American Dental Association, 1969.
13. Council on Dental Health, American Dental Association, *Departments of Community Dentistry in Dental Schools.* Chicago: American Dental Association, n.d. (mimeographed).
14. ———, *Official Policies of the American Dental Association on Dental Health Programs.* Chicago: American Dental Association, 1957.
15. Council on Legislation, American Dental Association, "Children's Dental Care Program," *Transactions of the American Dental Association*, 109 (1968), 127.
16. ———, "Current Bills of Interest During 85th Congress," *Transactions of the American Dental Association*, 98 (1958), 162–67.
17. ———, "Federal Aid to Dental Education," *Transactions of the American Dental Association*, 109 (1968), 127–28.
18. Dental Management, *The Business of*

Dental Practice. Stamford, Conn.: Dental Management, 1969.
19. Division of Dental Resources, Public Health Service, *A Study of Dental Manpower Requirements in the West*. Boulder, Colo.: Western Interstate Commission on Higher Education, 1956.
20. Division of Public Health Methods, Public Health Service, *Health Statistics from the U.S. National Health Survey: Dental Care: Interval and Frequency of Visits; United States, July 1957–June 1959*. Washington, D.C.: Government Printing Office, 1960.
21. Ennis, John, *The Story of the Fédération Dentaire Internationale, 1900–62*. London: Fédération Dentaire Internationale, 1967.
22. Haddon, William, Jr., J. P. Carlos, and D. B. Ast, "Frequency of Dental X-ray Examinations in a New York County," *Public Health Reports*, 77 (June, 1962), 525–32.
23. Heist, Paul, "Personality Characteristics of Dental Students," *The Educational Record*, 41 (July, 1960), 240–52.
24. Kegeles, S. S., "Why People Seek Dental Care; A Review of Present Knowledge," *American Journal of Public Health*, 51 (September, 1961), 1306–11.
25. Kesel, R. G., "Dental Practice," in B. S. Hollinshead, dir., *The Survey of Dental Practice: The Final Report*. Washington, D.C.: American Council on Education, 1961.
26. Mann, W. R., "Dental Education," in B. S. Hollinshead, dir., *The Survey of Dentistry: The Final Report*. Washington, D.C.: American Council on Education, 1961.
27. Mann, W. R. and G. Parkin, "The Dental School Applicant," *Journal of Dental Education*, 24 (March, 1960), 16–21.
28. Merton, R. K. et al., *The Student Physician*. Cambridge, Mass.: Harvard University Press, 1957.
29. Mitchell, G. E. and W. O. Young, *The 1957 Survey of Dental Practice in Idaho: Characteristics of Patients and Types of Services*. Boise: Idaho Department of Health, 1959 (mimeographed).
30. More, D. M., "Social Origins of Future Dentists," *The Midwest Sociologist*, 21 (July, 1959), 69–76.
31. ———, "The Dental Student," *Journal of the American College of Dentists*, 28 (March, 1961), 5–93.
32. ———, "The Dental Student Approaching Graduation," *Journal of the American College of Dentists*, 29 (September, 1962), 118–208.
33. More, D. M. and N. Kohn, Jr., "Some Motives for Entering Dentistry," *American Journal of Sociology*, 66 (July, 1960), 48–53.
34. National Center for Health Statistics, Public Health Service, *Health Manpower, United States, 1965–1967*. Washington, D.C.: Government Printing Office, 1968.
35. Patton, C. H., "Report of the President." *Transactions of the American Dental Association*, 102 (1961), 9–16.
36. Quarantelli, E., "The Career Choice Patterns of Dental Students," *Journal of Health and Human Behavior*, 2 (Summer, 1961), 124–32.
37. Sarner, Harvey, "Methods of Group Practice," *Journal of the American College of Dentists*, 36 (July, 1969), 206–14.
38. Sherlock, Basil J., "The Second Profession: Parallel Mobilities of the Dental Profession and Its Recruits," *Journal of Health and Social Behavior*, 10 (March, 1969), 41–51.
39. Sherlock, Basil J. and Alan Cohen, "The Strategy of Occupational Choice: Recruitment to Dentistry," *Social Forces*, 44 (March, 1966), 303–13.
40. Sherlock, Basil J. and Richard T. Morris, *Becoming a Dentist*. Springfield, Ill.: Charles C Thomas, Publisher, 1971.
41. *The American Dental Association Dental Health Program for Children*. Chicago: American Dental Association, n.d.
42. Warner, L., M. Meeker, and K. Eells, *Social Class in America*. Gloucester, Mass.: Peter Smith, 1957.
43. Young, W. O. and D. F. Striffler, *The Dentist, His Practice, and His Community*, 2nd ed. Philadelphia: W. B. Saunders Company, 1969.

11

LIMITED, MARGINAL, AND QUASI-PRACTITIONERS

Walter I. Wardwell

The proliferation of technical knowledge in the field of health has resulted in the development of many medical specialties and in a variety of aides and technical assistants ancillary to the profession of medicine. But there have also developed health practitioners who are independent of the medical profession. One such group of independent health practitioners are the *limited practitioners*, whose health services are usually confined to particular parts of the human body. Still others treat nearly the entire range of bodily functions and disorders, but because they employ forms of therapy unacceptable to orthodox medical practice they are considered *marginal practitioners*. Finally, there are the *quasi-practitioners*—those whose ministrations to the sick are pseudoscientific or incidental to another function, usually religious (See Table 11–1).

Although limited practitioners, in the sense we employ the term, occasionally function as part of a medical team, share offices with physicians, or operate in a strictly medical setting, more frequently they deal directly with self-referred patients seeking a relatively

TABLE 11-1 Comparative Data on the Major Health-Related Professions, United States, 1969*

	Medicine	*Pharmacy*	*Dentistry*	*Podiatry*	*Optometry*	*Clinical Psychology*	*Osteo-pathy*	*Chiro-practic*	*Christian Science*
Number licensed to practice	324,942	140,734	115,610	8,050	20,611	12,051	14,000	19,100	4,785
Number actively practicing	302,966	128,843	100,700	7,045	18,000	8,750	12,115	17,000	4,785
Number of U.S. colleges	99	75	53	5	11	102	6	11	0
Number of degrees awarded	8,059	4,301	3,433	251	445	842	427	540	—
Degrees awarded	M.D.	B.S., B. Pharm.	D.D.S., D.M.D.	D.P.M., Pod.D.	O.D.	Ph.D.	D.O.	D.C.	C.S., C.S.B.
Usual minimum number of years of college education	7	5	7	6	6	8	7	4 to 6	0
First college established in U.S.	1765	1821	1840	1912	1895	(A.P.A. founded in 1892)	1892	1897	1881 (none now)
First state regulatory law	1873†	1870‡	1868	1895	1901	1945	1896	1913	None
First university affiliation of college	1765	1868	1867	1915 (none now)	1910	—	1969	None	None
Rank on the North-Hatt Scale of Occupational Prestige§	93	—	86	—	—	85	—	—	—
Jonassen's Interpolated Ranks in the North-Hatt Scale§§	—	75	—	77	83	—	—	75	—
Reissman's Interpolated Ranks in the North-Hatt Scale♯	—	79	—	—	75	—	79	75	—
James's Ranking of Acceptance as a Profession**	97	72	97	—	85	87	75	56	—
Hartmann's Ranking of 25 Medical Specialties††	1 and 2	8	3	—	19	10	18	22	—

* Data from *Health Resources Statistics* [59] and the professional associations.
† In 1760 New York attempted state regulation unsuccessfully, as did several other states during the colonial period. Effective licensing began only in the 1870's [84].
‡ Earlier laws, beginning as early as 1808, were ineffective [25].
§ Data from North and Hatt [65].
§§ From Jonassen et. al. [50].
♯ From Reissman [77].
** From James [47].
†† From Hartmann [38].

specific service. If they see such patients first, they assume responsibility for deciding which ones they will treat and which ones they will refer to physicians for conditions beyond their competence or jurisdiction. Hence they exercise a degree of autonomous professional judgment that in this respect approaches medical diagnosis.

We can reach no final judgment concerning relationships among the various health professions because pressures for change continually arise both within and outside these professions. For example, the former division of the medical fraternity into the warring camps of allopathy, homeopathy, and eclecticism has all but disappeared, and fusion with osteopathy —until recently considered a "healing cult"—appears imminent [27, 42, 68, 4]. The major stimulus for change is the dynamic nature of medical knowledge itself, which requires that physicians constantly adapt to scientific innovation; this is particularly true of major breakthroughs requiring a reconceptualization of basic life processes, e.g., biochemistry, psychosomatic medicine, psychotherapy [21, 57]. The tendency toward exclusiveness and monopolization of discrete areas of practice, and the growing demand for specialized services not readily available from orthodox physicians (e.g., podiatry) increase the importance of the newer professions.

The pressure for professionalization, reinforced by licensing requirements, have raised the educational and ethical standards of the newer professions so that their public image, economic status, and social prestige vis-à-vis the medical profession have improved. In this constant shifting of ground, new health professions appear as new modes of treatment are discovered (e.g., psychology, audiology), some disappear as distinct groups (e.g., homeopathy), and the most acceptable approach fusion with orthodox medicine (e.g., dentistry, osteopathy). In the process of becoming professionalized, a new health profession may leave behind a less professional and less competent nucleus which carries on extralegally or affiliates with an even newer, probably lower-status group with a somewhat different orientation toward illness and therapy.

PHARMACY: A SPECIAL CASE

The pharmacist, strictly speaking, is as subordinate (i.e., ancillary) to the prescribing physician as the nurse, but his overall professional and social status is different. Although hospital pharmacists may indeed be as circumscribed in their functioning as other ancillary professions, retail pharmacists are not. Located apart from physicians, retail druggists supply commodities other than prescription medicines to their customers—a fact which casts them in an entrepreneurial as well as a professional role. Furthermore, druggists are often expected by their customers to suggest remedies for conditions that may not have been diagnosed by a physician—an expectation which was even more prevalent in the past, particularly in those parts of the country and in those social groups which lack easy access to physicians.

Pharmacy nevertheless is an adjunct to medicine: "All the responsibility and exercise of initiative and judgment belongs to the physician. . . . There is practically nothing he [the pharmacist] can do about a prescription if he is doubtful of it but get in touch with the doctor" [91]. The pharmacist's entrepreneurial role, however, and his frequent contacts with the public, put him in a position of strength vis-à-vis physicians. Not only can he refer patients to particular physicians, he can also reward physicians who send patients to him. For example, one pharmacist "bought a downtown building with a corner location and put four physicians upstairs on a rent-free basis" [45], others have leased telephone lines from doctors' offices and furnished them with prescription blanks on which the name of their own pharmacy appears. This is the kind of unethical behavior that is certainly deplored by physicians and pharmacists alike, but the very existence of such temptation reveals the relatively strong position which the druggist occupies in relation to the physician.

The principal source of the ethical problems of the retail pharmacist is the potential conflict between professional and commercial pressures [91]. Although there is a financial aspect to the practice of any profession, the problem is more acute for the retail pharmacist, principally because he sells merchandise other than pharmaceuticals in a setting which resembles other retail establishments more closely than it does a professional office. Salaried pharmacists who work in drug stores are not themselves entrepreneurs, but they are subject to some of the same situational pressures as their employers. (Pharmacists engaged in research and teaching do not experience these particular pressures.)

The professional training of the pharmacist emphasizes thoroughness, accuracy, cleanliness, and probity. It is a matter of professional pride, as well as a legal requirement, that the physician's prescription be filled with the utmost precision. Even if the physician has unnecessarily prescribed a trade-marked (perhaps more expensive) brand of a standard ingredient, the pharmacist is not supposed to substitute the standard ingredient for what is prescribed—even though it is a professionally approved goal to encourage physicians not to use brand names. How much such substitution actually occurs is not known, but Thorner [91] implies that it is rather frequent.

The pharmacist is not authorized to diagnose or prescribe for medical conditions but only to dispense medicines that physicians have prescribed, or which, if not legally proscribed, customers may request on their own initiative. If he is asked by a customer to recommend a medicine for a specific minor condition (e.g., poison ivy) he can usually recommend a suitable remedy without difficulty. In such cases he has not actually diagnosed the patient's condition or prescribed for him. But if the patient merely states his symptoms (e.g., dizziness, stomach pains, rectal bleeding), it would be unprofessional for the druggist to recommend a particular medicine. The line between the two cases is sometimes difficult for the pharmacist to discern.

Physicians naturally resent pharmacists who do more recommending of medicines than is necessary. Pharmacists, on the other hand, feel that physicians don't fully appreciate the knowledge and skill which a pharmacist must have in order to keep abreast of the latest scientific developments in pharmacology, and they resent the dispensing of pharmaceuticals for profit by physicians. *The General Report of the Pharmaceutical Survey, 1946–49*, concluded that "Medicine, as a profession, maintains an attitude of condescending superiority toward pharmacy as a profession. . . . The ancient controversies involving the dispensing physician and the prescribing pharmacist remain as controversies."

Social scientists have barely begun to study the fascinating profession of pharmacy. McCormack reported, in 1956, that 85 percent of the 117 freshmen entering one college of pharmacy saw themselves as future owners of retail drugstores [54]. Schwebel, using a sample of 450 New York State pharmacists who filled out the Strong Vocational Interest Blank, ascertained that "the typical pharmacist, as well as the typical satisfied pharmacist, has interests similar to those of the businessman" [82]. A more complete study of prescription pharmacists, based on a national sample of 450 druggists, was made by the National Opinion Research Center in 1955. In response to a question as to whether the general public regards the pharmacist mainly as a professional man or as a businessman, 48 percent answered "mainly professional," and 44 percent answered "mainly business"; the remainder stated that they didn't know. Two-thirds of those who answered "mainly business," said that they would prefer to be considered professionals, while the rest said it didn't matter [18]. In 1963, Quinney found prescription violators far more oriented to a business role than to their professional role [74].

Remmers and Gage, using the Kuder Preference Record to study the abilities and interests of freshman pharmacy students, found that their preference for "persuasive activities" was far less than that of drug store managers and pharmacists, for whom the Kuder Test Manual provided norms. They concluded:

> It may be that a substantial number of pharmacy freshmen will find themselves temporarily unfit for retail drugstore management because of insufficient interest in, and preference for, the persuasive type of activity for which, it appears, the typical drugstore manager has a strong preference [78].

However, Quinney found little difference in occupational satisfaction between retail pharmacists who favored a business orientation, or a professional orientation, or who favored them equally [74]. The five-year program of preprofessional and professional training, which has been required since 1960, has raised the level of professional competence of graduating pharmacists and may make them less satisfied with retail pharmacy. The opening up of opportunities in other phases of pharmacy, such as research and pharmaceutical manufacturing, provides alternatives for those students who are not psychologically well adapted to retail pharmacy.

Current emphasis is placed on a new development called "clinical pharmacy," which Tyler defines as follows:

> Clinical pharmacy is that division of pharmacy which deals with patient care with particular emphasis on drug therapy. In practice it is patient oriented and includes not only the dispensing of required medication but also advising the patient on the proper use of all medications, both prescribed and patient selected. It also utilizes the pharmacist as an information source for members of the medical and other health professions on all matters pertaining to drugs and their dosage forms [93].

A dozen or so pharmacy schools have revived the old degree, Pharm.D., based on six years of study, as appropriate to a more clinical approach to pharmacy.

With the recent development of so many new and potentially dangerous drugs, physicians need more authoritative consultants on drugs than the sales-oriented detail men from pharmaceutical firms; and patients could benefit from more expert advice from pharmacists on nonprescription drugs and on how to follow regimens prescribed by physicians. But the medical profession will certainly object to expansion of the pharmacist's role into the clinical area of diagnosis and prescription. And not only it but other professions as well would protest if pharmacists were to undertake, as has been recommended, "the fitting of surgical appliances and providing orthopedic services to institutionalized patients; performing audiometric examinations for patrons either at their request or at the request of the attending physician, and the operation of a clinical laboratory. . . . One of the most hotly debated proposals of recent months is that of the New Jersey Pharmaceutical Association—permitting the pharmacist to dispense immunizations in pharmacies" [35].

The exhortation "Let's Separate Pharmacies and Drugstores" [29] protests against pharmacies becoming department stores and against the pharmacist's job becoming almost exclusively to "count, pour, and label," something a (proposed) subprofessional assistant could do as well. The main problem facing pharmacy is to determine what functions of a professional nature pharmacists should perform for the public.

LIMITED PRACTITIONERS

Some health-related practitioners function independently of the medical profession but limit their area of practice to specified conditions or parts of the human body. In so doing they implicitly accept the authority of the physician over general conditions or systemic disorders. In the United States the best-established limited practitioners are dentists, podiatrists, optometrists, and psychologists. Other possible candidates for inclusion under this designation are speech pathologists (whose function does not conflict with that of organized medicine) [9], audiologists (those ancillary to medicine and those so-called "retail audiologists" who have barely started on the road to professionalization) [9], and midwives [75]. Although the range of professional status of such limited practitioners is obviously very great, they all have attained, or have the potential for attaining, a fairly stable *modus vivendi* with organized medicine.

Dentists

Dentistry, fully recognized as a profession, is the best established of the groups of independent health practitioners in terms of standards of professional training and requirements for licensure. Dental schools are without exception affiliated with universities—in many cases sharing their preclinical training facilities, instructors, and standards with the university medical school. From the very beginning, however, dental education and dental practice have been independent of medical control, partly because of the medical profession's almost complete lack of interest in dentistry [31]. The present course of professional training in dentistry requires at least two years of preprofessional college work, followed by four years in one of the fifty-three dental schools, for which the degree of Doctor of Dental Surgery (D.D.S.) or Doctor of Dental Medicine (D.M.D.) is awarded.

Dentistry is second only to medicine in public acceptance as a healing profession (see Table 11–1). Although Kriesberg and Treiman found that the public ascribes to the dental profession the same characteristics that it attributes to other high-status occupations [52], Quarantelli reports that only 10 percent of his sample of dental students felt that the public has a favorable image of the dentist [72, 73]. However, Sherlock states that "dentistry seems to be moving towards a greater elitism in its recruitment" and that one attraction, in comparison with medicine and law, is that dentistry offers "an essentially autonomous professional career" [83]. (See Chapter 10 for a further discussion of the dental profession.)

Podiatrists

Podiatry, sometimes called chiropody, is a well-established profession restricted to the diagnosis and treatment of certain types of foot ailments. Although podiatrists administer drugs, wield scalpels, and use casts and other appliances to correct various disabilities of the foot, they may not treat systemic ailments or perform amputations. First regulated by law in 1895 in New York, podiatry is licensed in all states and is accepted by organized medicine as an adjunct to medical care. With only 8,050 practitioners, it is still a relatively small field, however. Instruction is presently offered in the United States in only five colleges—none of which is affiliated with a university, although two have had university affiliation in the past.

Since 1964 all podiatric colleges have required a total of six years of preprofessional and professional education for the Doctor of Podiatric Medicine (D.P.M.) or Doctor of Podiatry (Pod. D.) degree. Reed reported, in 1933, that "on the whole the medical profession has used its influence to oppose the widening of the scope legally permitted the chiropodists," and that the president of the First Institute of Podiatry in New York City "has continued to maintain the position that the future of chiropody is that of a medical specialty and that, eventually, all who practice chiropody should be doctors of medicine" [75]. Obviously, this has not happened. The difficulty facing the profession appears to be that although the formal course of training is nearly as long as for a medical degree, podiatry does not offer the status and rewards of medicine. According to a thorough study of podiatric education made by a team of distinguished educators in 1961, all podiatric colleges are handicapped by limited financial support, part-time faculties, and inadequate facilities [85]. Furthermore, the study "disclosed that many of the students had undertaken professional studies previously in other institutions in such fields as dentistry, pharmacy, or veterinary medicine, and had demonstrated only limited success in their work prior to changing to a podiatry career."

Optometrists

Optometry is now well-established as an independent health profession. It is limited principally to making refractions and supplying eyeglasses and contact lenses to persons with defective vision. Licensed in all states since 1924, optometrists are trained at eleven colleges in the United States (plus two in Canada), seven of which are affilated with established universities. The minimum number of years of preprofessional and professional college training is six, following which the student receives a Doctor of Optometry (O.D.) degree.

The relationship of the optometrist with ophthalmologists and oculists (both of whom are physicians specializing in the treatment of the eyes), and with opticians (who grind lenses and make up spectacles in accordance with optical prescriptions), have been reasonably well clarified [62]. Optometrists should not diagnose or treat pathological conditions or use medicines to dilate the pupils, but they may prescribe corrective exercises for such conditions as crossed eyes. An examination of medical and optometric literature, however, reveals that the relationships between the two professions have not been resolved to the full satisfaction of both parties. Note the patronizing use of the phrase "skilled lay technicians" in this statement of the medical position:

> Optometrists who adhere to their proper field and do not attempt ocular diagnosis and treatment, or such basically medical procedures as the fitting of contact lenses, without supervision by ophthalmologists, may be considered skilled lay technicians who are acceptably engaging in the small segment of the field of eye care which they are permitted, by specific legal authorization, to share with ophthalmologists. They are entitled to ophthalmologic assistance and cooperation [61].

The attitude of organized medicine toward recognizing optometry and authorizing professional relationships with optometrists has been a wavering one. One of the earliest courses of training was available at the Northern Illinois College of Ophthalmology and Otology, "a postgraduate school for physicians" which "in the early '90's permitted enrollment by opticians, lengthening its course to three months in 1895" [66]. Apparently "refracting opticians," as they were then called, were not at that time perceived by physicians as a threat to their authority. In 1934, however, the House of Delegates of the American Medical Association declared it "unethical for members of the American Medical Association to give lectures or courses of instruction before optometric groups or to consult with them." In 1950 it reversed its position, only to forbid collaboration again in 1955 [61]. In 1966 came the latest reversal, when the AMA's House of Delegates declared: "Doctors of medicine may as teachers participate in the education of optometrists within the legitimate scope of optometric practice". The AMA's Judicial Council added: "It is not unethical for an ophthalmologist to employ an optometrist as ancillary personnel to assist him provided the optometrist is identified as an optometrist and not as a doctor of medicine," and "a doctor of medicine may refer his patients to a qualified and ethical optometrist solely for optometric care" [23]. Optometrists, however, are preserving a wait-and-see attitude.

The National Health Survey, using 1965–1966 data, found that 33.4 percent of persons using corrective lenses had been examined by ophthalmologists, and 56.7 percent had been examined by optometrists, with the remaining 10 percent "unknown" or seen by neither [60]. Any physician can legally prescribe glasses, despite the fact that "the training received by medical students does not qualify them to do refraction" [75]. Optometrists stoutly maintain that they are fully qualified to recognize pathology and that they often do a better refracting job than ophthalmologists:

> About one fourth of the optometrist's education is devoted to study of the body, eye diseases, and symptoms of other diseases revealed in the eyes. Thus the optometrist is thoroughly trained in the detection of disease so that he can refer patients for whatever other professional care they may require [3].

Perhaps because they are not permitted to employ drugs, optometrists emphasize that "vision examinations without the use of drugs are preferable," and say that they are concerned with "functional vision" [3]. The Committee on the Costs of Medical Care concluded, as early as 1933: "The ophthalmologist who devotes his time to refraction is doing work for which he is overtrained" [26].

The principal current source of difficulty within the optometric profession concerns "the corporate practice of optometry" by commercial organizations, such as department or jewelry stores that hire optometrists to fit and sell optical products. The problem is that their relationships with patients are potentially more commercial than professional. But such optometrists constitute only a small minority of the profession. A possible ethical dilemma for all optometrists arises from the fact that they must recommend whether or not patients should buy devices which they themselves sell for a profit.

There are no sociological studies of optometry except for Orzack and Uglum's overview of research possibilities in the field [67], but opinion surveys of occupational prestige confirm the public's acceptance of optometry as a profession. Indeed, James, studying the acceptance of professions, found that optometrists ranked above osteopaths, pharmacists, college teachers, and electrical engineers [47]. We may speculate that among the reasons for the high standing of optometry is that its practitioners must master the "hard" science of optics. Another reason may be that the eyes are symbolically a "good" and favorable part of the body, compared with those parts of the body treated by dentists, podiatrists, and physicians. Eyeglasses may even serve as a status symbol associated with learned and prestigious occupations. No drugs or knives are found in optometrist's offices, and little emotion, pain, or anxiety is generally associated with refractions. Next to dentistry, optometry is the most numerous of the limited professions, a fact which should make it better known to the public and therefore, perhaps, better accepted. Finally, the scope of optometry is rather easily delimited by patients and optometrists alike, a characteristic which reduces ambiguity and confusion about the optometrist's function. This should also serve to make the optometric profession less threatening to organized medicine.

Clinical Psychologists

Clinical psychology, another limited field of health practice, reflects its short history in several ways. First, its practitioners do not receive their training in separate professional schools (as has sometimes been urged), but in the graduate departments of psychology of some one hundred colleges of liberal arts and sciences. Second, their opportunities for psychoanalytic training in the United States are restricted by the fact that medical psychoanalytic institutes require that students already hold a medical degree or, alternatively, promise not to become practitioners. Third, certification and licensure of psychologists by state agencies, which did not begin until 1945, typically denies only the designation "psychologist" to the uncertified, and not their right to function as psychotherapists; the reason for this is the extreme difficulty of defining "clinical psychology" in such a way as to differentiate it from psychiatry, psychiatric social work, and the pastoral counseling of clergymen [33].

Physicians and psychiatrists view psychologists as ancillary to medicine —e.g., as capable only of performing psychometric or projective testing or limited psychotherapy following medical diagnosis—and have been "strongly opposed to the independent private practice of psychotherapy by clinical psychologists" [37]. Actually, relatively few psychologists are primarily engaged in independent private practice. The American Psychological Association estimated in 1968 that, of the 16,000 psychologists reporting that their work is related to mental health, "12,500 identify themselves as clinical, counseling, or school psychologists." Seventy percent (8,750) of these are clinical psychologists. On the other hand, only about 1,200 psychologists are in full-time independent, fee-for-service practice, while another 6,500 practice privately on a part-time basis [5].

Psychology's dilemma in relation to medicine is reflected in alternative definitions of psychology: as integrated with but subordinate to physicians (psychiatrists) as testers and diagnosticians, on the one hand, or as jealously competing with them as psychotherapists, on the other [39]. Watson found that, in nonmedical settings, including psychological clinics, "cooperation, not subordination, is the basis of relationship with medicine," and "in schools, colleges, and agencies dealing with the relatively normal there is little need for medical collaboration and certainly not supervision" [99]. Goode states that, in most clinical settings, the psychologist-therapist is not usually under real medical supervision: "Once a genuine team relationship is established, he works independently" [33].

Despite formal protestations, medicine appears to have given psychology *de facto* acceptance as a limited health profession rather than as merely an ancillary one. One reason for this may be that the psychologist does not usually touch the patient's body. Although mind and body are intertwined in any conceptualization of the malfunctioning of psyche or soma, the very concrete distinction between mere conversing and treating the body permits drawing a clear line of professional responsibility which the psychologist typically has no desire to cross. (Recent innovations in psychotherapy involving the "laying on of hands" resemble more closely religious healing than medical therapeutics.) An additional reason for medical acceptance of psychology has probably been the high standard of professional competence in psychology that has resulted from its historic locus in the graduate schools of established universities. Although psychologists have sometimes been criticized for having an inadequate clinical background, they have often been more intellectually alert and research-oriented than most practicing physicians or psychiatrists—probably as a consequence of their broad training in academic psychology and related subjects, and because of the requirement that they submit a comprehensive research dissertation for the doctorate. For example, "in 1959, for the third successive year, the Hofheimer Award (for an outstanding research contribution) of the American Psychiatric Association was given by an all-psychiatric jury to a psychologist" [33].

In any case, clinical psychology appears to have gained high standing as a profession. On the North-Hatt scale of occupational prestige, the psychologist is ranked 85, only one point below the dentist [65], while James, studying professionalization, found that the psychologist ranked higher than the clergyman, college teacher, electrical engineer, and osteopath [47].

MARGINAL PRACTITIONERS

Some practitioners, although they ordinarily treat nearly the entire range of human disease, have attained only marginal professional status because their whole approach to the problem of health and disease conflicts with that of orthodox medicine. Often referred to as members of *cults* or *sects*, they tend to reject such basic tenets of modern medicine as that disease is caused by bacterial agents which can be treated by drugs or prevented by inoculation, or they espouse a monocausal theory of illness and therapy. In a fundamental sense they thus constitute a more serious threat to organized medicine than the limited medical practitioners, who typically do not advocate therapeutic principles contrary to those of medicine. For these reasons the relationships between marginal practitioners and organized medicine are usually unstable, and the over-all professional standing of these groups tends to be ambiguous.

The best known marginal practitioners are the chiropractors, although osteopaths have historically also been considered cultists [27]. Naturopaths are very similar to chiropractors, and there have been several lesser known groups of marginal practitioners—e.g., neuropaths, naprapaths, vitopaths, mechanotherapists, spondylotherapists, and sanipractors. All have shared a tradition of hostility to the medical profession's liberal use of drugs, which they have regarded as "foreign" or "poisonous" substances. This hostility toward drugs has by now been almost completely abandoned by osteopaths, and it has been greatly weakened among some chiropractors, who are called "mixers."

Osteopaths

Osteopaths practice today as unlimited, nearly orthodox, medical practitioners in forty-eight states plus the District of Columbia [4]. A few states still do not permit osteopaths to use certain drugs or to perform major surgery; others have two types of osteopathic licenses, one permitting the licensee to perform major surgery [58]. The six osteopathic colleges provide high quality medical education and, in addition, teach traditional osteopathic theory and manipulative technique. To the dismay of many older osteopaths, today's young osteopathic graduate is more oriented toward allopathic medicine than toward body mechanics and manipulation, but the American Medical Association is in the process of welcoming osteopaths into the fold [51]. It now authorizes state medical societies to determine how far physicians can ethically go in associating with osteopaths as professional colleagues, and to decide which osteopaths are to be regarded as practicing scientific medicine: "The test should be: Does the individual doctor of osteopathy practice osteopathy or does he in fact practice a method of healing founded on a scientific basis?" [68]. In 1961, the medical and osteopathic associations of California voted to merge; the College of Osteopathic Physicians and Surgeons is now the University of California College of Medicine, Irvine.

The American Osteopathic Association strongly opposed these actions by its California affiliates: It chartered a new anti-medical osteopathic group in California, it successfully opposed an attempted merger of the two professions in the State of Washington, and it obtained a New York Supreme Court decision against recognition of the M.D. degrees granted retroactively to California osteopaths by the California College of Medicine. In 1967 the AOA's House of Delegates responded to further AMA moves to change osteopathic colleges into medical colleges with this unaminous statement: "This policy is clearly another attempt by that political group to dominate or control all aspects of American health care—a role that the AMA neither merits nor has the moral or legal right to enforce. . . . The osteopathic profession stands together in vigorously opposing this arrogant policy of academic piracy" [4]. A poll of Michigan osteopaths in 1966 revealed that 87 percent opposed merger with the medical profession. Backing statements with deeds, the osteopathic profession opened Michigan State University College of Osteopathic Medicine in 1969.

It is clear that osteopathy has grown away from the principles of its founder, Andrew Taylor Still, who once proclaimed: "No system of allopathy, with its fatal drugs, should ever enter our doors.... No orificial surgery, with its torture and disappointments to the afflicted, can possibly find an abiding place in the mind of the true, tried, and qualified osteopath" [88]. Indeed, there are indications that in some localities osteopaths are coming to occupy the role of the disappearing general medical practitioner. The dilemma faced by the osteopathic students who are trying to develop a professional self-image has been sensitively studied by Peter New [63, 64].

Chiropractors

Since its beginning in 1895, chiropractic has been beyond the medical pale [92, 96]. Whether or not it was "stolen" from Andrew Taylor Still's osteopathy, as has been charged [7], it has developed completely outside the field of medicine:

> Dr. Daniel David Palmer announced to the world a *separate, distinct*, and *independent* science, art, and philosophy of life.... Chiropractic holds nothing in common with any other system or health method.... If chiropractic bore any relation to medicine in any way, there would be no excuse for its existence. It is different, and in that difference lies its great success with cases given up by all other methods [15].

Organized medicine has stated almost as emphatically its disapproval of chiropractic [76]. Dr. Harvey Cushing is quoted as saying: "There is no pathological basis whatsoever for the theory of chiropractic, and it is silly to allude to it as a science" [14]. Constant repetition of such statements has intensified the hostility between medicine and chiropractic and has blinded physicians to certain basic facts about the chiropractic group. For example, one medical writer on chiropractic stated, in 1939, that "legal status . . . so far has been denied to it in nearly all the states" [79]. In reality, however, the first state law licensing chiropractors was passed in 1913, and by 1931 thirty-nine states had given chiropractors legal recognition. Today about 19,100 practicing chiropractors are licensed in forty-eight of the fifty states; they are educated in four-year colleges which, while neither well-equipped nor known for scholarly research, prepare students to take state licensing examinations; in addition, students must have credits for two years of preprofessional college work to qualify for licensure in thirty-five states, and credits for one year of such work in two additional states. In twenty-four states they must pass the same "basic science" examinations as physicians, osteopaths, and dentists [94]. These facts usually come as a shock to most physicians [43, 86]. But impressive as these requirements may be, they do not create anything like equality between chiropractic and medical education. Chiropractic clinical facilities are limited principally to ambulatory cases, hospital internships are practically nonexistent, and the chiropractic philosophy of disease and its treatment remains suspect.

In 1969 a comprehensive report prepared for the U.S. Public Health Service and Congress recommended that the Social Security Act *not* be amended so as to permit chiropractors to participate in Medicare [94]. The two chiropractic associations responded by issuing jointly a White Paper advancing such arguments as that chiropractors' services are already authorized in seventeen states under the Medicaid program of the Social

Security Act, that all departments of the Federal government accept statements from chiropractors for employee sick leaves, and that Workmen's Compensation claims for chiropractic services are paid in forty-eight states and the District of Columbia [16].

A small amount of sociological research on chiropractic has been published. In 1958 an extensive interview survey of over 500 California chiropractors was made by the Stanford Research Institute [6]. McCorkle has pointed to the congruence between chiropractic theories of illness and cultural values prevalent in rural Iowa [53]. The impact of his marginal status on the practicing chiropractor has been studied by Wardwell [95, 97], who distinguished several shared patterns of reaction which sometimes appear to contribute to the marginality of the role: (1) Chiropractors realistically unite to fight for self-protection, legal recognition, and public acceptance; (2) chiropractors share such faith in their philosophy of illness and therapy that empirical evidence to the contrary threatens it very little, failures being explained as due to the lack of skill of the particular chiropractor or to the fact that the case didn't get to the chiropractor soon enough, with the result that irreversible pathology may have set in; (3) chiropractors can feel that if their therapy is completely different from that of medicine they should not be expected to study the same subjects as physicians or meet the same licensing requirements; nor, if the two professions are completely different, need they feel inferior to the physician; (4) chiropractors share what the writer has called an "ideology of an oppressed minority"—a comprehensive explanation for their inferior social standing and lack of professional acceptance. The ideology attributes organized medicine's disapproval of chiropractic to pecuniary motives, and it righteously upholds chiropractic's struggle against medical "oppression." The ideology gives the chiropractor, in his daily practice, a sense of carrying out an important mission—that of bringing help to the afflicted that medicine cannot cure.

Clark has criticized Wardwell's formulations, questioning that chiropractors suffer problems of personal adjustment merely because they occupy a marginal social role. Using data derived from interviews with over 500 California chiropractors, he showed that those chiropractors who adhere most closely to the behavior patterns described by Wardwell as characteristic of the chiropractic group are no more satisfied with their community standing than the chiropractors who deviate from the patterns [11].

The dilemma faced by organized medicine and by legislators is whether to continue to fight a rearguard action against the legal and social recognition of chiropractors or to approve legislation recognizing them, and thereby help the chiropractic profession to raise educational standards and eliminate incompetent practitioners [30, 94, 98]. The American Medical Association acts as though chiropractors were nonexistent or, if their existence must be recognized, as though they were out-and-out quacks rendering nothing but incidental psychological benefit to their patients. Organized medicine thus loses the goodwill of many patients who have received other than merely psychological benefit from chiropractors [e.g., for sacroiliac strains]. Weiant has found extensive documentation of benefits derived from spinal manipulation, in the scientific medical literature [100].

The fears of organized medicine that "chiropractic is attempting to evolve into the practice of medicine without restriction" [86] are probably exaggerated, since the vast majority of practicing chiropractors do not appear to want to practice medicine. Ideologically they are pretty well committed to a drugless therapy, to a philosophy of "dis-ease," as they sometimes spell it, and to a style of manipulative treatment which is their familiar stock-in-trade. There are strong vested interests —e.g., the chiropractic schools—eager to keep chiropractic a separate and distinct healing profession. Hence it will be many years before chiropractic attains, if it ever does, the degree of professional recognition that osteopathy has achieved: Schools would have to be vastly improved, licensing laws would have to be broadened in scope and tightened up, the mono-causal theory of illness would have to become greatly attenuated, and at least a generation of chiropractors would have to be displaced.

Medical acceptance of osteopathy may impede acceptance of chiropractic, by bringing more experts in manipulative therapy within the medical profession. On the other hand, the disappearance of osteopathy as a separate profession might bring about a gradual upgrading of the more progressive chiropractors (perhaps joined by dissident osteopaths), and the creation by more orthodox chiropractors of a new association of drugless practitioners hostile toward physicians and the chiropractic "mixers" alike. One can hypothesize that the cycle would then repeat itself, with the trend toward the professionalization and scientific upgrading of drugless practitioners continually counterbalanced by the emergence of additional cultic groups adapting new variants of drugless therapy to the cure of mankind's ills.

QUASI-PRACTITIONERS

A varied collection of nonmedical healers use methods that have not been or cannot be empirically validated. Some of these practitioners invoke the symbols and terminology of modern science and claim empirical validation for their therapy; others attribute their achievements to specifically nonscientific factors, such as religious faith, supernatural beings, or magical rites. In both cases the essential benefits which their patients receive are clearly psychological, although they are not conceptualized as such by the practitioners.

Psychotherapy can be intended or unintended. In his comparative study *Persuasion and Healing*, Frank offers a comprehensive definition of psychotherapy and states that its characteristics are common "also to methods of primitive healing, religious conversion, and even so-called brain-washing"; and that "the administration of an inert medicine by a doctor to a patient is also a form of psychotherapy" [28]. He lists physicians, osteopaths, chiropractors, naturopaths, clergymen, marriage counselors, parole officers, and group workers among those conducting psychotherapy. But it is essential to distinguish between those (including most quasi-practitioners) who conduct psychotherapy in this broad sense, perhaps unconsciously, and those whose therapy is conceptualized in terms of modern psychology and who are scientifically trained in its theory and practice. It is of course possible for persons in other professions —e.g., clergymen—to practice psychotherapy scientifically if they are trained to do so. The Academy of Religion and Mental Health exemplifies the overlapping interests of clergymen and psychotherapists [101].

Faith Healers

One subgroup of quasi-practitioners is comprised of religious, or faith, healers. They ascribe to religious faith or supernatural intervention the benefits they confer on their patients. The means they employ are almost exclusively spiritual, such as prayer. Conventionally, such healers are regarded as filling some other primary role—e.g., clergyman or other religious specialist—rather than that of physician. Laws pertaining to medical practice ordinarily exempt religious practitioners from their purview even when healing is their prime stock in trade and is done for a fee—as, for example, Christian Science practitioners.

Miraculous healing has been a potent Christian tradition. Healing shrines such as those at Lourdes in France and at Ste. Anne de Beaupré in Canada attract thousands of sick people, some of whom benefit from the emotional effect of the pilgrimages and the impressive ceremonies in which they participate with other believers [17]. The evangelist Oral Roberts has conducted healing demonstrations before vast television audiences [46]. Christian Science, the most prominent contemporary American example of the link between religion and healing, has had its counterparts in "Jewish Science", "Divine Science," "New Thought," and the "spiritual healing" at one time emphasized by Jehovah's Witnesses [32, 36, 48, 69, 89].

Lesser-known groups combine religion with the occult, with astrology, and with pseudopsychology for the purpose of eliminating all man's ills—not only physiological, but also mental, spiritual, and financial. For example, the Foundation for Divine Meditation, in Santa Isabel, California—which shares quarters with the Academy of Self-Attainment and the National Institute of Christian Healing—offers to train practitioners in "instant healing," "psycho-metaphysics," or "suggestive passivity induction." From Indianapolis, the College of Divine Metaphysics has offered correspondence courses in "metaphysical healing," "practical metaphysics," and "the psychology of business success." Its course in "metaphysical healing" includes lessons in "mental chemistry," "mental surgery," and "the mental cure" of numerous specific diseases and disorders. Completion of two such courses and payment of fees of $50 per course earns the student a Doctor of Psychology (Ps.D.) degree, authorizing him to enter practice immediately. One additional course merits the Doctor of Metaphysics degree, while another two courses are rewarded with the degree of Doctor of Divinity. Five courses and three doctorates for $250!

The Rosicrucians, who reportedly date from the fourteenth century, combine religion, astrology, healing, and vegetarianism in one package, offering instruction through correspondence or in residence. Their extensive list of publications includes one entitled "Occult Principles of Health and Healing."

Primitive and Magical Healers

A second subgroup of quasi-practitioners not only invoke supernatural powers but also typically employ various material substances in conjunction with them. Hence they may be regarded as magical rather than as religious healers, although the line of demarcation is indistinct. In the magical group are included the primitive healers, such as witch doctors, medicine men, and shamans [20, 80], the specialized practitioners of folk medicine, such as the Spanish-American *medicas* and *curanderas* in the Southwestern United States described by Saunders [81], and other contemporary employers of magic.

Quacks

A third subgroup of quasi-practitioners comprises those who "pretend" to be scientific but are not. The word "pretend" is put in quotation marks because frequently the practitioner is himself deceived about the scientific merits of his procedure or equipment. This type of practitioner ascribes the benefits of his practice to "natural" rather than to "supernatural" forces. Prominent are mechanical devices of an electrical nature believed to emit beneficial impulses, waves, or radiations which somehow stimulate restorative processes in the patient's body. Some members of this subgroup, such as the famous Hoxsey Cancer Clinic in Dallas, Texas, dispense medicine or nostrums for which they claim special benefits not recognized by orthodox medical practitioners. Of course, such practitioners sometimes actually do effect cures among those who believe. Faith can be as central to the healing power of an unscientific technique (or for that matter a scientific technique!) as to the healing power of God. "Quackery" is the common term for such pseudoscientific practices, although that term has also sometimes been used for practices that later gained acceptance by orthodox medical circles [41]. In the field of psychotherapy "quack psychologists" are those who employ pseudopsychological principles in an untrained manner, as the practitioners of dianetics have been accused of doing [44]. Steiner's investigation of the variety of ill-trained persons to whom people "take their troubles" is a major contribution to information about this field [87].

These three subgroups of quasi-practitioners vary greatly in their therapeutic techniques, in their rationale for employing them, and in the degree to which they sincerely believe in their therapy. But in each case there is little doubt that the benefits derived by their patients are basically psychotherapeutic in nature, even though they may not be conceptualized or intended by the practitioner as *scientific* psychotherapy. As Frank has pointed out, suggestion is not absent from any type of therapy, including medicine. The psyche is always involved when the body suffers, and probably vice versa. The whole person is treated by any therapist, even when the lesion is clearly somatic and the method wholly pharmacological; thus, all therapy is also psychotherapy.

Christian Science Practitioners

Christian Science is examined here within the context of medicine, although it is obviously impossible to separate its medical from its religious philosophy. It is well-known that Christian Science denies the existence of matter, sin, death, and sickness, and asserts that all is mind, spirit, God, and good. "The word 'healing' as used in Christian Science extends to the healing of family and business problems, of social injustices, intellectual limitations, psychological tensions, and moral confusions" [10]. Despite the prominent attention given in Christian Science testimonials to the social and material benefits received by true believers, it is for its spiritual healing of disease that Christian Science is best known. Unfortunately, the relatively large bibliography on Christian Science, which includes several unpublished sociological treatments, places primary emphasis on its development as a religious sect rather than on its healing *per se* [12, 13, 20, 24, 40, 70, 90].

The techniques of Christian Science healing are remarkably unlike those of other spiritual healing. Although the emphasis is on prayer and mental concentration, along with reading from the Bible and from Mary Baker Eddy's *Science and Health with Key to the Scriptures*, the group ceremonials and the emotional ecstasy that accompany most primitive and contemporary faith-healing are lacking. Even the function of the practitioner himself is minimized, for he does not have to be physically present. He can focus his mental energy on the patient's problem while remaining in his own home, or he can even be dispensed with altogether, since the patient is competent to attain correct belief by himself and is encouraged to do so through studying authorized writings. However, practitioners can help a person afflicted by a "claim" (an illness) and practitioners play a significant role in most "demonstrations" (cures).

Christian Science practitioners usually take "primary class instruction" from a qualified teacher. Such instruction, which lasts about two weeks, is based on twenty-four questions and answers from the chapter entitled "Recapitulation" in Mary Baker Eddy's *Science and Health.* Pupils who have received primary class instruction may put "C.S." (Christian Scientist) after their names. Although class instruction is not a requirement for being officially listed in the *Christian Science Journal,* such listing is the equivalent of certification as a qualified practitioner. Not all who take class instruction become practitioners, and some who practice do so only part time. Some 4,785 such practitioners are listed in the United States, and another 1,115 or so are distributed around the world.

After three years of full-time practice, practitioners may apply for the Normal Class, which is given only once every three years to a limited number of pupils. The Normal Class usually lasts six days and merits the degree of C.S.B., Bachelor of Christian Science. A graduate of the Normal Class is certified as a "teacher" and may give primary class instruction to not more than thirty pupils once a year.

Class instruction of practitioners has always been surrounded by secrecy despite the fact that, in principle, any Christian Scientist can educate himself solely through study of the Bible, *Science and Health,* and other Christian Science texts. For example, note-taking in class has been either forbidden or severely restricted. Furthermore, "teachers are required to teach pupils to defend themselves 'against malpractice' " [102], for just as a practitioner's thought can produce benefit for a person, so also can it produce evil, intentionally or unintentionally. (In the very earliest days of Christian Science students were taught physical manipulation of the head and solar plexus "to produce a state of receptivity." Mrs. Eddy reasoned that since the belief to be rubbed out is located in the brain, "you lay your hands where the belief is to rub it out forever" [8]). A conscientious practitioner avoids "promiscuous mental treatment." "Malicious mental malpractice," or "malicious animal magnetism" (usually abbreviated "M.A.M."), is presumably employed only by the enemies of Christian Science, never by loyal members of the faith.

A special feature of the system of qualification of Christian Science practitioners is that the bond between teacher and pupil is considered to be so close that if the teacher later falls out of favor with the Church authorities and becomes disqualified, all the pupils he has ever trained are disqualified as well. Only by being "retaught" by a teacher in favor with the Board (again paying the instruction fee) can the pupil return to the privileged position of which he has been deprived through no fault of his own. Every teacher, of course, has his own position and welfare to consider, but he must also move with supreme caution lest his pupils be penalized for his actual or supposed defection [8]. Nevertheless, a number of Christian Science practitioners who have been excommunicated from the Church or whose names have been removed from the *Journal* for some other reason continue to practice.

The right of Christian Scientists to practice has been established in nearly all the states. As one judge ruled: "I deny the power of the Legislature to make it a crime to treat disease by prayer" [8]. But there is evidence in recent court rulings that the climate of public opinion is changing, particularly where children are concerned [8]. Additional recognition is shown in the fact that:

> ... practitioners are authorized by statute to sign certificates for sick leave and for disability claims in seven states ... and for federal employees. In health, accident, and hospitalization policies, some insurance companies today recognize the services of a Christian Science practitioner in lieu of a physician or surgeon [8].

Women have always played an especially prominent role in Christian Science both as leaders and as members, and they have nearly monopolized Christian Science healing. In 1953, 77 percent of all practitioners were married women, and another 11 percent were single women—a total of 88 percent [102]. Furthermore, practitioners tend to be of middle-class or higher status, and rather frequently have independent incomes.

The growth of Christian Science as a religious movement has largely been a result of the tireless dedication of its teachers and practitioners, the social characteristics of those affiliated with the movement, and the compatibility between the practical, this-worldly ethos of Christian Science and the American middle-class ethic of the late nineteenth century. All observers agree that the center of social gravity of Christian Science has been in the urban middle classes. Fifty-five years ago, Pierre Janet observed that Christian Science had:

> ... an eminently practical character, well adapted to please persons of an ambitious and active type and whose main concern was with material success. It is not a religion for weaklings and repiners.... It thus ministers to the sense of satisfaction and well-being characteristic of the prosperous classes of the United States" [49].

It is not difficult to see why "manual workers, factory workers, the poor, and the uneducated are not drawn to Christian Science, which demands something of a willingness to attribute poverty to the wrong set of mental attitudes" [102]. "To paraphrase Marx, it is an opiate for those whose lives are already sheltered" [20]. Thorner concludes: "Christian Science is the polar development of ascetic Protestant tendencies toward the transformation of the omnipotent and transcendental personal God of the Old Testament into a dependable impersonal and immanent force available for man's disposal"; the net result is a "toughly self-reliant and responsible" type of person who directs his energies in a pragmatic, this-worldly direction [90].

The Christian Scientist seeks empirical goals using nonempirical means. And there is no question that the empirical goals sought are often attained. Physicians have sent patients to and have themselves sometimes become Christian Science practitioners. But there is no doubt that Scientific therapy is separate and distinct from scientific therapy. The problem concerns the efficacy of the means employed by Christian Science. How does Christian Science cure? "It has been estimated that sickness, suffering, sin, and death are denied at least three thousand times in the pages of *Science and Health*" [102]: e.g., "Efface from thought all forms and types of disease . . . Avoid speaking aloud the name of the disease" [22]. During treatment the patient repeatedly is told, or tells himself, that sickness is not real and that he is well and whole. Such ritualistic denial of objective reality must carry great meaning not only for the patient but for the practitioner as well. In psychological terms, it suggests an almost schizoid withdrawal from reality.

Denial probably occurs at several different psychological levels. First, the practitioner denies his own weaknesses and inadequacies and finds opportunities to treat them nurturantly in patients. Secondly, when the Christian Scientist insists on man's inner perfection, goodness, and spirituality, he in effect denies his own aggressive and other unacceptable impulses. These may be projected, according to well-known psychodynamic mechanisms, onto others, who are then perceived as dangerous. Malicious animal magnetism (referred to, interestingly enough, as "the dragon") resembles nothing so much as paranoid delusions of persecution by imaginary enemies. Denial, and projection to the "outside," of all hostility, sickness, and evil is a tenuous psychodynamic solution that needs continual reinforcement by a repetitious denial of the reality of evil. Lacking the emotional ecstasy that is usually part of faith healing, the Christian Scientist intellectualizes denial through an abstract and impersonal metaphysics.

Above and beyond the high proportion of women who are leaders and practitioners, Christian Science has a strong feminine orientation in general. The direction was initially set by Mary Baker Eddy, who referred to herself as "a God-like woman, God-anointed" [8], and who apparently considered herself the feminine representative in Christianity, as Jesus was the masculine representative. References to "Father-Mother-God" are made in the rewritten Lord's Prayer for Christian Science use. Identification of the church as feminine is not unusual in Christian denominations, for symbolically the church can be mother as well as a pillar of strength; but the feminine emphasis seems strongest of all in Christian Science—in its founder, in its theology, in its practitioners, and in its overt repetition of loving sentiments in interpersonal relationships.

An emphasis on the gentle, more feminine virtues and the tendency to deny and project hostile impulses are both common in those strata in which Christian Science has attained its greatest success—the urban American middle classes in which, as Gorer and Mead have pointed out, there is much psychological dependence of men on women as well as considerable confusion over sex roles generally [34, 56].

The psychological factors in any religious affiliation are notoriously difficult to study, but in Christian Science they need more empirical investigation. Thus far, sociological studies of Christian Science have dealt mainly with such objective factors as the growth of the movement and the social background of its adherents, paying little attention to the personal meaning of its therapy. Dakin has provided an excellent analysis of the meaning of the faith for Mary Baker Eddy herself [19]. It is high time for someone to analyze its meaning for other Christian Scientists.

RESEARCH PROBLEMS

Nearly all the types of studies that have been made of the medical profession could also be made of the limited, marginal, and quasi-practitioners, with great theoretical and practical benefit. In addition, comparative research on several such professions representing different degrees of professionalization, prestige, or marginality could ascertain the correlates of differential recruitment, adult socialization, professional self-image, the choice of therapist by patients, and the therapist-patient relationship. Akers' and Quinney's ranking of medicine, dentistry, optometry, pharmacy, and chiropractic in terms of group cohesion exemplifies the type of sociological variable that can be meaningfully related to other social or personality variables [1].

Other topics deserving investigation center on the social forces producing changes in the status of these professions: (1) the relationship between rational and nonrational factors in the acceptance or rejection of new modes of therapy; (2) the role of charismatic leadership in legitimizing therapeutic innovation and in establishing new health-related professions; (3) the effect of the activities of organized medicine and of state regulatory agencies on the establishment, evolution, and possible disappearance of limited, marginal, and quasi-practitioners; and (4) the comparative study of these professions in other societies for the light which cross-cultural investigation can shed on the forces and factors operative in the American scene.

REFERENCES

1. AKERS, RONALD L. AND RICHARD QUINNEY, "Differential Organization of Health Professions: A Comparative Analysis," *American Sociological Review*, 33 (February, 1968), 104–21.
2. American Council on Education, *The General Report of the Pharmaceutical Survey: 1946–49.* Washington, D.C., 1950.
3. American Optometric Association, *Your Eyes and Optometry.* St. Louis, 1958.
4. American Osteopathic Association, *White Paper: AOA–AMA Relationships, No. 2.* Chicago, 1968.
5. American Psychological Association, *The Psychologist and Voluntary Health Insurance.* Washington, D.C., 1968.
6. BARSALOU, FRANK W. et al., *Chiropractic in California.* Los Angeles: The Haynes Foundation, 1960.
7. BOYD, C. E., *The Cult of Chiropractic.* Shreveport, La.: American Medical Association and Louisiana State Medical Society, n.d.
8. BRADEN, CHARLES S., *Christian Science Today.* Dallas: Southern Methodist University Press, 1958.
9. CARHART, RAYMOND, "Speech Pathology and Audiology," *ASHA: A Journal of the Speech and Hearing Association*, 2 (April, 1960), 99–102.
10. Christian Science Publishing Society, *Facts about Christian Science.* Boston, 1959.
11. CLARK, ALEXANDER L., "Marginality and Induced Stress." Paper read at the St. Louis meeting of the Society for the Study of Social Problems, August 28, 1961.
12. CLEMENS, SAMUEL [MARK TWAIN], "Christian Science and the Book of Mrs. Eddy," *Cosmopolitan*, October, 1899, 585–94.
13. ———, *Christian Science.* New York: Harper & Row, Publishers, 1907.
14. COMMITTEE ON LEGISLATION OF THE MEDICAL SOCIETY OF VIRGINIA, *Chiropractors and Naturopaths.* Richmond, Va., 1947.
15. COOLEY, C. S., "Science Sidelights," *Journal of the National Chiropractic Association*, 19 (April, 1949), 35–38.
16. Council of State Chiropractic Examining Boards, *Chiropractic's "White Paper" on Health, Education, and Welfare Secretary's Report "Independent Practitioners under Medicare."* Cheyenne, Wyo., 1969.
17. CRANSTON, RUTH, *The Miracle of Lourdes.* New York: McGraw-Hill Book Company, 1955.
18. CROATMAN, WALLACE AND PAUL B. SHEATSLEY, *The Prescription Pharmacist*

Today. New York: Health Information Foundation, 1958.

19. DAKIN, EDWIN F., *Mrs. Eddy: The Biography of a Virginal Mind.* New York: Charles Scribner's Sons, 1930.
20. DENOOD, NEAL B., *"The Diffusion of a System of Belief."* Unpublished Ph.D. dissertation, Harvard University, 1937.
21. DUBOS, RENE J., "Health and Disease," *Journal of the American Medical Association*, 147 (October 1, 1960), 505–7.
22. EDDY, MARY BAKER, *Science and Health with Key to the Scriptures.* Boston: Christian Science Publishing Society, 1934.
23. EGER, MILTON J., "AOA–AMA Relationship: AOA Objective Evaluated," *Journal of the American Optometric Association*, 39 (April, 1968) 324–25.
24. ENGLAND, R. W., "Some Aspects of Christian Science as Reflected in Letters of Testimony," *American Journal of Sociology*, 59 (March, 1954), 448–53.
25. EVANS-PRITCHARD, E. E., *Witchcraft, Oracles, and Magic among the Azande.* London: Oxford University Press, 1937.
26. FALK, I. S., C. F. ROREM, AND M. D. RING, *The Costs of Medical Care.* A summary of publications of the Committee on the Costs of Medical Care. Chicago: University of Chicago Press, 1933.
27. FLEXNER, ABRAHAM, "A Layman's View of Osteopathy," *Journal of the American Medical Association*, 42 (June 6, 1914), 1831–33.
28. FRANK, JEROME D., *Persuasion and Healing: A Comparative Study of Psychotherapy.* Baltimore: Johns Hopkins Press, 1961.
29. FRANCKE, D. E., "Let's Separate Pharmacies and Drug Stores," *American Journal of Pharmacy*, 141 (September–October, 1969), 161–76.
30. GEIGER, ARTHUR J., "Chiropractic: Its Cause and Cure," *Medical Economics* (February, April, June, and August, 1942).
31. GIES, WILLIAM J., *Dental Education in the United States and Canada.* New York: Carnegie Foundation for the Advancement of Teaching, 1926.
32. GODDARD, HENRY H., "The Effects of Mind on Body as Evidenced by Faith Cures," *American Journal of Psychology*, 10 (April, 1899), 431–502.
33. GOODE, WILLIAM J., "Encroachment, Charlatanism, and the Emerging Professions: Psychology, Sociology, and Medicine," *American Sociological Review*, 25 (December, 1960), 902–14.
34. GORER, GEOFFREY, *The American People.* New York: W. W. Norton & Company, Inc., 1948.
35. GRIFFENHAGEN, GEORGE B., "Discovering Our Full Potentialities," *Journal of the American Pharmaceutical Association*, NS8 (June, 1968), 283.
36. GRISWALD, ALFRED W., "New Thought: A Cult of Success," *American Journal of Sociology*, 40 (November, 1934), 309–18.
37. Group for the Advancement of Psychiatry, Committee on Clinical Psychology, "The Relation of Clinical Psychology to Psychiatry," *American Journal of Orthopsychiatry*, 20 (April, 1950), 346–54.
38. HARTMANN, GEORGE W., "The Relative Social Prestige of Representative Medical Specialties," *Journal of Applied Psychology*, 20 (December, 1936), 659–63.
39. HILDRETH, JANE D., "Psychology's Relations with Psychiatry: A Summary Report," in Bernard Lubin and Eugene E. Levitt, eds., *The Clinical Psychologist: Background, Roles, and Functions.* Chicago: Aldine Publishing Company, 1967.
40. HOFFMAN, LOIS, "Problem Patient: The Christian Scientist," *Medical Economics*, 33 (December, 1956), 265–83.
41. HOLBROOK, STEWART H., *The Golden Age of Quackery.* New York: The Macmillan Company, 1959.
42. HOLMES, OLIVER WENDELL, SR., "Homeopathy and Kindred Delusions," in *The Writings of Oliver Wendell Holmes.* Cambridge, Mass.: Riverside Press, 1891, Vol. IX, Chap. 1.
43. HOMEWOOD, A. E., "Chiropractic," *University of Toronto Medical Journal*, 38 (February, 1961), 165–73.
44. HUBBARD, L. RON, *Dianetics: The*

Modern Science of Mental Health. New York: Hermitage House, 1950.

45. HULL, WILLIAM H., *Public Relations for the Pharmacist.* Philadelphia: J. B. Lippincott Co., 1955.
46. JACOBS, HAYES B., "Oral Roberts: High Priest of Faith Healing," *Harpers' Magazine*, February, 1962, 37–43.
47. JAMES, WARREN E., "Differential Acceptance of Occupations as Professions." Unpublished Ph.D. dissertation, Ohio State University, 1957.
48. JAMES, WILLIAM, *The Varieties of Religious Experience.* New York: Modern Library, Inc., 1902.
49. JANET, PIERRE, *Psychological Healing*, trans. Eden and Cedar Paul. New York: The MacMillan Company, 1925.
50. JONASSEN, CHRISTEN, ROBERT BULLOCK, JEROME FOLKMAN, WILLIAM KENKEL, ALFRED CLARKE, AND RUSSELL DYNES, "Interpolations in the North-Hatt Scale." Unpublished ms.
51. KEESECKER, RAYMOND P., *The Osteopathic Movement in Medicine.* Chicago: American Osteopathic Association, 1957.
52. KRIESBERG, LOUIS AND BEATRICE R. TREIMAN, "The Public's Views of Dentistry as a Profession," *Journal of Dental Education*, 25 (September, 1961), 247–68.
53. MCCORKLE, THOMAS, "Chiropractic: A Deviant Theory of Disease and Treatment in Contemporary Western Culture," *Human Organization*, 20 (Spring, 1961), 20–23.
54. MCCORMACK, THELMA H., "The Druggists' Dilemma: Problems of a Marginal Occupation," *American Journal of Sociology*, 61 (January, 1956), 308–15.
55. MCDOWELL, HAROLD D., "Osteopathy: A Study of a Semi-Orthodox Healing Agency and the Recruitment of Its Clientele." Unpublished M.A. thesis, University of Chicago, 1950.
56. MEAD, MARGARET, *Male and Female.* New York: William Morrow & Co., 1949.
57. MENZEL, HERBERT AND ELIHU KATZ, "Social Relations and Innovation in the Medical Profession: The Epidemiology of a New Drug," *Public Opinion Quarterly*, 19 (Winter, 1955–56), 337–52.
58. MILLS, LAWRENCE W., *The Osteopathic Profession and Its Colleges.* Chicago: American Osteopathic Association, 1959.
59. National Center for Health Statistics, *Health Resources Statistics: Health Manpower and Health Facilities, 1970*, U.S. Public Health Service Publication, No. 1509. Washington, D.C.: Government Printing Office, 1970.
60. ———, *Characteristics of Persons with Corrective Lenses: United States, July 1965–June 1966*, Series 10, Number 53. Washington, D.C.: Government Printing Office, 1969.
61. National Medical Foundation for Eye Care, *Medicine, Optometry, and the Public Welfare.* New York, 1957.
62. ———, *The Ancillary Worker in Ophthalmologic Medical Practice: Part I. The Optician*, Report No. 6. New York, 1959.
63. NEW, PETER, "The Osteopathic Students: A Study in Dilemma," in E. Gartly Jaco, ed., *Patients, Physicians, and Illness.* New York: The Free Press, 1958.
64. ———, "The Application of Reference Group Theory to Shifts in Values: The Case of the Osteopathic Student." Unpublished Ph.D. dissertation, University of Missouri, 1960.
65. NORTH, C. C. AND P. K. HATT, "Jobs and Occupations: A Popular Evaluation," *Public Opinion News*, 9 (September 1, 1947), 3–13.
66. *Optometry, the Profession: Its Antecedents, Birth, and Development.* A series of editorial articles that appeared under the title "The Basis of Optometry's Public Relations" in *The Optical Journal and Review of Optometry* (October 1, 1945–January 1, 1947).
67. ORZACK, LOUIS H. AND JOHN R. UGLUM, *Sociological Perspectives of the Profession of Optometry, American Journal of Optometry and Archives of American Academy of Optometry*, Monograph No. 230, 35 (August, 1958), 407–24.
68. "Osteopathy: Special Report of the Judicial Council to the AMA House of Delegates," *Journal of American Medi-*

cal Association, 177 (September 16, 1961), 774–76.

69. PAULSEN, ALICE E., "Religious Healing," *Journal of the American Medical Association*, 86 (May 15, 22, and 29, 1926), 1519–24, 1617–23, 1692–97.
70. PFAUTZ, HAROLD W., "Christian Science: A Case Study of the Social Psychological Aspect of Secularization," *Social Forces*, 34 (March, 1956), 246–51.
71. ———, "Christian Science: The Sociology of a Social Movement and a Religious Sect." Unpublished Ph.D. dissertation, University of Chicago, 1953.
72. QUARANTELLI, ENRICO L., "The Dental Student: A Social Psychological Study." Unpublished Ph.D. dissertation, University of Chicago, 1959.
73. ———, "The Dental Student Image of the Dentist-Patient Relationship," *American Journal of Public Health*, 51 (September, 1961), 1312–19.
74. QUINNEY, EARL R., "Occupational Structure and Criminal Behavior: Prescription Violation by Retail Pharmacists," *Social Problems*, 11 (Fall, 1963), 179–85.
75. REED, LOUIS, *Midwives, Chiropodists, and Optometrists*, Publication No. 15 of the Committee on the Costs of Medical Care. Chicago: University of Chicago Press, 1932.
76. ———, *The Healing Cults*, Publication No. 16 of the Committee on the Costs of Medical Care. Chicago: University of Chicago Press, 1932.
77. REISSMAN, LEONARD, *Class in American Society*. New York: The Free Press, 1959.
78. REMMERS, H. H. AND N. L. GAGE, *Student Personnel Studies of the Pharmaceutical Survey*. Washington, D.C.: American Council on Education, 1949.
79. RIESMAN, DAVID, *Medicine in Modern Society*. Princeton, N.J.: Princeton University Press, 1939.
80. RIVERS, W. H. R., *Medicine, Magic, and Religion*. London: Routledge & Kegan Paul, Ltd., 1924.
81. SAUNDERS, LYLE, "Healing Ways in the Spanish Southwest," in E. Gartly Jaco, ed., *Patients, Physicians, and Illness*. New York: The Free Press, 1958.
82. SCHWEBEL, MILTON, *The Interests of Pharmacists*. New York: King's Crown Press, 1951.
83. SHERLOCK, BASIL J., "The Second Profession: Parallel Mobilities of the Dental Profession and Its Recruits," *Journal of Health and Social Behavior*, 10 (March, 1969), 41–51.
84. SIGERIST, HENRY E., "The History oı Medical Licensure," *Journal of the American Medical Association*, 104 (March 30, 1935), 1056–60.
85. Special Commission on Status of Podiatry Education, *Podiatry Education in the 1960's*. Washington, D.C.: American Podiatry Association, 1961.
86. STALVEY, RICHARD M., "What's New in Chiropractic?" *New York State Journal of Medicine*, 57 (January 1, 1957), 49–59.
87. STEINER, LEE R., *Where Do People Take Their Troubles?* Boston: Houghton Mifflin Company, 1945.
88. STILL, ANDREW T., *Autobiography of A.T. Still*. Kirksville, Mo.: Published by the author, 1908.
89. STROUP, HERBERT H., *The Jehovah's Witnesses*. New York: Columbia University Press, 1945.
90. THORNER, ISADOR, "Christian Science and Ascetic Protestantism." Unpublished Ph.D. dissertation, Harvard University, 1950.
91. ———, "Pharmacy: The Functional Significance of an Institutional Pattern," *Social Forces*, 20 (March, 1942), 321–28.
92. TURNER, CHITTENDEN, *The Rise of Chiropractic*. Los Angeles: Powell Publishing Company, 1931.
93. TYLER, VARRO E., "Clinical Pharmacy: The Need and an Evaluation of the Professional Concept," *American Journal of Pharmaceutical Education*, 32 (December, 1968), 764–71.
94. U.S. Department of Health, Education, and Welfare, *Independent Practitioners under Medicare*, A Report to Congress. Washington, D.C.: Government Printing Office, 1969.
95. WARDWELL, WALTER I., "Social Strain and Social Adjustment in the Marginal

Role of the Chiropractor." Unpublished Ph.D. dissertation, Harvard University, 1951.
96. ———, "A Marginal Professional Role: The Chiropractor," *Social Forces*, 30 (March, 1952), 339–48.
97. ———, "The Reduction of Strain in a Marginal Social Role," *American Journal of Sociology*, 61 (July, 1955), 16–25.
98. ———, "Public Regulation of Chiropractic," *Journal of the National Medical Association*, 53 (March, 1961), 166–72.
99. WATSON, ROBERT I., *Psychology as a Profession*. Garden City, N.Y.: Doubleday & Company, 1954.
100. WEIANT, CLARENCE W., *Medicine and Chiropractic*. New York: Published by the author, 1958.
101. WESTBERG, GRANGER, "Religious Aspects of Medical Teaching," *Journal of Medical Education*, 32 (March, 1957), 204–9.
102. WILSON, BRYAN R., *Sects and Society: A Sociological Study of Elim Tabernacle, Christian Science, and Christadelphians*. Berkeley: University of California Press, 1961.

12

THE HOSPITAL AS A SOCIAL SYSTEM

Sydney H. Croog and Donna F. Ver Steeg

In many respects the hospital contains within its walls a microcosm of the world outside. Most people in the United States are born in a hospital, many of them die there. Patients eat and sleep there, as do some members of the staff. People fall in love in hospitals, and some have married there. Suspected criminals are imprisoned in hospitals. Courts convene there. Church services are held there. Families gather within hospitals, and for some these are the only occasions for meeting. Governments have risen and fallen on the events which have transpired there. The hospital, while a social system in itself, is intricately involved with the world beyond its walls, and an understanding of its system must be linked to an examination of its larger connections with society.

Hospitals have been analyzed as social systems, as complex organizations, and as small societies [33, 36, 45, 86, 87, 94, 179]. The methods of operations research and systems analysis have been applied [22, 201, 225]. Decision models, power structure models, and socialization models have constituted other modern means of approach to hospitals [15, 276]. Compared with other points of emphasis, it appears that in the literature relatively less attention has been given to the larger context within which hospitals operate. In this chapter, as one means of examining the hospital in terms of both its internal and external environments, we have chosen to employ an open systems model [87, 252].

With this approach, an organization such as a hospital may be viewed not only as an entity itself, within which a certain technology is practiced, but also in terms of its contacts and overlapping with other organizations. From some of these outside organizations it receives inputs (e.g., funds, patients, supplies, professionals, students). With others it engages in negotiations, of a more or less peaceful nature, about which organization shall exercise control over a given domain. To other organizations it also sends outputs (patients, services, trained professionals, etc.).[1]

While the hospital shares a basic core of characteristics with other large-scale formal systems, it has its own distinctive traits which place it in a special category for analysis. Among others, Georgopoulos and Mann [86] and Georgopoulos and Matijko [87] have reviewed some of the characteristics that are useful in comparing the community general hospital and other large-scale organizations. For example, the hospital is a care- and treatment-giving organization. It processes individual people rather than some uniform and nonreactive product. It operates with the mandate of the community. Provision of service is commonly expected to take priority over consideration of costs or efficiency. Demands for care tend to be emergency in nature and nondeferrable. Decisions are required which have moral as well as functional and secular implications [3, 76, 119, 132, 139, 143, 224, 260, 261]. To balance the unpredictability inherent in the work to be done, hospitals in Western civilizations aim towards a high degree of standardization (and therefore predictability) in those areas which can be controlled [166]. Hospitals have traditionally utilized management practices which are authoritarian and blame fixing in nature [2, 157, 158]. Division of authority, power, and discretion between the administrative structure and the medical care structure results in a high degree of interdependence and the need for coordination between all groups.[2] This problem is, of course, typical of all complex organizations.

CHARACTERISTICS OF HOSPITALS IN THE UNITED STATES

Hospitals can be classified in many ways: by type of service, type of management or control, type of financial support, physical size, type of facilities, staff composition, and numerous other features. In the United States there are approximately 7,000 hospitals, about 5,800 of which are of the nonfederal, short-term, general hospital type [173]. On the national level the number of persons involved in hospital settings is large as compared with other industries and economic activities. The hospitals of the United States employ approximately 1.6 million full-time

[1] For an expanded discussion of some organizations outside the hospital which interact with it and affect what goes on within its walls, the reader is referred elsewhere in this handbook, especially to Chaps. 8, 9, 13, 14, and 15.

[2] Mechanisms for dealing with such conflict have been discussed by Litwak and others [42, 148, 159]. The dysfunctions which result from attempts to satisfy conflicting demands were earlier discussed by Barnard [14].

FIGURE 12-1 Classification of Health Care Institutions by Function

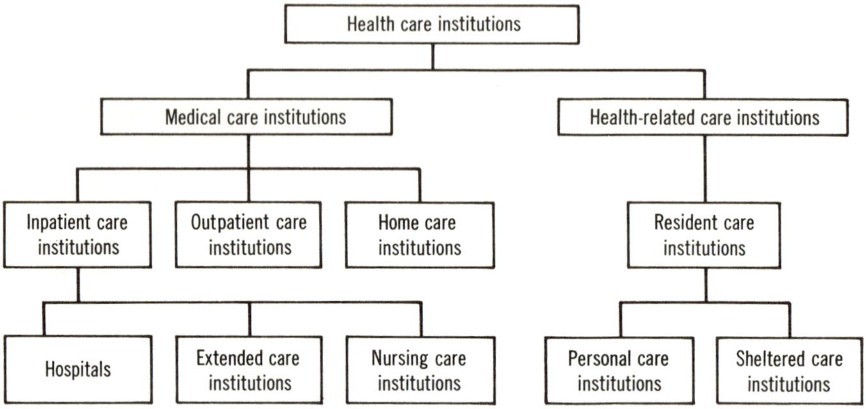

Source: American Hospital Association, *Classification of Health Care Institutions,* 1968 edition.

Each of the terminal boxes in the left-hand side of this figure can be further divided into "general" and "special," according to whether or not the patient population is limited to those suffering from specific diseases.

workers. About 31 million patients are admitted each year. In addition, many thousands of doctors, volunteers, visitors, and other categories of permanent and temporary personnel participate, for differing periods, in various types of activities and relationships in these institutions.

The modal type of hospital in the United States is the short-term general hospital. A *short-term hospital* is defined as one in which over 50 percent of the patients stay less than thirty days. *General hospitals* are contrasted to *special hospitals,* which limit their services to groups requiring specialized care (psychiatric; tuberculosis; maternity; ear, nose, and throat; children's; orthopedic; chronic; etc.). For certain statistical purposes another distinction is made between hospitals by type of management. Thus, *community hospitals* may be described as all short-term, nonfederal institutions providing general and selected special services, and *noncommunity hospitals* include all federal institutions, all psychiatric institutions, and all other long-term, nonfederal hospitals.

The increasing involvement of third party (governmental and private insurance) agencies made exact definitions of the different types of institutions a legal necessity. *Classification of Health Care Institutions, 1968 edition* [5], was published by the American Hospital Association, with the sponsorship of the Public Health Service and the Social Security Administration. It attempts to clarify the nature of health care institutions, and classifies them in two ways—by function (Figure 12–1) and by control (Figure 12–2).[3]

Hospital organizational charts vary by size and type and on a cross-national basis, but there are some basic uniformities among them, at least in the United States. Some of these uniformities have been encouraged by the recommendations of the Joint Commission on Accreditation of Hospitals [130, 193]. Figure 12–3 [254] is an example of a fairly typical organization chart.

[3] For examples of how this varies from other countries, see [8, 25, 79, 135, 160, 228].

FIGURE 12-2 CLASSIFICATION OF HEALTH CARE INSTITUTIONS BY CONTROL

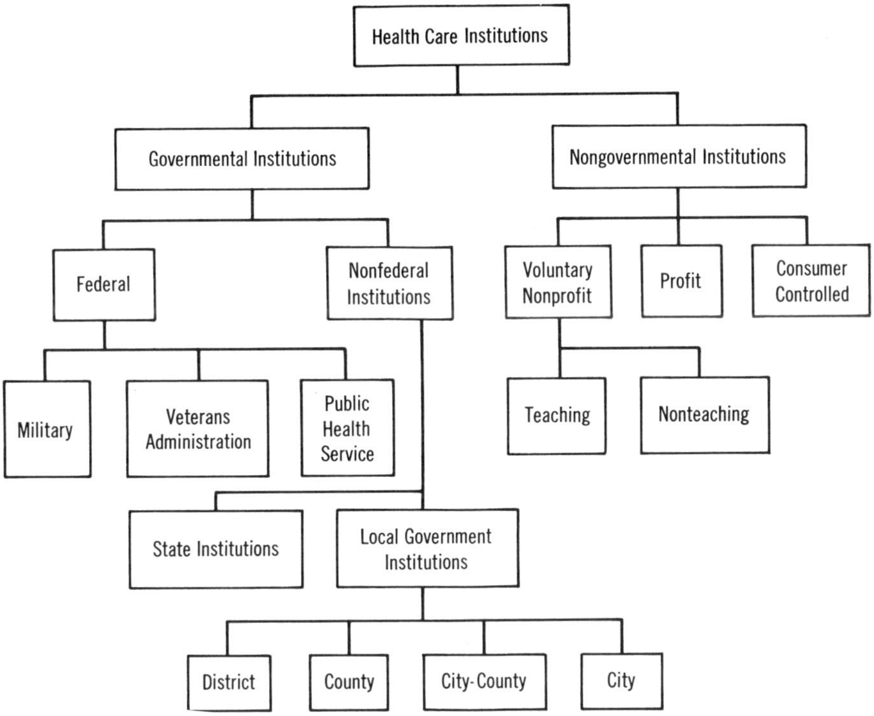

Source: American Hospital Association, *Classification of Health Care Institutions,* 1968 edition.

In recent years a number of distinctive and important trends in the character of hospitals have become evident [18, 85, 138, 153, 259]. These find their roots in such factors as changes in the technology of care; efforts to improve efficiency; increased recognition of social, psychological, and economic needs; and efforts to measure hospital output with a view toward accurate assessments of quantity and quality. Among these trends are the development of refined diagnostic and treatment facilities, progressive patient care (including intensive care units) [245], home care programs, transformation of governmental into community hospitals, use of outpatient facilities as drop-in clinics by all sectors of the community, and the increasing use of salaried physicians [4, 30, 39, 136].

Outpatient visits in the United States increased by 64 percent between 1960 and 1969. During that same period, hospital personnel increased by 52 percent. Payroll expenses increased 147 percent, while total expenses increased 162.5 percent. All this occurred with only a 4 percent increase in the number of hospitals and a net loss of 0.5 percent in the total number of beds. During that time also, changing treatment technologies and basic philosophies of care brought psychiatric, rehabilitation, and extended care units to the community hospitals, enhancing their transformation to community health centers. Tuberculosis hospitals were closing with the advent of new drug therapies. In 1946, there were 412 nonfederal tuberculosis hospitals, by 1969 this number had been reduced to 107 [173].

Hospitalization has become increasingly common. In 1946, there was one hospital admission for every 10 persons in the population. By 1966 this had risen to one admission for every 6.5 persons [253]. While the average length of stay has remained quite stable (8 days ±1 day), hospital expenses per patient day have risen markedly [173]. Some of this has been due to belated increases in salaries and wages of hospital employees, but the larger portion has been caused by increased costs of hospital operation brought on by new diagnostic and treatment facilities and equipment [142, 253, 275]. The increasing complexity of the internal organization (Figure 12–3) has been more than matched by enormous changes in the number and complexity of the interactions of the hospital with outside agencies (Table 12–1). The agencies listed are only those which involve reporting relationships. To these must be added the myriad organizations with which more or less purely economic relationships exist (e.g., those concerned with supplies, equipment drugs, capital financing, etc.).

The average hospital stay of patients sixty-five or older (13 days in 1968) was almost double that of patients under sixty-five (6.6 days) [121]. As a consequence, in many short-term hospitals, there is a relatively high proportion of elderly patients as compared with previous years. Transfers to extended care facilities or nursing homes were intended to relieve this situation but some difficulties have arisen [150]. Ro has determined that length of stay is significantly correlated with a number of variables including size of hospital, age of patient, employment status, whether living alone, and method of payment [205]. Whether the hospital has an outpatient clinic and/or a home care program is also important.

With the occurrence of these and other changes in hospitals and the changing nature of the demands upon them, many professional workers and health care planners have been concentrating upon how to reframe the social organization of hospitals to improve their effectiveness. Some proposals, for instance, are aimed at decentralizing decision making in order to make hospital services more responsive to patient needs and to improve the job satisfaction of paramedical personnel [29, 68, 86, 239].[4] It is claimed that these changes would also encourage motivation, constructive competition, and productivity incentives, and enhance the ability of the hospital to measure true output. Unit management teams composed of a salaried physician, a nurse, and an assistant hospital administrator have been suggested. Others would include a pharmacist and perhaps a "resident fiduciary intermediary" at the unit level to deal with the increasingly specialized knowledge required for the clinical use of drugs and for third-party pay (insurance) problems.

Perrow has pointed out, in another context [185], that changes such as those outlined above are effective only with a nonroutine technology. This would appear to be antithetical to pressures for routinization. Such pressures are implicit in many measures of quality of patient care.

Measuring the Quality of Patient Care

Another continuing and problematic feature of hospitals is the difference in quality and respectability among these institutions and their staffs. These constitute important variables, not only in terms of contacts the hospital and its

[4] Some extrahospital examples of problems with changes in decision-making structures can be found in [147].

FIGURE 12-3 Typical Large Ceneral Hospital Organized into Five Divisions

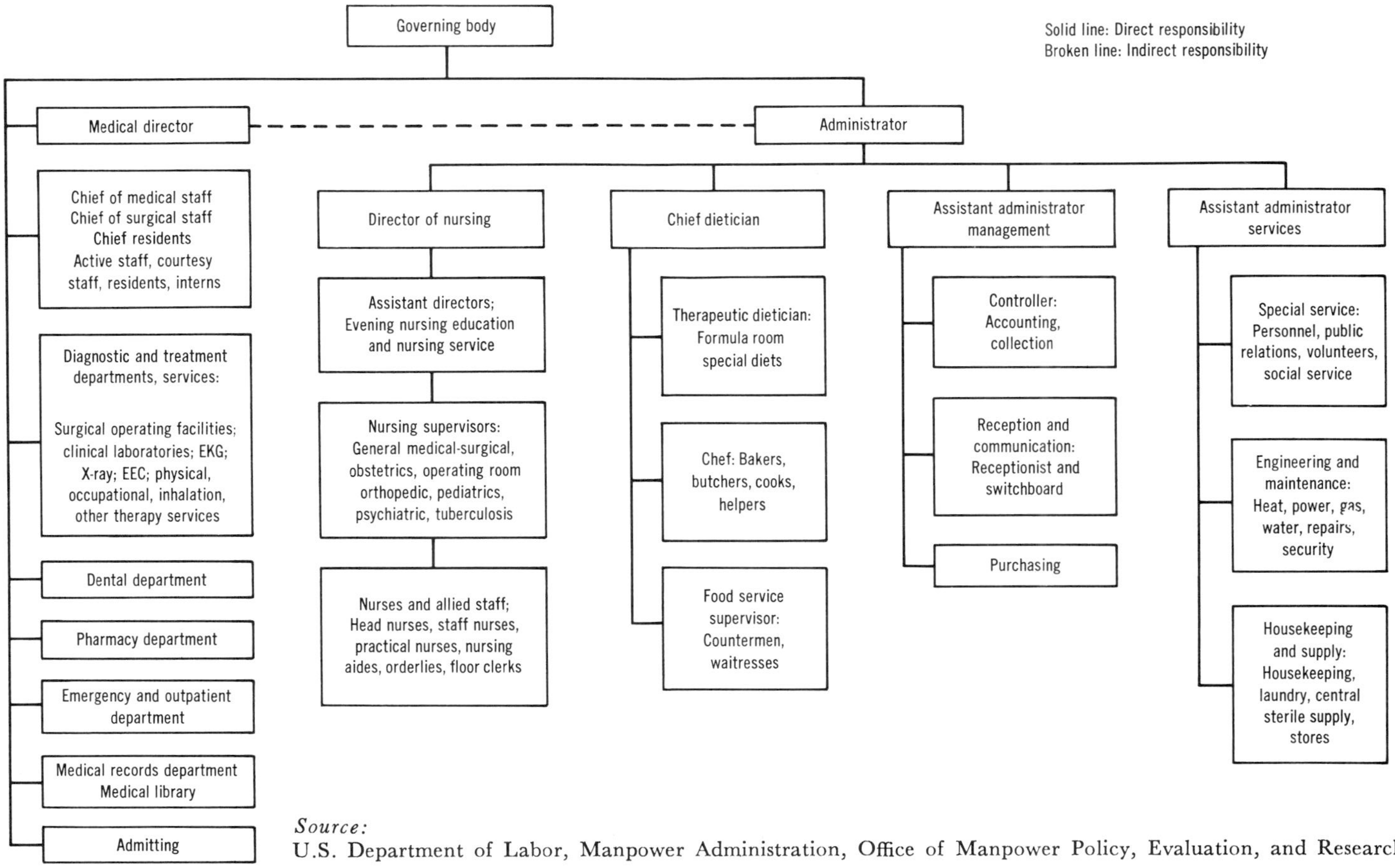

Source:
U.S. Department of Labor, Manpower Administration, Office of Manpower Policy, Evaluation, and Research.

TABLE 12-1 Partial Listing of Outside Agencies with Which Hospitals May Interact[5]

Governmental Agencies	Voluntary Agencies
National	
Atomic Energy Commission (Division of Biology and Medicine) (Office of Isotopes Development) Department of Commerce (Bureau of Standards) Department of Health, Education, and Welfare (Social Security Administration) (Food and Drug Administration) Department of Housing and Urban Development Department of Justice (Bureau of Narcotics) Office of Emergency Preparedness Office of Civilian Defense	Joint Commission on Accreditation of Hospitals American College of Surgeons (Cancer program) American Medical Association (Residency approval) (Interne approval) (Medical School approval) National League for Nursing (Nursing school approval) Association of American Medical Colleges (Teaching hospitals) Blue Cross Association American Osteopathic Association Other professional associations and educational, accreditation, and certifying agencies (e.g., medical specialty boards, junior college affiliations, baccalaureate affiliations for other professional training)
State	
Medical licensure boards Nursing licensure boards Health hospital facilities (Hill-Burton) programs (usually under Department of Health or its equivalent) Hospital licensure Crippled Children's Service Maternal and Child Health Mental Health Vocational Rehabilitation Regional Medical Programs (Public Law 89–239)	State Medical Society State Nursing Association Blue Shield Blue Cross Area Wide Planning Agencies Hospital associations and councils
Local	
Fire Department Building and plumbing codes Health Department Air Pollution Board Sanitation Department Licensing agencies Maternal and Child Health programs Law enforcement agencies	Neighborhood Health Councils Visiting Nurse Associations Nursing Homes Extended Care Facilities Red Cross Organized labor Local educational institutions: university, college, junior college, trade school

5 See Chap. 15 for a discussion of this. See also [27, 53, 101, 102, 173, 258].

staff have with the outside community but also in terms of what goes on inside hospital walls. The social position of its staff and of those who enter the hospital as patients differ across these variables—and not necessarily in the same direction nor in a linear fashion. A huge county hospital (turned community hospital to qualify for federal monies) may care primarily for the medically indigent. Its staff may include both the academic elite from the nearby university and the local general practitioner, who has gained admission to the staff by reason of nondiscrimination clauses required by use of federal funds. The care this hospital gives may vary from that of poorly staffed beds-in-the-hall wards to elaborately equipped clinical research units.

Quality of hospital care has proven difficult to measure. The chief difficulty arises with the selection of measurable attributes. In selecting any given set of measurements, the investigator has, in fact, defined the quality of care he is measuring. Two appendectomy patients may be judged to have had comparable care because they stayed in the hospital the same length of time—or because they underwent the same therapeutic regime—or stayed in hospitals with comparable facilities—or because they lost the same number of days of work.

Criteria for measuring quality of care may involve an assessment of the content, process, structure, and outcome or impact of health care [58, 64, 98, 237].

1. Content and process involve medical judgment, which has proven difficult to quantify. Evaluation is usually based on normative criteria [31, 59, 104, 133, 188, 266, 278].
2. Structure includes both physical facilities and organizational and professional qualification criteria. Structure is easiest to measure, but it measures the *probability* of quality care, not its execution. (The Joint Commission for the Accreditation of Hospitals standards are an example of such criteria [130, 193].)
3. Outcome and impact depend on other important, and perhaps determining, factors besides quality of care (culture, family, housing, productivity, etc.) [10].

Another serious difficulty in assessing hospital efficiency and effectiveness arises from the fact that only recently have hospitals begun to keep records of a nature that would begin to permit an accurate cost-benefit analysis. As governmental and private insurance plans found their cost rising, they moved toward the policy of paying only for services received, as opposed to earlier flat fee reimbursements [89, 118, 138]. Hospitals discovered that in many cases they literally did not know what various services cost nor how to evaluate alternative methods of providing the same service. This situation like many others has its roots in the religious-charitable origins of hospitals. The situation is complicated by the fact that hospitals may have limited control over their workload. Computerized systems and techniques, however, are making more sophisticated studies possible [63, 206].

In an economy of scarce health resources, where the costs of delivery have to be balanced against benefits to individual patients (and/or to society), such a situation had to be resolved. The complex interrelationships involved have made it evident that simplistic accounting methods were inadequate [90, 171, 206, 236].

Improvements in record keeping make possible the use of other relevant criteria in assessing the quality of care, i.e., organizational coordination, composition and distribution of nursing and medical staffs, absenteeism and turnover among nursing personnel, and adequacy of financial support. Intraorganizational strain and complementarity of work expectations between medical and nursing staffs have also been utilized in such studies [64, 86, 87, 222, 223, 237].

Revans, in a series of studies, demonstrated high correlations between length of patient stay for given medical and surgical diagnosis and a number of indicators of nursing staff morale. These included job turnover at all levels, illness rates among students, and dropouts among student nurses. Perceptions of blocked communication channels within the nursing hierarchy and between nurses and physicians were felt to be the root cause of many of the difficulties uncovered [201, 202]. Support for this hypothesis was offered in independent evidence that length of stay of medical patients was more closely related to the morale indicators than was that of surgical patients. (Medical patient stay was felt to be more dependent on accurate observation and reporting.) Commonly offered reasons for turnover in nursing staff (low pay, long hours, competing opportunities for employment in the larger community, etc.), were not supported by the evidence.

The presumed inability of clients to assess the quality of hospital professional service received has long been a critical issue. Professionals have used this claim to support their right to evaluation by peers. There is some evidence, however, that clients may be more sensitive in this respect than has been supposed. Kisch and Reeder found that welfare patients' reports on whether or not they received the care they desired from physicians correlated highly with professional criteria of professional performance. Although no claim has been made that this study tested lay evaluation, it does point up the necessity for further research in this area [137].

THE HOSPITAL AND ITS EXTERNAL ENVIRONMENT

The influence of the external environment upon the internal system of the hospital is pervasive, affecting many aspects of the structure and content of the interpersonal environment within the institution. The external setting in which hospitals exist can be differentiated at a number of levels. At one extreme, hospitals can be seen in the context of vast divisions, such as Western society or Western culture. They can also be analyzed in relation to national, regional, or community contexts. At a more microcosmic level, the pertinent external environment of American hospitals can be seen as the county, town, and neighborhood. In the matter of supply of personnel, for example, the immediate local neighborhood may be the crucial area for determining the composition of the semiskilled and unskilled staff. On the other hand, the conditions in the state, region, or even the nation may constitute factors influencing the size, composition, and quality of the medical staff in a particular hospital.

Values and Cross-Cultural Perspectives

The existence of the hospital is dependent upon such elements as the values, felt needs, and the level of technological development in a society. Humanitarianism, compassion, and belief in the worth of the individual are themes which historically have been associated with the founding and development of hospitals in Western countries [26, 77, 92, 226]. Faith in science, belief in good health and the prolonging of life, and convictions about the power of rationally determined action are also important themes which are often ultimately reflected in the organization of activities in hospitals and in interpersonal relations within them.

In the United States, hospitals are organized to fill certain community needs, and their continued operation is dependent upon their ability to conform to the standards, expectations, and customs of the society outside. Federal, state, and local laws specify that certain values will be fulfilled, particularly those relating to standards of professional practice, maintenance of the safety of life and property, and the prudent management of resources. Professional groups such as medical societies and nursing associations are among the many agencies outside the hospital which also have regulatory power over activities within it (cf. Table 12–1) [46].

Numerous reports, based on both research and random observation, offer rich evidence of ways in which the interpersonal environment of hospitals may differ on a cross-cultural basis. Variations in the character of interpersonal relations in hospitals appear in many cases to be associated with the political, religious, economic, family, age-sex, and status systems of each larger society as well as the prevailing conceptions of the nature of disease [32, 37, 78, 93, 196]. Glaser has reported a number of such examples and has devised a number of propositions to guide further research [93]. Utilizing a method similar but not identical to that of March and Simon [163], he lists six major classifications of hospital organization variables (inputs, organization, authority structure, performance of employees, relations between hospitals, and output). To these he relates determining nonmedical variables from religion, the family, economics, and urbanism. For example, he proposes that "the greater the number of religions in a society, . . . the more diffused the ownership and management of hospitals."

As one consequence of the close interrelationship between the internal system of the hospital and the complex of social institutions of the larger society outside, changes in one area might eventually lead to changes in the other. Thus, the patterning of roles within the hospital may alter as the functions of a major social institution alter. More specifically, it has been suggested that the roles of doctor and patient as well as the more general mission of the hospital are all sensitive to changes occurring in the family system [181]. As some of the functions of the American family have been transferred to outside agencies, the hospital has become an adjunct to the home, a center for therapeutic activities which for various reasons can no longer be carried out in the family setting. These large institutional changes have many implications for the structuring of the traditional roles of doctor, patient, nurse, and other participants in hospital systems.

An instance of direct association between the governmental institution and aspects of doctor-patient relationships may be seen in a report by Field on medical practice in the Soviet Union [78]. Doctors providing services for factory workers were required to conform to a quota system: At any particular time only a limited number of persons could be certified as being ill enough to be excused from their job. By this means, the Soviet state was able to assure that a work force of predictable size would always be available for service. This same system of regulation, however, constitutes an effort by government to define the limits of morbidity in a substantial segment of the population. Field reports that workers used various maneuvers and even subterfuges to persuade physicians that they were sufficiently ill to merit being excused from labor. On the other hand, the physicians themselves were constrained to keep within the quota by the prospect of being penalized. Consequently, the interaction of doctor and patient in some cases involves subtle interplay whose content is influenced by the political structure as well as by the usual interpersonal elements associated with the seeking and supplying of medical care [135].

Daniels provides another example in her comparison between the private and the military psychiatrist. She outlines the effect of the military organization on the decisions made by the professional [51]. The cosmopolitan-local frame of reference is utilized to distinguish between those military psychiatrists who persist in treating soldiers as clients and those who recognize that the organization (the Army) is their true client.[6]

Organizational patterns in the external environment are reflected in hospital structure. The team concept [19], for example, has been given wide currency in industry, government, the armed services, and educational institutions. It has also diffused into hospitals, particularly by departments of nursing. At one level, attempts to develop the team principle in the hospital may be seen as a reflection of the needs of the system for the effective organization of work. At the same time, however, the attempts appear to represent one form of adaptation to problems of labor shortages. Emphasis on the importance of teamwork in the hospital may serve as a device for attracting and holding workers, as it stresses the value of the individual (regardless of his formal occupational status) to the system.

[6] The reader is referred to Grusky and Miller for an overview of the basic organization-profession literature [105].

The Status System of the External Environment

Many of the influences upon interpersonal relations stemming from the external environment are inextricably intermeshed with social structural elements in the community. A formal organization such as the hospital must rely entirely upon the external environment for personnel. The hospital competes with other formal organizations for staff, since there are limits to the size of the population potentially available and optimally qualified for service. The size and character of this population varies on a regional basis, and there are some marked differences between communities as well [32, 254]. The processes in the external environment which operate to bring people into the institution are critical in that they determine who will participate in the interaction systems within the hospital.

Numerous links exist between the status system of the community and the structure and content of the interpersonal environment of the hospital. In many cases, for example, the relative prestige of a hospital and the type of financial support it receives are related to its being identified with a particular segment or stratum of the community [73]. This identification, in turn, has implications for the staffing of the institution at various occupational levels [72, 74]. The most prestigious and respected hospitals in a community may have relatively less difficulty than low-status institutions in attracting trustees, staff physicians, volunteer workers, and salaried employees.

Social status in the external community is also apparently related to position within the institution. Following an analysis by Hughes, Hall has observed:

> To a conspicuous degree, the hospital is so structured that it articulates neatly with the class structure of the community: the patrons are of upper class status, the functionaries belong to the professional group in society, and both act to help provide services for the clients who, by and large, belong to strata below both [110].

This statement is a more accurate portrayal of the voluntary hospital in the nineteenth century than it is of the modern prototype. The class origins of persons in professional groups in the hospital and those who are patients are not so distinctly at variance as is implied. The phenomenon is probably more marked in more traditional, more rigidly stratified societies than the United States. In India, for example, occupation within the institution is associated positively with the position of the individual in the caste system of the society. Further, there are caste restrictions upon both interpersonal contacts and upon kinds of tasks which can be performed [93].

The social, economic, and ideological changes which have led to burgeoning hospitalization insurance in the United States constitute another type of extra-hospital influence upon the ecology of patients and upon the structure of interaction situations. Decades ago there were two major categories of patients in many hospitals: A marked social gulf existed between the groups classified as "ward patients" and "private patients," reflected in part by differences in facilities, cuisine, and visiting privileges. The spread of hospitalization insurance, however, has served to reduce the number of "ward patients," and, in most general hospitals, patients of diverse social status in the community are located in close proximity. In a sense, the semiprivate room has become a melting pot of patients from diverse social backgrounds.

Hall, reporting on the multiple factors related to the appointment of particular physicians to particular hospitals in one community, indicates that considerations of ethnic origins, informal associations, and other types of social qualifications operate along with an evaluation of professional qualifications [109, 111]. On the basis of a study of Chicago hospitals, Solomon points out that "the ethnic and class segmentation and stratification of the city" play roles in determining access to particular hospital facilities. Thus, staff composition in part rests upon various social background characteristics including graduation from the "right" medical school, postgraduate training in the "right" type of hospital, and the sponsorship of key senior members of the staff [203, 233]. However, recent federal legislation has had some influence in this area. For example, successful legal actions have been filed not only on the basis of race but of geographic area of practice. Both have been cited as illegal barriers to membership on the medical staffs of participating hospitals [189].

In other ways as well, values of the community outside the hospital determine the nature of its internal social form. For example, in southern mental hospitals similar to one described by Belknap, patients have in the past been distributed to specific ward areas not only on the basis of official diagnosis but on the basis of such criteria as race and, to a lesser extent, age [17]. The fact that in the southern area of the United States, black and white hospital patients may be segregated is as much a product of community values as is the widespread segregation of adult patients by sex. In such instances, the standards of the external community rather than considerations of therapeutic potential are perhaps the more critical determinants of the nature of interaction systems.

Such practices came under attack with the changes brought about by Supreme Court rulings on racial segregation and civil rights. As late as 1970, however, some states still carried on their books, laws requiring separate facilities for the white and Negro races [189]. The minute detail with which such practices can be carried out is illustrated by the fact that as late as 1969 the state of Louisiana still had a law requiring that blood for transfusions be labeled as to whether its donor was Caucasian, Negroid, Mongoloid, etc. Potential recipients had the right to refuse blood which came from a donor of a different race [101].

Numerous studies, reports, and newspaper accounts have revealed the sometimes tragic and pathetic experiences of the disadvantaged in hospitals. Space is not adequate to deal with this matter here, and more ample references and descriptions may be found in works specifically concerned with the medical and hospital care of the poor and disadvantaged, e.g., Kosa, Antonovsky, Zola, and others [22, 97, 141, 183, 196, 241, 242, 258].

Research on social structural factors in the external system and their consequences for the character of the experience of patients in the hospital was originally focused on mental patients. On the basis of a large-scale investigation Hollingshead and Redlich point out the relationship between social-class origins and such elements as length of hospitalization, type of diagnosis, and the nature of the hospital in which the mental patient is treated [120]. A study of mental hospital patients in New York State was carried out by Hardt and Feinhandler as a partial replication of the Hollingshead-Redlich work, and it confirmed the general hypothesis that the social-class level of the patient is inversely related to the risk of continuous long-term hospitalization [112]. The specific context of staff and patient groups, the duration of contact of members, and the amount of therapeutic interaction of patients with physicians and psychiatrists also appear to vary, depending upon the segment of society from which the mental patient comes.

In their ten-year follow-up study of the patients in the Hollingshead-Redlich study group, Myers and Bean [172] reported that social-class differences continued to show a relationship to clinical status over time. Class continued to be inversely related to hospitalization (upper class had lower rates) at the end of the ten-year period. Further, this relationship was additive because chances of discharge were greater for higher-status persons and of those who were discharged, chances of readmission were as great or greater for lower-status persons. Methods of treatment were also correlated with social class. Adjustment to the community (in comparison to a control group) was also found to be generally inversely related to social class [172].

Roth and Eddy and Scott, in their separate studies of rehabilitation, also report concerning relationships between the treatment offered patients and their ties to the community social structure [214, 220]. According to these authors, patients with higher social status, those with professional ties to the health community, and those who had families willing and able to intercede for them with the health professionals received care which appeared more nearly to meet their expressed needs.

While hospital staff members perceive each other in terms of formal occupational characteristics, they also respond to one another according to their perceptions of each other's "latent social identities" [100]. Sexual, ethnic, class, and religious identities of staff members are attained outside the institution, and they are commonly proscribed as theoretically irrelevant to status in the hospital. But as Gouldner has demonstrated, latent social identities intrude upon and influence behavior in the organization in many ways. In the United States, the role performance of female physicians, for example, is often colored by problems involving these social identities [6, 20, 156, 268, 269, 273]. The relations of female doctors with their male peers, with subordinate workers, and with patients are complicated by the relative importance of female status as opposed to professional status. Comparable problems arise for female hospital administrators and for male nurses [62]. Glaser, in his cross-cultural studies [92, 93] has demonstrated that these differences may be culture specific and subject to manipulation over time. In some countries, male nurses have been the rule rather than the exception. Female doctors are far more common in other countries than they are in the United States, although top medical administrative positions are generally reserved for men [6, 78, 79, 93, 273].

The fact that status criteria of the external community can influence interaction patterns within the hospital has some direct implications for administrative attempts to manipulate the social milieu for therapeutic ends. Some effects of these extrahospital criteria have been explored in the context of formal groups of patients in mental hospital settings. In a study of a patient-government organization in two "open" psychiatric wards, Croog found that the degree of participation and the nature of the leadership structure were associated with educational level, occupational status, and ethnic origins [49]. This finding regarding participation is consistent with observations made in other types of settings, such as jury sessions [244].

In the situation of the "closed" wards of the mental hospital, however, it appears that other variables may be more highly associated with degree of participation. Rosenberg reports, for example, that in a patient-council group composed of seriously disturbed patients in the closed ward of a "total institution," participation had special appeal to low-status patients [209]. The organization was regarded by professional personnel as one instrument for counteracting severe withdrawal by patients. In a sense, patients were able to indicate their progress in recovery through demonstrating their social affiliative skills in the council. In this context, status criteria of the external community were apparently less salient than in the "open" ward milieu.

Cultural Subsystems and Differential Participation

In recent years it has become increasingly apparent that certain strains and difficulties in hospitals can be traced to differential participation in the larger society on the part of personnel. The origins of many problems involving mutual misunderstandings, failure in communication, and failure in the fulfillment of role expectations lie in the differential internalization of norms and values by members of various subcultural groups. Social interactions in the hospital may be profoundly influenced by the tendency of individuals to respond to similar stimuli in ways conforming to the social class, ethnic, or religious subcultures in which they have been socialized [23, 247].

Evidence from many sources indicates that the meaning of illness, evaluation of symptoms, and attitudes toward the hospital vary greatly among the societies of the world and among groups within a single society [48, 182, 217, 277, 279]. For example, Suchman reports in studies of ethnic groups in New York that their medical care orientation was linked to their "parochial" or "cosmopolitan" life orientations [246, 247]. Within the patient population of a hospital there may be found a number of distinctive conceptions of illness and sets of beliefs regarding behavior appropriate to the sick role. Thus, Zborowski discovered that Italian and Jewish patients in a Veterans Administration Hospital were far more expressive regarding their symptoms and suffering than were patients of Irish and "Old American" ethnic origins [277]. He concludes that variations in reaction to pain, attitudes toward disease, and perceptions of the physician may be linked to such elements as time-orientation among ethnic groups, child-rearing practices, and the configuration of the "ideal pattern" to which members of particular subcultural groups are expected to conform.

Various practical problems in quality of care can arise from differences in the value systems of hospital personnel and patients. For example, the patient who conforms to the norms of his own group by describing his symptoms in great detail may be regarded as a hypochondriac and a nuisance by doctors and nurses who were socialized in cultural settings where stoicism and a "stiff upper lip" are regarded as the intelligent responses to illness. They may prefer to deal with the patient down the hall who has exactly the same disease but who is silent and uncommunicative about his symptoms. In such a case the medications and routine therapeutic procedures prescribed for the two patients might by exactly the same; however, the quality of care received by each might be very different.

The Role of the Consumer

An important development of the late 1960's was the increased demand of consumers for a voice in the planning and delivery of health care. The bases for these new demands were many and complex. They have variously been ascribed to such factors as rising expectations, a revolt against an impersonal system, the effects of the mass media, prepaid health insurance, the demand for equal rights, and higher levels of education.

In the hospital setting this trend has been most evident in demands for (1) the provision of health care to surrounding neighborhoods or "catchment" areas and (2) strong representation of the "community" on governing boards. In both areas, the problems have been complex and difficult, complicated by the expertise mystique and by the credibility gap that frequently exists between the traditionally elite members of hospital boards and medical staffs and the newly vocal community members who are pressing for change [129].

The expertise mystique can be illustrated in part by the case of the planner who writes that the duty of the planner is to make those decisions which the client would make *if he had all the facts* [251]. Implicit in such professional judgment is the belief that the professional knows better than the client what is best for the client [24; but see also 210, 215]. Under such circumstances the client may be provided with certain services and denied others without being given any choice in the matter. The client may complain, as he is more frequently doing, or he may simply not use the services provided, thereby validating the idea that he does not know what is best for him [38, 57].

In many hospitals the trustees are

faced with serious dilemmas in meeting the various needs of physicians and consumers and the demands of third-party insurers, while at the same time acting as stewards of the hospital's resources [12, 70]. Where the community has become involved with setting goals and selecting the means for achieving those goals some widely varying results have emerged. For example, a large-scale project that had long-term support from a wide base of lay community leaders and health professionals and that was accompanied by educational efforts, feedback, etc. was judged a general success [88]. Another project involving a community advisory council (set up because of federal contract requirements) ran into difficulties because the institutional members (the university and the Office of Economic Opportunity) maintained full control. The citizens on the advisory council were caught between their concern for making inputs and their lack of knowledge of how to go about it [57]. Eventually, they succeeded in having a training program organized for themselves, but this had not been provided for in the initial planning. Several other reports in the literature indicate that where consumers have been allowed to establish health priorities, problems have arisen when these priorities have not matched those of the professionals [134]. Pressure for more formal participation of consumers as lay members of professional licensing boards is developing as another means of providing consumer input to health care systems [114, 144].

The Role of Government

The expanding role of government in the hospital has been a major feature of the past several decades [184, 255, 256, 257]. This has come about partly through the efforts of various groups [11, 102, 113, 138, 253, 258]. These include associations of health professionals, health care consumer organizations such as unions, and others who have turned to legislative solutions for medical care delivery problems [102, 115, 263]. An extended discussion of range and depth of governmental involvement is beyond the scope of this chapter; the interested reader is referred elsewhere in this handbook and to the works of Forgotson, Roemer, Newman, and others [80, 81, 149, 235]. Donabedian provides a historical chronology which demonstrates the interplay of private and public action in the development of medical care administration in the United States [63].

An indication of the kinds of governmental agencies that may be involved may be had by referring to Table 12–1. It has been reported that one hospital was required to make or submit to 105 reports or inspections by governmental agencies in a single year. This was in addition to 38 reports or inspections by voluntary agencies [192].

One other aspect of the interplay of government and hospitals is the part hospital personnel must play in law enforcement. Gunshot wounds, attempted suicides, bungled criminal abortions, drug abuse victims—all present prima facie evidence that a crime has been committed. The hospital is required by law to report such cases, sometimes creating a conflict between the medical ethos and legal requirements. And how the reporting is handled may vary with the social status of both hospital and client.

THE HOSPITAL AS A SOCIAL INSTITUTION: THE INTERNAL ENVIRONMENT

Formal Organization and Authority

The general hospital has been one of the most highly stratified and rigid of formal organizations. Like other large bureaucratic institutions, it works toward achieving its goals through reliance upon such structural devices as a complex system of division of labor, an elaborate hierarchy of authority, formal channels of communication, and sets of policies, rules, and regulations. Although arrangements in formal structure enable the institution to attain a relativly high degree of efficiency and speed in the performance of its major functions, at the same time those arrangements have multiple consequences.

In tracing the history of organizational control in one hospital, Perrow reported that it proceeded through four stages. These have relevance here as illustrating a type of development characteristic of other hospitals as well.

Trustee domination had its roots in the tradition of charity hospitals to serve the poor.
Medical domination developed as medical knowledge increased in quantity and complexity.
Administrative challenge was the result of increasing need for sound management practices and cost control.
Multiple leadership resulted from the effects of a power struggle between the three. This proved relatively ineffective in terms of long-range planning [186].

In the general hospital, as Smith has pointed out, a system of dual authority has been used as a basic device for controlling and directing the activities of diverse types of personnel [231]. One line of authority, the administrative one, runs from trustees down to hospital workers. The second is the line of professional authority, in which the primary power figures are the physicians. The system of professional authority has permitted the physician to exercise power throughout the hospital structure.

In her study of the professional medical staff of a large university teaching center, Goss suggested that in that setting, certain structural mechanisms are required to effect a working relationship between these forms of authority. She saw these as making up a semibureaucracy—partly representative and partly advisory in nature—with superiors having professional expertise and functions as well as administrative duties [99].

Inevitably, conflict between the two systems of authority permeates many aspects of hospital life. Lay and professional lines of authority come into conflict, for example, since they tend to have overlapping jurisdiction over certain areas and certain personnel. Each system is oriented to a different set of values, one emphasizing the maintenance of the operation of the organization, the other emphasizing the provision of service [145, 146].

Henry has also pointed out various consequences of certain administrative arrangements in hospitals, particularly in regard to the areas of interpersonal relations and communication [116, 117]. For example, where the authority system operates through multiple subordination, one worker is subject to directions from many chiefs, and certain powerful stresses result. The performance of tasks becomes complicated by problems of inconsistent orders, overlapping of responsibility, and inadequate coordination of activities. The difficulties stemming from structural arrangements become associated with interpersonal stresses, with the level of morale, with the attitudes of staff members toward one another, and ultimately with the quality of care received by patients [198].

In a report on administrative arrangements in the medical and surgical wards of a large general hospital, Coser illustrates ways in which two different types of authority structure affected role behavior and the relations of role groups with one another [44]. She points out that in the medical ward there was consistent delegation of authority downward through levels in the medical hierarchy. In the surgical section, there was little delegation of authority, and decision was made by fiat. One effect in the surgical ward, for example, was the development of a "colleague type of relationship between nurses and doctors." Since only little authority could be exercised by assistant surgical residents and interns, "they could not be consistently superior to the nurse," and this condition was associated with the development of relatively equalitarian relationships between resident, intern, and nurse.

A series of studies by Seeman and Evans represents one attempt to relate specific social structural features to the performance of medical tasks [222]. In one article, the authors conclude that the stratification system of the hospital does make a difference in medical performance. They report, for example, that "where staff stratification is low, the communication to and about the patient appears to be, relatively speaking, full and clear . . . and the teaching function is said to be well-performed. The reverse, of course, holds on the high stratification wards." Moreover, they remark that attitudes toward stratification on the part of the intern seem to be related to his performance in patient care. Thus, interns who appear to prefer highly stratified ward situations tend to be those who report spending less time than their fellows in giving psychological support to patients.

Duff and Hollingshead [65] identified four patterns of physician sponsorship of patients in the hospital—meaning by this the manner in which physicians exercised and/or delegated responsibility for the care of their patients. The first is "committee sponsorship," a type that is traditionally found on teaching wards. Medical care of a given patient is not supervised by a single physician but by a rotating group of physicians who are identified not with individual patients but with particular positions of responsibility in the school of medicine.

The other three forms are found on semiprivate and private floors. "Semicommittee sponsorship" is a step removed from committee sponsorship. The patient is nominally under the care of a private physician who admits and dismisses him, but his in-hospital care is supervised by the house staff. Neither the private physician nor the house staff consider this patient as their full responsibility, and the medical supervision reflects this lack.

"Casual sponsorship" is the term used to reflect a distant type of management exercised by the disease-oriented physician, one who treats the disease rather than the "whole patient." House staff are involved in such care in a purely technical sense, with the private physician exercising full primary authority, but little personal involvement.

"Committed sponsorship" involves "a determined assumption of responsibility for the patient by the physician" and represents a close type of physician-patient relationship. Duff and Hollingshead point out that while such a relationship has the best potential for the cooperation of patient and physician in the diagnosis and treatment of the patient's disease, it is also vulnerable to abuse by either party. In a few cases it has resulted in actual danger to the patient's health, as when patients pressed for and succeeded in getting treatments which may not have been entirely necessary considering their clinical status [65].

Formal Roles and Interpersonal Relations

The continuing operation of a complex organization such as a hospital is contingent upon the differentiation of tasks, the assignment of tasks to particular occupational groups, and the performance of those tasks by members of each group in a routine manner which fulfills the expectations of other personnel. Formal occupational roles serve to channel and control interaction in ways which assure that the major functions of the organization will be performed. At the same time they appear to divide the institution into groups with relatively distinctive associational patterns and frames of reference.

Goffman, alluding to the mental hospital as a type of "total institution," indicates the significant degree to which staff and patients live in separate social worlds [95]. Wessen has noted some consequences of the hierarchical structure in terms of the patterns of interaction which occur on the wards of one general hospital [267]. He reports that on the ward the doctor is three times more likely to speak to another physician than to a nurse, and his interaction with personnel in other occupational groups is minimal. Similarly, the frequency of conversational interaction of a nurse with other nurses on the ward is approximately twice that of a nurse with other types of co-workers. The channelizing of interaction among personnel of various occupational levels along the lines noted is assumed by numerous observers to have dysfunctional consequences for patient care. The flow of communication upward regarding the condition of patients and the effects of administrative policies is inhibited, and the social barriers between occupational groups may tend to limit the development of a team approach [19, 60, 153, 161, 201].

Along with patterns of limited interaction among hospital personnel of varying ranks, differential interaction involving members of the same occupational group is a common feature of large hospitals. Persons within the same status, who share common interests and often the same departmental affiliation, tend to affiliate themselves in formal groupings and cliques. For example, in line with this tendency, surgeons are most likely to have lunch with other surgeons in the hospital cafeteria, rather than with doctors in other specialties [33, 202, 267]. Patterns of differential association tend to promote solidarity within in-groups, and they may have numerous other functional consequences as well. However, they may at the same time constitute a type of divisive influence. The tendency of physicians in the same specialty to associate with one another may raise barriers against the informal exchange of information concerning patients, and thus may limit the opportunities for members of one specialty to maintain familiarity with the viewpoints, approaches, and technical advances in other fields.

Lack of conformity to role expectations constitutes one of the sources of interpersonal strain in hospitals, as it does in other types of institutions. Relations between staff members and patients are notably susceptible to stresses arising from this source. Persons in the various role groups of the hospital, as acculturated functionaries of the system, have explicit expectations in regard to patient behavior. But people who enter the hospital or clinic as patients, if they are aware of the formal requirements of the role, may be unwilling or unable for various reasons to conform. They are also likely to have differing conceptions of staff with which they come in contact [230, 262]. As Reader, Pratt, and Mudd have pointed out, differences in expectations may lead directly to difficulties and misunderstandings in relations between patients and staff, and this may be expressed in both manifest and covert ways [199]. Degree of conformity to role expectations is a particularly critical matter for patients in the mental hospital [155, 191]. At least one measure of improvement in the condition of mental patients consists of the evaluation of their capacity to conform to the role expectations of staff. Unless patients meet these expectations adequately, they may never be discharged.

The Professional in the Hospital Setting

The lodgement of control over the activities of the professional in the organization has been studied from various perspectives [91, 96, 140, 187]. In both mental and general hospitals this control has been described as more complicated than might appear from the organization charts. (See Strauss et al., Stanton and Schwartz, Roth, Sudnow, Duff and Hollingshead, etc. [15, 213, 238, 243, 249].) While formal rules and professional protocols exist, what actually takes place in hospitals between administration, medical staff, nursing staff, other professionals, semiprofessionals and nonprofessionals and clients is a matter of negotiation (overt) and influence (covert negotiation) [13, 28, 153, 272].

Hughes [123] has suggested that it is a common characteristic of occupations to attempt to hand down the less desirable tasks (the dirty work) to persons of lower status. One of the common ways of examining the hospital hierarchy is to view the proliferation of occupations and professions as a sort of "network" of clean work ascription and dirty work assignation. This network in part has been made possible by (1) the many advances in technology and (2) the shortage of professional people to do the work [122, 179, 254, 255].

Newly discovered treatments and diagnostic procedures are carried out at first only by top level professionals. As the procedure becomes better understood and codification becomes possible (i.e., decisions about the procedure become predictable rather than problematic), the procedure can be delegated to a lower skill level [41, 52, 272].

It has often been observed that individual departments, units, and professional groups in hospitals vie with one another for increased recognition, new privileges, and for more advantageous positions in the power system [125]. Some of the stresses have been associated with the pressures for change exerted by so-called emergent professions. It is widely known, for example, that changes in the role of nursing and social work departments have been accompanied by periods of resentment and stress [13]. Macgregor, in attempting to account for the "dim view" taken by a "great many physicians" toward recent trends in nursing, remarks that "some see it as an attempt by nurses to usurp some of the doctor's functions or to become pseudo-physicians" [107, 159]. Wilson, in discussing changes in the traditional role of the physician in the hospital, has shown that the rise of hospital administration to the status of a profession has resulted in strains and in readjustments in the nature of work and authority relationships between doctors and administrators [68, 168, 271].

This problem is exacerbated by such

developments as the proliferation of intensive care units (cardiac care units, respiratory care units, kidney dialysis units, etc.) [178]. On these special units, as throughout the hospital to a lesser degree, for many years nurses have been performing acts that are legally medical in nature. The degree to which this is done tends to vary with such factors as the size of the hospital, the complexity of its medical organization, and the availability of house officers and medical students. In recent years the American Hospital Association, the American Medical Association, and the American Nursing Association, through their state bodies, have joined forces to define the terms under which nurses may perform these acts [131]. However, in a presentation before a legislative committee in California, the California Nurses Association had this to say about the continuing ambiguities of the role of the nurse in the cardiac care unit:

> Although she is assigned specific nursing responsibilities, she functions as a team member in patient care. The unique role of the nurse and her status on the team need to be clarified with medical staff to avoid friction which may develop because many of her new responsibilities are medical therapies which were formerly seen as responsibilities delegated to the physician's role on the team [240].

Engel studied physicians' self-perceptions of autonomy in settings exhibiting different degrees of bureaucracy. She found support for her hypothesis that a moderate degree of bureaucracy facilitates the autonomous practice of medicine by providing the physician with access to expensive equipment, specialized technicians, and consultants which the solo practitioner could not afford. There can be too much bureaucracy, however, and physicians in highly bureaucratized settings considered themselves less autonomous in their clinical practice than either solo or moderately bureaucratic physicians. This situation was reversed when opportunities for clinical research were examined. In this study highly bureaucratized physicians reported the greatest autonomy and moderately bureaucratized physicians, the least, as far as clinical research was concerned [75].

On the basis of other studies [65, 84], it may be postulated that the moderately bureaucratized physician is also more free of the pressures exerted by clients on solo practitioners. That is, in addition to providing facilities and services, the moderately bureaucratic setting protects the physician from client pressures and provides a regular income and regular hours. In return for *this* freedom, the physician gives up his right to practice in private; i.e., his practice is visible to and subject to review by his colleagues [70, 71].

The roles of the various professions and occupations in the hospital setting are often a matter of legal definition, and like other legal interpretations, they alter through challenge in the courts [80, 81, 113, 189]. Both medical and nursing journals, as well as the hospital administration journals, maintain legal columns which attempt to keep their readers abreast of these decisions. The legal provisions written into Medicare and Medicaid served to further circumscribe professional autonomy.

As Smith has pointed out in reference to the phenomenon of "blocked mobility," the hospital consists of a series of relatively discrete occupational groups. Personnel cannot be promoted from one occupational status level to another [231]. Movement from one level to another can be accomplished only if an individual in one group leaves the system, obtains training outside, and reenters at a different level. Occupational groups tend to be discrete from one another, not only in terms of function but in their patterns of association, in their values, and in their perceptions of the institution and of each other.

Increasing concern with the effect of such blocking on the recruitment and retention of qualified health workers has led to a number of proposals for "unblocking." Opposition to this upward mobility by the professions who feel threatened by it is being overcome by increasing recognition that without such programs, it will be impossible to meet the needs of the patient population [47]. Proposed solutions range from "the professionalization of everyone" to the construction of a single health career ladder, with rungs designated in serial fashion like civil service ratings [268]. Glaser reports that the latter system is being used in Russia [93]. One point of view, as expressed by Darley, Eisele, and others is that the increasing responsibility of the hospital organization for the performance of both its employed workers and its medical staff will force the development of some kind of ongoing proficiency rating scheme [53, 54, 70, 232]. Where authority rests so heavily on expertise, and blame is determined by authority, expertise can no longer be taken as "given" but must be subject to regular review. The means of providing such review has led to considerable controversy. Most palatable to the professions themselves are peer review and/or license renewal contingent on evidence of continuing postgraduate education. Both of these, of course, rely on the professionals to police themselves—something that consumers appear to find increasingly unsatisfactory [84].

Informal Organization

Side by side with the formal organizational structure of hospitals there exists informal organization, an apparently universal component of complex social systems. Informal organization has norms, goals, leadership structure, and traditions of its own. It is characterized by intimate relationships and normative controls, and it may support or subvert organizational functioning and the achievement of formal goals. Informal organization constitutes a network of relationships of considerable size and complexity, and it has long been recognized as constituting a powerful influence in bureaucratic systems [14, 152, 164, 165].

Hospital studies dealing with aspects of informal organization have typically focused upon its implications for therapy. In the case of the mental hospital, as Caudill and others have demonstrated, membership by patients in cliques which are antagonistic to the institution can do much to negate the therapeutic aims of the institution [36]. In his report on a state mental hospital, Belknap has illustrated ways in which individual ward areas in one state mental hospital are controlled through informal punishment and reward systems by the psychiatric attendants [17]. Patients who wish to avoid electric shock therapy and who wish to move toward discharge from the hospital behave in terms of an awareness that the immediate power figure whom they must please is the ward attendant. This apparent usurpation of power by the attendants occurs even though the formal regulations of the hospital dictate that decisions regarding therapy and discharge are the responsibility of staff psychiatrists. In this case, informal organization in the wards operates in ways which are at variance with the formal program of methods and goals laid out by the hospital. Similar processes have been noted by others [218].

The functioning of informal organization in the context of the general hospital has been subjected to extensive analysis by Fox [82]. In the small metabolic ward where she carried out her research, patients suffered from chronic and debilitating diseases which were only imperfectly understood and only partially controllable by physicians at the time. The patients were the objects of research and experiment, and the character of life in the ward was influenced to a considerable extent by universal recognition of the seriousness of the diseases and the uncertain outcome of therapy. In this context, informal organization among patients played an important role in enabling individuals to come to terms with their precarious life chances. Patients shared a deep mutual commitment and interest in one another, and they utilized as means of stress reduction a number of socially patterned responses, such as shared humor, prayer, friendly competition for recognition as a distinctive case, and the development of close, colleague type relations with their physicians. So integrated and close-knit was this group that for some patients it served at least partially to impede the formal therapeutic goals of the ward. Some became reluctant to leave and to adjust anew to life on the outside, and some suffered severely when the condition of another member of the ward community took a negative turn.

Tenure and the Turnover Within Role Groups

When it is viewed as a total social system, the hospital can be seen as a structure through which various personnel groups move at differing rates of speed. The degree of stability differs within such major categories of personnel as trustees, physicians, nurses, patients, and business office workers. Hospitals, like other large organizations, may be characterized as consisting of (1) a "core group" of relatively stable personnel with a high degree of commitment to the institution and (2) a highly transient population which in many ways is distinctive in orientation, commitment, and life goals. The core group in the nursing population of hospitals has sometimes been described as the "home guard" [86, 124].

Although rates of turnover have been reported for individual institutions, most studies have focused on turnover rates for specific occupations, particularly those of the professional nurse, the aide, and the attendant [61, 151]. Stability in job tenure has been found to be associated with a number of variables. High turnover rates are most commonly evident in large hospitals, particularly those with schools of nursing. Turnover is greatest among nurses in the youngest age groups, and rates for staff nurses exceed those for supervisory personnel. High occupancy rates and low staff-patient ratios appear to be positively associated with high rates of voluntary turnover among the professional nurses [61]. This latter finding suggests that the amount of pressure placed on the nurse may be a factor in her decision to terminate her employment. (See also [86, 142, 174, 176, 254, 275].)

Personnel flow has at least several major effects upon the nature of interpersonal relations. It has important influence upon the quality of relationships in that it may hinder the development of primary-group feeling among ward workers. Personnel in areas of high turnover must devote more effort toward integrating their activities than those in areas where long-established relationships exist and where sets of mutual expectations are well established. In the general hospital the workers who have most contact with patients are usually at the junior levels of the nursing staff, and it is in this group that a high proportion of turnover occurs. Consequently, patients constantly come into contact with workers who are still in the process of learning the norms and values of the hospital.

Flow and turnover are basic to the life process of organizations. Nevertheless, because job instability and geographic mobility appear inordinately high in certain employee groups, there is widespread concern among hospital administrators and leaders in the nursing profession about the impact of turnover upon the effective operation of hospitals and the providing of optimal patient care.

Hospitals and Individual Subcultural Systems

Each institution has an individual history, sets of formal regulations and informal customs, and a fabric of traditions and folklore which render it distinctive. Further, individual departments, subdepartments, units, and subunits may develop traditions and customs of a sort which cause them to appear as microcosmic cultural systems within larger systems. To some extent, each is characterized by a jargon or a code language of its own, and new staff members must learn the special meanings of these words as they become enculturated [17, 33, 67, 197]. The use of this jargon also has serious implications for communication with the patient population, who normally have less time to learn it [16, 190, 195, 216, 230].

One trait common to the culture of hospitals is the informal system of classifying patients. Patients are commonly evaluated by various levels of staff in terms of such characteristics as manageability, personality traits, types of disease or disability, and their potential interest as teaching material. Thus, in a teaching hospital the patient with the rare disease or mysterious disorder often stands in a high position in the hierarchy of ratings, and the patient who is considered a "crock" occupies a low position. In the mental hospital, the degree of manageability of the patient is an especially important criterion in informal ratings [17, 207, 264]. Long before student nurses and medical students enter the hospital for training, they are aware of the value system relating to patients and have begun to internalize it [167]. The differential evaluation of patients is often reflected in specific behavior patterns on the ward, and the relationships of "crocks" with staff members are likely to be distinctive from those experienced by the more highly rated types of patients.

As in the case of the larger cultural systems of which they are a part, the individual cultures of hospitals are characteristically marked by conflicts in values. Many of these value conflicts are reflected in problems of interpersonal behavior, and they may have direct implications for the administrative management of patients. Rapoport, in his report on a planned mental hospital community, deals at length with problems of values and the multiple implications of conflict between them [197]. For example, in the hospital which he studied, "permissiveness" was a major theme. A number of hospital policies were based on the assumption that reduction of bureaucratic restrictions and the encouraging of expression by patients would have certain therapeutic, diagnostic, and rehabilitative benefits. At the same time, the staff of the hospital remained legally responsible for the safety of patients and property, as well as for the orderly maintenance of the organization. Thus, there were necessary and real limits to permissiveness. Situations were constantly arising in which administrative and system maintenance values came into conflict with the permissiveness value. Autocratic administrative action then became necessary to reinstate controls.

As in the case of other cultural systems, some of the customs which are frequently practiced in hospitals are essentially contradictory and even nonrational in nature. For instance, in tuberculosis hospitals, sets of regulations based on an elaborate belief system prescribed procedures for controlling contagion through the use of protective clothing and masks. However, in at least one hospital, the incidence of use of such clothing by staff members in contact with patients appeared to be related to occupational status levels and to the nature of the interaction. Staff members of high rank were particularly likely to avoid wearing gowns and masks. Moreover, the wearing of protective clothing by a staff member appeared to be related in part to whether or not the interaction involved formal business or informal socializing [212].

Some procedures of a ritual nature were also found in an operating room, where custom rather than fact was found to determine whether certain items were considered sterile or contaminated [170]. Similarly, nurses aides and orderlies, by tradition, have not always participated in change of shift reports, although they see more of the patient than most of the rest of the staff.

A number of reports comment on the classifications and assumptions made by staff about patients and patients about staff on the basis of dress, observed behavior, speech, habits of hygiene, manners, etc. [190]. Confusion caused by the wrong interpretation of these cues is the subject of cautionary tales told by patients and staff alike. This occurs not only in mental institutions [94] but in general hospitals as well. Every hospital has its tale of the man who dressed like a doctor and (1) being a patient, left the hospital without permission or (2) being a thief, absconded with drugs or equipment or records. Similar stories are told of patients mistakenly admitted to wards or private rooms or prepared for surgery by mistake on the basis of some nonverbal cue.

While distinctions such as the above may be unwitting, both patients and staff also consciously use nonverbal cues to attempt to influence the behavior of others. Patients will deliberately "put on a good face" or, conversely, try to "look peaked." Medical students are notorious for the number of "doctor" tools they display in their pockets. In the days before drip-dry fabrics, nurses could be ranked by the amount of starch in their uniforms. Surgeons have been known to put on scrub suits to visit the patient units, giving the impression that they had just left surgery when this was not the case [249].

In their efforts to obtain information, patients may make elaborate interpretations of looks, tones of voice, and casual or unguarded words on the part of hospital staff. They do this with all the care and attention to detail of a top diplomatic mission [45, 219]. One study, using a noise meter and recorded medication data, reports a relationship between requests for pain medication and noise levels in a postoperative recovery room. The noise of casual conversations among staff was found to be positively correlated with requests for medication [169].

The existence of linkage between personality type and particular forms of interaction or social structure is widely assumed by hospital personnel. Thus, social scientists carrying out research in general hospitals may be informed that the personality of the head nurse sets the tone of a ward. Or they may be informed by physicians that the way to understand the institution is to study the character of the chiefs of the various professional services, for the chiefs determine the nature of the organization. Widespread stereotypes exist which portray doctors as independent, individualistic people. Such traits are presumed to limit their capacity for being integrated into the ward team and are presumed to make them rebellious against administrative regulation [33]. There are also widely disseminated stereotypes, of psychiatric tinge, which portray such specialists as surgeons, pediatricians, obstetricians, and proctologists as each having differing kinds of unconscious needs.

A common bit of folklore circulated among employees themselves is that hospital people are "different" from those who work in other types of settings. When expressed by a sympathetic observer, this usually refers to an assumption that those who choose to work in hospitals are somehow more sympathetic, altruistic, and humane than workers in industry or in business [262]. As in the case of much folklore and stereotyping, beliefs about personality types and patterns often form the justification and basis for behavior on the part of members of various role groups of the hospital [126]. For example, as Merton has pointed out, in their choice of future medical specialty, medical students are influenced in some degree by their beliefs regarding modal personality among such varied specialists as surgeons, internists, and psychiatrists [167].

On the whole, attempts at delineating personality characteristics of particular groups of hospital personnel have represented one portion of larger studies seeking to examine personality in relation to such elements of organizational life as job satisfaction, task performance, or ideological commitment. For example, personality characteristics of attendants in mental hospitals have been the subject of research. Studies carried out by Gilbert, Levinson, and Pine have been concerned in part with the investigation of relationships between the ideology of the attendant regarding the nature of mental illness and regarding the aims and policies of the hospital and certain aspects of his personality. One segment of the research effort centered on the association between "authoritarian" or "equalitarian" personality types and the holding of distinctive ideologies which the authors characterize as "custodialism" and "humanism" [89]. They found a significant association between custodial ideology and personal authoritarianism as measured by the "F" scale. A study by Carstairs and Heron in a British mental hospital replicated the American research in part, reaching conclusions which differed in a number of respects but which pointed in the same general direction [34].

Personality of the Patient, Disease Syndrome, and Interpersonal Relations

Turning to the influence of the personality of the patient upon the hospital interpersonal environment, issues of a somewhat different order may be seen. The hypothesis that certain model personalities or personality profiles are associated with particular ailments has stimulated much research on the relations between emotional state and physical illness of disability. The question of which personality characteristics are associated with particular illnesses is currently the subject of much controversy, and the optimum mode of conceptualizing the particular pattern has yet to be determined [227]. Nevertheless, research in psychosomatic medicine has provided increasingly strong evidence of apparent linkage between disease type and personality type [3, 26, 66]. Such findings have many implications for the understanding of the structure and emotional tone of interpersonal relations involving patients and hospital personnel. For example, if patients with peptic ulcers do indeed exhibit marked dependency traits, as has often been suggested in the psychiatric literature, then it is likely that the emotional tone of the interaction systems in which such patients participate will be distinct from those in which patients with other types of personality structure take part.

One aspect of the patient role which has been the subject of recent research and theoretical commentary is the nature of response to illness and the ward situation. The entrance of professional and paramedical workers into their occupational roles is largely a "voluntary" one, while entrance into the role of patient is determined by social definition as well as by physiological, affective, and cognitive processes within the person who becomes ill. The patient enters the hospital with a set of conceptions regarding the institution, the personnel, his illness, and his body. His experiences in the institution and his subjective perception of those experiences help to determine the nature of his conduct in situations of interpersonal relations [82, 179, 221, 227].

Entrance into the patient role is often accompanied by many shades of stress and anxiety. Moving into the alien atmosphere of the hospital away from the familiar things of home and family represents one sort of strain [250]. The requirements of adopting the dependent, infantilized behavior patterns which may be forced upon adults who become hospital patients represent another. Besides those stresses involving unfamiliar social setting and role, many hospital patients must deal with dangers to life itself. Cancer, heart disease, and the host of other ailments with potentially terminal consequences are real and frightening entities which can stimulate primitive psychological response. Even minor ailments can have threatening and anxiety-laden aspects whose consequences can be as serious as those associated with major illnesses.

The contingencies of unconscious processes upon the structure and content of interation involving patients are many. For example, as Dunbar has pointed out: "... the meaning of disease varies according to the personality strutcure. For some patients it will activate a well-concealed neurotic or psychotic trend and for others it may seem a happy solution to a situation of intolerable stress" [66]. The course of convalescence may be profoundly influenced by the emergence of differing types of defenses which have been developed in early life. On superficial observation these defenses might appear to be rational responses to the ward situation. But complaints about treatment or expressions of well-being on the part of patients may depend not so much on the real character of the ward as upon the way in which the realities are perceived by the patient and the ways in which they mesh with his unconscious needs [66].

In an article on psychiatric aspects of medical practice in a general hospital, Bibring reviews the types of behavior patterns exhibited by four patients with tuberculosis. These patterns constitute modes of adjustment to stress, and they had been developed by each patient over the course of his life. Though all are suffering from the same physical disease, each patient brings to the ward situation distinctive techniques for handling anxiety. To ward personnel and to fellow patients, one of the four would seem overconcerned and worrying, another would appear self-willed and independent, and so forth [21]. An intensive psychoanalytic study of the reactions of a woman who experienced surgery was carried out by Janis, and one area of research interest was the relationship between the patient and the surgeon [128]. It was seen that the patient's postoperative perceptions of her relationship with the surgeon were linked to unconscious components such as her emotional dependency and certain regressive reactions heightened by the stress situation.

A somewhat different approach to the study of patients in the hospital social system has been to view the hospital experience as part of the patient's illness career [94]. Socialization models and learning theory are then used as frameworks for explaining patient interaction with the physical and psychosocial environment. Most of the work in this area has involved patients with long-term handicapping diseases. F. Davis's report on polio patients, Cogswell's work with paraplegics, and Roth's on tuberculosis patients are examples of what has been done in this area [40, 55, 213]. These authors identify career stages within the hospital setting that fit in with the larger illness career pictures being developed through the work reported by Suchman and by Croog, Levine and Lurie, and others [50, 248]. The validation of these models and Janis's anticipatory fear model, through attempts to manipulate the patients' experience, have been the subject of a number of reports in the medical and nursing literature as well as in sociological journals [69, 127, 128, 175, 204, 220, 221, 229].

The patient career concept has been used by Rosengren and Lefton in a somewhat different fashion. They postulate a fourfold categorization of hospital orientation to patients in terms of laterality (social space) and longitudinality (social time). Laterality is used to distinguish between hospitals whose interest in the patient is disease specific, e.g., the emergency room and those which have a commitment to the total patient, e.g., a psychiatric hospital. Longitudinality refers to the temporal length of involvement, i.e., short-term (acute) and long term (chronic). It is their belief supported by considerable theoretical discussion that these distinctions are far more useful than the more traditional ones of functions and control cited earlier in this chapter [210].

Unconscious Mechanisms and Social Process: Insights From Mental Hospital Settings

In recent years a number of social scientists have been exploring some of the relationships between unconscious mechanisms and structured social behavior in the hospital. The bulk of this work has been carried out in mental hospital settings rather than in the general hospital or in other types of medical settings. One conceptual product to which many authors have contributed is the delineation of the phenomenon of "collective disturbance." In periods of such disturbance, feelings of unrest and agitation sweep through a ward area and sometimes throughout an entire hospital. These feelings are communicated in considerable part by affective, nonverbal means. Although the origins of such feelings are obscure, their effects are obvious, and such episodes represent a major problem for management [35, 238]. Their regular patterning has led at least one observer to characterize them as "oscillations" [197]. In many mental hospitals recognition of a shift by patients toward the manic side is often given expression in such comments by staff members as "The ward is high today."

On the basis of his study of a small psychiatric ward, Caudill points out that primitive instinctual behavior of mental patients can become accepted and integrated into the ward social system [35]. Consequently, the social subsystem in which patients participate may come to contain elements of insulated regressive behavior which can frustrate the purposes of formal organization. Caudill has also postulated the existence of "covert emotional structure" which underlies overt formal and informal structure in the hospital. Stanton and Schwartz have developed a "staff consensus" hypothesis, which holds that periods of disagreement among staff members of a mental hospital will tend to lead to episodes of disturbed behavior among patients [238].

The exact nature of these phenomena remains to be clarified and tested through replication in multiple settings, not only in psychiatric hospitals but in general hospitals as well. At least one recent attempt at testing a version of the Stanton-Schwartz hypothesis on staff consensus has been made [265]. This yielded essentially negative results, for the authors could find no significant statistical relationship between the direction of change in staff consensus concerning the individual mental patient and the direction of change in the level of disturbance in the patient. However, further work can be expected which will explore the dimensions of the influences of unconscious processes upon interaction in hospital settings.

CONCLUSION

In this chapter we have attempted to use a broad frame to portray some selected features of the hospital as a social institution. In particular, the concern has been with the nature of the internal structure, interrelationships of the internal system with elements in the external environment, and some relationships between personality systems and the internal system. Some aspects of movement and flow of personnel through the system have been considered, and in at least a rudimentary way, we have indicated some features of this structure moving through time and in the context of larger social changes. Some of the more decisive changes that may most significantly alter American hospitals over future years have been those in the external environment, including the developing interest of the consumer in management and the pervasive influence of government upon major dimensions of hospital functions, including self-maintenance, therapy, teaching, and research.

Though the hospital is in many ways a unique organization, much of the theory and findings which emerge from hospital studies have direct application for the understanding of other types of formal organizations and social systems. Similarly, the many developments in studies of other types of organizations can enrich understanding of the hospital. Moreover, the hospital is important as a core element in the health care system and as a formal organization worthy of study in its own right. Yet, reviewing the work of the past two decades, a case can easily be made that the creative work of the 1950's, based chiefly on mental hospital studies, has provided innovative studies which only with distinctive exceptions have been equaled in the succeeding decade. Hence, it seems desirable still to press for creative approaches, for continued movement beyond repetitive studies in the same narrow lines, for movement beyond ethnocentrism into cross-national and cross-cultural research, and for further work on the complex interactions between personality, internal systems, and the larger sociocultural environment. From such work there will emerge a body of empirical material which, hopefully, will stimulate more sophisticated theory about the hospital as a social system and, equally important, more sophistication and innovation in hospital planning and management.

REFERENCES

1. Advisory Commission on Intergovernmental Relations, *Intergovernmental Problems in Medicaid.* Washington, D.C., September, 1968.
2. ALEXANDER, FRANZ, ed., *Psychosomatic Medicine.* New York: W. W. Norton & Company, Inc., 1950.
3. ALEXANDER, L., "Medical Science Under Dictatorship," *New England Journal of Medicine*, 241 (July, 1949), 39–47.
4. ALPERT, JOEL J., JOHN KOSA, ROBERT J. HAGGERTY, LEON ROBERTSON, AND MARGARET C. HEAGARTY, "The Types of Families That Use an Emergency Clinic," *Medical Care*, 7 (January–February, 1969), 55–61.
5. American Hospital Association, *Classification of Health Care Institutions.* Chicago, 1968 ed.
6. American Medical Women's Association, *Conference on Meeting Medical Manpower Needs: The Fuller Utilization of the Woman Physician.* Washington, D.C., 1968.
7. AMMER, DEAN S., "Hospital-Operated Nursing School No Guarantee of Full Staff, Study Shows," *Hospitals*, 42 (May 1, 1968), 55–57.
8. ANDERSEN, RONALD AND JOHN HULL, "Hospital Utilization and Cost Trends in Canada and the United States," *Health Services Research*, 4 (Fall, 1969), 198–222.
9. ANDERSON, ODIN W., "Compulsory Medical Care Insurance, 1910–1950," *Annals American Academy of Political and Social Sciences*, 273 (January, 1951), 106–13.
10. AVNET, HELEN HERSHFIELD, *Physician Service Patterns and Illness Rates: A Research Report on Medical Data Retrieved from Insurance Records.* New York: Health Insurance, 1967.
11. BADGLEY, ROBIN F. AND SAMUEL WOLFE, *Doctors Strike: Medical Care and Conflict in Saskatchewan.* New York: Atherton Press, Inc., 1967.
12. BAILEY, DAVID R., "A Future Course for Boards of Trustees," *Hospital Administration*, 14 (Fall, 1969), 76–89.
13. BAKER, CONSTANCE AND MARLENE KRAMER, "To Define or Not to Define: The Role of the Clinical Specialist," *Nursing Forum*, 9 (1970), 41–45.
14. BARNARD, CHESTER, *The Functions of the Executive.* Cambridge: Harvard University Press, 1938.
15. BAUERSCHMIDT, ALAN D., "The Hospital as a Prototype Organization," *Hospital Administration*, 15 (Spring, 1970).
16. BAZIAK, ANNA TERESA AND ROBERT KNOX DENTON, "The Language of the Hospital and Its Effects on the Patient," *ETC: A Review of General Semantics*, 17 (September, 1960), 261–68. Reprinted in J. K. Skipper and Robert C. Leonard, eds., *Social Interaction and Patient Care.* Philadelphia: J. B. Lippincott Co., 1965, pp. 272–77.
17. BELKNAP, IVAN, *Human Problems of a State Mental Hospital.* New York: McGraw-Hill Book Company, 1956.
18. BELLIN, SEYMOUR S., H. J. GEIGER, AND COUNT D. GIBSON, "Impact of Ambulatory Health-Care Services on the Demand for Hospital Beds," *New England Journal of Medicine* (April 10, 1969).
19. BELOFF, J. S. AND MARION WILLET, "Yale Studies in Family Health Care, No. 3—The Health Care Team," *Journal of the American Medical Association*, 205 (September 2, 1968), 663–69.
20. BESHIRI, PATRICIA H., *The Woman Doctor: Her Career in Modern Medicine.* New York: Cowles Book Company, Inc., 1969.
21. BIBRING, GRETE L., "Psychiatry and

Medical Practice in a General Hospital," *New England Journal of Medicine*, 254 (February 23, 1956), 366–72.

22. Bithell, J. F., "A Survey of In-Patients of a London Teaching Hospital: General Results," *British Journal of Preventive and Social Medicine*, 23 (1969), 101–5.
23. Blackwell, Barbara Louise, "Upper Middle Class Expectations about Entering the Sick Role for Physical and Psychiatric Dysfunctions," *Journal of Health and Social Behavior*, 8 (June, 1967).
24. Blau, Peter M. and W. Richard Scott, *Formal Organizations*. San Francisco: Chandler Publishing Company, 1962.
25. Blishen, Bernard, *Doctors and Doctrines: The Ideology of Medical Care in Canada*. Toronto: University of Toronto Press, 1969.
26. Bockoven, J. Sanbourne, "Some Relationships Between Cultural Attitudes Toward Individuality and Care of the Mentally Ill: An Historical Study," in Milton Greenblatt, Daniel J. Levinson, and Richard H. Williams, eds., *The Patient and the Mental Hospital*. New York: The Free Press, 1957, pp. 517–26.
27. Bodenheimer, Thomas S., "Regional Medical Programs: No Road to Regionalization," *Medical Care Review*, 26 (December, 1969), 1125–66.
28. Breytspraak, Linda M. and Louis R. Pondy, "Sociological Evaluation of the Physician's Assistants' Role Relations," *Group Practice* (March, 1969), 32–41.
29. Brown, Esther Lucille, *Newer Dimensions of Patient Care, Part 2—Improving Staff Motivation and Competence in the General Hospital*. New York: Russell Sage Foundation, 1962.
30. Brown, Howard J., "Planning for Rational Organization of Urban Health Services: The Health Services Administration of New York City," *Medical Care*, 5 (1969).
31. Bunker, John P., "Surgical Manpower: A Comparison of Operations and Surgeons in the United States and in England and Wales," *New England Journal of Medicine*, 282 (January 15, 1969), 135–44.
32. Bureau of Labor Statistics, *Industry Wage Survey, Hospitals, July 1966*, Bulletin No. 1553, Washington, D.C.: Government Printing Office, 1967.
33. Burling, Temple, Edith M. Lentz, and Robert N. Wilson, *The Give and Take in Hospitals*. New York: G. P. Putnam's Sons, 1956.
34. Carstairs, G. M. and Alastair Heron, "The Social Environment of Mental Hospital Patients: A Measure of Staff Attitudes," in Milton Greenblatt, Daniel J. Levinson, and Richard H. Williams, eds., *The Patient and the Mental Hospital*. New York: The Free Press, 1957, pp. 218–29.
35. Caudill, William, "Around the Clock Patient Care in Japanese Psychiatric Hospitals: The Role of the Tsukisoi," *American Sociological Review*, 26 (April, 1961), 204–14.
36. ———, *The Psychiatric Hospital as a Small Society*. Cambridge: Harvard University Press, 1958.
37. Coe, Rodney M., *Sociology of Medicine*. New York: McGraw-Hill Book Company, 1970.
38. ——— and Albert F. Wesson, "Social-Psychological Factors Influencing the Use of Community Health Resources," *American Journal of Public Health*, 55 (July, 1965), 1024–31.
39. Coggeshall, Lowell T., *Planning for Medical Progress through Education*. Report to Education Committee, Association of American Medical Colleges (April, 1965).
40. Cogswell, Betty E., "Some Structural Properties Influencing Socialization," *Administrative Science Quarterly*, 13 (December, 1968), 417–40.
41. Connelly, John P., John D. Stoeckle, Edna Shepper, and Ruth M. Farrisey, "The Physician and the Nurse—Their Inter-Professional Work in Office and Hospital Ambulatory Settings," *New England Journal of Medicine*, 275 (October 6, 1966), 765–69.
42. Contini, B., "Threats and Organizational Design," *Behavioral Science*, 12 (November, 1967), 453–62.
43. Cordice, John W. V., Jr., Chairman. "Community Participation and National Health Policy," 1970 Annual Health Conference, *New York Academy of*

Medicine Bulletin, 46(December, 1970), entire issue.
44. COSER, ROSE LAUB, "Authority and Decision-Making in a Hospital," *American Sociological Review*, 23 (February, 1958), 36–63.
45. ———, *Life in the Ward*, East Lansing, Mich.: Michigan State University Press, 1962.
46. Council on Medical Education, American Medical Association, *Directory of Accredited Allied Medical Educational Programs*, 1969–70.
47. CREECH, D., JR., "Presidential Address: The Surgical Residency Revisited," *Annals of Surgery*, 166 (September, 1967), 301–11.
48. CROOG, SYDNEY H., "Ethnic Origins, Educational Level, and Response to a Health Questionnaire," *Human Organization*, 20 (Summer, 1961), 65–69.
49. ———, "Patient Government—Some Aspects of Participation and Social Background on Two Psychiatric Wards," *Psychiatry*, 19 (May, 1956), 203–7.
50. ———, SOL LEVINE, AND ZIFRE LURIE, "The Heart Patient and the Recovery Process: A Review of the Directions of Research on Social and Psychological Factors," *Social Science and Medicine*, 2 (1968), 111–64.
51. DANIELS, ARLENE K., "The Captive Professional: Bureaucratic Limitations in The Practice of Military Psychiatry," *Journal of Health and Human Behavior*, 10 (December, 1969), 255–65.
52. DARLEY, WARD, "Allied Health Personnel and Their Employment for the Improvement of Medical Care," *New England Journal of Medicine*, 281 (August 21, 1969), 443–45.
53. ———, "The Hospital Staff, Community Medicine, and Continuing Education," *American Medical Association Journal*, 204 (May 13, 1968), 590–94.
54. *Darling* v. *Charleston Memorial Hospital*, 33 Ill. 2d 326, 211 N.E. 2d 253 (1965), cert. den. 383 U.S. 946 (1966).
55. DAVIS, FRED, *Passage through Crisis: Polio Victims and Their Families*. Indianapolis: The Bobbs-Merrill Company, Inc., 1963.
56. DAVIS, MILTON S., "Variations in Patients' Compliance with Doctors' Advice: An Empirical Analysis of Patterns of Communication," *American Journal of Public Health*, 58 (February, 1968), 274–88.
57. ——— AND ROBERT E. TRANQUADA, "A Sociological Evaluation of the Watts Neighborhood Health Center," *Medical Care*, 7 (March–April, 1969), 105–17.
58. DE GEYNDT, WILLY, "Five Approaches for Assessing the Quality of Care," *Hospital Administration*, 15 (Winter, 1970).
59. DENTON, JOHN C., AMASA FORD, RALPH E. LISKE, AND ROBERT S. ORT, "Predicting Judged Quality of Patient Care in General Hospitals," *Health Services Research*, 2 (Spring, 1967).
60. DILWORTH, AVA S., "Joint Preparation for Clinical Nurse Specialist," *Nursing Outlook*, 18 (September, 1970), 22–25.
61. DODGE, JOAN S., "Why Nurses Leave—and What to Do about It," *Modern Hospital*, 94 (May, 1960), 116ff.
62. DOLSON, MIRIAM TERRY, "Where Women Stand in Administration," *Modern Hospital*, 108 (May, 1967), 100.
63. DONABEDIAN, AVEDIS, ed., *A Guide to Medical Care Administration*: Vols. I-II. Medical Care Appraisal—Quality and Utilization. New York: The American Public Health Association, Inc., 1969.
64. ———, "Promoting Quality through Evaluating the Process of Patient Care," *Medical Care*, 6 (1968), 181–202.
65. DUFF, RAYMOND S. AND AUGUST B. HOLLINGSHEAD, *Sickness and Society*. New York: Harper & Row, Publishers, 1968.
66. DUNBAR, FLANDERS, *Psychiatry in the Medical Specialties*. New York: McGraw-Hill Book Company, 1959.
67. DUNHAM, H. WARREN AND S. KIRSON WEINBERG, *The Culture of the State Mental Hospital*. Detroit: Wayne State University Press, 1960.
68. DURBIN, RICHARD L. AND W. HERBERT SPRINGHALL, *Organization and Administration of Health Care: Theory, Practice, Environment*. St. Louis: The C. V. Mosby Company, 1969.
69. EGBERT, L. D., G. E. BATLET, O. E. WELCH, AND M. K. BARTLETT, "Reduction of Postoperative Pain by Encouragement and Instruction of Patients: A Study of Doctor–Patient Rapport," *New England Journal of Medicine*, 270 (April 16, 1964), 825–27.

70. Eisele, C. Wesley, "How Changing Times Are Changing Staffs," *Modern Hospital* (May, 1967).
71. ———, ed., *The Medical Staff in the Modern Hospital.* New York: McGraw-Hill Book Company, Blakiston, 1967.
72. Elling, Ray H., "The Hospital-Support Game in The Urban Center," in Eliot Freidson, ed., *The Hospital in Modern Society.* New York: The Free Press, 1963.
73. ——— and Sander Nalebsky, "Organizational Differentiation and Support," *Administrative Science Quarterly,* 6 (September, 1961), 185–209.
74. ——— and William P. Shepard, "A Study of Public Health Careers: Hospital Administrators in Public Health," *American Journal of Public Health,* 58 (May, 1968), 915–29.
75. Engel, Gloria V., "The Effect of Bureaucracy on the Professional Autonomy of Physicians," *Journal of Health and Social Behavior,* 10 (March, 1969), 30–40.
76. Epstein, L. C. and L. Lasagna, "Obtaining Informed Consent, Form or Substance," *Archives of Internal Medicine (Chicago),* 123 (June, 1969), 682–88.
77. Faxon, Nathaniel W., ed., *The Hospital in Contemporary Life.* Cambridge: Harvard University Press, 1949.
78. Field, Mark G., *Doctor and Patient in Soviet Russia.* Cambridge: Harvard University Press, 1957.
79. ———, *Soviet Socialized Medicine: An Introduction.* New York: The Free Press, 1967.
80. Forgotson, Edward H., Ruth Roemer, Roger W. Newman, and John L. Cook, "Licensure of Other Medical Personnel," *Report of the National Advisory Commission on Health Manpower,* 2. Washington, D.C.: Government Printing Office, 1967.
81. Forgotson, Edward H., Ruth Roemer, and Roger W. Newman, "Innovations in the Organization of Health Services: Inhibiting vs. Permissive Regulation," *Washington University Law Quarterly,* 1967:3 (Summer, 1967), 400–13.
82. Fox, Renée C., *Experiment Perilous.* New York: The The Free Press, 1959.
83. Friedson, Eliot, ed., *The Hospital in Modern Society.* New York: The Free Press, 1963.
84. ———, *Profession of Medicine: A Study of the Sociology of Applied Knowledge.* New York: Dodd, Mead & Co., 1970.
85. Friedman, Jay W., "Multiple Determinants of Hospital Programs," *Social Science and Medicine,* 3 (1969), 49–63.
86. Georgopoulos, Basil S. and Aleksander Matijko, "The American General Hospital as a Complex Social System," *Health Services Research* (Spring, 1967), 76–112.
87. Georgopoulos, Basil S. and Floyd C. Mann, *The Community General Hospital.* New York: The Macmillan Company, 1962.
88. Getting, V. A., "Regional Planning of Community Health Services in Michigan: A Four-Year Report," *American Journal of Public Health,* 58 (June, 1968), 1077–84.
89. Gilbert, Doris C. and Daniel J. Levinson, "Role Performance, Ideology, and Personality in Mental Hospital Aides," in Milton Greenblatt, Daniel J. Levinson, and Richard H. Williams, eds., *The Patient and the Mental Hospital.* New York: The Free Press, pp. 197–208.
90. Ginzberg, Eli, "Facts and Fancies about Medical Care." *American Journal of Public Health,* 59 (May, 1969), 785–94.
91. Glaser, Barney G., *Organizational Scientists: Their Professional Careers.* Indianapolis: The Bobbs-Merrill Company, Inc., 1964.
92. Glaser, William A., "American and Foreign Hospitals: Some Sociological Comparisons," in Eliot Freidson, ed., *The Hospital in Modern Society.* New York: The Free Press, 1963.
93. ———, *Social Settings and Medical Organization: A Cross-National Study of the Hospital.* New York: Alberton Press, Inc., 1970.
94. Goffman, Irving, *Asylums.* Garden City, N.Y.: Doubleday & Company, Inc., Anchor Books, 1961.

95. ———, "Characteristics of Total Institutions," Symposium on Preventive and Social Psychiatry, April, 1957, Walter Reed Army Institute of Research. Washington, D.C.: Government Printing Office, pp. 46–47.
96. GOLDNER, FRED H. AND R. R. RITTI, "Professionalization as Career Immobility," *American Journal of Sociology*, 73 (March, 1967), 489–502.
97. GOODRICH, CHARLES H., MARGARET C. OLENDZKI, AND GEORGE G. READER, *Welfare Medical Care*. Cambridge: Harvard University Press, 1970.
98. GOSS, MARY E. W., "Organizational Goals and the Quality of Medical Care," *Journal of Health and Social Behavior*, 11 (December, 1970), 255–68.
99. ———, "Patterns of Bureaucracy among Hospital Staff Physicians," in Eliot Freidson, ed., *The Hospital in Modern Society*. New York: The Free Press, 1963.
100. GOULDNER, ALVIN W., "Cosmopolitans and Locals: Toward an Analysis of Latent Social Roles, I," *Administrative Science Quarterly*, 2 (December, 1957), 281–306.
101. GOVERNMENT IMPACT ON HOSPITAL PRACTICE, "Segregated Blood: A Backlash Backfires," *Hospital Practice*, 2 (July, 1969), 21.
102. GRAEF, IRVING, Chairman, "Creative Federalism: Partnership in Health, Slogans or Solutions," *New York Academy of Medicine Bulletin*, 45 (November, 1969), entire issue.
103. GREENBLATT, MILTON, DANIEL J. LEVINSON, AND RICHARD H. WILLIAMS, eds., *The Patient and the Mental Hospital*. New York: The Free Press, 1957.
104. GRIFFITH, JOHN R., "Research in Hospital Management: Is Utilization Review Worth It?," *Hospital Administration*, 14 (Fall, 1969), 4–9.
105. GRUSKY, OSCAR AND GEORGE A. MILLER, *The Sociology of Organizations: Basic Studies*. New York: The Free Press, 1970.
106. HABENSTEIN, ROBERT W. AND EDWIN A. CHRIST, *Professionalizer, Traditionalizer, and Utilizer: An Interpretive Study of the General Hospital*. Columbia, Mo.: University of Missouri Press, 1963.
107. HALE, THOMAS, "Problems of Supply and Demand in the Education of Nurses," *New England Journal of Medicine*, 275 (November 16, 1966), 1044–48.
108. HALEVI, H. S., "Patterns of Hospitalization in England and Israel," *British Journal of Social and Preventive Medicine*, 23 (1969), 196–202.
109. HALL, OSWALD, "The Informal Organization of Medical Practice in an American City." Unpublished Ph.D. dissertation, University of Chicago, 1944.
110. ———, "Sociological Research in the Field of Medicine: Progress and Prospects," *American Sociological Review*, 16 (October, 1951), 639–43.
111. ———, "The Stages of a Medical Career," *American Journal of Sociology*, 53 (March, 1958), 327–36.
112. HARDT, ROBERT H. AND SHERWIN J. FEINHANLER, "Class and Mental Hospitalization Prognosis," *American Sociological Review*, 24 (December, 1959), 815–21.
113. HAVIGHURST, CLARK C., ed., *Medical Progress and the Law*. Dobbs Ferry, N.Y.: Oceana Publications, Inc., 1969.
114. HAYNES, M. A., "Professionals and the Community Confront Change," *American Journal of Public Health*, 60 (March, 1970), 519–23.
115. HAYNES, ROY, "Law Protecting Rights of Mental Patients Hit," *Los Angeles Times*, November 11, 1960.
116. HENRY, JULES, "The Formal Structure of a Psychiatric Hospital," *Psychiatry*, 17 (May, 1954), 139–51.
117. ———, "Types of Institutional Structure," *Psychiatry*, 20 (February, 1957), 47–60.
118. HILL, LAWRENCE A., "Hospital Costs and Controls in Canada and the United States," *Health Services Research*, 4 (Fall, 1969), 170–76.
119. HOGNESS, J. R., "Role of the Dean and Faculty in Governance of the Medical School," *Journal of the American Medical Association*, 204 (May 27, 1968), 785–88.
120. HOLLINGSHEAD, AUGUST B. AND

Frederick C. Redlich, *Social Class and Mental Illness.* New York: John Wiley & Sons, Inc., 1958.

121. Hospital Indicators, *Hospitals*, 43 (February 16, 1969).

122. Hoxsie, Russell S., "A Time for Study and the Need for Change," *New England Journal of Medicine*, 280 (May 15, 1969), 1099–1101.

123. Hughes, Everett C., *Men and Their Work.* New York: The Free Press, 1958.

124. ———, Helen McGill Highes, and Irwin Deutscher, *Twenty Thousand Nurses Tell Their Story.* Philadelphia: J. B. Lippincott Company, 1958.

125. Hykawy, E., "A Problem Solving Approach," *Canadian Nursing*, 63 (August, 1967), 35–38.

126. Inkeles, Alex and Daniel J. Levinson, "National Character: The Study of Modal Personality and Socio-cultural Systems," in Gardner Lindsey and Elliot Aronson, *Handbook of Social Psychology*, 2nd ed. Reading, Mass.: Addison-Wesley Publishing Company, Inc., 1969, pp. 418–506.

127. Janis, Irving L., "Effects of Fear Arousal on Attitude Changes: Recent Developments in Theory and Experimental Research," in Leonard Berkowitz, ed., *Advances in Experimental Social Psychology.* New York: Academic Press, Inc., 1967.

128. ———, *Psychological Stress: Psychoanalytic and Behavioral Studies of Surgical Patients.* New York: John Wiley & Sons, Inc., 1958.

129. Johnson, Everett A., "Giving the Consumer a Voice in the Hospital Business," *Hospital Administration*, 15 (Spring, 1970).

130. Joint Commission for the Accreditation of Hospitals, *Standards for the Accreditation of Hospitals: Accepted for Field Testing with Interpretive Material.* Chicago: Joint Commission for the Accreditation of Hospitals, October, 1969.

131. *Joint Statement of Intravenous Administration of Fluids, Including the Addition of Drugs and the Starting and Administration of Blood by Registered Nurses Licensed to Practice in California.* Statement January 1, 1957, as amended through January, 1965. California Medical Association, California Hospital Association, and California Nurses Association.

132. Katz, Jay, "The Education of the Physician Investigator," in *Ethical Aspects of Experimentation with Human Subjects, Daedalus*, Proceedings of the American Academy of Arts and Sciences, 98 (Spring, 1969), 480–501.

133. Kelman, Howard R., Elliott Cameran, Sonrad Herr, William Perry, and Kathleen Sward, "Monitoring Patient Care," *Medical Care*, 7 (January–February, 1969), 1–13.

134. Kent, J. A. and C. H. Smith, "Involving the Urban Poor in Health Services through Accommodation—The Employment of Neighborhood Representatives," *American Journal of Public Health*, 57 (June, 1967), 997–1003.

135. King, Maurice, ed., *Medical Care in Developing Countries: A Primer on the Medicine of Poverty and a Symposium from Makerere.* Nairobi: Oxford University Press, 1966, reprinted 1968.

136. Kirkpatrick, John R. and Leon J. Taubenhaus, "The Non-Urgent Patient on the Emergency Floor," *Medical Care*, 5 (January–February, 1967), 19–24.

137. Kisch, Arnold I. and Leo G. Reeder, "Client Evaluation of Physician Performance," *Journal of Health and Social Behavior*, 10 (March, 1969), 51–58.

138. Klarman, Herbert E., "Approaches to Moderating the Increases in Medical Care Costs," *Medical Care*, 7 (May–June, 1969), 183–90.

139. Knutson, Andie L., "Body Transplants and Ethical Values," *Social Science and Medicine*, 2 (1968), 393–414.

140. Kornhauser, William, *Scientists in Industry.* Berkeley: University of California Press, 1962.

141. Kosa, John, Aaron Antonovsky, and Irving Kenneth Zola, eds., *Poverty and Health: A Sociological Analysis.* Cambridge: Harvard University Press, 1969.

142. Kossoris, Max D., "The San Francisco Bay Area 1966 Nurses' Negotiations," *Monthly Labor Review*, U.S. Department of Labor, Bureau of Labor Statistics, 90 (June, 1967), 8–12.

143. KOTTKE, F. J., "Research Training in Medical Post-Graduate Programs," *Archives of Physical Medicine*, 50 (July, 1969), 406–8.
144. KOVNER, ANTHONY R., GERALD KATZ, STANLEY B. KAHANE, AND CECIL G. SHEPS, "Relating a Neighborhood Health Center to a General Hospital: A Case History," *Medical Care*, 7 (March–April, 1969).
145. KRAMER, MARLENE, "Collegiate Graduate Nurses in Medical Center Hospitals: Mutual Challenge or Duel," *Nursing Research*, 18 (May–June, 1969), 196–210.
146. ———, "Role Conceptions of Baccalaureate Nurses and Success in Hospital Nursing," *Nursing Research*, 19 (September–October, 1970), 428–39.
147. LAMMERS, C. J., "Power and Participation in Decision-Making in Formal Organizations," *American Journal of Sociology*, 73 (September, 1967), 201–16.
148. LARRABEE, L. L. AND R. E. LEFTON, "Managing Intergroup Conflict within Your Organization," *Hospital Progress*, 49 (April, 1968), 62–66 *passim*.
149. LEGAL REGULATION OF HEALTH PERSONNEL: INTRODUCTION, *Washington University Law Review*, 1967 (Summer, 1967), 247–48.
150. LE ROCCO, AUGUST, *Planning for Hospital Discharge. A Bibliography with Abstracts and Research Interviews.* Library of the Center for Community Health and Medical Care, Harvard University. Department of Health, Education, and Welfare, August, 1970, HSRD-70-17.
151. LEVINE, EUGENE, "Turnover among Nursing Personnel in General Hospitals," *Hospitals*, 31 (September 1, 1957), 50ff.
152. LEVINSON, HARRY, "How to Undermine an Organization," *Think* (July–August, 1966), 15–19.
153. LEWIS, C. E. AND BARBARA. A. RESNIK, "Nurse Clinics and Progressive Ambulatory Care," *New England Journal of Medicine*, 277 (December 7, 1967), 1236–41.
154. LITWAK, EUGENE, "Models of Bureaucracy Which Permit Conflict," *American Journal of Sociology*, 68 (September, 1962), 177–84.
155. LOEB, MARTIN B., "Role Definition in the Social World of a Psychiatric Hospital," in Milton Greenblatt, Daniel J. Levinson, and Richard H. Williams, eds., *The Patient and the Mental Hospital.* New York: The Free Press, 1957, pp. 14–19.
156. LUTKER, EDYTHE, *Women Gain a Place in Medicine.* New York: McGraw-Hill Book Company, 1969.
157. MACEACHARN, MALCOLM T., "History of Hospitals," in *Hospital Organization and Management.* Chicago: Physician Record Company, 1957, pp. 1–28.
158. MCGIBONY, JOHN R., *Principles of Hospital Administration*, 2nd ed. New York: G. P. Putnam's Sons, 1969.
159. MACGREGOR, FRANCES COOKE, *Social Science in Nursing.* New York: Russell Sage Foundation, 1960.
160. MCKEOWN, THOMAS, "Current Trends in British Medical Planning," in John W. V. Cordice, Jr., Irving Graef, Joseph G. Benton, and Richard S. Gubner, eds., *Education in the Health Related Professions,* New York Academy of Sciences, 16 (December 31, 1969).
161. MCINTYRE, HATTIE MILDRED, "The Nurse Clinician—One Point of View," *Nursing Outlook*, 18 (September, 1970), 26–29.
162. MADISON, DONALD L., "Organized Health Care and the Poor," *Medical Care Review*, 26 (August, 1969), 783–803.
163. MARCH, JAMES C. AND HERBERT A. SIMON, *Organizations.* New York: John Wiley & Sons, Inc., 1958.
164. MECHANIC, DAVID, *Medical Sociology: A Selective View.* New York: The Free Press, 1968.
165. ———, "Sources of Power of Lower Participants in Complex Organizations," *Administrative Science Quarterly*, 7 (1967), 349–64.
166. MENZIES, I. E. P., "A Case Study in the Functioning of Social Systems as a Defense Against Anxiety: A Report on a Study of the Nursing of a General Hospital," *Human Relations*, 13 (May, 1960), 95–122.
167. MERTON, ROBERT K., GEORGE C.

Reader, and Patricia L. Kendall, The *Student Physician: Introductory Studies in the Sociology of Medical Education.* Cambridge: Harvard University Press, 1957.

168. Metsch, J. M., "Professionalism in Administration," *Hospital Topics*, 47 (September, 1969), 50–53.

169. Minckley, Barbara, "A Study of Noise and Its Relationship to Patient Discomfort in the Recovery Room," *Nursing Research*, 17 (May–June, 1968), 247–50.

170. ———, "A Study of Practices of Handling and Opening Suture Packets in the Operating Room," *Nursing Research*, 18 (May–June, 1969), 267–70.

171. Muller, Charlotte, "Health Care at What Price? Some Notes for Comprehensive Health Planners," *American Journal of Public Health*, 59 (April, 1969).

172. Myers, Jerome K. and Lee L. Bean, *A Decade Later: A Follow-up of Social Class and Mental Illness.* New York: John Wiley & Sons, Inc., 1968.

173. "The Nation's Hospitals: A Statistical Profile," *Hospitals*, 44, part 2 (August 1, 1970), Hospital Guide Issue.

174. New, Peter Kong-Ming, Gladys Nite, and Josephine M. Callahan, *Nursing Service and Patient Care: A Staffing Experiment.* Kansas City: Community Studies, Inc., 119, 1959.

175. New, Peter Kong-Ming, Anthony T. Ruscio, Rhea Pendergrass Priest, Dora Petritsi, and Linda A. George, "The Support Structure of Heart and Stroke Patients: A Study of the Role of Significant Others in Patient Rehabilitation," *Social Science and Medicine*, 2 (1968), 185–200.

176. Nightingale, Florence, *Notes on Nursing: What It Is and What It Is Not.* London: Harrison, 1859. Facsimile Reprint, Philadelphia: J. B. Lippincott Company, 1946.

177. O'Donahue, John D., "Developing a Conceptual Framework for Planning," *Hospital Administration*, 14 (Fall, 1969), 35–54.

178. Olson, S. W., "Educating the Physician for Comprehensive Care," *New Zealand Medical Journal*, 70 (August, 1969), 73–78.

179. Parsons, Talcott, *The Social System.* New York: The Free Press, 1951.

180. ———, *Structure and Process in Modern Societies.* New York: The Free Press, 1960.

181. ——— and Renee Fox, "Illness, Therapy, and the Modern Urban American Family," *Journal of Social Issues*, 8 (1952), 31–44. Reprinted in E. Gartly Jaco, ed., *Patients, Physicians, and Illness.* New York: The Free Press, 1958.

182. Paul, Benjamin D., ed., *Health, Culture, and Community.* New York: Russell Sage Foundation, 1953.

183. Pavenstedt, E., "The Drifters: Children of Disorganized Lower-Class Families," *International Psychiatric Clinics*, 4 (1967), 255–96.

184. Pennell, Maryland Y. and David B. Hoover, *Allied Health Manpower 1950–1980.* Health Manpower Source Book Section 21, U.S. Public Health Service Publication no. 263. Washington, D.C.: Government Printing Office, 1970.

185. Perrow, Charles, "A Framework for the Comparative Analysis of Organizations," *American Sociological Review*, 32 (April, 1967), 194–208.

186. ———, "Goals and Power Structures: A Historical Case Study," in Eliot Freidson, ed., *The Hospital in Modern Society.* New York: The Free Press, 1963.

187. ———, "Hospitals: Technology, Structure and Goals," in James G. March, ed., *Handbook of Organizations.* Skokie, Ill.: Rand McNally & Company, 1965.

188. Piedmont, Eugene B. and Bright M. Dorablaser, "Evaluation of Patient Welfare," *Health Services Research*, 5 (Fall, 1970), 248–57.

189. Pittsburgh University, Health Law Center, *Hospital Law Manual*, published quarterly since 1959, 2 eds, Hospital Administration and Hospital Attorneys.

190. Plaja, Antonio Ordonez, Lucy M. Cohen, and Julian Samora, "Communication between Physicians and Patients in Outpatient Clinics: Social and Cultural Factors," *Milbank Memorial*

Fund Quarterly, Part 1, 46 (April, 1968), 161–213.

191. POLANSKY, HERMAN A., ROBERT B. WHITE, AND STUART C. MILLER, "Determinants of the Role-Image of the Patient in a Psychiatric Hospital," in Milton Greenblatt, Daniel J. Levinson, and Richard H. Williams, eds., *The Patient and the Mental Hospital*. New York: The Free Press, 1957, pp. 380–481.

192. POMRINSE, S. DAVID, "To What Degree Are Hospitals Publicly Accountable," *Hospitals*, 43 (February 16, 1969), 41–44.

193. PORTERFIELD, JOHN D. III, "The New JCAH Standards," *Hospitals*, 43 (October 16, 1969), 69–74.

194. PUBLIC HEALTH SERVICE, U.S. DEPARTMENT OF HEALTH, EDUCATION, AND WELFARE, *Health Manpower Source Book*, Section 2: Nursing Personnel (revised January, 1966). Public Health Services Publication No. 263. Washington, D.C.: Government Printing Office.

195. QUINT, JEANNE C., "Institutionalized Practices of Information Control," *Psychiatry*, 28 (1965), 119–32.

196. RAINWATER, LEE, "The Lower Class: Health, Illness, and Medical Institutions," in Irwin Deutscher and Elizabeth J. Thompson, *Among the People: Encounters with the Poor*. New York: Basic Books, Inc., Publishers, 1968.

197. RAPOPORT, ROBERT N., RHONA RAPOPORT, AND IRVING ROSOW, *Community as Doctor*. London: Tavistock Publications, 1959.

198. RAVICH, RUTH, HELEN REHR, AND CHARLES H. GOODRICH, "Hospital Ombudsman Smooths Flow of Services and Communications," *Hospitals*, 43 (March 1, 1969), 56–61.

199. READER, GEORGE G., LOIS PRATT, AND MARGARET C. MUDD, "What Patients Expect from Their Doctors," *Modern Hospital*, 89 (July, 1957), 88–94.

200. *Report of the National Advisory Commission on Health Manpower*, Vols. I and II. Washington, D.C.: Government Printing Office, 1968.

201. REVANS, R. W., "Hospital Attitudes and Communications," in J. R. Lawrence, ed., *Operations Research and the Social Sciences*. London: Tavistock Publications, 1966.

202. ———, *Standards for Morale: Cause and Effect in Hospitals*. Published for the Naffield Provincial Hospitals Trust. London: Oxford University Press, 1964.

203. RICHARD, MICHEL PAUL, "The Negro Physician: Babbitt or Revolutionary," *Journal of Health and Social Behavior*, 10 (December, 1969), 265–74.

204. RIE, HERBERT E., HAROLD DOVERMAN, BURTON J. GROSSMAN, AND NATIVIDAD OZOA, "Immediate and Long-Term Effects of Intervention Early in Prolonged Hospitalization," *Pediatrics*, 41 (April, 1968), 755–64.

205. RO, KONG-KYUN, "Patient Characteristics, Hospital Characteristics, and Hospital Use," *Medical Care*, 7 (July–August, 1969), 295–312.

206. ——— AND RICHARD AUSTER, "An Output Approach to Incentive Reimbursement for Hospitals," *Health Services Research* (Fall, 1969), 177–87.

207. ROCKART, JOHN F. AND PAUL B. HOFFMAN, "Physician and Patient Behavior under Different Scheduling Systems in a Hospital Outpatient Department," *Medical Care*, 7 (November–December, 1969), 463–70.

208. ROSEN, GEORGE, "The Hospital: Historical Sociology of a Community Institution," in Eliot Freidson, ed., *The Hospital in Modern Society*. New York: The Free Press, 1963.

209. ROSENBERG, LARRY, "Social Status and Participation among a Group of Chronic Schizophrenics," *Human Relations*, 15 (1962), 365–77.

210. ROSENGREN, WILLIAM R. AND MARK LEFTON, *Hospitals and Patients*. New York: Atherton Press, 1969.

211. ———, *Organizations and Clients: Essays in the Sociology of Service*. Columbus, Ohio: Charles E. Merrill Books, Inc., 1970.

212. ROTH, JULIUS A., "Ritual and Magic in the Control of Contagion," *American Sociological Review*, 22 (June, 1957), 310–14.

213. ———, *Timetables: Structuring the Passage of Time in Hospital Treatment*

and Other Careers. Indianapolis: The Bobbs–Merrill Company, Inc., 1963.

214. ——— AND ELIZABETH M. EDDY, *Rehabilitation for the Unwanted.* New York: Atherton Press, Inc., 1967.

215. RUTSTEIN, DAVID D., *The Coming Revolution in Medicine,* Cambridge: The M.I.T. Press, 1967.

216. SAMORA, JULIAN, LYLE SAUNDERS, AND RICHARD LARSON, "Medical Vocabulary Knowledge among Hospital Patients," *Journal of Health and Human Behavior,* 2 (1961), 83–92.

217. SAUNDERS, LYLE, *Cultural Difference and Medical Care.* New York: Russell Sage Foundation, 1954.

218. SCHEFF, THOMAS J., "Control over Policy by Attendants in a Mental Hospital," *Journal of Health and Human Behavior,* 2 (Summer, 1961), 93–105.

219. ———, "Preferred Errors in Diagnosis," *Medical Care,* 2 (August, 1964), 166–72.

220. SCOTT, ROBERT A., *The Making of Blind Men: A Study of Adult Socialization.* New York: Russell Sage Foundation, 1969.

221. SEEMAN, MELVIN AND JOHN W. EVANS, "Alienation and Learning in a Hospital Setting," *American Sociological Review,* 26 (December, 1962), 772–82.

222. ———, "Stratification and Hospital Care: I. The Performance of the Medical Intern," *American Sociological Review,* 26 (February, 1961), 67–80.

223. ———, "Stratification and Hospital Care: II. The Objective Criteria of Performance," *American Sociological Review,* 26 (April, 1961), 193–204.

224. SHARPE, DAVID J. AND ROBERT F. HARGEST III, "Lifesaving Treatment for Unwilling Patients," *Fordham Law Review,* 36 (1968), 695–706.

225. SHELDON, ALAN, FRANK BAKER, AND CURTIS B. MCLAUGHLIN, *Systems and Medical Care.* Cambridge: The M.I.T. Press, 1970.

226. SHRYOCK, RICHARD H., *The Development of Modern Medicine.* New York: Alfred A. Knopf, Inc., 1947.

227. SIMMONS, LEO W. AND HAROLD G. WOLFF, Social Science in Medicine. New York: Russell Sage Foundation, 1952.

228. SIMPSON, J., A. MAER, R. G. THOMAS, H. N. WILLARD, AND H. J. BAKST, *Custom and Practice in Medical Care: A Comparative Study of Two Hospitals in Arboath, Scotland, and Waterville, Maine.* London: Oxford University Press, 1968 (for Nuffield Provincial Hospitals Trust).

229. SKIPPER, JAMES A., JR., AND ROBERT C. LEONARD, "Children, Stress, and Hospitalization: A Field Experiment," *Journal of Health and Social Behavior,* 9 (December, 1968), 275–86.

230. SKIPPER, J. K., HANS O. MAUKSCH, AND DAISY TOGLIAROZZO, "Some Barriers to Communication between Patients and Hospital Functionaries," *Nursing Forum,* 11 (1963), 14–23.

231. SMITH, HARVEY L., "Two Lines of Authority: The Hospital's Dilemma," *The Modern Hospital,* 84 (March, 1955), 59–64. Reprinted in E. Gartly Jaco, ed., *Patients, Physicians, and Illness.* New York: The Free Press, 1958.

232. SNELL, BERNARD, "The Changing Position of the Physician in Canadian Hospitals," *Medical Care,* 7 (November–December, 1969), 43–49.

233. SOLOMON, DAVID N., "Ethnic and Class Differences among Hospitals as Contingencies in Medical Careers," *American Journal of Sociology,* 65 (March, 1961), 463–71.

234. SOMERS, ANNE R., "Hospital Costs and Payment: Suggestions for Stabilizing the Uneasy Balance," *Medical Care,* 7 (September–October, 1969), 348–60.

235. ———, *Hospital Regulation: The Dilemma of Public Policy.* Princeton: Princeton University, Industrial Relations Section, 1969.

236. SPILLANE, E. J., "The A-NAT-O-MY of a Decision," *Hospital Progress,* 50 (April, 1969), 47–50.

237. SPITZER, WALTER O., "The Small General Hospital: Problems and Solutions," *Milbank Memorial Fund Quarterly,* 48, Part 1 (October 19, 1970), 413–47.

238. STANTON, ALFRED H. AND MORRIS S. SCHWARTZ, *The Mental Hospital.* New York: Basic Books, Inc., Publishers, 1954.

239. STARKWEATHER, DAVID B., "The

Rationale for Decentralization in Large Hospitals," *Hospital Administration* (Spring, 1970), 27–44.

240. Statement of the California Nurses Association to the Assembly Committee on Health and Welfare concerning the Physician's Assistant Concept, Appendix D, December 4, 1969.

241. STRAUSS, ANSELM L., "Medical Organization, Medical Care, and Lower-Income Groups," *Social Science and Medicine*, 3 (1969), 143–77.

242. ———, *Where Medicine Fails.* Chicago: Aldine Publishing Company, 1970.

243. ———, LEONARD SCHATZMAN, DANUTA EHRLICH, RUE BACHER, AND MELVIN SABSHIN, "The Hospital and its Negotiated Order," in Eliot Freidson, ed., *The Hospital in Modern Society.* New York: The Free Press, 1963.

244. STREDTBECK, FRED L., RITA M. JAMES, AND CHARLES HAWKINS, "Social Status in Jury Deliberations," in Eleanor E. Maccoby, Theodore M. Newcomb, and Eubene L. Hartley, eds., *Readings in Social Psychology.* New York: Holt, Rinehart & Winston, Inc., 1958, pp. 379–88.

245. STURDAVANT, MADELYNE AND HAROLD C. MICKEY, "An Experiment in Minimal Care," *Hospitals*, 40 (February, 1966), 72–78 passim.

246. SUCHMAN, EDWARD A., "Sociomedical Variations among Ethnic Groups," *American Journal of Sociology*, 70 (November, 1964), 319–31.

247. ———, "Social Patterns of Illness and Medical Care," *Journal of Health and Human Behavior*, 6 (1965), 2–16.

248. ———, "Stages of Illness and Medical Care," *Journal of Health and Human Behavior*, 6 (1965), 114–28.

249. SUDNOW, DAVID, *Passing On: The Social Organization of Dying.* Englewood Cliffs, N.J.: Prentice-Hall, Inc., 1967.

250. TAYLOR, CAROL, *The Horizontal Orbit.* New York: Holt, Rinehart & Winston, Inc., 1970.

251. THOMAS, WILLIAM, "Health Planning and Realism," *Hospital Administration*, 14 (Fall, 1969), 16–34.

252. THOMPSON, JAMES D., *Organizations in Action: Social Science Bases of Administrative Theory.* New York: McGraw-Hill Book Company, 1967.

253. U.S. DEPARTMENT OF HEALTH, EDUCATION, AND WELFARE, *Secretary's Advisory Committee on Hospital Effectiveness.* Washington, D.C.: Government Printing Office, 1968.

254. U.S. DEPARTMENT OF LABOR, MANPOWER ADMINISTRATION, *Technology and Manpower in the Health Service Industry*, Manpower Research Bulletin No. 14. May, 1967.

255. U.S. PUBLIC HEALTH SERVICE, *Health Resource Statistics: Health Manpower and Health Facilities*, Publication 1509, 1969 ed. Washington, D.C.: Government Printing Office, 1970.

256. U.S. PUBLIC HEALTH SERVICE, *State Licensing of Health Occupations*, Publication No. 1758. Washington, D.C.: Government Printing Office, 1967.

257. U.S. PUBLIC HEALTH SERVICE, *Hill-Burton Program Progress Report, July 1, 1947–June 30, 1969*, Publication No. 930-F-3, revised 1969. Washington, D.C.: Government Printing Office.

258. U.S. SENATE COMMITTEE ON GOVERNMENT OPERATIONS, *Federal Role in Health.* Senate Report No. 91–809, 91st Cong., 2d sess., 1970. Washington, D.C.: Government Printing Office.

259. U.S. SURGEON GENERAL'S OFFICE, *A Decade of Change in U.S. Hospitals, 1953–1963.* Washington, D.C.: Government Printing Office, 1965.

260. VAN LEEUWEN, J. A. C. DE KOCK, "Some Social and Emotional Aspects of Health Manpower Planning," *Medical Care*, 7 (May–June, 1969).

261. VAUX, KENNETH, ed., *Who Shall Live: Medicine, Technology, Ethics.* Philadelphia: Fortress Press, 1970.

262. VER STEEG, DONNA F., "The Fictional Nurse: Is She for Real?" *Nursing Outlook*, 16 (August, 1968), 20–23.

263. VISTEAR, ARTHUR J., ARNOLD J. KISCH, AND MILTON I. ROEMER, The *Watts Hospital: A Health Facility Is Planned for a Metropolitan Slum Area*, Medical Care Administration Case Study No. 5. U.S. Department of Health, Education, and Welfare, 1967.

264. WAGER, L. WESLEY AND GEORGE A. MILLER, "Hypothetical Situations and

Particularistic Requests: A Test in Three Hospitals," *Human Organizations*, 28 (Summer, 1969), 119–27.

265. Wallace, Anthony F. C. and Harold A. Rashkis, "The Relation of Staff Consensus to Patient Disturbance on Mental Hospital Wards," *American Sociological Review*, 24 (December, 1959), 829–35.

266. Wenkert, Walter, John G. Hill, and Robert L. Berg, "Concepts and Methodology in Planning Patient Care Services," *Medical Care*, 7 (July–August, 1969).

267. Wessen, Albert F., "Hospital Ideology and Communication between Ward Personnel," in E. Gartly Jaco, ed., *Patients, Physicians, and Illness*. New York: The Free Press, 1958, pp. 448–68.

268. Wilensky, Harold L., "The Professionalization of Everyone?," *American Journal of Sociology*, 70 (September, 1964), 137–58.

269. Williams, Josephine J., "The Woman Physician's Dilemma," *Journal of Social Issues*, 6 (1950), 38–44.

270. ———, "Patients and Prejudice: Lay Attitudes toward Women Physicians," *American Journal of Sociology*, 51 (January, 1946), 283–87.

271. Wilson, Robert N., "The Physician's Changing Hospital Role," *Human Organization*, 18 (Winter, 1959–60), 177–83.

272. Wise, Harold, "Physicians in Health Centers," *Postgraduate Medicine* (June, 1970), 130–37.

273. Women's Bureau, U.S. Department of Labor, *Facts on Prospective and Practicing Women in Medicine*, in Report prepared for the Conference on Meeting Medical Manpower Needs: *The Fuller Utilization of the Woman Physician*, January, 1968.

274. Wylie, Charles Murray, "Evaluating Time Trends in a Rehabilitation Center," *Medical Care*, 5 (July–August, 1967), 249–54.

275. Yett, Donald E., "The Nursing Shortage and the Nurse Training Act of 1964," *Industrial and Labor Relations Review*, 19 (January, 1966), 190–220.

276. Young, John P., "A Conceptual Framework for Hospital Administrative Decision Systems," *Health Services Research*, 3 (Summer, 1968), 79–93.

277. Zborowski, Mark, "Cultural Components in Responses to Pain," *Journal of Social Issues*, 8 (1952), 16–30.

278. Zimmer, James G. and Emrett W. Groomes, "An Observer Reliability Study of Physicians and Nurses Decisions in Utilization Review of Chronic Care Facilities," *Medical Care*, 7 (January–February, 1969), 14–20.

279. Zola, Irving Kenneth, "Culture and Symptoms: An Analysis of Patients Presenting Complaints," *American Sociological Review*, 21 (October, 1966), 615–30.

13

PATIENT-PRACTITIONER RELATIONSHIPS

Samuel W. Bloom and Robert N. Wilson

> In every medical action there are always two parties involved, the physician and the patient or, in a broader sense, the medical corps and society. Medicine is nothing else than the manifold relations between these two groups. The history of medicine, therefore, cannot limit itself to the history of the science, institutions and characters of medicine, but must include the history of the patient in society, that of the psysician, and the history of the relations between physician and patient [47].

Sigerist's assertion that health care is essentially a social relationship deserves special emphasis today because our era is distinguished by its focus on the technology of medicine. In the dense web of machinery, technique, testing, and computer processing that enfolds modern medicine, it often is easy to forget that the nub of the health system is found in the interplay between helper and helped. Thus, Sigerist's admonition about the centrality of the doctor-patient relationship has been largely unheeded by historians of medicine; they have chosen instead, as Freidson notes, "to pass through the centuries picking out the 'valid' elements of medical knowledge and assembling a chronology of truths that add up to become present-day scientific medicine" [25]. Quite the opposite occurs in the sociology of medicine.

Since Henderson [33], a large sociological literature has accumulated in which the relations between the medical professional and his client are treated as the crux of medicine. In its first stages, this type of inquiry was dominated by theories of social systems. Henderson, himself an outstanding biochemist, became fascinated with the idea of adapting Pareto's theory of sentiments to the Gibbs model of physiochemical systems [32]. After publishing his first formulations of the doctor-patient relationship as a social system in 1934 and 1935, Henderson, in 1937, started a course at Harvard in what he called "concrete sociology," described as "a few lectures and numerous cases discussed by various members of the University group and others" [7]. Talcott Parsons attended this seminar and very soon after incorporated the "case of medicine" as the main illustrative example in his theory of the social systems [53].

For Henderson, system analysis focused on the internal processes of interaction between doctor and patient. Parsons expanded the perspective to view medicine as "an important subsystem of modern Western society." For both, the homeostatic principle was central to their conceptions. But with Parsons, this principle became more clearly and fully connected with the assumptions of a functional analysis of social systems. "Illness," Parsons concluded, "is a state of disturbance in the 'normal' functioning of the total human individual, including both the state of the organism as a biological system and of his personal and social adjustments. It is thus partly biologically and partly socially defined. Participation in the social system is always potentially relevant to the state of illness, to its etiology, and to the conditions of successful therapy, as well as to other things" [53].

According to Parsons, patient-practitioner relationships are best viewed in the framework of social roles, in the attitudes and activities the two parties bring to the situation of care. This interaction of two or more persons centered on the health needs of a single individual is far from being a spontaneous happening. It is, rather, a more or less well-rehearsed confrontation in which the key participants have learned to expect certain things and to act in certain ways. Just as health and illness are subject to various definitions, so the pattern of activities designed to intervene in ill processes is phrased in different ways—and is always a social definition.

For a variety of investigators, faith in Parsonian role analysis continues unabated [42, 43, 63, 64]. A parallel channel of inquiry took exception to the functionalism of Parsons but retained and expanded the conception of illness as deviance. Especially as developed by Freidson, the propositions of symbolic interactionism and conflict theory appear [23, 25]. Freidson retains a role analysis. At issue is not the question whether patterned expectations exist but, rather, the assumptions which different theoretical positions take about the nature of these expectations. In place of the mutuality and reciprocity dynamics of the Parsonian analysis, Freidson substitutes hostility, ambivalence, and conflict.

The theoretical issues, therefore, are familiar in the general terms of modern sociology. The exposition of the contrasting arguments of functionalism and "structural" conflict theory [38] as they apply to the doctor-patient relationship—or if one prefers the more generic term, "patient-practitioner relations"—is chosen as the method of this paper because, first, the major work of the field is covered thereby, and second (and more important), by such theoretically oriented exegesis, the state of the field may be clarified and critical problems identified for future study.

A FUNCTIONAL MODEL: THE PARSONIAN FRAMEWORK

The basic conceptual framework of a functional analysis of health in society is succinctly stated by Parsons.

> ... The problem of health is intimately involved in the functional prerequisites of the social system.... Certainly by almost any definition health is included in the functional needs of the individual member of the society so that from the point of view of functioning of the social system, too low a general level of health, too high an incidence of illness is dysfunctional. This is in the first instance because illness incapacitates for the effective performance of social roles. It could of course be that this incidence was completely uncontrollable by social action, an independently given condition of social life. But insofar as it is controllable, through rational action or otherwise, it is clear that there is a functional interest of the society in its control, broadly in the minimization of illness [53].

Within this frame of reference, what is the implication of construing health care as a social role relationship? It means, first, that this interaction between a helping agent and a person needing help is *patterned* and, hence, *shows predictable regularities.* Sickness and health are too important in human affairs to be left to improvised chance encounters; rather, they are treated in ways that form part of man's culture, that have been passed among individuals as a social heritage. If patient-practitioner relations are a patterned sector of culture, then they must be transmitted from those who know about them to those who do not. These roles are learned sequences of behavior.

The system, in Parsons's interpretation, is not static: that is, role reciprocity is seen as a dynamic process, with predictable obstructing as well as facilitating factors. For example, one of the prime difficulties in helping relationships, almost a leitmotif in modern medicine and public health, is that the parties to the transaction often do not learn the same things in the same ways. Thus, when they confront one another, they manifest attitudes and actions that are inappropriate to the other's perception of the health care situation. A great deal of helping takes place between people whose relationship is marked, at least initially, by formidable *barriers* to *communication* and *mutual satisfaction.* Within a given society, say, the United States, the barriers may consist of differences in health sophistication (the physician is a professional, while the patient is an amateur), differences in social status, and in racial or ethnic group membership. Between societies, as in the thrust to introduce Western medicine into the developing countries, all these barriers are compounded by divergent cultural milieux, which may promote radically different assumptions about the nature of illness and about who should treat whom.

It may be well to underscore that this formulation entails a *basic mutuality,* a *meshing of viewpoints and activities.* Each of the persons entering upon a role transaction either must be familiar with his own and the other's expectations and probable sequences of behavior, or an adaptive process must occur, in which the necessary role behavior is learned. Within such a social system, it is apparent that neither of the parties can define his own role independently of his role partner. The helping agent's view of himself does not make up all of his role; the full meaning of acting as doctor or nurse rests also upon the patient's conception of what a doctor or nurse is. Similarly, the role of the patient is composed both of subjective models of patienthood and of the helper's notions about what constitutes a good—or bad—client.

Distribution of Authority Within the System: The Asymmetry of Therapeutic Relations

The Parsonian assertion that the roles of treater and client must be mutually understood and mutually rewarded does not at all mean that practitioners and patients are equals in the therapeutic situation. In the nature of the case, it is calculated that some significant change is to be promoted in the behavior, the total state of health, of the patient. As the skilled person meets the unskilled and tries to alter the latter, the parties can no more be equals than are parent and child or teacher and student. The helping agent, it is asserted, must have leverage to induce change; this leverage is generated by over-all circumstances, notably the *professional prestige* and *situational authority* of the health agent and the *situational dependency* of the patient.

Health professionals, especially the physician, tend to rank generally fairly high in the prestige hierarchies of industrial societies, although this is much more true of the West than of, for example, the Soviet Union. But what is at issue in the therapeutic relationship is not only the aura of high status; rather, it is the specific technical qualifications of the healer, Parsons contends, which lend him a position of *power rooted in his having what the patient wants and needs.* Thus, even the ward attendant in a psychiatric hospital, whose general rank in society may be considerably lower than that of most of his patients, is, in the ward situation, endowed with a profound control over resources of reward and punishment.

The patient is assumed to take a passively dependent posture in many if not most health care interactions for several reasons. The very existence of the relationship is premised on the patient's being "out of his field," on his not knowing what the treater knows. Further, the expert in any delivery of services has a certain initiative; even a shoeshine boy tells the customer how to place his feet. Much more important, however, is the vulnerable social and psychological stance of an individual who has defined himself, or who has come to be defined by others, as ill. Any brand of disease, from traumatic bodily injury to psychoneurosis, appears to foster a regression in the patient, a reversion in some degree to the role of dependent child. There are properties of being ill that threaten the integrity of the person. He who adopts the sick role, for whatever reason, feels himself at least temporarily less than whole, weakened, open to incursions of fear and trembling. The threat of physical illness strips him of "normal" defenses, rendering him more frail and childlike. If the illness is severe, of course, it carries the realization of that final fear of death itself, of nonbeing. Mental illness renders the individual unsure, disoriented; as the sufferer is gauged incompetent and sees the incompetence mirrored in others' behavior toward him, he cannot but doubt himself. Again, as the child, he requires the special reassurance of support and affection, of confirming evidence that he is worthy and that he really exists in a viable organization of selfhood.

Therapeutic relationships, in modern Western society, are thus presented as both culturally and situationally derived. As we shall see, however, critics see the Parsonian model as, in fact, an ideal type based on the assumption of an underlying rationality, which is so emphasized that other factors, including the structure of the situation, are assigned only token significance. The theoretical problem is centered first in the question about what is the major determining variable—culture or situation—and, second, in the question of what is the guiding behavioral process—homeostatic adaptation or encounter bargaining.

The model is not complete, however, without further description of the institutionalized expectations of behavior in the patient's and doctor's role. The patient, considered from a sociological standpoint, is a deviant individual. The physician is a professional. It is around these two themes that Parsons builds his institutional structures for the patient-practitioner social system.

The Social Role of the Patient

Sociologically viewed, the patient is a deviant individual. The onus implied in his deviance is clearly more forceful in mental than in physical illness, but, in any case, it is considerable, especially if the state of illness is prolonged. The essential reason for his being called a deviant is not obscure: A patient is by definition an individual whose incapacity thwarts his performance of the social roles with which he is normally charged. His illness diminishes the body social by one, and in a tightly integrated society the withdrawal of particular persons from full functioning may have a pervasive effect. It is thus eminently reasonable to believe, with Parsons, that a society cannot long afford an endemic or epidemic taking of the patient's role, that society must construe this role as undesirable, temporary, and basically disruptive.

But how does one "become a patient?" With the possible exception of certain severe congential defects, no one is "born" a patient. Nor can he expect to assume the patient's role as a consequence of a normal developmental sequence, as the result of schooling in patienthood. The role is usually temporary, only loosely circumscribed by accepted definitions of its content, and ascribed to the individual rather than achieved by him. It is not consciously sought by many persons in society, although the secondary gains of illness—especially the security of a protected dependency—may lead some persons to an unconscious desire to be ill. The decisive element in assuming the role of patient is probably not the sheer fact of sickness or accident but the recognition by the affected individual and/or certain other people of a particular need for help in coping with the condition.

Parsons' analysis of the sick role deals with the social meaning of the patient's situation [53]. He notes that when in any highly industrialized, rational society, the sick role is institutionalized, it is delimited in such a way that the well population is "insulated" from the contagion of the ill. The ill person is defined as "needing help," as obligated to accept this help and to cooperate with the therapeutic agent. The patient is made dependent on the nonsick society.

1. This incapacity is interpreted as beyond his powers to overcome by the process of decision-making alone; in this sense he cannot be "held responsible" for the incapacity. Some kind of "therapeutic" process, spontaneous or aided, is conceived to be necessary to recovery.
2. Incapacity defined as illness is interpreted as a legitimate basis for the *exemp-*

tion of the sick individual, to varying degrees, in varying ways, and for varying periods according to the nature of the illness, from his normal role and task obligations.

3. To be ill is thus to be in a partially and conditionally *legitimated* state. The essential condition of its legitimation, however, is the recognition by the sick person that to be ill is inherently *undesirable*, that he therefore has an obligation to try to "get well" and to cooperate with others to this end.

4. So far as spontaneous forces, the *vis medicatrix naturea* cannot be expected to operate adequately and quickly; the sick person, and those with responsibility for his welfare, above all, members of his family, have an obligation to *seek competent help* and to cooperate with competent agencies in their attempts to help him get well; in our society, of course, principally medical agencies. The valuation of health, of course, also implies that it is an obligation to try to prevent threatened illness where this is possible [53].

In a society which is marked by an interdependent series of highly complex social roles, the patient is under particularly heavy pressure to regain capacity. In keeping with the emphasis on the value of health in American culture, and in Western European culture generally, the patient has the corresponding advantage of a developed scientific armamentarium and a host of helping agents. The ill person, then, recognizing his illness or having it enunciated by others, prepares to define himself as a more or less compliant partner in a therapeutic relationship. At this point in his career as patient, he typically confronts some helping agent—often, but not always, a physician.

For Parsons, however, social roles are *internalized*, and, therefore, emergent in behavior as "motivated." Socialization is, for Parsons, therefore a key process in understanding behavior at all stages of the life cycle, and with reference to all social roles. In childhood, the cultural norms of patienthood are learned as part of the standard sequence of cultural training, but, Parsons contends, socialization in the sick role continues as an aspect of therapy itself. Socialization, in this second type of usage, like therapy, is seen as a direct process of social control, as asymmetrical relationships, as emotionally laden and directed toward a terminus in which the dependent party has become independent as a fully functioning member of his society. Writing with Fox on illness and the modern urban family [54], Parsons states that the emotional relearning of psychotherapy comes closer to the model of socialization than does general medical practice, but therapy of any sort is illumined by the comparison. Four major features of the relationship are singled out for analysis; these features have the activity of the-rapist or parent as their point of reference. They are support, permissiveness, manipulation of reward, and denial of reciprocity. Briefly, they entail.

Support: the therapist expresses his obligation to be of assistance, to provide a stable figure on whom the patient may lean. He will be available, helpful, nurturant toward the patient's needs for dependency. It is understood, however, that the support is temporary and contingent on the patient's continuing efforts to get well.

Permissiveness: the therapist allows the patient to express feelings and indulge in actions which would not be acceptable in a nontherapeutic relationship. Again the dispensation is temporary and rooted in the idea that patient or child is for the moment unable to adhere strictly to ordinary norms of social intercourse. Permissiveness is granted with the justification that the patient, by reason of his illness, "can't help" doing certain things and cannot be held to usual expectations of responsibility.

Manipulation of reward: the therapist exerts leverage on the ill person by controlling certain rewards which are especially significant to the dependent party. As in child-rearing, the primary reward is probably approval, which can be offered or withheld at the discretion of the socializing or therapeutic agent. Rewards are given for doing the "right thing," for trying to "grow up" or to "get well."

Denial of reciprocity: the therapist, as a condition of the granting of *support* and *permissiveness*, withholds from the patient his own full interpersonal responsiveness. He keeps the relationship asymmetrical by refusing either to feel all the patient feels or to allow the patient access to his, the therapist's, true feelings. He will not meet fire with fire, irritation with irritation, adoration with adoration; for to do so would be to sacrifice the independent terrain on which he stands, and with it the potential for helping the other [54].

Assuredly the patient and child are not the same thing; one departs from a disturbed maturity, while the other is by definition "immature." Doctor and parent are unlike in the magnitude of their involvement with the dependent party, the depth of their emotional linkage, the range of their concerns for the other. Yet, Parsons and Fox argue, the processes of inducting an individual into society and of returning him to a full and sanctioned functioning in society are remarkably parallel. In particular, the patient's being as a child seems to be inseparable from the physical and emotional insult of illness, and the physician's being as a parent seems intrinsically commensurate with his superior knowledge and experience in the domain of health.

The Social Role of the Practitioner

All of the major sociological analyses of the physician's role [25, 30, 48, 50, 53] use the definition of "professions" by Carr-Saunders and Wilson [10, 11] as the point of departure. Parsons focuses on medicine's institutionalization of the "technical-specificity" of professional behavior as the base of its achieved status and autonomy, especially its right to police its own practitioners. Parsons further emphasizes the legitimizing function of the physician. Indeed, having defined the patient as a social deviant, it is natural to think of the practitioner first as an agent of social control. He is implicitly charged by society with the job of returning the affected person to full functioning, of reversing the tide of withdrawal so that the patient may again take up the threads of social obligations. The practitioner is the representative of dominant cultural values, and although there is increasing sophistication and self-consciousness—especially at certain junctures in psychotherapy—about the way in which he expresses these values, they are ordinarily intrinsic and need no deliberate articulation. That is, the practitioner is the symbol of the well and normal, of the non-ill encountering the ill. It might be guessed that his role as symbol of health is actually equal in importance to—and indeed inseparable from—his role as a technically equipped curative agent.

The professional attitude toward the patient has many facets, but its core is probably to be found in what Parsons has termed "affective neutrality." This orientation is the vital distancing mechanism which prevents the practitioner from becoming the patient's colleague in illness, from entering an emotional compact whose mute provisions would destroy his objective judgment and his therapeutic-educative leverage. Affective neutrality constitutes the physician's prime safeguard against the antitherapeutic dangers of countertransference. (In the type-case of psychoanalytic countertransference, Freud warns the male physician against returning the erotic overtures of a neurotic female patient [26, 27]. The practitioner's neutral posture does not mean that he is resolutely unfeeling, although the medical student may undergo a stage of flamboyant callousness in his struggle to adopt professional norms of conduct. It does mean that his primitive emotive response is controlled and complicated, that his feelings are at least partially prevented from affecting his technical judgment. Strictly speaking, one might say that the ideal practitioner exhibits sympathy but not empathy, intuitive understanding without full-scale involvement; he should understand the patient's feelings without feeling them himself. There are many ways in which this ideal of measured neutrality may be disturbed. And it may be the most artificial as well as the most essential element in the professional role—one of the hardest aspects to be "learned" during professional education [46].

Two other important dimensions of the professional attitude have been isolated by Parsons, who terms them the orientations toward "universalism" and "functional specificity." The universalistic theme connotes the practitioner's tendency to treat all patients alike; this does not, of course, mean the prescription of identical therapies but, rather, the viewing of patients as in some sense equal members of a universe of health and illness. Criteria that lie outside the field of health are considered irrelevant to the treatment process; judgment is guided by technical medical factors, and these are invariably applied to cases arrayed according to rational modes of classification. Again, a compelling adherence to universalistic norms is not easy to achieve; it may be summarily vitiated not only by the intrusion of ideally extraneous factors, such as the patient's ethnicity or financial capacity, but by problematic junctures in medicine itself. The efflorescence of social medicine, psychosomatic medicine, and psychiatry, with their emphases on family context and total social configurations in which the client is implicated, now calls into question both traditional schemes of disease classification and traditional models of uniform orientation toward patients.

The norm of functional specificity impels the professional to limit his attention and activities to a rigidly circumscribed sphere—to those things which are strictly "medical." The practitioner is not expected to be expert in religious or political counsel or to intrude into the patient's private affairs any further than the medical problem demands. Functional specificity is clearly most characteristic of Western medicine; it rests on the fine-grained division of labor found in industrial societies and on the development of a comprehensive science of medicine. There are significant currents working for and against this norm in modern professional life. Specialization, which is the butt of so much humor and the object of so much genuine concern, sometimes carries the mandate of specificity to extreme lengths. On the other hand, the increasing stress upon the whole patient and all his psychosocial circumstance means that the practitioner may become legitimately interested in a wider range of factors. In programs of total medical care, ancillary professionals such as the social worker may make the physician indirectly privy to a much more detailed case history than seems appropriate to the model of functional specificity. The line separating the medical sphere from the nonmedical is, then, a shifting one; especially in psychotherapy, the practitioner may at times be drawn into a set of global concerns more nearly comparable to those of the priest-healer than those of the hospital technician.

This completes, in outline, a description of the Parsonian model of the doctor-patient relationship. Although some questions and exceptions have been noted along the way, it has been presented in essentially unchanged (and unchallenged form). We turn now to a review of alternate models and to the critical literature which amplifies and changes the role analysis of patient-practitioner relationships.

THE SZASZ-HOLLENDER MODEL: BEHAVIORAL IMPLICATIONS OF ORGANIC SYMPTOMS

Parsons noted at the beginning of his formulation that illness is "partly biologically defined," and that the "state of the organism as a biological system" is related to the social systems of medical practice. His illustrations on this point tended to concentrate on two types of cases: first, *sexuality* as a threat to the obligation of the doctor to be affectively neutral and, second, the special case of *emotional* (psychiatric) *illness* as it differs in its implications from physical illness.

Szasz and Hollender, both physicians, saw more extensive behavioral implications of organic symptoms which they incorporated in a model of doctor-patient relationships based on a threefold typology.

1. ACTIVITY-PASSIVITY. Here the orientation is one in which the physician is active and the patient is passive. It has originated in, and is entirely appropriate for, emergencies (severe injuries, marked blood loss, delirium or coma). The patient is more or less completely helpless and the physician *does* something to him. Treatment takes place regardless of the patient's contribution. The relationship of the doctor to the patient is similar to that of the parent to the helpless infant.

2. GUIDANCE-COOPERATION. This model usually underlies the doctor-patient relationship when the circumstances are less desperate than those described above. It applies to most acute disorders and especially to those of an infectious type. Although the patient is ill, he is still keenly aware of what is going on, and he is capable of following directions and of exercising some judgment. Moreover, when the approach is geared at this level, the patient is expected to look up to his physician and to obey him. In essence, the patient says: "You know what is best for me. That is why I come to you. Tell me what to do and I will follow your directions." This model has its prototype in the relationship of the parent and his child (or adolescent).

3. MUTUAL PARTICIPATION. This approach is often useful for the management of chronic illness in which the treatment program is carried out by the patient with only occasional consultation with a physician (i.e., diabetes mellitus, myasthenia gravis, psoriasis, etc.). According to this model, the physician *helps the patient* to *help himself*. Since it requires a complex psychological and social organization on the part of the patient, it is rarely appropriate for children or for people who are mentally deficient, very poorly educated, or profoundly immature. Its prototype is the relationship of adult to adult (with one having specialized knowledge that the other needs) [67, 34].

One of Szasz and Hollender's clearest illustrations of the typology is diabetes mellitus, requiring, in their interpretation, mutual participation in the doctor-patient relationship. It is a well-known observation that response to illness is commonly more related to symptoms than to the seriousness of an illness. Pain, for example, often serves as a reminder to the patient that he is ill and, consequently, motivates him to follow treatment which he either knows or believes will help cure or assuage the illness. The symptoms of diabetes mellitus, except in emergency states, are not severe. With treatment, the diabetic can be relatively symptom-free. As a consequence, the patient's motivation for prolonged, usually lifelong, treatment is not supported by the symptoms of the illness. As long as the diabetic is faithful to his treatment, he usually does not feel sick, nor indeed does he show any signs to others that he is sick. It is required, however, that the diabetic patient participate in the treatment of his disease to an unusual extent. Although treatment methods are usually effective, it is necessary for the patient to be a willing, active partner in his own treatment [34].

When one considers that treatment is normally so hopeful, it seems paradoxical that a majority of diabetic patients do *not* achieve the major objective of treatment, normoglycemia. Commenting on this fact, a psychiatrist and an internist recently asserted that technical problems—regulation of insulin dosage, diet, and so on—probably account for only a small number of failures. "This suggests," they continued, "that the patient's attitude, the physician's approach and the interaction of physician and patient should be carefully scrutinized to determine their part in this problem"[35].

In other words, the effect of this disease upon the human organism (the patient's symptoms) and the known requirements for treatment (the application of the physician's technological skill and knowledge) produce a situation that, in turn, has requirements of its own. The situation determines to a large extent how the physician and the patient must act toward each other. In this case, for example, the patient is required to be active. He must participate with his physician, or his relationship with his physician will deteriorate and, with it, the medical treatment and his health. With another kind of illness, a different basic situation would be created [5].

Like Parsons, Szasz and Hollender analyze the problem in basically functional terms. Thus, the choice of a type of relationship that is inappropriate to the situation produces dysfunctional consequences. For example, consider guidance-cooperation rather than the mutual participation which Szasz and Hollender believe is required with diabetes mellitus. In the conception of the model, guidance-cooperation is appropriate mainly for acute processes in which suffering provides the motivation. There are many pitfalls when this approach is applied to a chronic illness like diabetes mellitus:

> Both physician and patient regard the treatment program as imposed by the physician (which is actually so). This creates the danger that the physician rather than the illness will be viewed as the frustrator and restrictor. Thus, instead of being an ally, the physician may be regarded as someone who is pitted against the patient, and a power struggle may ensue. In this way, an internal conflict about following a plan of treatment is externalized, and a battle is waged against the physician with seemingly little awareness of the self-destructive consequences. . . . *The emphasis here is on being a good or a bad patient and not on maintaining the best possible health* [34].

The Szasz-Hollender model further parallels Parsons in its asymmetry, leaning heavily on the parent-child analogy, with similar implications for the necessity of status difference between the roles, with the professional in firm control.

THE CHALLENGE TO PARSONS: STRUCTURE VERSUS FUNCTION

While, on the one hand, Spiegel, Kluckhohn, and others [5, 31, 42, 43,

63, 64, 67] built directly upon the Parsonian model, linking it with the small-group theory emerging from the laboratories of Bales and his co-workers [2, 52], and Szasz and Hollender confirmed the Parsonian assumptions unknowingly, a chorus of dissent was also finding its voice. Freidson, in our view, makes the most complete case, both against Parsons and for a different approach to the problem, although Mechanic, Zola, and Davis contribute significantly [16, 25, 48, 70].

Freidson, in his study of three types of medical practice as perceived by patients in one geographic area of New York City, found the Parsonian model deficient in its sensitivity to "salient features of reality" [23]. His critical stance is summarized in the following passage.

> A rather popular way of conceptualizing the doctor-patient relationship lies in constructing a formal model based on how physician and patient *should* behave. This sort of model underlies much of the hortatory writing of professionals about themselves and their patients. In a more neutral, elegant, and empirically useful way it also forms the basis for Talcott Parsons' analysis. . . .
>
> The virtue of this kind of analysis is that it provides us with a definition of (philosophically) the "essence" of the relationship. We may use it as a fixed standard by which we may measure the variable deviation of reality. However, it cannot really explain reality. It can only say what reality should be and note exceptions: it can note that the patient should submit to professional authority but, in fact, does not.
>
> The deficiency of the approach does not entirely lie in its emphasis on ideal expectations rather than actual behavior. Parsons seems to derive his definition of the sick role from one quite limited perspective—the physician's. Much more of reality could be traced intelligibly if definition of the doctor-patient relationship could pay attention to all the perspectives involved in what Merton calls the "role-set" [49]. The sick role, for example, might be defined not in general or from one point of view, but from the points of view of the patient himself, of his lay associates, of the physician, and, if in a hospital, of the nurses and any other persons significant to the process of treatment. By so doing, we could anticipate and explain the conflict that appears in the doctor-patient relationship by pointing to the varying expectations of all the members of the role-set.
>
> Superior as this modified approach may be, however, it is still not quite enough. It does not allow us to determine the weight we must assign to each perspective, and so does not allow us to assess the importance of each perspective in exacerbating or reducing conflict. An expectation, like an attitude or an opinion, has no influence in itself. Simply the fact that two patients expect with about the same intensity that their doctor take an interest in them does not mean that their doctor will take equal interest in each. The response to an expectation is at least a partial function of the influence lying behind the person with that expectation. Influence does not inhere in the expectation, but in the position of the person holding it. In addition, the very possibility of conforming to an expectation is a partial function of the limits imposed by the situation in which that expectation is expressed.
>
> In order to understand and predict the chance that an expectation will be met, then, it is not enough to specify the expectations of everyone included in the doctor's or patient's role-set. Attention must be paid to the social structure in which those perspectives are located, and there must be systematic specification of the variable situation and position of influence in which doctors and patients find themselves. Furthermore, . . . it is realistic to see the relationship as a form of conflict [14], the compromise of practice shifting now one way, now another, as the influence of the participants' positions shifts [23].

Parsons thus is accused of seeing the

doctor-patient relationship from too limited a perspective (that of the physician), assigning to expectations a force for the influence of behavior which does not exist, and of failing to perceive that influence derives from the position of the person in a relationship. Most important, Freidson accuses him of ignoring the necessity of conflict in human relationships. In his own words, "the professional expects patients to accept what he recommends on his terms; patients seek services on their own terms. In that each seeks to gain his own terms, there is conflict" [23].

To fully understand the theoretical implications of Freidson's position, it is important to keep in mind his own explanation of how he uses theory in an applied setting:

> There is little doubt that ultimate explanation of problems of applied medicine lies in the examination of more than one level of reality. . . . By concentrating on the structural level I hope not only to emphasize something that has not received the attention in medical sociology that it deserves, but also to avoid the confusion of a more eclectic approach. What this concentration may gain in clarity, however, it risks losing by distortion. The risk may be attenuated somewhat by specifying the nature of the distortion so that it may be taken into account in evaluating the results.
>
> Structural analysis deals with constraints. Such personal characteristics as spontaneity and creativity, perceptiveness and honesty are seen either as consequences of the analytical variable itself, or as irrelevant to an analysis that holds such variables equal. What are stressed are boundaries to possible behavior. As Selznick put it, "Attention being focused on the structural conditions which influence behavior, we are directed to emphasize constraints, the limitations of alternatives imposed by the system upon its participants. This will tend to give pessimistic overtones to the analysis, since such factors as good will and intelligence will be deemphasized. As a consequence of the central status of constraint, tension and dilemmas will be highlighted" [61]. Differences that bear on behavior independently of social structure—differences between the conscientious and the slovenly doctor, the cooperative and intelligent, and the resistant and ignorant patient—will be largely ignored. This obviously influences the shape and sense of the discussion [23].

Having cautioned his readers concerning the negative cast of structural analysis, Freidson plunges ahead and concludes that the doctor-patient relationship is most effectively analyzed within the framework of a "clash of perspectives." As he himself states, however, the evaluation of this approach requires "data first, then conceptual analysis," so we must ask: What kind of data does he bring to bear in the argument of this approach?

Freidson's basic challenge to Parsons derives from his study of the attitudes and behavior of patients who had connections with Montefiore Hospital in the Bronx (New York City), through three different types of organized medical care. For one group everyday care was provided by *an interprofessional team* working in a prepaid, centralized medical group; everyday care was provided to members of the second group by *individual* pediatricians and internists who worked within the framework of a prepaid, centralized medical group; and in the third, everyday care was provided by individual practitioners working in their own scattered offices in situation conventional, solo, fee-for-service practice. The design allowed for focus on "structural differences between practices. When patients chose to use one practice rather than another, it was possible to illuminate their choice by reference to the way in which the structure of the chosen practice fitted into the structure of patient life." Four questionnaires were administered to the various types of patients (according to form of medical care), and intensive interviews were conducted in the homes of a selected subsample, chosen to represent the different types.

One of the main findings of this study centers on the patients' criteria for evaluating medical care. "... In every intensive interview," Freidson writes, "there were expressed two major criteria: first, in desirable medical care the practitioner must have *interest* in his patients; second, in desirable medical care the physician must be *competent*." Moreover, these did not appear to be most accurately discussed as two separate entities: "... where simple statements could be most fully explored the patients were rather insistent that one [interest] could not very well exist without the other [competence]" [23]. It might well be asked, Is this finding not a clear supporting evidence for the validity of Parsons' pattern variable, affective neutrality?

Concerning the implications of the organization of medical care, from the view of the patient, Freidson found that his subjects saw the solo practitioner as one likely to take more personal interest in them than would practitioners in the prepaid medical group. And, in what seemed a paradox, the same patients, even though they think prepayment encourages a "charity attitude," also think that it encourages technically superior care.

But for Freidson, the most important of his data appeared to describe what he refers to as a "lay referral system." Many instances are cited from his interviews to show that each patient goes through a set of rather definite steps in handling his illness. "The steps constitute stages of forming an opinion about the nature of the complaint and what to do about it. Consultation with other laymen is often crucial to the opinion that is formed and to subsequent consultation with professional practitioners. The concept of the lay referral system may be used to analyze the events that occur during the history of a complaint" [23]. Warning that it is easy to underestimate the significance of lay influence in the utilization of medical care, Freidson says that such interpersonal influence is organized in the same patterned sequence that the professional side of medical care contains. Within this network, the doctor is but one of many consultants, and what is more, each consultant, whether formally a professional or not, is a potential source of diagnosis, prescription, and also referrals.

It is at this point that Freidson diverges most strikingly from the Parsonian model. Whereas Parsons sees each patient as behaving out of a socialization pattern that is part of culture and subculture, Freidson sees the patient responding on the basis of more immediate sources of reference—his *lay referral structure*. Freidson accepts the concept of differences according to variables of culture, socioeconomic status, and other societal systems which are dealt with in the Parsonian analysis. The differences between them would appear to be based upon varying assumptions about the potency of immediate situations and interpersonal networks.

Parsons ultimately relies on a concept of the psychological internalization of patterned socialization experience deriving from the normative values of the greater society. Freidson, in contrast, bypasses the psychological and sees more direct influence, change, and reinforcement from interpersonal networks that are part of everyday life.

The lay referral system, of course, lends itself as a concept to a picture of patient-practitioner relationships in which two distinct social systems are involved, rather than one. There is a professional system containing the doctor and a lay system containing the patient. Although these systems are part of a larger whole from which doctor and patient derive latent identities, they have an immediate relevance which stimulates a process of bargaining between interests based essentially upon the structure of each role situation rather than upon the common, *reciprocal* needs of a combined professional-client system. In other words, the distinction is the classic one between functional analysis within what is called social system theory (Parsons) and the structural analysis that has come to be associated with the University of Chicago Department of Sociology and its students, a form of analysis which generally leads to concepts of a conflict theory.

For Parsons, illness is most essentially a biological state with social implications and consequences; the sick role involves a separate motivational step. In this conception, there is choice and variable behavior in the sick role; in illness, substantially there is none. Thus Parsons argues for the legitimacy of the physician's authority as the agent of social control over *illness*, by his (the physician's) achieved expertise (functional specificity) in judging what the valid connections are between illness and sick-role behavior.

Freidson, on the other hand, asserts that medicine is a monopoly with the right to create illness as an official social role. In his words:

> Unlike Parsons, I do not argue merely that medicine has the power to legitimize one's acting sick by conceding that he really is sick. My argument goes further than that. I argue here that by virtue of being the authority on what illness "really" is, *medicine creates the social possibilities for acting sick.* In this sense, medicine's monopoly includes the right to create illness as an *official social role*.... It is part of being a profession to be given the official power to define and therefore create the shape of problematic segments of social behavior: the judge determines what is legal and who is guilty, the priest what is holy and who is profane, the physician what is normal and who is sick [25, 37].

In these terms, Freidson articulates the basic sociological position underlying the "labeling theory" of Szasz, Scheff, and Goffman in their analyses of mental illness [29, 58, 59, 66]. This is developed most extensively in Freidson's recent writings on illness as social deviance [24, 25].

THE ROLE-SET: THE CLASSIC DYAD EXPANDED

Like the Parsonian model, much, probably most, analysis of the doctor-patient relationship has focused on the situation of the solo private practice of medicine. This perception of medical treatment as an essentially two-person interaction is remarkably persistent, notwithstanding a broad consensus that the validity of the treatment dyad has been narrowed to an increasingly small range of medical care problems. The acute illness fits best the dyadic model, but we are in a phase of medical history in which the threat of death by acute, infectious illness has been reduced dramatically, while the threat to life of chronic and debilitating physical and mental illnesses has moved to center stage. Prevention has become the watchword as cure-potential has advanced for the infectious diseases. Rehabilitation has similarly become the competitor of curative treatment as chronicity shoulders the acute conditions from the spotlight of concern. But prevention directs attention to patient populations, and rehabilitation is a process that generally involves professional teams. Where then can one fit the patient-practitioner dyad?

The answer is not simple. It involves a sometimes subtle and ambiguous division of tasks and their assigned values by both parties. Thus, as we have seen, Freidson's data show that patients separate issues of practitioner concern and competence. They prefer that both should be joined in one practitioner, and they *perceive* the solo practitioner as being more concerned and interested in his patients, but on the other hand, they believe that the *competence* of doctors in a prepaid medical group is superior. In medical crisis, they seek group-practice care; in more routine medical situations, they are likely to go outside the prepaid system and consult solo physicians.

On the practitioner's side, a similar division of labor appears to occur. It is most clear in problems of chronicity and especially where disability is involved. This is the classic situation of rehabilitation medicine.

It has been observed that concepts of rehabilitation have been derived mainly from work done with the physically disabled and have to do largely with an individual's *capacity* to function in relation to his *actual* functioning [22, 60, 64]. This asserts a two-step process: First, the specific task of establishing capability and, second, a teaching-learning process of utilizing capabilities. The first step is defined as the specifically medical aspect of the process; the second, specifically the "rehabilitative," aspect tends to be assigned to the "auxiliary" therapist. In effect, this preserves the main practitioner-patient relationship as a doctor-patient dyad. The practitioner team is a separate and second step in the process—second in importance as well as in the natural time order. Moreover, even in the second part of the rehabilitation process, the formal dyad persists as a model. The so-called paramedical specialists or "auxiliary professionals" are trained to approach the patient very much on the same basis as the doctor does. The patient is described as though he existed alone, separated from any kind of social world. All of the emphasis is on the individual and his traits. A true integration of functions in a team is rare. In other words, the emphasis remains on the formal dyadic social structure as the main instrument of both treatment and rehabilitation, with the former conceived in strictly medical terms and the latter defined as a learning process [6].

This picture of the supremely dominant physician and the isolated individual patient undoubtedly represents the peak point in the history of the growth of modern science as a partner of the medical profession. The physician scientist became the high priest of the hospital as the major institution of medical care, while the function of the family in illness was attenuated, and the sick role was isolated from lay sources of care. This point of concentration of the authority of the doctor's role occurred in the generation just prior to World War II. Since the war, however, the role of the physician has changed [67], and with it, the status of the patient. As persistent as the formal dyad is, concepts of "therapeutic community," team medicine, and patient culture press strongly for official sanction by the medical profession in the organization of medical care.

These are, however, changes in normative expectations about the sick role. *Does this mean that the Parsonian model needs only revisions that reflect changed historical or cultural conditions, but that its basic functional assumptions are valid?*

In effect, this is not the place in

which a complete answer to this theoretical question can be attempted. The addition of role-set as a concept certainly would appear to be compatible with the Parsonian model. Freidson again demurs, however, although he regards the Merton role-set concept with strong favor. The exception that Freidson takes to a Parsonian adaptation of the role-set framework to the sick role model is contained in his conception of the clash of perspectives.

Discussions in depth of the institutional components of the patient-practitioner role-set occur elsewhere in this volume. Included are the hospital (Chap. 12), medical profession and related occupational groups (Chaps. 9, 11, 14), and the community (Chap. 15). To conclude our own discussion we will look selectively at some examples of research that seem particularly relevant to the issues which have been raised.

TRENDS IN EMPIRICAL INQUIRY

Evidence has accumulated which supports the argument that doctors are strongly moved by individual preferences in their ability to relate to patients. Taken together with descriptive studies of medical education, which show that interpersonal skills are not seriously or rigorously taught as part of professional training, questions have been raised about universalism and affective neutrality as intrinsic attributes of the doctor's role [48]. According to the Parsonian model, these are internalized professional ethics in professional autonomy. However, studies by Caplovitz, Davis, Levine, and Mumford may be interpreted to cast doubt on this formulation [9, 17, 45, 51]. Social control of the physician's behavior would seem to be as important as the function of the physician to control the sick role. The role-set of the doctor may be argued to be basically a day-to-day environment and a "membership" reference group, *not* a generalized professional norm.

At the critical points of career decision, the interpersonal side of medicine is a significant motivating factor. Medical students see themselves, as they begin their studies, as "intellectual humanitarians," as scientist-healers who will be expert but also "doing something that helps." However, American medical schools and the clinical institution they have spawned—the university hospital—have become "temples of science" [8, 12]. As such, their effects upon the basic humanitarianism of the practitioner's self-image have been the subject of concern in the profession. With anxiety, the dehumanizing effect of medical training has been called the "cynical-training" of doctors.

Although the evidence is not complete, data have been suggested which support the concern that medical education has tended toward training in cynicism [20]. The problem, however, is more complicated than one of attitudinal teaching-learning, which is dominated by one or another ethical theme. Thus, Becker and others argue that the process is more one of *maturation* than of loss of idealism [4]. In somewhat similar terms, Fox also describes a developmental process, rather than a distinct change from humanitarianism to cynicism [21, 46]. But Fox describes a purposeful and specific maturation, whereas Becker and others see the process as a relatively random order of experiences which serve to correct youthfully naïve stereotypes.

The question is whether the professional identity of the physician is an individual product arrived at in an orderly process of adult socialization (medical education) or whether the behavior of the physician is primarily dominated by the structural components of his working situations when he finally is practicing medicine.

Caplovitz, in one of the few intensive studies that touch on this issue, provides evidence that clearly challenges the notion that the medical school is the socialization agent of the values of medicine [9]. He conducted his study at "an outstanding medical school in the Eastern United States," seeking to find out "which components of the physician's role are emphasized during medical school." His analysis focused on "the faculty members nominated by students as outstanding role performers—men they are likely to take as role models—and the students judged by the faculty to be particularly promising physicians." His basic finding was "that the acquisition of technical knowledge and skills is given much more emphasis than the acquisition of medical values at this stage in the socialization process. Both students and faculty," Caplovitz concluded, "evaluate each other as professionals on the basis of skills and knowledge and not on the basis of values. In other words, values are not a major aspect of socialization in the medical school."

Mumford, in a recent study of the education of interns, adds some of the most important data now available in our efforts to understand the process of becoming a physician in modern society [51]. She compared the experience of interns in a university hospital with that of interns in a community hospital having no medical school affiliation. She analyzed the development of two increasingly separate traditions in medical care—represented, on the one hand, by academic medicine and, on the other, by everyday medicine in the community. The implications for attitudes and behavior toward patients are striking.

The two medicines of these unlike hospitals are mediated by very different institutional reward patterns. In the university hospital the reward pattern is that of the "creators" in medicine, the cosmopolitan scientists of teaching and research. In the community hospital, the attendings are "purveyors" of medicine, supported by the rewards of individual esteem from other *local* practitioners and from patients, and not, as in the academic centers, rewarded for priorities in scientific advance. The consequences for the doctor-patient relationship are obvious. The young physician in the university hospital is thinking constantly of how his behavior will be judged by his superiors. In the community hospital, the house officer, working much more on his own, comes to think of himself as a "true doctor" sooner than his university counterpart. He learns to get along well with all sorts of patients, he is more likely to try to make sure that the patient understand his illness and treatment, and in other ways is constrained by the situation to feel more sensitivity to patient's feelings than does his colleague in the academic setting, with its emphasis on "interesting cases," orderly and knowledgeable procedure, and technique. Kendall, in another one-of-a-kind study—in this case involving intensive interviews in a variety of medical practice settings—documents further the nature and actual consequences of tensions between academic and nonacademic medicine in the United States [41].

From these types of evidence, recent students of the problem have concluded that it is the structure of the organization of medical care which exerts the primary influence on the physician's behavior toward patients [25, 48]. Whatever his personal attitudes, the constraints upon ongoing behavior are part of the organized setting in which he works. He *must* abide by these constraints. Opposition involves the threat of sanction; agreement promises rewards.

Studies of physician behavior, *in situ*, are sparse [13, 55]; therefore arguments about the doctor's role, when supported by any evidence at all, still rely heavily on an abstract level of analysis, with much extrapolation from existing research.

In contrast, research on patient attitudes and behavior is very active and varied in approach—too much so to allow for more than a brief, selected view here. Sociological research about patients has followed a pattern which, in effect, recapitulates the "career" of patienthood; in the first instance, the major focus was on differential perceptions of illness, according to variables especially of class and culture [44, 57]. Most recently, a large number of studies have been concerned either primarily or in an important but secondary sense with what has been called "patient compliance"; that is, to what extent and for what reasons the patient follows the prescribed regimen of the doctor [18, 19, 40, 51]. Between the perception of illness and the consequences of the doctor-patient relationship, the question of how patients choose their doctors [3], and the communication process within the relationship have been explored in a variety of forms of inquiry.

In large measure, the issues of illness perception and illness behavior [48] are overlapping in the importance to both of class and cultural variables. The early studies by Koos for the former and of Saunders for the latter are now classics [44, 57]. Koos initiated a deep channel of inquiry concerning class differences in the perception and weighting of specific symptoms, and Saunders similarly anticipated a rich variety of descriptions of how culture affects both the perceptions of and responses to such fundamental aspects of illness as pain, bleeding, and swelling.

At this point, it is notable that the theoretical issues between functional and structural analysis are not, as far as one can tell, important for the process of inquiry. Both views incorporate the issues of class and culture in their formulations. This can be seen in a brief exploration of the two themes.

CONVERSATIONS ACROSS CLASSES

If the health professional and the patient differ in their mastery of health knowledge and techniques, this basic imbalance may be exaggerated by other dissimilarities in the social worlds from which they come. And, indeed, the gulf in technical vocabulary and in the conceptual framework through which illness is viewed tends to widen as the social-class origins of the two parties become more remote from one another. To a very considerable extent, the best-known conceptions of the sick role reflect a middle-class value pattern on which physician and client agree; this pattern emphasizes the merits of individual responsibility, deliberate striving and grooming of the self toward health, mastery and activism in the carrying out of normal social roles—particularly in the occupational sphere. Above all, the pattern assumes that rational problem solving is the only viable behavior in the face of difficulty. Health is to be sought and illness expeditiously cured: the fate of misfortune is not to be passively bemoaned or stoically accepted.

Yet, of course, the motivations and expectations that underlie this posture can be taken for granted only in a slice of the population. This slice is the advantaged, privileged sector of our society, overwhelmingly white, educated, and affluent. Patients are well-fed and well-clothed, comfortably housed, and steadily employed. If the world is not quite everywhere and always their oyster, it is at any rate a social universe to be mastered, manipulated, and controlled in the interest of attaining the prestige and possessions that advertisers knowingly term "the good things of life." What of the large numbers of Americans who lie outside this advantaged sector but who exhibit an abundance of health needs?

There is a good deal of evidence that individuals of lower socioeconomic status not only face heightened risks from the majority of illnesses but also are least likely to seek and receive adequate health care. Beyond the strictly economic aspects of the situation (and these are still not at all negligible, despite the movement toward a more solid flooring of services for the poor), we find a whole complex of motivational and life-style features that render patient-practitioner relations uneasy. Helper and helped do not speak the same language—and this is not merely a question of technical vocabulary. To be sure, research indicates that the poor and members of some minority ethnic groups misunderstand a major fraction of the terms conventionally used by doctors and nurses [56, 62]. Probably more important, however, are differences in the assumptions that lie behind the words. To take a single example, there is a distinctive concept of "time" and its meaning implicit in the traditional medical helping arrangement. This concept assumes that people are highly aware of the passage of time, and that they monitor time as a normal aspect of their behavior; such awareness is clearly essential to self-medication and the keeping of medical appointments. Further, it assumes a specific orientation toward future time, for which people build toward a desirable state of affairs; for instance, they do exercises for the progressive reattainment of muscle function or look forward to completing a course of unpleasant or inconvenient medication. But this view represents a middle-class orientation to the clock and the calendar; millions of lower-class patients do not habitually monitor time, living instead by sun, season, and the fabric of significant life events [39]. Millions, too, as described by Allison Davis [15], do not defer present pleasures or schedule themselves in favor of a desired future; their lives have not taught them that a concept of the future is workable, since in their experience of hazardous daily living, the future has never arrived, the rewards for this sort of husbanding of self and resources have not been received.

Instances of such divergence in orientation could be multiplied. In psychotherapy, it has commonly been found that many lower-class patients lack habits of self-expression and introspection, and are simply not used to objectifying their emotional life. In many helping relationships, the avenues of discussion and flow of information are clogged by the disadvantaged patient's often well-founded mistrust and fear of authority figures; his evasive or mutely accepting posture does not augur well for a sustained therapeutic interchange.

And, to be sure, conversations between the classes are not thwarted solely by obdurate or unaware behavior on the part of lower-class clients. The health professional wears his own perceptual blinders. Not only may he be limited to a middle-class stereotype of the responsive and responsible patient, and yearn for the client to be more nearly like himself, but he customarily carries a certain moral freight. The message on this freight is that the disadvantaged patient is not just different, but is morally bad or inferior. The pattern of illness itself may be unconsciously interpreted as a tangible sign of the lack of grace: If the patient had cared for himself and ordered his life differently, perhaps his health state would be better.

It seems plain that patient-practitioner relations between individuals of widely varying social-class identities are colored by a series of difficulties. Some of these may be overcome by shrewd and persistent education of *both* the health professional and his prospective client, by education to make them more aware of each other. Some may be mitigated through employing new varieties of health workers; for example, there is increasing effort to train auxiliary personnel as a species of health intermediaries who can stand between the classes and interpret in both directions. Perhaps most critical, however, will be attempts to discover or invent new models of the doctor-patient relationship itself, to find effective alternatives to the classic model of therapeutic asymmetry.

CONVERSATIONS ACROSS CULTURES

An important share of American medicine's activities is directed to the health care of patients whose culture differs markedly from the prevailing culture of the United States. Part of the process of development in the "developing" nations is a health process; this must be the case, both because industrial productivity demands a population functioning at high levels of wellness and because westernization itself generates health risks as a fraction of the human price exacted for rapid change. There no longer really seems to be any point in debating the desirability of the great tide of change from traditional agricultural societies to urban industrial ones. The change is, in fact, desired by those who must change, and no romantic nostalgia for a less hurried and harried way of life appears to stand a chance when stacked against automobiles, refrigerators, and the civility of the city.

The basic consideration in the introduction of Western scientific medicine to non-Western cultures is that the health techniques and knowledge cannot be transferred as isolated parcels. That is, Western models of medical practice or of health theory do not stand alone as cultural fragments but are woven into a larger system of custom and value. Patient-practitioner relations represent peculiarly interesting and complicated conversations across cultures [62]. Lyle Saunders has provided perhaps the clearest and most comprehensive statement of what cultural differences mean for the social role of the practitioner:

> When the practice of medicine involves the application of elements of the institution of medicine in one culture to the people of another, or from one subculture to members of another subculture within the same cultural group, what is done or attempted by those in the healing roles may not be fully understood or correctly evaluated by those in the patient roles. Conversely, the responses of those on the patient side of the interaction may not conform to the expectations of those on the healing side. To the extent that this occurs, the relationship may be unsatisfactory to everyone concerned.
>
> When persons of widely dissimilar cultural or subcultural orientations are brought together in a therapeutic relationship, the probability of a mutually satisfactory outcome may be increased if those in the healing roles know something of their own culture and that of the patient and are aware of the extent to which behavior on both sides of the relationship is influenced by cultural factors. An even higher probability of satisfaction may result if the pro-

fessional people are willing and able to modify elements from their medicine so as to make them fit the expectations of the laymen with whom they are working [57].

The hazards we marked in the health care of the lower-class patient by a middle-class professional are repeated and magnified in cross-cultural medicine. Once again, the helping agent is called on to examine his own unstated assumptions about the "proper" roles of the parties to the transaction, to strip out the necessary therapeutic aspects of the relationship from the merely conventional features. Health professionals in foreign settings must, as Saunders avers, look closely at their own culture and attempt an empathic reaching out toward understanding of the patient's culture. Above all, they must be sensitive to the fact that a given item of health behavior is part of a system that transcends health affairs as such; not only does this systematic character shape the meaning of health events but it also implies that health changes will influence (and be influenced by) other sorts of social change.

Examples of patient-practitioner relations going wrong in cross-cultural interactions are legion; examples of successful health care are far fewer. One of the familiar difficulties for the male physician is the reluctance of women in many traditional cultures to be examined and treated if this involves intimate access to the body. Another prominent sequence of misunderstanding occurs when the Western health agent underestimates the relevance of kinship ties to patient behavior; he may regard the patient's relatives as rank intruders if they accompany the patient to his office or insist on always being present on home visits. Yet in many societies the illness of one member is a profoundly family affair, in which relatives lend strength —rather than disrupt therapy—through their presence.

Once again, as in the cross-social class situation, effective helping can often be achieved by utilizing health intermediaries who stand between Western medical professionals and an indigenous population. Creating new auxiliary health roles of this kind has proved to be of value in several settings; a notable example is the Cornell Many Farms project, in which a Navajo intermediary termed a health visitor served in a tuberculosis treatment program as go-between for Western practitioners in the clinic and Navajo patients in their widely scattered homes [1].

CONCLUSIONS

The goals of this discussion have been centered upon outlining the conceptual frameworks which have emerged from more than three decades of diverse and intensive analysis by sociologists of the patient-practitioner relationship. We have only touched upon the empirical studies which, as though thrust by the momentum of earlier theoretical polemics, are building an increasingly varied literature. Fortunately, two recent books provide thorough coverage of this literature and clear, incisive interpretations [25, 48].

The arguments of functional and structural analysis, as we have discussed them, have important implications, we believe, for the future of medical practice. The implications of each are quite different for issues of policy; and there is no doubt that questions of policy are pressing academic sociology for meaningful contributions to decision making in the everyday operation of medicine's major institutions. Although it is well known that policy making is not inherently rational, the social sciences have traditionally accepted their assignment precisely as a challenge toward grasping and clarifying the patterns of the nonlogical and nonrational in human behavior. How the junction of tasks between policy operation and scientific interpretation will occur in medical practice—if it will at all—is not known. All we can say, in conclusion, is that sociologists have accumulated a considerable bank of knowledge about the nature of patient-practitioner relationships in modern Western society.

REFERENCES

1. Adair, John and Kurt Deuschle, *The People's Health: Anthropology and Medicine in a Navajo Community.* New York: Appleton-Century-Crofts, 1970.
2. Bales, Robert F., *Interaction Process Analysis.* Reading, Mass. : Addison-Wesley Publishing Company, Inc., 1950.
3. Balint, Michael, *The Doctor, His Patient and the Illness.* New York: International Universities Press, 1957.
4. Becker, Howard S., Everett C. Hughes, and Anselm L. Strauss, *Boys in White: Student Culture in Medical School.* Chicago: University of Chicago Press, 1961, pp. 15–16, 34, 419–20.
5. Bloom, Samuel W., *The Doctor and His Patient: A Sociological Interpretation.* New York: Russell Sage Foundation, 1963, and (paperback edition) The Free Press, 1965.
6. ———, "Rehabilitation as an Interpersonal Process," in Marvin Sussman, ed., *Sociology and Rehabilitation.* Washington, D.C.: The American Sociological Association, 1966, pp. 114–31.
7. Bock, Arlie V., "Lawrence Joseph Henderson, 1878–1942," *Transactions of the Academy of American Physicians,* 57 (1942), 17–19.
8. Burling, Temple, Edith M. Lentz, and Robert N. Wilson, *The Give and Take in Hospitals.* New York: G. P. Putnam's Sons, 1956.
9. Caplovitz, David, "Student-Faculty Relations in Medical School: A Study of Professional Socialization." Unpublished doctoral dissertation Columbia University, 1961.
10. Carr-Saunders, A. M. and P. A. Wilson, *The Professions.* London: Oxford University Press, 1933.
11. ———, "Professions," *Encyclopedia of the Social Sciences* (1934), Vol. 12, pp. 476–80.
12. Churchill, Edward D., "The Development of the Hospital," in Nathaniel W. Faxon, ed., *The Hospital in Contemporary Life.* Cambridge: Harvard University Press, 1949.
13. Clute, Kenneth, F., *The General Practitioner: A Study of Medical Education in Ontario and Nova Scotia.* Toronto: University of Toronto Press, 1963.
14. Dahrendorf, Ralf, "Out of Utopia: Toward a Reorientation of Sociological Analysis," *American Journal of Sociology,* 64 (September, 1958), 115–27.
15. Davis, Allison, "The Motivation of the Underprivileged Worker," in William Foote Whyte, ed., *Industry and Society.* New York: McGraw-Hill Book Company, 1946, pp. 84–106.
16. Davis, Fred, "Deviance Disavowal: The Management of Strained Interaction by the Visibly Physically Handicapped," in Howard Becker, ed., *The Other Side.* New York: The Free Press, 1964, pp. 119–37.
17. Davis, Milton S., "Attitudinal and Behavioral Aspects of the Doctor-Patient Relationship as Expressed and Exhibited by Medical Students and Their Mentors," *Journal of Medical Education,* 43 (March, 1968), 338.
18. ———, "Variations in Patients' Compliance with Doctors' Advice," *American Journal of Public Health,* 58 (February, 1968), 274–88.
19. ———, "Predicting Non-Compliant Behavior," *Journal of Health and Social Behavior,* 8 (December, 1967), 265–71.

20. ERON, LEONARD D., "The Effect of Medical Education on Attitudes: A Follow-up Study," *Journal of Medical Education*, 33, Part 2 (October, 1958) 25–33.
21. FOX, RENEE C., "Training for Uncertainty," in Robert K. Merton, George G. Reader, and Patricia L. Kendall, eds., *The Student Physician*. Cambridge: Harvard University Press, 1957, pp. 207–41.
22. FREEMAN, HOWARD E. AND OZZIE G. SIMMONS, *The Mental Patient Comes Home*. New York: John Wiley & Sons, Inc., 1963, p. 34.
23. FREIDSON, ELIOT, *Patient Views of Medical Practice*. New York: Russell Sage Foundation, 1961.
24. ———, "Disability as Social Deviance," in Marvin B. Sussman, ed., *Sociology and Rehabilitation*. Washington, D.C.: American Sociological Association, 1965.
25. ———, *Profession of Medicine*. New York: Dodd, Mead & Company, 1970.
26. FREUD, SIGMUND, "Observations on Transference-Love" (Further Recommendations on the Technique of Psychoanalysis, III) in James Strachey, ed., *The Complete Psychological Works of Sigmund Freud*, Vol. 12. London: The Hogarth Press, Ltd., 1958. See especially pp. 165–66.
27. ———, "The Dynamics of Transference," in James Strachey, ed., *The Complete Psychological Works of Sigmund Freud,* Vol. 12. London: The Hogarth Press, Ltd., 1958, p. 105.
28. ———, "Analysis Terminable and Interminable," *International Journal of Psychoanalysis*, 18 (1937).
29. GOFFMAN, ERVING, *Asylums*. Garden City, N.Y.: Doubleday & Company, Inc., Anchor Books, 1961.
30. GOODE, WILLIAM J., "Encroachment, Charlatanism, and the Emerging Profession: Psychology, Sociology, and Medicine," *American Sociological Review*, 25 (December, 1960), 902–3.
31. GORDON, GERALD, *Role Theory and Illness*. New Haven, Conn.: College and University Press, 1966.
32. HENDERSON, LAWRENCE J., *Pareto's General Sociology: a Physiologist's Interpretation*. Cambridge: Harvard University Press, 1937.
33. ———, "Physician and Patient as a Social System," *New England Journal of Medicine*, 212 (1935), 819–23.
34. HOLLENDER, MARC H., *The Psychology of Medical Practice*. Philadelphia: W.B. Saunders Company, 1958.
35. ——— AND LEONARD A. STINE, "The Medical Patient," in Marc H. Hollender, ed., *The Psychology of Medical Practice*. Philadelphia: W.B. Saunders Company, 1958, pp. 35–88.
36. HOLLINGSHEAD, AUGUST B. AND FREDERICK C. REDLICH, *Social Class and Mental Illness*. New York: John Wiley & Sons, Inc., 1958.
37. HOLZNER, BURKART, *Reality Construction in Society*. Cambridge: Schenkman Publishing Company, Inc., 1968, p. 68.
38. HOMANS, GEORGE CASPAR, "Contemporary Theory in Sociology," in Robert E. L. Faris, ed., *Handbook of Modern Sociology*. Chicago: Rand McNally & Company, 1964, pp. 951–77.
39. HORTON, JOHN, "Time and Cool People," *Transaction*, 4 (April, 1967), 5–12.
40. JOHANNSEN, W. J., G. A. HELLMUTH, AND T. SORAUFF, "On Accepting Medical Recommendations: Experiences with Patients in a Cardiac Work Classification Unit," *Archives of Environmental Health*, 12 (January, 1966), 63–69.
41. KENDALL, PATRICIA L., *The Relationship Between Medical Educators and Medical Practitioners: Sources of Strain and Occasions for Cooperation*. Evanston, Ill.: Association of American Medical Colleges, 1965.
42. KLUCKHOHN, FLORENCE R., "Variations in the Basic Values of Family Systems," *Social Casework*, 39 (February, 1958), 63–72.
43. ———, AND JOHN P. SPIEGEL, *Integration and Conflict in Family Behavior*, Group for the Advancement of Psychiatry, Report No. 27. Topeka, Kans., August, 1954.
44. KOOS, EARL L., *The Health of Region-*

ville. New York: Columbia University Press, 1954.

45. LEVINE, GENE N., "The Good Physician: A Study of Physician-Patient Interaction," Working Paper No. 3, Evaluation Studies of the Cornell Comprehensive Care and Teaching Program, Bureau of Applied Social Research, Columbia University, June, 1957 (mimeo).
46. LIEF, HAROLD I. AND RENEE FOX, "The Medical Student's Training for Detached Concern," in H. I. Lief, V. F. Lief, and N. L. Lief, eds., *The Psychological Basis of Medical Practice.* New York: Harper & Row, Publishers, Hoeber Medical Books, 1963, pp. 12–35.
47. MARTI-IBANEZ, FELIX, ed., *Henry Sigerist on the History of Medicine.* New York: M.D. Publications, Inc., 1960, p. 26.
48. MECHANIC, DAVID, *Medical Sociology: A Selective View.* New York, The Free Press, 1968.
49. MERTON, ROBERT K., "The Role-Set: Problems in Sociological Theory," *British Journal of Sociology*, 8 (June, 1957), 112 ff.
50. ———, "Some Preliminaries to a Sociology of Medical Education," Robert K. Merton, George G. Reader, and Patricia L. Kendall, eds., *The Student Physician.* Cambridge: Harvard University Press, 1957.
51. MUMFORD, EMILY, *Interns: From Students to Physicians.* Cambridge: Harvard University Press, 1970.
52. OLMSTEAD, MICHAEL S., *The Small Group.* New York: Random House, Inc., 1959.
53. PARSONS, TALCOTT, *The Social System.* New York: The Free Press, 1951, pp. 428–73.
54. ———, AND RENEE FOX, "Therapy, and the Modern Urban Family," *Journal of Social Issues*, 8 (1952), 31–44.
55. PETERSON, OSLER L., LEON P. ANDREWS, ROBERT S. SPAIN, AND BERNARD G. GREENBERG, "An Analytical Study of North Carolina General Practice," *Journal of Medical Education*, 31, Part 2 (December, 1956).
56. SAMORA, J., L. SAUNDERS, AND R. LARSON, "Medical Vocabulary Knowledge among Hospital Patients," *Journal of Health and Human Behavior*, 2, (Summer, 1961).
57. SAUNDERS, LYLE, *Cultural Differences and Medical Care.* New York: Russell Sage Foundation, 1954, p. 8.
58. SCHEFF, THOMAS J., *Being Mentally Ill: A Sociological Theory.* Chicago: Aldine Publishing Company, 1966.
59. SCHUR, EDWIN M., "Psychiatrists Under Attack: The Rebellious Dr. Szasz," *The Atlantic*, 217 (June, 1966), 72–76.
60. SCHWARTZ, CHARLOTTE GREEN, *Rehabilitation of Mental Hospital Patients*, Public Health Monograph No. 17. Washington, D.C.: Government Printing Office, 1953.
61. SELZNICK, PHILIP, "A Theory of Organizational Commitment," in Robert K. Merton et al., eds., *Reader in Bureaucracy.* New York: The Free Press, 1952, p. 196.
62. SHUVAL, JUDITH T., *Social Functions of Medical Practice: Doctor-Patient Relationships in Israel.* San Francisco: Jossey–Bass, Inc., 1970.
63. SPIEGEL, JOHN, "Some Cultural Aspects of Transference and Countertransference," in Jules H. Masserman, ed., *Individual and Familial Dynamics.* New York: Grune & Stratton, Inc., 1959, pp. 160–82.
64. ———, "The Social Role of Doctor and Patient in Psychoanalysis and Psychotherapy," *Psychiatry*, 17 (November, 1954), 369–76.
65. SUSSMAN, MARVIN B., ed., *Sociology and Rehabilitation.* Washington, D.C.: American Sociological Association, 1965.
66. SZASZ, T. S., *The Myth of Mental Illness.* New York: Harper & Row, Publishers, Hoeber Medical Books, 1961.
67. ——— AND M. H. HOLLENDER, "A Contribution to the Philosophy of Medicine: The Basic Models of the Doctor-Patient Relationship," *A.M.A. Archives of Internal Medicine*, 97 (May, 1956), 585.
68. WILSON, ROBERT N., "The Physician's Changing Hospital Role," *Human Organization*, 18 (Winter, 1959–60), 177–83.

69. ———, "Teamwork in the Operating Room," *Human Organization*, 12 (Winter, 1954), 9–14.
70. ZOLA, IRVING K., "Culture and Symptoms—An Analysis of Patients' Presenting Complaints," *American Sociological Review*, 31 (October, 1966), 615–30.

part three

SOCIOLOGY OF MEDICAL CARE

14

THE ORGANIZATION OF MEDICAL PRACTICE

Eliot Freidson

Medicine is practiced in privacy. Work in the other established professions is carried on publicly—in the court, the church, and the lecture hall—as often as in the office; the work of the doctor is characteristically conducted in the consulting room or the bedchamber. Furthermore, the physician usually renders personal services to individuals, rather than to congregations or classes. Perhaps because of these characteristics, medicine is more likely than other established professions to be seen as involving a simple practitioner-client relationship (this relationship is discussed extensively in Chapter 13). But it is much more than that: Medicine is practiced within an organized framework which influences both doctor and patient. Indeed, the framework of practice in the United States seems to be moving toward more elaborate forms which may be expected to change the doctor-patient relationship.

THE CONSOLIDATION OF PROFESSIONAL AUTHORITY

Only recently has the physician obtained widespread professional authority. Until the nineteenth century, he had too little sure knowledge and technique to sustain the authority he sought. As L. J. Henderson put it, it was not until around 1910 or 1912 that a random American with a random disease consulting a doctor chosen at random stood better than a 50–50 chance of benefiting from the encounter. At least until the latter half of the nineteenth century, the physician was used by a rather small proportion of the population, and in the United States he was fighting—often unsuccessfully—for licensing laws [45].

Generally speaking, the physician had neither de jure nor de facto control over the practice of healing: Even his "science" was unpopular, as the various healing movements and the thriving patent-medicine business of the century testify. Without a truly scientific foundation and without basic standards in the training of physicians, how could medicine justify its desire for occupational monopoly and lay submission? Certainly not by success, nor by ethics, nor by reference to superior education. In prosecuting Jacoba Felicia de Almania, the medical faculty of the University of Paris had to content itself with the claim—which now appears ludicrous—that she should not practice because she was not instructed in medieval theory. She never made promises, she asked for a fee only in the event of success, she cured cases which physicians could not, but she was too "ignorant" to practice [28].

By the end of the nineteenth century, however, the physician's monopoly over healing was fairly well established. Unlike the lawyer and clergyman [24], he was rising in public esteem. By the time medical education in the United States was reformed, the physician was in the virtually unprecedented position of being the symbol of healing to people in all social classes. While a few early medical specialties were in direct competition with folk specialties, the general medical practitioner acquired wholesale the clientele of a variety of folk specialists. The nostalgic and sentimental image of the old-fashioned family doctor who was all things to all men is based upon the fleeting period in history when folk practice had declined but medical specialization was still in an incipient stage.

THE FRAGMENTATION OF MEDICAL RESPONSIBILITY

During earlier times, the physician could learn most of what he needed to know during his training period: If he was wise and creative, he could temper his sparse formal education by continually reflecting on his experience as he acquired it. Furthermore, significant advances in medical knowledge were few. Equipped with a small shelf of basic technical books, the early physician could conceivably work in total isolation as efficiently as the knowledge of his age would permit, occasionally watching the work of an itinerent surgeon or dentist or glancing through one of the few medical journals of the time. By and large, he could handle—as well as the next man—any ailment that presented itself to him. But by the time the general practitioner had reached his peak of authority in the public eye, the development of medical science had led to the training of specialized men who seized fragments of his domain.

Specialization, as such, was hardly new. The Hippocratic oath itself implied a specialty involving lithotomy (or, as Nittis argued [35], castrating slaves for the eunuch market). Indeed, in the eighteenth and nineteenth centuries, there were perhaps as many "specialties" among folk practitioners as now exist among physicians. Witness the specialist bone-setters, blood-stoppers, baruchers, wart-doctors, and others cited by Jones [25]. What was new was the refinement of knowledge and technique underlying specialization, and its growth within the control of a single profession [15].

In addition to specialists, there arose diagnostic and therapeutic tools which, unlike the instruments in the hallowed black bag, were too expensive for any individual to own and use at his own convenience, and too complex for him to operate even if he could afford them. The hospital came to serve as a locus for such capital equipment, and new specialists like radiologists and pathologists became essential personnel in treatment centers. The physician came to depend upon the hospital and upon the new specialists for access to new medical technology.

Clearly, with the rise of modern medicine, it became difficult to practice alone and, what is more positively unrealistic, to attempt to handle the whole range of human ills. Over the past fifty years, general practice has declined and practice limited to particular organs, specific illnesses, or special procedures has increased remarkably. In 1923, for example, only 11 percent of all physicians were engaged in limited practice. By 1967, however, the proportion of all active physicians engaged in giving patient care in some specialty had risen to 71 percent [51].

THE GROWING PROBLEM OF COORDINATION

The displacement of the general practitioner by the specialist renders continuity and comprehensiveness of care difficult, if not impossible. First, members of the same family are less and less likely to be able to go to one physician—for general problems, children go to a pediatrician, and the adults to internists. For anything uncommon, both children and adults go to other specialists. This has led to the fragmentation of the individual patient. When the various parts of the individual have been examined by those with specially competent knowledge of those parts, how are they to be put together again? Without someone with continuing responsibility for the patient through all his consultations with specialists, the parts are unlikely to be put together at all. In many cases there is no doubt that the parts need not be put together, sentimentalists notwithstanding, but in those fairly common disorders which seem beyond the germ theory, it does seem necessary to see and treat the patient as a whole. The idea of comprehensive care expresses the prevailing uneasiness in medical educational and policy circles about the lack of continuous and well-rounded communication between patients and their doctors.

When more than one doctor is handling a case, each must communicate with the other if the case is to be handled efficiently and well. The hospital has become a place where many physicians are brought together around the same bed, and consequently a place which facilitates communication about the patient and coordination of his regimen is facilitated. (Communication within the hospital is discussed in more detail in Chapter 12). Conceivably, the hospital outpatient department may also provide a milieu for such communication. But in the United States, the bulk of patient care is provided by medical practice outside the hospital. It is precisely in extra-hospital practice that the greatest problems of coordination and communication seem likely to occur as the general practitioner disappears.

SOLO PRACTICE: MYTH AND REALITY

Symbolically, the typical mode of medical practice in the United States is "solo practice." This involves a man working by himself in an office which he secures and equips with his own capital and with patients who have freely chosen him as their personal physician and for whom he assumes responsibility. Stereotypically he lacks any formal connection with colleagues.

The phrase "solo practice" is as often used in an ideological as in a descriptive mode. It is, as Evang put it, a "sacred cow" to the medical profession in more than one country [12]. Its ideological connotations have interesting implications. One of the central themes is independence—the notion of "professional autonomy." A man can do as he pleases. For autonomy to exist, the practitioner must work alone and have no long-term obligation to his clients: He must be able to sever the relationship to his client at any time, and vice versa. A fee-for-service rather than a contractual financial arrangement is thus likely to encourage autonomous practice.

A truly autonomous fee-for-service solo arrangement is inherently unstable, however: It is eventually bound to fall under the control of either patients or colleagues. In a system of free competition, the physician may neither count on the loyalty of his patients (with whom he has no contract) nor on that of his colleagues (with whom he has no ties and who are competing with him). Since his collegues are competitors, he is not likely to solicit their advice or trade information with them, and he certainly will not refer his patients to them for consultations. Thus he remains isolated from his colleagues and relatively free of their control—but at the same time he is very vulnerable to control by his clients. To keep them, he must give them what they want, or someone else will attract them away. Obviously, conscientious practice under these conditions is difficult and frustrating. It is hardly right to describe it as "autonomy" [14].

The simple restriction of competition by banding together against the tyranny of the client's choice, however, results in the tyranny of the colleague. Autonomy from colleagues can exist only under very special circumstances. It seems plausible that, when the supply of physicians is sufficiently restricted to fail to meet demand, control by the client may be avoided. If, in addition to a scarcity of physicians and other potential competitors, no large capital is required for initiating a practice, and no consultation or institutions like hospitals are necessary for its pursuit, control by colleagues can be avoided and "total autonomy" approached.

In the United States today, the supply of physicians in many areas is such that control by the client can be avoided; but, increasingly, control by colleagues cannot. Dependence on colleagues in one way or another is the rule, for consultations, hospitals, and capital equipment are essential to modern practice. In short, present practice is not really solo: It embraces a large variety of organized relationships, most of which currently involve control by colleagues rather than by clients.

SOURCES OF COOPERATIVE ARRANGEMENT AMONG PRACTITIONERS

How do cooperative arrangements develop? Let us start with an ostensibly solo, fee-for-service practice in a situation where the supply of physicians is reasonably restricted. One's practice is only partially secure, however, because the continual entrance of younger men into a system which does not include the predictable retirement of the older practitioner always involves some threat of competition. In answer to the threat, one keeps his patients to himself, but this means a deadly grind—perpetual availability for service. In order to take an evening or a weekend off, or a vacation, in order to be sick, one's practice must be "covered" by colleagues who can be relied on to avoid "stealing" patients. A cooperative arrangement is necessary.

The need for such organization becomes even more pressing when specialization is involved. Patients who must see more than one physician in the normal course of obtaining medical care might become particularly attracted to any one of them. The danger of losing patients by referring them to a young internist seems to have led at least some general practitioners to avoid referring patients at all. In one study of Negro doctors, it was found that some refer patients to white rather than Negro consultants, assuming that the former do not want to keep Negro patients [38]. To try to avoid referrals is patently unsatisfactory, however, since the conscientious practitioner, on one occasion or another, knows that his patient needs help he cannot give himself. He can send some, but not all, patients to a clinic or an outpatient department whose staffs presumably will not "steal" them. A rather natural and conventional arrangement is a fairly definite reciprocal one: The general practitioner habitually refers his patients to a limited number of specialists who may be trusted to act "ethically" by eventually returning his patients to him, and who, in turn, will refer patients needing general services to him.

The time has passed in the United States when the general practitioner was in a strong enough position to be the key "feeder" to a network of specialists. The patient has developed more sophistication, and the number of accessible specialists has increased; the patient now circumvents the general practitioner and seeks out his own specialists. Indeed, the general practitioner's place is being taken by the internist and the pediatrician, and nonprofessional referrals are the major source, in urban settings, of patients for the average ophthalmologist, otorhinolaryngologist and orthopedist, if not the obstetrician-gynecologist, allergist, and dermatologist.

Since there has ceased to be a single key "feeder" in the division of labor, there is danger of considerable confusion and irregularity in the disposition of the patient. Fairly well-integrated arrangements among physicians are important, not only as a way of gaining and regulating economic access to patients but also as a way of coordinating the care of the patient and his illness.

THE COLLEAGUE NETWORK

The "colleague network" described by Hall may be used as the prototype of an informal but well-integrated arrangement among American physicians in solo practice [21, 22, 23].

> Insofar as the doctors of a given community are established and possess relatively loyal clienteles, they form a system. This system can effectively exclude the intruding newcomer. On the one hand they have control of the hospital system through occupying the dominant posts therein. On the other they tend to develop, in the course of time, through association, a sort of informal organization. Rights to position, status, and power become recognized and upheld; mechanisms of legitimate succession and patterns of recruitment become established.
>
> The provision of medical facilities in a given community, insofar as a system

or an order has been established, depends heavily on such an organization. As a matter of fact, the two matters discussed above, i.e., institutions and clienteles, are intimately related to the working of the informal organization. The allocation of positions in the institutions, the pace at which one receives promotions, the extent to which one has patients referred to him, all hinge on the workings of the informal organization. . . .

Sponsorship is not necessarily a one-sided process. It permits the newcomer to share in the established system of practicing medicine, but it also imposes responsibilities upon him. It obligates him to fulfill the minor positions in the institutional system. Where he needs expert advice or assistance it obligates him to turn to his sponsor. And if he is designated as successor to an established member of the profession he necessarily takes over the duties and obligations involved there. Hence the protégé is essential to the continued functioning of the established inner fraternity of the profession [21].

The kind of network Hall describes is more likely to exist in localities having a variety of hospitals and other hierarchically ordered medical institutions. It is much less likely to be so definite and articulated in small cities where hospitals are virtual open, community institutions. Even in large cities, the municipal and proprietary institutions at the bottom of the prestige hierarchy provide fairly free access to physicians, irrespective of their location in colleague networks [23, 48]. For this reason, it is safe to assume that the looser form of colleague network portrayed in the sociometric studies of Coleman, Katz, and Menzel is the more common form in the United States [8].

ELEMENTARY FORMS OF COOPERATIVE PRACTICE

Because it is entirely informal, the colleague network is the most elementary type of cooperative practice. It also has sufficient weakness to make it uncomfortably vulnerable to collapse. Under the solo system of practice, patients and hospitals are not always completely monopolized. Often the colleague network cannot completely control the treatment environment, and so may lack the reliable patronage necessary to gain the cooperation of hungry young men. Furthermore, the good faith among peers upon which an informal system depends may break down in petty jealousies and antipathies.

The large solo practice in the United States has developed some formal techniques of protecting itself. The successful physician may, as Hall suggested, send his overflow to a young physician in whom he takes an interest, but he also may—and often does—avoid sending out any cases at all by hiring the younger man to work in his office, handle the routine cases, and make the grueling house and emergency calls. This lightens his burden while it reduces the danger of permanently losing patients. The employer-physician's position is particularly strong when the man he hires is not fully qualified to practice on his own (like some English medical assistants) or when it is very expensive or otherwise difficult to set up a practice (as in localities where practices must be bought or where competition is severe).

When the junior is in a position to break away and become a competitor, however, the hiring physician is very vulnerable. Each young man he introduces to his patients may leave and take some of those patients with him. One way to prevent that is to draw up a legal document whereby the younger man agrees not to set up an independent practice in the same community. Another way, which by no means rules out the first, is to take the young man into partnership, sharing expenses and profits according to some prearranged schedule, and thereby giving him a direct stake in the maintenance and growth of the practice.

The most common type of formal cooperative arrangement among peers is not the partnership, but what might be called the association—an arrangement whereby physicians have their own patients, from whom they collect their own fees, but share the expense of maintaining such common facilities as offices, equipment, assisting personnel, and the like. In addition, when one physician is away the other may cover for him by seeing his patients in his absence. In one form or another, this rudimentary type of formal cooperation is very widespread in the United States, particularly in city "professional buildings" with fairly elaborate suites and in "medical centers" owned by the resident physicians [27].

From the association it is a short, though by no means simple, step to the small legal partnership—sharing profits from fees as well as overhead expenses. The division of pooled fees is likely to be a constant bone of contention, however, since the practices of the partners, though overlapping, are not identical. This is particularly true when specialties are involved, for one specialist may feel he brings in more money than the other and so deserves a larger proportion of the profits.

If such problems can be overcome, however, the partnership is more reliable and predictable than simpler forms of cooperation. In a colleague network, doctors can arrange trustworthy coverage for each other so as to be able to enjoy their leisure hours despite the unpredictability of their patients' demands. In the simple association this virtue is carried over; moreover, the sharing of overhead costs reduces each doctor's ordinary expenses and makes it possible to have more laboratory and diagnostic equipment. The partnership adds to these virtues increased long-term financial security. When practitioners of different ages are involved, the younger man may see many patients instead of few, and earn a considerable income at a time when he could otherwise expect little. The older man may have a higher income at a time when patients would be leaving him or when he himself would be forced, by his decreasing energy, to relinquish them. Moreover, when more than one specialty is involved, each can function as a referring agent to the other, with mutual advantage: The dubious ethics of fee-splitting, often found in informal cooperative arrangements, is regularized in the partnership without raising an ethical problem. The partnership constitutes some protection against the competition of other practitioners, and it also facilitates communication among practitioners.

GROUP PRACTICE

One requirement common to all these forms of cooperation is access to a fairly large number of patients. Cooperative practice is comparatively large-scale, involving the ordering of expenses, referrals, consultations and—in the case of partnerships—profits, into a system which meets the needs of a larger number of people than one man alone can handle. The more formal the arrangement, the more systematized and rational it becomes. At a certain point in the expansion of scale, however, a qualitative change in the form of cooperative practice occurs.

"Group practice" very often designates a form of association that goes beyond the scope of the two-man partnership, but definitions have not been very helpful in delineating the differences. The value of the term, like "solo practice," is limited by its ideological overtones. Rather than autonomy and independence, it is "groupness" and interdependence which are emphasized. But if "group medical practice is the application of medical services by three or more *full-time* physicians formally organized to provide medical care, consultation, diagnosis, and/or treatment through the joint use of equipment and personnel, and with the income from medical practice distributed in accordance with methods previously determined by members of the group" [2], it is hard to see how it differs from the partnership. The difference between a two- and a three-man partnership does not seem significant. And since 76 percent of the "medical groups" recently surveyed by the A.M.A. had only three to five full-time physicians, obviously a large proportion are insignificantly different from simple partnerships [2]. This semantic confusion of group practice with a modestly growing office partnership seems to be responsible for much of the talk about the rapid growth of a genuinely new and significantly different form of practice.

If numbers are to be used to define group practice, Jordan's suggestion of the minimum number of five full-time physicians seems reasonable [26]. Five full-time physicians—not all of them giving day-to-day routine medical care—can serve an ordinary population of anywhere from 5,000 to 20,000, depending on the proportion of general practitioners, internists, and pediatricians, the financial arrangements with patients, and the general style of practice. As the number of patients and doctors increases further, it seems likely that some of the technical characteristics of bureaucracy will emerge: hierarchical organization, extensive division of labor, systematic rules and procedures, and the like.

THE THIRD PARTY

Large-scale group practice is not widespread in the United States, but it is becoming more common [2] and its potential impact is great. It has been growing out of two quite different sources. One is the traditional entrepreneurial basis of professional practice: Like a successful business, the successful practice may expand by hiring or by taking into partnership many other practitioners. Some of the most famous clinics in the United States grew this way. The other source is the increasingly important role being played by agencies which assume responsibility for the welfare of a population. This is the so-called "third party." Some agencies have organized and staffed large-scale bureaucratic practices to serve a particular clientele. Others have provided, in the form of health insurance, the large-scale financing which makes entrepreneurial bureaucratic practice practical. (For a more detailed discussion of utilization of health services, see Chapter 16.)

On occasion, governments have sought to provide medical care for their citizens, as have employers for their employees and consumer groups for their members [46, 51]. In some instances, the doctor was contracted to provide care to a population for a flat salary. In others, he was paid a retainer by a city in order that he would stay in the locality and make himself available, free nonetheless to charge each patient a fee. Many physicians in rural, "underdoctored" areas in the United States are in a position similar to that of the "public physician" of ancient Greece [7]—attracted to a town by its promises of guaranteed income, housing, and well-equipped medical facilities.

Recent developments in third-party care in the United States have enormously increased its scale and scope. The rise of the centralized nation-state, committed to a modicum of welfare service for its citizens and empowered to mobilize physicians for the public good, is a significant factor, though as yet less in the United States than Europe. Here, much the same role is being performed by the giant corporations, insurance companies, and trade unions which, though lacking the political power to mobilize physicians, nonetheless possess sufficient economic power to negotiate the terms of the practice of medicine. Even the voluntary hospital seems to be becoming something of a third party, mediating between the lay community supporting it and the physicians who depend upon it. And, of course, Medicare and Medicaid are new federal programs for the elderly and poor which are developing new third party relationships.

There are two ways in which the role of the third party is important. First, the third party might be seen as a force which offsets an imbalance. As we have noted, the development of the modern medical profession has been accompanied by greater control of the practitioner by colleagues than by clients. The third party at its best has the client's welfare in mind and, unlike the client himself, also has available expert guidance in determining a policy which advances the health of community members [39]. Thus, it can be better equipped than individual clients ever could be to counterbalance the material interests of the practitioner without detracting from the scientific quality of practice. Does it work out that way? This question leads to the second point about the significance of the third party—its influence over the nature of medical practice [13].

A third party can simply arrange some scheme for paying the doctor for his services or—less commonly—can go so far as to set up medical practice units of its own [43]. The arrangement which has the least influence on the organization of practice continues the fee-for-service tradition: The doctor claims from the third party a standard fee for each service he renders a client. Obviously, all that is added to practice is some paperwork and a somewhat less flexible fee schedule than ordinarily. But while the fee-for-service method is desirable to the physician, it has not been considered desirable administratively: it is too "open-ended" and too difficult to supervise. More acceptable, administratively, is paying the physician a given sum for each patient to whom he renders services over a period of time (a capitation scheme) or putting the physician on salary. In short, a method of easily predictable payment, subject to little fluctuation except by negotiation, is most desirable to the third party. In the United States, the number of salaried practitioners and practitioners paid on a capitation basis may be growing [48]; beyond that, the increasingly large role of the third party seems likely to introduce an element of greater economic regularity into medical practice. The net effect, varying with the precise role of the third party, seems to be that much of the physician's traditional entrepreneurial freedom is being lost.

The scanty evidence that exists suggests that a restriction of the physician's entrepreneurial freedom does not neccessarily impinge upon his freedom of judgment. On the whole, there seems to be no imperative reason why the mere existence of a third party need influence diagnosis, prescription, or therapy. Indeed, it has been argued that the existence of a responsible third party allows the physician to devote himself wholly to his art, without having to preocupy himself with business.

THE DIFFERENT FORMS OF PRACTICE

Thus far a number of forms of practice and some of their functional characteristics have been discussed. They may be seen to distribute themselves between two logically but not numerically important extremes. At one end there is a rarity, true solo practice. It is unstable, merging into more common, loose forms of informal cooperation with colleagues. The colleague network is a tighter but still informal type of cooperative practice. The "association" is a simple variety of formal cooperation; the small partnership, and then the group practice, are tighter and more complex forms. Finally, there is the tightest and most formal variety of practice, which may be called organizational or bureaucratic. We can divide all these types of practice into two groups by making a common-sense distinction between solo and group practice: the former to include true solo and all types of informally cooperative practice; the latter to include, from the "association" on, all types of formally cooperative practice. Using this simple distinction, we may make the comparisons which are perhaps most important for social policy.

FORM OF PRACTICE AND THE QUALITY OF CARE

The foremost question about such a pursuit as medical practice is its technical consequences—the quality of service it provides. It is, unfortunately, the question about which there is least information. However, the opinion is fairly widespread that a physician cannot practice the best possible medicine without easy access to modern diagnostic and therapeutic facilities. In this sense, it is reasonable to assume that the solo practitioner who lacks access to such facilities is least likely to do the best for his patient. Formal cooperative arrangements, whether simple or complex, are more likely to provide the capital to buy an extensive amount of equipment. Furthermore, the isolation of the practicing physician from his colleagues is believed to affect the quality of care. It is presently believed that a physician must continually keep abreast of advances in scientific knowledge, relying less on "education" by drug manufacturers and their representatives and more upon "education" by colleagues and professional associations. (see Chapter 8).

As we have seen, however, solo practice, as such, cannot be readily classified as more or less isolated. A considerable degree of informal, but nonetheless real and important, interaction can take place among loose networks of practitioners. While much of it, as Peterson and his associates observed, is bound to be about fishing, bridge, and golf, some is certainly about medicine [36]. It is the fact that isolation in solo practice is possible that marks it off from "group practice," whether that be small partnership or a large-scale medical group. In this sense, group, more than solo, practice contains within it conditions that may encourage quality of care. Indeed, Peterson and his associates reported a tendency for those in group practice to give care of better quality than those working alone [36], though Clute did not find such a tendency [6].

In addition, care by a variety of specialists is held to be necessary these days. While solo practice does not preclude the use of specialists, group practice facilitates frequent consultation and the exchange of professional information. When a number of physicians of varied specialties work together within the same organization, it is not only easier to refer patients, but also to communicate and coordinate information about them. Coleman, Katz, and Menzel have demonstrated the importance of colleague relations to one facet of care—prescribing drugs [8]. Thus, it is to be expected that in group practice the fragmentation of care following upon specialization can be compensated for and that so-called "comprehensive care" is more likely to ensue.

Finally, there is the element of supervision, the quality which Seeman and Evans have shown influences medical performance [42]. The most reputable medical institutions—e.g., medical school clinics and teaching hospitals—are characterized by doctors working in close association with each other and by the fairly systematic supervision of their work by chiefs of service, tissue committees, and the like. Except in a purely educational context, where it is ideologically acceptable, the nature of supervision in such medical bureaucracies has received little attention [40, 41], but it is indubitable that at least some administrative supervision almost always exists, even if in varied degree [16, 17, 32]. Furthermore, the cultivation of a medical-records system and the continuous accumulation of information in records is in itself supervisory, for while the records may not be subject to routine inspection, they may always be examined if some doubt arises about a physician's work. If, as Peterson assumes, systematic and complete records are an important element of competent medical care, bureaucratic practices—which are far more likely to encourage record keeping—can to this extent provide better care.

In theory, then, formal and cooperative, rather than informal, arrangements are more likely to provide good medical care. However, there are only scattered bits of evidence to support this theory [11, 52]. One of the rare comparative studies was made by the Health Insurance Plan of Greater New York, in which the hospitalization and perinatal mortality of a population served by medical groups under contract with the insurance plan compared favorably with that of the New York City population [9, 44]. That study, however, was concerned with an additional element in the arrangement of medical care—the prepaid service contract. It is believed that when people can be insured, so that no financial barrier stands between them and medical care, they will not hesitate to seek help. Thus, they can obtain the care they need early in the course of illness and prevent complications. Consequently, a comprehensive prepaid service contract is believed to be—of itself—conducive to better medical care. When the existence of insurance is not differentiated from organizational variables, the influence of either on the quality of care is difficult to establish.

The same difficulty exists when the mode of compensating the physician is undifferentiated from organization. A study by Densen and his associates compared the hospitalization of members of a single union who were under two different medical insurance plans—one involving medical group practice compensated on a per capita basis, and the other solo fee-for-service practice [10]. Hospitalization of the first group proved to be less, even though the comprehensiveness of the insurance was much the same. But it is difficult to tell whether the lowered rate of hospitalization resulted from group practice, as such, or from the fact that the group plan provided no additional compensation to the group physician for in-hospital surgery. Clearly, present evidence is inadequate.

FORM OF PRACTICE AND PATIENT SATISFACTION

Whether or not people are deeply involved emotionally with their doctors, they must in any case be sufficiently happy with the care they receive from a physician to consult him. The patient's satisfaction assumes additional importance when medicine becomes a political issue. In a number of national surveys in the United States, most people have expressed general satisfaction with medical services which are typically organized on only a loosely cooperative fee-for-service basis. And the solo general practitioner, of course, is part of the national folklore. Still, fairly large proportions of the population cite grounds for dissatisfaction. They complain that doctors keep them waiting too long, are difficult to reach during the night and on weekends, and don't give enough time to them. Koos [29, 30] reports the largest proportions of dissatisfaction, and the Gaffin study showed that people are less likely to complain about their own doctors than about doctors in general [18].

This material, however, like the data on in-hospital surgery, bears on solo practice only insofar as it is the most common and most characteristic form in the United States. Comparative studies provide the most useful evidence. Anderson and Sheatsley compared two groups of socioeconomically equivalent, insured patients, one served by solo physicians compensated by an insurance organization on a fee-for-service basis, the other by physicians in medical groups, paid on a per capita basis [1]. The finding was that the solo fee-for-service program was more satisfactory to the patients than the group practice. The patients of the latter were prone to complain of a lack of personal interest, insufficient explanation of their condition by the doctor, waiting in the office, and difficulty in obtaining house calls. In a study by this author, in which patients contrasted their experience with these two types of practice, there was also a tendency to feel that the doctor in solo fee-for-service practice took more "personal interest" in them. But there was also some feeling that medical care of a technically higher quality could be obtained from the medical group [14]. In both studies, however, the solo fee-for-service practice was compared to a per capita payment group practice, and the financial variable was not controlled.

Plainly, the material on the patient's satisfaction is equivocal, but none contradicts the idea that he seems more likely to be satisfied by a physician who can be more immediately responsive to him than the group physicians, who have obligations to a work organization, can be [14]. The English population seems as satisfied with its solo per capita payment practice as the American with its solo fee-for-service practice; it seems that the arrangement of payment is less important than the organization of the work [34].

FORM OF PRACTICE AND PHYSICIAN SATISFACTION

The physician's satisfaction, also, may be more influenced by the arrangement of his work than by the arrangement of his payment. In assessing job satisfaction, however, we must first recognize that it is much easier for the physician to free-lance than the professor or the minister, both of whom require congregations rather than an assortment of successive individuals, and neither of whom can count on the fairly strong motivation provided by illness. This alone means that even in an environment where the state sets the terms of work for the average practitioner (as in Great Britain and the Soviet Union), it is possible for the physician to be able to stay outside the scheme if he wishes. In this sense, a physician in any organized scheme of practice always has an alternative.

It may be noted, furthermore, that job satisfaction is inevitably a function of the alternative careers which exist at any particular time, and of the symbolic and material rewards of these alternatives. In the United States today, for example, the form symbolically valued by physicians is the successful solo, fee-for-service, specialty practice. The general practitioner may genuinely enjoy the procession of minor cases (called "garbage" by specialists), the laying-on of hands, and the genial calls at humble homes—the human rather than the scientific side of medicine—but in depressed moments he may realize that he is not a social success because he is not a "scientific" specialist with a limited practice and prominent clients. Thus, environment must be considered a factor in job satisfaction, because of the way it defines the form of practice and because of the alternatives it contains [32].

No matter what the tyranny of the patient, solo practice has the aura of potentially complete autonomy. The physician working in the privacy of his own consulting-room can examine, diagnose, prescribe, and treat as he sees fit. There is no one to soften his patient's pressure to make him honor lay prejudices, of course, and when his practice is insecure it is likely that he will feel obliged to do what he does not really want to do. But theoretically, the solo physician may dismiss his patient rather than give in to him. Autonomy perhaps more extensive than in any other profession thus exists, at least *in potentia*, in solo practice [12]. This is what was stressed by medical students in response to survey questions on why they would reject salaried positions in organizations [5].

In contrast to this apparently gratifying side of solo entrepreneurial practice are a number of potential handicaps—isolation from one's colleagues and thus from their information and support, the necessity to be preoccupied daily with the financial basis of practice, the financial basis of practice, the financial leanness of the early and late stages of the career and, chiefly, the difficulty of controlling and regularizing one's work hours. These are the very things which are said to be solved by group practice—indeed, medical students who preferred salaried positions stressed the opportunity to work in close association with colleagues, to obtain a regular income, and to work regular hours [5].

On the whole, one should expect that a doctor-owned, fee-for-service partnership or group practice would provide most of the gratifications of both and fewest of the deficiencies of the two extremes—solo practice and bureaucratic practice. It seems to allow the greatest amount of room for self-determination without in turn sacrificing the major virtues of cooperative practice. The 1956 survey of a "cross-section of American male students in all four years of the entire group of approved medical schools in the United States," by Cahalan and his associates, reported that of those who preferred a nonsalaried practice, only 26 percent preferred solo practice to group practice, partnership, or some other form of formally cooperative practice [5]. Since more freshmen than seniors preferred solo practice, we can assume that interest in cooperative forms increases as the medical student comes closer to being a physician. However, the students who preferred group practice were less likely to expect that their preference would be realized than students preferring the solo form. Testimony to the realism of their expectation is provided by the A.M.A.'s finding that 61 percent of those engaged in private practice in 1966 were practicing entirely alone [50].

RESEARCH NEEDS

Systematic and reliable information about medical practice in the United States is incredibly scanty. The extraordinary bulk of published material is composed almost entirely of special pleading or unsystematic individual impressions; the only reliable body of extensive information bears on the financing, distribution, and utilization of health services. From any point of view, two as yet unperformed research tasks are fundamental—studies of the polar extremes of purely solo practice and bureaucratic practice. The former merits study both for its persistence and its symbolism, the latter for its reputed but as yet undemonstrated potentialities.

From the sociological point of view, solo practice is a very old way of organizing skilled work. It is based on the almost ludicrous assumption that a long period of professional training develops such stable professional values in the physician that his work—entirely escaping observation by colleagues—will be performed adequately even under the most harrowing or tempting circumstances. Structurally, it is on the surface a one-man "organization": It is more accurately a case in which one man forms the focus for an organization composed of himself and prospective clients, an organization whose boundaries blur as they merge into the surrounding community. As modern organizations go, solo practice is a primordial form which, in spite of the strong professional identity shared with all physicians [19], grows by becoming part of the lay environment. A careful and systematic examination of the way in which the true solo practitioner captures and organizes segments of the environment—and is in turn captured and organized by it—would be valuable indeed.

Ideologically, solo practice implies full professional autonomy; bureaucratic practice limits autonomy [3]. Indeed, bureaucracy, with its essential reliance on the authority of office, seems to contradict the idea of the authority of knowledge [20]. The physician, with his high social status, his strong subjective sense of importance, the privacy of his daily work and its immediately fateful consequences, seems better able to resist bureaucratic authority than any of the other professionals [4]. Consequently, a careful study of bureaucratic practice should shed much light on the varieties of influence and authority which can exist in a bureaucratic organization, as well as on some of the limits of professional freedom in a bureaucratic setting.

REFERENCES

1. Anderson, Odin W. and Paul B. Sheatsley, "Comprehensive Medical Insurance," *Health Information Foundation Research Series*, 9 (1959).
2. Balfe, B. E. and M. E. McNamara, *Survey of Medical Groups in the U.S.: 1965*. Chicago: American Medical Association, 1968.
3. Ben-David, Joseph, "The Professional Role of the Physician in Bureaucratized Medicine: A Study in Role Conflict," *Human Relations*, 11 (1958), 255–74.
4. Bucher, Rue and Joan Stelling, "Characteristics of Professional Organizations," *Journal of Health and Social Behavior*, 10 (1969), 3–15.
5. Cahalan, Don, Patricia Collette, and Norman Hilmar, "Career Interest and Expectations of U.S. Medical Students," *Journal of Medical Education*, 32 (August, 1957), 557–63.
6. Clute, Kenneth F., *The General Practitioner*. Toronto: University of Toronto Press, 1963.
7. Cohn-Haft, Louis, *The Public Physician of Ancient Greece*, Smith College Studies in History, No. 42. Northampton, Mass.: Smith College, 1956.
8. Coleman, James, Elihu Katz, and Herbert Menzel, *Medical Innovation: A Diffusion Study*. Indianapolis: The Bobbs–Merrill Co., Inc., 1966.

9. Committee for the Special Research Project in H.I.P., *Health and Medical Care in New York City.* Cambridge, Mass.: Harvard University Press, 1957.
10. DENSEN, PAUL M., ELLEN W. JONES, EVE BALAMUTH AND SAM SHAPIRO, "Prepaid Medical Care and Hospital Utilization in a Dual Choice Situation," *American Journal of Public Health,* 50 (November, 1960), 1710–26.
11. DONABEDIAN, AVEDIS, *A Review of Some Experiences with Prepaid Group Practice,* Bureau of Public Health Economics Research Series, No. 12. Ann Arbor: University of Michigan Press, 1965.
12. EVANG, KARL, *Health Service, Society and Medicine.* London: Oxford University Press, 1960.
13. FIELD, MARK G., "The Doctor-Patient Relationship in the Perspective of 'Fee-for-Service' and 'Third Party' Medicine," *Journal of Health and Human Behavior,* 2 (Winter, 1961), 252–62.
14. FREIDSON, ELIOT, *Patients' Views of Medical Practice.* New York: Russell Sage Foundation, 1961.
15. ———, *Profession of Medicine: A Study of the Sociology of Applied Knowledge.* New York: Dodd, Mead & Co., 1970.
16. ——— AND BUFORD RHEA, "Processes of Control in a Company of Equals," *Social Problems,* 11 (Fall, 1963), 119–31.
17. ———, "Knowledge and Judgment in Professional Evaluations," *Administrative Science Quarterly,* 10 (June, 1965), 107–24.
18. BEN GAFFIN ASSOCIATES, *What Americans Think of the Medical Profession.* American Medical Association brochure, n.d.
19. GOODE, WILLIAM J., "Community within a Community: The Professions," *American Sociological Review,* 22 (April, 1957), 194–200.
20. GOSS, MARY E. W., "Influence and Authority among Physicians in an Outpatient Clinic," *American Sociological Review,* 26 (February, 1961), 39–50.
21. HALL, OSWALD, "The Informal Organization of the Medical Profession," *Canadian Journal of Economics and Political Science,* 12 (February, 1946), 30–41.
22. ———, "The Stages of the Medical Career," *American Journal of Sociology,* 53 (March, 1948), 327–36.
23. ———, "Types of Medical Careers," *American Journal of Sociology,* 55 (November, 1949), 243–53.
24. HOFSTADTER, RICHARD, *The Age of Reform.* New York: Alfred A. Knopf, Inc., 1955.
25. JONES, LOUIS C., "Practitioners of Folk Medicine," *Bulletin of the History of Medicine,* 23 (September–October, 1949), 480–93.
26. JORDAN, EDWIN P., ed., *The Physician and Group Practice.* Chicago: Year Book Publishers, Inc., 1958.
27. KATZ, GERALD, "Pilot Study of Medical Practices in Medical Arts Buildings," *Public Health Reports,* 81 (November, 1966), 1025–30.
28. KIBRE, PEARL, "The Faculty of Medicine at Paris, Charlatanism, and Unlicensed Medical Practices in the Later Middle Ages," *Bulletin of the History of Medicine,* 27 (January–February, 1953), 1–20.
29. KOOS, EARL LOMON, *The Health of Regionville.* New York: Columbia University Press, 1954.
30. ———, "Metropolis: What City People Think of Their Medical Services," *American Journal of Public Health,* 45 (December, 1955), 1551–57.
31. LIEBERSON, STANLEY, "Ethnic Groups and the Practice of Medicine," *American Sociological Review,* 23 (October, 1958), 542–49.
32. MCNERNEY, WALTER J. et al, *Hospital and Medical Economics.* Chicago: Hospital Research and Educational Trust, 1962, Vol. 2, 1205–1459.
34. MECHANIC, DAVID, "General Medical Practice in England and Wales," *New England Journal of Medicine,* 279 (September 26, 1968), 683.
35. NITTIS, SAVAS, "The Hippocratic Oath in Reference to Lithotomy," *Bulletin of the History of Medicine,* 6 (July, 1939), 719–28.
36. PETERSON, OSLER L., LEON P. AND-

REWS, ROBERT S. SPAIN, AND BERNARD G. GREENBERG, "An Analytical Study of North Carolina General Practice: 1953–1954," *The Journal of Medical Education*, 31 (December, 1956), Part 2 (entire issue).

37. POLLACK, JEROME, "How Prepayment and Insurance Carriers Can Participate in Prepaid Group Practice," in Social Security Administration, *Private Health Insurance and Medical Care*. Washington, D.C.: Government Printing Office, 1968, pp. 75–88.

38. REITZES, DIETRICH, *Negroes and Medicine*. Cambridge: Harvard University Press, 1958.

39. SCHWARTZ, JEROME L., *Medical Plans and Health Care*. Springfield: Charles C Thomas, Publisher, 1968.

40. SCOTT, W. RICHARD, "Reactions to Supervision in a Heteronomous Professional Organization," *Administrative Science Quarterly*, 10 (June, 1965), 65–68.

41. ———, Some Implications of Organization Theory for Research on Health Services," *Milbank Memorial Fund Quarterly*, 44 (October, 1966), Part 2, 35–59.

42. SEEMAN, MELVIN AND JOHN W. EVANS, "Stratification and Hospital Care: I. The Performance of the Medical Interne," *American Sociological Review*, 26 (February, 1961), 67–80; II. The Objective Criteria of Performance," *ibid*., 26 (April, 1961), 193–204.

43. SEHAM, MAX, "An American Doctor Looks at Eleven Foreign Health Systems," *Social Science and Medicine*, 3 (April, 1969), 65–81.

44. SHAPIRO, S., L. WEINER, AND P. M. DENSEN, "Comparison of Prematurity and Perinatal Mortality in General Population and in Population of Prepaid Group Practice," *American Journal of Public Health*, 48 (February, 1958), 170–87.

45. SHRYOCK, RICHARD H., *The Development of Modern Medicine*. New York: Alfred A. Knopf, Inc., 1947.

46. SIGERIST, HENRY N., A *History of Medicine*. Fairlawn, N.J.: Oxford University Press, 1951.

47. SOLOMON, DAVID N., "Ethnic and Class Differences among Hospitals as Contingencies in Medical Careers," *The American Journal of Sociology*, 66 (March, 1961), 463–71.

48. SOMERS, HERMAN MILES, AND ANNE RAMSAY SOMERS, *Doctors, Patients and Health Insurance*. Washington, D.C.: Brookings Institution, 1961.

49. STEWART, WILLIAM H., "Keynote Address," *Promoting The Group Practice of Medicine*, U.S. Public Health Service Publication No. 1750. Washington, D.C.: Government Printing Office, 1968, pp. 75–88.

50. THEODORE, CHRIST N. AND GERALD E. SUTTER, "A Report on the First Periodic Survey of Physicians," *Journal of the American Medical Association*, 202 (November 6, 1967), 180–88.

51. U.S. Department of Health, Education, and Welfare, *Health Resources Statistics: 1968*, U.S. Public Health Service Publication No. 1509. Washington, D.C.: Government Printing Office, 1968, p. 128.

52. WEINERMAN, E. RICHARD, "Research into the Organization of Medical Practice," *Milbank Memorial Fund Quarterly*, 44, Part 2, (October, 1966), 104–40.

53. WEISKOTTEN, HERMAN G., WALTER S. WIGGINS, MARION E. ALTENDERFER, MARJORIE GOUCH, AND ANNE TIPNER, "Trends in Medical Practice: An Analysis of the Distribution and Characteristics of Medical College Graduates, 1915–1950," *Journal of Medical Education*, 35 (December, 1960), 1071–121.

54. WHITE, KERR L., "Patterns of Medical Practice," in Duncan W. Clark and Brian MacMahon, eds., *Preventive Medicine*. Boston: Little, Brown and Company, 1967, pp. 849–70.

55. WILLIAMS, JOSEPHINE J., "Patients and Prejudice: Attitudes Towards Women Physicians," *American Journal of Sociology*, 51 (January, 1946), 283–87.

15

THE COMMUNITY OF HEALTH ORGANIZATIONS

Sol Levine and Paul E. White

A complex network of health agencies and organizations renders medical services within the typical American community. These organizations vary in size, form, function, autonomy, and professional composition, interact with one another, and comprise a health-agency system serving the general community and individuals within it. This system, which includes the hospitals, provides a host of services not available in the offices of individual practitioners.

The best point of departure for describing the organizations that constitute the health system is, perhaps, the ready-made system of classification which health professionals employ in their daily parlance. Health professionals refer to four main types of health organizations that are pertinent to our consideration of the community health system: (1) official or public agencies; (2) voluntary, or nonprofit agencies; (3) hospitals and nursing homes; and (4) health-related organizations. In our discussion of these classes of health organizations, we shall employ such sociological considerations as size, function, professional composition, and locus of authority.

OFFICIAL AGENCIES

Within most medium or large communities in the United States, there are official health-oriented agencies which, like other governmental organizations, depend upon tax funds and operate within relatively clear legal limits and regulations. Official agencies are organized on many levels. Traditionally, they existed on the federal, state, county, and city level but, in recent years, regions of various sizes—from parts of single states to several states—have been represented.

Federal Official Agencies

Federal agencies, for the most part, affect the local community only indirectly. Most federal health agencies (where "the most confused organizational picture in the United States is found" [43]) operate primarily through state agencies, but occasionally branches of these agencies serve local communities directly.

The Department of Health, Education, and Welfare is the most important of these agencies. Among its many important and encompassing activities are research, demonstration projects, and financial grants-in-aid to states. The Children's Bureau, for example, as one of its main functions, encourages the improvement and extension of services to mothers and children on the state and local level. This is accomplished by financial assistance, sponsorship of health programs, demonstration projects, and extensive research and educational activities. Another federal agency of considerable significance on the local scene is the Rehabilitation Services Administration, which makes grants-in-aid to states for the purpose of rehabilitating vocationally handicapped persons with physical or mental disabilities. Another organization is the Veterans Administration, which operates hospitals and outpatient departments and administers various kinds of training benefits for former members of the armed forces. These are only a few of the federal agencies whose activities have import for and are intertwined with the services offered by other agencies on the local level.

State Official Agencies

The pattern of official health organizations on the state level is a highly complex arrangement which varies markedly from state to state: "A study made by the Public Health Service in 1950 indicated a total of sixty different types of state agencies contributing in some way to state health programs." [43]. Direct health or health-related services are offered by a vast array of state departments, and the same health service is often the focus of the activities of a number of agencies. The organization of primary concern on the state level is the Department of Health, in which responsibility for public-health services is invariably invested.

Personal health services provided by state health departments vary greatly in kind and magnitude, but in general they tend to be confined to the provision of mobile personnel and equipment to specific localities at periodic intervals. In this manner, for example, many dental services, diagnostic X-rays, and other health services may be made available to a selected part of the population. Where full-time local health departments are lacking, however, the state health department may offer a greater volume of direct health services on a more permanent basis. In fact, one of the main functions of the state health department in many states is to promote the establishment of full-time health departments in areas where there are none and, perhaps even more important, to assist local health departments in the planning and execution of their programs. In order to meet this latter objective, the state health department may grant considerable financial aid to local health departments and provide them with various kinds of personnel resources, including consultative and specialized services and in-service training programs.

Local Official Agencies

Local public health departments have traditionally carried out six fundamental services: (1) the recording and analysis of vital statistics; (2) the control of communicable disease; (3) the maintenance and supervision of environmental sanitation; (4) public-health laboratory services; (5) maternal and child health services; and (6) health education of the general public [43]. The types and number of personnel necessary to carry out these services vary, of course, with the size of the jurisdiction—but all usually have the full or part-time services of a health director and at least the part-time services of nursing personnel, sanitary engineers or other sanitary personnel, and office workers.

In recent years, there has been increased concern with the role and scope of the health department [43]. As the morbidity pattern in the United States has changed, existing programs have been reexamined and health leaders have attempted to chart new ones. With the decrease in the incidence of communicable diseases, public-health programs have been developed to control cancer, heart disease, mental illness, and accidents. Administrators have placed increased emphasis upon early detection, prevention, comprehensive care, and rehabilitation, and they have initiated new activities such as cancer-detection clinics, glaucoma-screening programs, accident-control programs and services involving ambulatory and home care of the patient. Family-planning programs have also been defined as health programs and have been added to health-department activities. There has been a corresponding influx into the larger public-health agencies of such new public-health personnel as medical social workers, health educators, nutritionists, and even social scientists.

The scope of the programs conducted by a local public health department depends in large part upon the training of its chief administrator, the health officer. The larger proportion of local health agencies throughout the country is under the direction of physicians who have not had formal training in public-health methods, and others are administered by untrained laymen. The ideal of the public-health profession is to have local public-health units under the full-time direction of physicians with graduate training in public health. In the changing curriculum offered by schools of public health for prospective health officers, stress is placed on community organization, the organization of medical services, and the social sciences, in addition to the usual spectrum of laboratory courses.

Official health units also have shown increasing concern with coordinating the activities of the many and diverse types of community health agencies in an attempt to reduce the gaps and overlaps in the services provided. Since the local public-health unit is the agency with the greatest legal responsibility for the health of the population, the belief has grown among public-health professionals that the task of achieving maximal coordination of these various health and health-related agencies should reside in the local health department. This goal has not been realized, however. As Elling has pointed out, the question of which agencies will emerge as local coordinators is still open [24]. On a regional level, though, there have been three major attempts to coordinate and rationalize health resources and services: the Hill-Burton Program, the Regional Medical Programs, and the Comprehensive Heath Planning programs. These programs seek to influence various aspects of local programs through grants and consultation services.

VOLUNTARY AGENCIES

Existing side-by-side with official agencies are a multitude of nongovernmental, or voluntary, health agencies which are legally incorporated as nonprofit organizations on the local, state, or national level and which are supported by funds solicited from the public. What large community does not have a chapter or affiliate of the American Cancer Society, The National Foundation, The Visiting Nurse Association, or The Tuberculosis and Health Association? Other organizations associated with more esoteric illnesses or conditions are rapidly becoming embedded into the voluntary-health activity of communities across the country: e.g., Muscular Dystrophy, Cystic Fibrosis, Multiple Sclerosis, and so on. The great variation in these agencies is reflected in their size and in their executives—who range from nurse, social worker, or community organizer to interested layman. Some agencies are small, consisting of only a part-time director and secretary, whereas others are larger than many official health departments.

Voluntary agencies vary considerably in the services they perform and the activities in which they engage. A good number, such as Muscular Dystrophy and Cystic Fibrosis, raise funds to sponsor research, distribute considerable educational material and, in some cases, give financial assistance to special classes of patients; still others, such as the Tuberculosis and Health Association, engage in case finding and assist in the rehabilitation of the afflicted. A few, such as the Visiting Nurse Association, provide direct services to a large number of patients.

Voluntary health agency activity in the United States is extensive, involving the time and energy of hundreds of thousands of laymen serving on boards and committees, and of literally millions of volunteers. Personnel and laymen associated with these agencies tend to express the general belief that voluntary agencies possess advantages which are not shared by their official counterparts. For example, it is often said that voluntary organizations are more flexible, more free to experiment, and more able to pioneer in the health field, and that they supplement the activities of, and provide a needed stimulus to tax-supported agencies. On the other hand, leaders of voluntary health agencies generally grant that official agencies, because of their greater resources in money and personnel, are better equipped to undertake longer-range and more broadly based direct-service programs. Whether these are, indeed, respective advantages of the two types of organizations is worthy of systematic research. It would be desirable to document the kinds and magnitude of experimental programs undertaken by voluntary agencies, for example [41].

HOSPITALS

Hospitals are the major treatment centers of the community. Some are official, and some voluntary; some are addressed to specific diseases, others are more general in their scope; some do not have outpatient facilities, others offer extra-hospital programs. (For a detailed description of the structure of the hospital, see Chapter 10).

The changes in the morbidity picture due to urbanization, the growing philosophy of comprehensive care, the heightened efforts to decrease the number of in-patients, and the gradual extension of health insurance to cover medical costs outside the hospital setting have combined to cause many hospitals to go beyond the mere provision of inpatient services and to expand the scope of existing outpatient departments [78, 88]. Over the years, the services of outpatient departments have been broadened to include a wide range of diagnostic and therapeutic services to ambulatory patients in the general community. The new functions assumed by the outpatient clinics have established them more firmly in a network of relationships with other hospitals and community agencies.

HEALTH-RELATED ORGANIZATIONS

Side-by-side and overlapping with the complex of health agencies is a constellation of welfare and social agencies. While these agencies are not primarily devoted to health, they directly affect the health agencies through their control of resources, primarily patients and money.

The Welfare Department

One such agency is the official welfare department, which exists everywhere on the state level and can also be found as an autonomous agency on the local level in most medium-sized communities. Although the welfare department was historically associated exclusively with relief for the indigent and such concomitant activities as the administration of almshouses and the operation of orphanages, it has drastically expanded its scope and services within the last thirty years. The Social Security Act of 1935 heralded the inauguration of significant new programs for older people, the disabled, and dependent children. "The Act also contains provisions for unemployment compensation, old age pensions, care for the crippled, maternal and child welfare services, venereal disease control, and other activities" [80]. Subsequent provisions also include federal grants to states to defray the costs of preventive, therapeutic, and rehabilitative services to the indigent [80]. The welfare department subsidizes the cost of much of the medical care given by other agencies to welfare recipients, and is one of the main sources of referrals to agencies offering direct health services to the community. It also administers funds made available by Medicaid (Title XIX of the Social Security Amendments of 1965), a medical-care program for the "medically indigent," a category of persons determined for each state. In most states it is administered by the welfare department. The costs of the program are paid by the federal government and the states on a matching basis, the percentages paid by each party varying with the per capita income of the state. The program pays all costs for the comprehensive care of patients included in it.

Medicare (Title XVIII of the Social Security Amendments of 1965) is a system of financing medical care under the Social Security principle. Payroll deductions finance Part A of the plan, under which all persons sixty-five years of age or older are eligible for a limited amount of hospital care, nursing home care, and related services. The Social

Security Agency administers the plan, although health departments certify the providers. Part B is a voluntary plan for which a fee is exacted from the enrollee. Part B is not completely self-financing.

The Schools

The activities of the educational system overlap those of the health agencies of the community at many points. Although administrative arrangements vary, most schools are required by law to have some kind of health program for their students. This inevitably brings the school into contact with the health department, as well as with other official or voluntary agencies. In addition, school counseling or guidance programs have reciprocal contact with special community agencies serving children and their families. In some cases, the special health problems of students may produce heavy traffic between the school and agencies offering such specialized services as speech therapy, remedial reading, or other forms of aid to handicapped children.

The Voluntary Agencies

There are also a large number of voluntary agencies devoted to social-welfare or social-service activities—among them, the Salvation Army, the Family Service Society, the YMCA, and the Traveler's Aid Society. Many of these agencies had their "start in religious groups, in settlement houses or in efforts by citizens to deal with the mass migrations of the past" [80]. In recent years, they have extended their collective scope to encompass such diverse activities as financial assistance, rehabilitation, counseling, recreational activities, and varied types of help to needy parents and underprivileged children.

Other health-related voluntary and official agencies also supplement the health agencies. These include the courts, commercial organizations, and religious associations.

THE SOCIOLOGICAL STUDY OF HEALTH ORGANIZATIONS

The various health organizations, despite their complexity and heterogeneity, are amenable to logical classification and analysis. Sociological studies have focused on several aspects of community health agencies. Drawing upon the general field of organizational sociology and specific studies of the health field, the spectrum of health agencies can be analyzed under the following main subject areas:

1. The internal structure of the health agency.
2. The organization and its community environment.
3. Vertical relationship with parent bodies.
4. Interagency relationships.

Our consideration of health agencies focuses on organizations within the community. We shall, therefore, refer to studies which analyze community health organizations, individually and as parts of a system.

THE INTERNAL STRUCTURE OF THE HEALTH AGENCY[1]

The components of each organiza-

[1] Much of the ensuing discussion is based on a three-year study of some 130 health and welfare agencies and their interaction patterns in four Northeastern communities. The project was sponsored by the Social Science Program of the Harvard School of Public Health and supported by Grant 8676 from the National Institutes of Health. Sol Levine was the principal investigator of the project and Benjamin D. Paul, former director of the Social Science Program, was co-investigator.

tional structure are basically the same: the board, the executive director, and the staff. There are variations and elaborations of these components, to be sure: some official agencies have no boards, for example. In general, however, these organizational components are remarkably consistent from agency to agency.

The Board and the Executive

The boards are the formal policy makers of the organizations and, within limits imposed by their respective organizational affiliations, are commissioned to formulate and modify the charter and bylaws of the organization and allocate its expenditures. Boards vary in size but generally have up to thirty or forty members who are usually appointed for terms ranging from three to six years. An institutionalized mechanism of rotating membership generally requires members to retire from the board for a period of one term after having served two or three terms. This is intended to prevent the board from becoming "self-perpetuating," but desirable members are often asked to resume membership after token periods of retirement.

Since large boards are often unwieldy, decision-making power is frequently delegated to an executive committee. The executive, or paid director, of the agency is responsible to the board and acts within the limitations it imposes. Once the basic functions and scope of the organization are determined, the executive may exercise a good deal of latitude in administering the operations of the agency and supervising his staff, however. Moreover, because he is frequently a professional and the person most knowledgeable about the day-to-day occurrences within the agency, the information he conveys to the board may be the main basis for its policy decisions. While all executives appreciate the value of having influential citizens on their boards—it serves to indicate the climate of the dominant community and the potential receptivity of the population—some executives view boards as barriers to the achievement of imaginative programs. One of the main tasks of the energetic executive is therefore to continually educate his board and enlist its support for desirable programs.

In official agencies, the board is sometimes appointed by the relevant governmental unit—city, county, state—or, at other times, consists of a committee drawn from the membership of the elected governmental body itself. Consequently, the executives of official agencies normally contend with board members who are less committed than the members of the boards of voluntary agencies.

Board composition is being affected by the issue of community control and consumer representation. For the most part it is the new health centers that have such representatives, but other types of organizations will increasingly reflect this trend.

The Executive and the Staff

A variation in executive-staff relationships is found in hospitals because, in many instances, a good number of staff physicians are not employees of the hospital. In these cases the executive deals with the physicians as a group, usually through a committee. The physicians are not individually responsible to the executive except for adhering to administrative procedures governing the treatment of patients and the utilization of hospital facilities. Otherwise, the individual physician retains control over the disposition of his private patient within the hospital.

Smith has drawn attention to the fact that two lines of authority—lay and professional—exist within the hospital structure, a condition which, he demonstrates, may pose a dilemma for hospital personnel [89].

Each organization, depending on its functions, contains a range of professional positions. Many of these may be occupied by persons without formal training; one of the main reasons for this is the acute shortage of trained personnel in this field [2]. When interviewed, executives in some 130 agencies indicated that the largest organizational problem is staff shortage; the next is budgetary difficulties [56].

Most community health organizations, particularly the voluntary agencies, also have part-time volunteer workers who perform varied services without remuneration and thus supplement the work of staff and board members. The part-time volunteer helps substantially with the basic organizational chores, including clerical work, home visits, sundry clinical duties, and door-to-door fund raising. Although there have been various studies of volunteers in different types of voluntary organizations, the only intensive investigation of volunteers in a health agency is Sills's study of the National Foundation. Starting with the assumption that the characteristics of an organization are determined largely by the social character of its membership and the gratifications of participation, Sills intensively examined the volunteers, why and how they were recruited, and the psychological satisfactions they derived from participating [87].

Organizational Research

Although the characteristics of participants in voluntary agencies have been studied, the agencies themselves have not been the object of sociological investigation, other than Sills's work and a few case studies of individual national health agencies [12, 21, 36]. Sociological studies of health organizations have focused primarily on hospitals and outpatient departments, to the relative exclusion of other types of agencies.

Studies of other health agencies have been made, however. Some studies of innovation in community agencies have been carried out, but they report seemingly different results [50, 66, 69]. Mohr, in his study of ninety-four full-time local health departments, analyzed the determinants of innovation in services and concluded that "organizational size proved to be an excellent indicator of the relevant resources available to local health departments for the adoption of a large number of non-traditional programs" [66]. Kaplan, in his study of program change in community agencies, stated: "The executive director . . . is the most significant factor in variability in program innovation in community agencies" [50]. Perhaps the question of innovation and its determinants might more successfully be resolved by studies of process rather than of structural variables associated with innovation.

Another approach to organizational change was utilized by New and May. They studied local boards of health from the viewpoint of factors that have led to their continuation and persistence in the face of State Health Department pressures to discontinue them [70].

That health-agency environments are appropriate settings for the testing and refinement of sociological hypotheses is evidenced in a study by Bennis and his associates, in which they employed the concepts of "locals" and "cosmopolitans" in classifying nurses in several outpatient departments. It was expected, for example, that "locals" would show greater in-group loyalty and involvement in organizational goals and that "cosmopolitans" would be more interested in outside groups. But the findings were contrary to expectations. "Cosmopolitans" maintained in-group loyalties and shared organization goals, while "locals" revealed less in-group loyalty and were more interested in groups, such as nursing associations, external to the outpatient setting. The authors interpret these surprising findings in the light of the distinctive nature of the nursing profession and its intra-organizational environments. They sugest that the anticipated local-cosmopolitan schema tends to hold less in settings where organizational goals are unclear, where individual success is not dependent upon the organization, and "where the main body of the membership perceives the profession chiefly as embodying ultimate values rather than criteria for skills, research, and the development of a body of knowledge" [5].

Another study of the outpatient department, by Solon and his coworkers focuses on the staff's perception of patients and their use of medical services. Distinct differences appear in the perceptions and attitudes of physicians, nurses, and social workers. Solon suggests that these may be related to the values and experiences of the different professional groups. In brief, the physician, his outlook anchored in his private practice, seems to be least sympathetic to the various practices of patients in utilizing medical care, such as "shopping around" for medical care or obtaining free care. The social worker, on the other hand, shows a strong identification with the patient, while the nurse appears "to articulate her strong concern for the patient with a strong organizational identification" [90].

THE AGENCY AND THE COMMUNITY

The promotion of health and the prevention and cure of disease are the ideal goals of the health-agency system, but few, if any, agencies possess access to all the resources they need to enable them to attain these objectives fully. They must be realistic and limit their activities, selecting particular functions that permit them to achieve certain ends as fully as possible.

The Functions of the Agency

"By function is meant a set of interrelated services or activities that are instrumental, or believed to be instrumental, for the realization of an organization's objectives" [54]. In more operational terms, "function" consists of the services offered and the specific categories of recipients or population groups served. The functions selected by an agency represent its decision about the allocation of its resources for serving its community. By characterizing organizations by their primary functions, some order and clarification can be introduced into the otherwise diverse array of agencies in the community.

The nature of the disease involved and the existing medical technology partially determine the range of services which an organization may offer to the community. The disease process itself usually has a natural history, and the sequence of the individual's organic reactions provides the health specialist with specific opportunities for intervention. The functions of an organization represent its mode of intervening with respect to the disease or illness. There are seven main functions which an organization may perform: (1) *education*, the transmission of medicoscientific information intended to produce behavior reducing the risk of illness; (2) *prevention*, the employment of scientific technology to make the individual impervious to disease; (3) *treatment*, the utilization of medicoscientific technology to control the disease in its acute stage and to restore the individual, so far as possible, to his previous state of functioning; (4) *rehabilitation*, the application of medicoscientific technology to restore the organism to maximum functioning after the illness has struck and produced some effects; (5) *resource giving*, the facilitation of the receipt of medicoscientific technology by the removal of financial and other impediments; (6) *research*, the building of medicoscientific knowledge and technology with regard to a specific illness; and (7) *coordination*, the integration of medicoscientific resources of different agencies.

The Population Served

These functions, with the exception of the last two, are services rendered directly to specific population groups. Although there are various criteria for classifying the recipient populations, age and illness are the ones generally used.

Classification by age parallels the divisions which are found in the larger society. The customary age breakdown within the health system in the United States is: (1) infant and preschool; (2) school; (3) adult; and (4) elderly. The first group is generally supervised by a parent or guardian; the second is in school at predictable times; the third, especially its male members, is at a place of employment; and the fourth is fairly sedentary, either at home or in hospitals, nursing homes, or other institutions.

Income, another differentiating characteristic used by health agencies, cuts across age and illness. People are classified as self-supporting, medically indigent (unable to afford necessary health services but not otherwise indigent), and financially indigent (unable to afford medical services and even unable to pay for the other necessities). Some other more specialized bases of classification may be adopted by sectarian or church-sponsored agencies whose services may be aimed mainly at specific racial, ethnic, or religious groups.

But an agency may not adhere rigidly to these criteria; indeed, it may depart drastically from them at any time for all kinds of reasons—a diminishing case load, an unclear or changing agency policy, lack of knowledge, or the whim of its personnel [39]. Then, too, an agency may generally screen the clients referred by other agencies but automatically accept those referred by a specific agency with which it enjoys an established and favorable relationship. In general, however, illness, age, and income constitute the framework within which agencies order the world of clients or patients around them.

The Community as a Resource

The goals and related functions of an organization not only determine its services to the community but also affect what the organization needs and seeks to obtain from the community. An organization requires three main resources: patients or clients, personnel, and such nonhuman resources as money, space, equipment, and information [54]. Although these may be obtained from other health agencies, it is the general community as a source which concerns us here.

One variable that is related to an organization's receiving the resources it needs is prestige. Whether the relationship is causal or not is problematic. Elling has described the strategies and processes by which competing hospitals in a community gained financial support and, on a more general level, Elling and Halebsky have studied the factors affecting the support received by governmental and voluntary hospitals [23, 26]. They report that voluntary nondenominational hospitals receive more financial support than their official or governmental counterparts. A similar relationship obtains when patient channeling (referral) is used as a measure of support and when the criterion of community participation is considered (but the authors have no comparative data on the composition of hospital volunteers). They point out that, as hospitals evolved in the present century:

> ... voluntary hospitals tended to draw business, industrial and society leaders on to their boards and did not leave any channel of formal control open to the public. City and county hospitals, on the other hand, have remained the "people's" hospitals in the sense that popular control and identification has been partially retained through the election of governmental officials [26].

They also suggest that the higher prestige of the voluntary hospitals may possibly explain, in part, the greater support they receive.

That voluntary hospitals do enjoy more prestige than governmental hospitals is supported by data obtained in studies of health agencies in four communities, based on ratings by agency executives, board members, and community leaders [57]. In this respect, Perrow's comment on the importance of organizational prestige is most pertinent:

> One of the many ways of controlling dependency is to create and maintain a favorable image of the organization in the salient publics. If an organization and its products are well regarded, it may more easily attract personnel, influence relevant legislation, wield informal power in the community, and insure adequate numbers of clients, customers, donors, or investors [72].

He also shows that concern with the organizational image and prestige may be dysfunctional—from the point of view of fulfilling the organization's basic goals [72].

The personnel of the agencies consists of board members, the policy makers of the organization, and the staff, either paid or volunteer, which implements the policy. The boards which link the agency to the community, whether appointed or co-opted are drawn mainly from the business and industrial sectors of the community, sometimes from the professional groups, and rarely from the lower-income levels of the population [18, 55, 103]. Recently, however, the question of the effect of members of the community on local organizations has been receiving increasing attention [3, 4, 25, 45, 73, 103]. Litwak and Meyer have described a conceptual approach for studying the links between interlocking as overlapping boards and the exchange of resources among agencies [58].

Freeman and Lambert, in a survey of views of lower-income mothers, assessed the positive and negative influences of organizational endorsement of health issues. They concluded that advocates of health measures should avoid endorsement by most voluntary associations. Positive influence, they found, is generally exerted only on the members of the organization. Therefore, assessments of effects of such endorsements must take into account the possible negative impact on nonmembers [31].

A different order of problems that is currently receiving much attention is the participation of community and consumer representatives on advisory and policy-making boards of local, particularly neighborhood, health organizations. Goldberg, Trowbridge, and Buxbaum, delineating major issues in the development of neighborhood health centers, emphasize that the issue of control is a major source of conflict in community-professional relationships [34]. Davis and Tranquada describe conflicts in a neighborhood health center which resulted in large part from a poorly defined division of authority and responsibility. The situation is typical of many centers, sponsored by the Office of Economic Opportunity. They state:

> ... the OEO granted money to the University at large, with administration of the project to be by the Medical School. Although there was a general commitment of responsibility toward the project by the larger University, in actuality, the project was never interpreted as other than a Medical School project. The Medical School does not have the manpower or resources necessary to train and prepare the Council for an eventual takeover; nor were funds directly allocated in the budget for this purpose, an oversight that neither the OEO nor the University recognized [19].

Geiger and Bellin have described the experiences of the Columbia Point Project and indicated the problems involved in relationships between the poor and the university [4, 32, 33].

In addition to their need for members of their advisory and policy-making boards, voluntary health agencies rely heavily on volunteers who perform the daily activities of the organization. As Sills points out, voluntary health agencies do not have the alternatives of other kinds of organizations for recruiting members:

> Unlike a church for example, a voluntary health association cannot depend upon the occupational structure for recruits; ... unlike a military organization, it has no such coercive mechanism as conscription legislation; unlike a government bureaucracy, a business firm or a professional or trade association, it cannot depend upon the occupational structure for recruits ... [87].

It tends, therefore, to make use of personal relationships. Of all volunteers recruited by the National Foundation, 52 percent joined at the invitation of someone they knew personally; 20 percent were asked to join by some other community member; 18 percent were invited by an organizational or work colleague; and only 10 percent joined on their own initiative [87]. In this respect, the typology of voluntary agencies offered by Gordon and Babchuck is most relevant [36]. They characterize agencies by whether they are mainly expressive or instrumental, by the social status they enjoy, and by their accessibility. Voluntary agencies in general would appear to be organizations of relatively low accessibility, despite their obvious need for membership. Sills, in his interesting study of members recruited by the Foundation, focused on the typology of joiners, the acquisition of new interests and attitudes as a result of membership, and the psychological gratifications of participation [87]. Comparable information on volunteers in other voluntary agencies would be most desirable.

Financing

The financing of health agencies has been the object of considerable attention and controversy in recent years. With the exception of proprietary hospitals, nursing homes, or special clinics, none of the agencies of the health system is a profit-making organization. The three main sources of funds for health agencies are: public tax funds, contributions from the general community, and fees for service from individual clients or recipients.

Most government agencies rely almost entirely upon tax funds for their support. Theoretically, an official agency is only required to submit a budget to the appropriate allocating group, either an administrative or legislative body, for review and approval. But agency executives usually expect that some budgetary items will be deleted or decreased, and they are known to exaggerate their needs accordingly. A good number of executives of official agencies also confide that they find it easier to obtain funds for projected services which are likely to yield concrete results than for services having less tangible consequences, say, education. Were the concerns of the executives of official agencies limited just to satisfying the vote-oriented objectives of the legislators, their fund-raising task would be difficult enough. In some communities, however, their problems are further complicated by other factors which arise mainly from the relationship of official agencies to the political patronage system. Agency executives who adhere to the norms of the patronage system are more likely to be successful in their requests for funds, and those who fail to conform are more likely to encounter difficulties.

Historically, the voluntary health agencies have depended mostly upon private philanthropy and individual contributions. Charitable funds, often in the form of bequests, together with the personal services of volunteers, enabled an appreciable part of the voluntary health system to operate. As the population grew, however, the volume of health services increased. Most of the roles in the health system became professionalized, thereby diminishing the importance of many of the volunteer services and creating the need for more funds to hire new professionals. Simultaneously, technological developments in medicine necessitated the procurement of costly machinery and physical plants.

Philanthropy has itself accommodated to changing community conditions [41]. With the demise and decrease in importance of locally owned industries in many communities, the paternalistic system associated with them has become less prevalent and less capable of supporting the wide gamut of health services. The concurrent rise of national corporations has also affected the system of local philanthrophy, as local branches of these corporations gradually replaced locally owned industry. These local branches are more likely to have charity quotas, allotted more or less impartially to the whole array of voluntary agencies in the community. The agencies' reliance on large individual donations, therefore, has gradually been superseded by fund raising which is more carefully organized and community-wide in scope. The two predominant modes of soliciting funds are independent fund raising by the agency itself and membership in a community chest or fund organizations.

Independent fund raising takes three general forms: special offers, often from board members and their friends, to obtain large individual contributions from a few well-to-do persons; solicitation of the general public by mail; and door-to-door canvassing. The calendar year has been divided into fund-raising seasons, each the domain of a particular agency. Usually the national or parent bodies of the local organizations determine when fund raising is to take place. Thus the TB Association claims Christmas with its seals, Crippled Children monopolizes Easter. Other organizations do not necessarily synchronize their fund raising with holidays; they may proclaim and publicize a special period, such as Mental Health or Heart Sunday, when they concentrate on programs to "educate" the public to the value of their special endeavors. The campaign then concludes with an appeal for donations. There seems to be no general rule for determining which kinds of agency will conduct which sort of campaign.

There is a real difference, however, between the agencies that conduct independent campaigns and those that solicit through the community chest or fund. Community chests and funds originated as a response to the gradual proliferation of fund-raising agencies. They were initiated primarily by the business and industrial segments of various communities in order to expedite the collection of funds by decreasing the number of solicitations to which a given business enterprise might be subjected. The intent was to consolidate fund drives into a single endeavor, so that the community would be approached but once a year and the money apportioned among the various community agencies.

The plan has succeeded to some extent. A great proportion of the funds solicited in the community are collected through the community chest or fund, although the monies acquired through independent fund drives are also considerable [41]. Agencies with proportionately large local expenditures of local funds tend to belong to the community chest or fund, but the financial arrangements they make with the fund or chest are most varied. The arrangements in one city may be cited to illustrate the complexity of arrangements. In this city upon joining the chest, an agency is generally guaranteed, for a stipulated number of years, an annual income equivalent to its prior yearly budget. In subsequent years, expenditures become subject to revision, and funds for specific purposes may be deleted from the agency's budget. After this initial period of financial adjustment, an agency's budget is normally approved automatically, so long as the agency does not modify its services. If the chest should fail to meet its fund-raising goal, the budgets of member agencies are usually decreased in proportion to the deficit.

The funds are a financial partnership. The budgets of member agencies are not usually subject to review or revision, and the member agencies usually receive relatively fixed proportions of the proceeds of the funds' drives. Member agencies tend to be those which could well conduct independent fund drives. They derive their strength either from their strong appeal to a particular group or from the fact that they solicit from a wide area or region of which the community is only a part. In most cases, membership in a fund represents a compromise with local pressure groups. It is a concession to integrated fund raising but a rejection of local control. In some areas, both a chest and a fund exist. In such cases, chest agencies as a whole constitute one member of the fund.

Those agencies which conduct independent fund drives almost exclusively concentrate on single, specific disease syndromes, though there are some noteworthy exceptions such as the Red Cross and the Salvation Army. These agencies are often prohibited by their national parent bodies from participating in the community chest or fund. Several considerations underlie such a policy. The reason most frequently given by specific-disease agency personnel is that membership would result in the loss of their "agency identity"; they would become submerged in the mass of chest agencies and the special appeal of their agency would be forfeited. However, there are other reasons as well. Specific-disease agencies often do considerable research, for the diseases they concentrate on are usually incurable. They consequently wish to spend their funds in centralized research endeavors, and to achieve this end they must delimit the programs of the local affiliates in order to drain off as few funds as possible. An independent drive is advantageous to these research-orientated agencies; it frees them of any stipulations which a local community chest might impose and thereby permits them to expend their funds in accordance with their own goals.

The conflict between proponents of independent and federated fund raising is one of the greatest sources of friction within the health and welfare agency world [41]. Community chests and united funds have exerted pressure on the independent agencies at the local level in an attempt to induce them to adopt federated fund raising. The controversy stems mainly from the different goals of the two types of agencies: The federated agencies are mainly concerned with serving local interests, whereas the independent-drive agencies are geared to accomplishing national objectives. United funds and community chests recently have established a number of local "research and health foundations," often as a means of competing with the research appeal of independent national voluntary agencies [41]. On the other hand, independent voluntary agencies, in order to capitalize on the public appeal of direct service, have attempted to indicate that their efforts also bear fruit on the local level.

White has noted that efforts to consolidate fund drives may be dysfunctional from the point of view of the rational coordination of community health services. The critical variable in determining the manner of solicitation seems to be whether time is available, rather than amount of money collected. The consolidation of separate fund drives makes free periods available in the calendar, and these are filled by new, relatively autonomous agencies seeking entry to the community [101]. The allocation of funds to agency members of the consolidated drives, because of the local balance of power among the agencies, does not often lead to the discontinuance of outmoded services or to the stimulation of integrated programs.

THE RELATIONSHIP BETWEEN LOCAL ORGANIZATIONS AND NATIONAL BODIES

All organizations, including health agencies, operate within a changing environment and are faced with the recurrent need to reappraise their goals and objectives and establish new ones [8, 84, 85, 95]. In general, the products of health agencies would appear less tangible than, for example, those of business organizations and, accordingly, the task of goal reappraisal would be rendered more difficult [95]. But organizations do not respond merely to the changing environment; they often produce the very changes in the environment which in turn command their adaption. When the goals of a health agency, particularly a voluntary agency, are realized, there are two main courses it may follow: It may disband as an organization or it may develop new goals or objectives. The more usual course is the latter—which Blau defines as the "succession of goal." It is vital for the organization to have its new goals, like the old ones, legitimized by the rest of the health-agency system or the general community, for the goals represent the agency's claim to resources without which it cannot survive. The National Foundation is an excellent example of a large voluntary health agency which realized its good —the development of the Salk vaccine which heralded the eventual disappearance of polio—and which is presently attempting to redefine its goals in the midst of a changing environment which it helped to produce [87].

Sills's intensive study of the National Foundation shows how a national voluntary organization may exercise control over its affiliates so that it undergoes a minimum of goal displacement [87]. He distinguishes between two types of national voluntary organizations: corporate organizations, which delegate authority downward from the national to the local level; and federated organizations, which delegate authority upward from the local to the national level. In the corporate-type structure, the local units tend to have been formed at the initiative of the national body. In a federated organization, the local affiliates tend to have created the national unit as a coordinating body [11]. Examples of corporate organizations are the American Red Cross, the American Cancer Society, and the American Heart Association; examples of federated structures are the Visting Nurses Association, the National Tuberculosis Association, and United Cerebral Palsy. National corporate and federated health and welfare organizations tend to differ in the stipulations or requirements they establish for their local affiliates or chapters. In contrast with federated organizations, corporate agencies tend to forbid the local to incorporate or own property. The explanation seems to be that the more the local retains and accumulates resources, the more it responds to local pressures, is enabled to exist independently of national support, and becomes more independent of national direction [11]. Local affiliates of corporate agencies are also required to give a greater percentage of the funds they raise to the national organization, and they are also more restricted in how they may use whatever funds they retain.

Corporate agencies seem less interested in having professionally trained persons as local executive directors or on the local staff. The few agencies that do indicate the desirability of having professionally trained staff on the local level are of the federated type [11]. A study of community agencies reveals that none of the executive directors of corporate agencies is professionally trained, whereas a considerable proportion of the heads of federated agencies have graduate training in one of the health or health-related professions such as nursing, social work, or health education. Of course, types of personnel are also related to other organizational characteristics (e.g., function) but it is to be noted that, by not having professionals as members of the permanent staff, corporate agencies minimize the threat that other objectives may replace their original organizational goals. Nonprofessionals seem to display "local patterns" of behavior, having greater interest in and allegiance to the organization *per se*. Professionals approximate the "cosmopolitan," who is bound by the norms of his profession and may feel free to move to other organizations. Professionals would thus appear to be less dependent upon national parent bodies and, under certain circumstances, more ready to question national policy.

There is some evidence, on both national and local levels, that an organization's functions are correlated with its structures. Single-disease agencies tend to have a corporate structure and to state as their primary goal that of "finding a cure." Federated organizations are more likely to state as their major objective "prevention" or "maximum relief of suffering" [11]. Although most local affiliates perform some services in their communities to justify their fund raising, these services also seem to vary in accordance with the structure of the national organization. As we would expect, there is a greater tendency for federated organizations to operate clinics or other programs which entail cooperation with other agencies, whereas the health services of corporate agencies are most often confined to educational programs or the payment of individual medical bills incurred elsewhere [11]. Because of their different orientations, corporate organizations are less likely than federated to join consolidated fund-raising efforts such as the Community Chest. Local constraints and commitments are thereby minimized.

The variation in the degree of control exerted by a national organization over its local chapters, as Johns and de Marche have noted, can be characterized as: (1) high degree of control; (2) mixed local-national control; and (3) local control. Some of the sanctions which national organizations exercising high degrees of control may employ to effect conformity are: withholding charters, failing to provide field service, excluding local units and staff members from official rosters, and restricting the participation of workers in personnel services and pension plans. In organizations characterized by mixed control, national plans and policies are submitted to local chapters as required actions or recommendations. These policies are generally arrived at through regular meetings with local representatives, and considerable leeway is permitted in adapting the policy to local conditions. Among organizations where local control prevails, the role of the national organization is limited to making recommendations and arranging meetings where mutual problems may be discussed and experiences exchanged [49]. Warren describes and analyzes the experiences of a project in which a state-level voluntary organization offered program consultation to community-level agencies. He indicates the conditions under which such endeavors are relatively successful and unsuccessful [99].

Similar patterns are evident among official agencies. An official state rehabilitation organization, for example, has as its main objective the return to employment of persons who have suffered a serious illness. The agency has a corporate-type organization, and the local branch must justify its existence to its parent body, and eventually to the state legislators, by showing that a large number of persons have been successfully rehabilitated. The local organization, therefore, only reluctantly accepts seriously debilitated clients that are referred to it, for it cannot commit its resources to the consuming task of rehabilitating "poor risks." It may share the values of other community agencies and want approval from them, but it is the parent agency and other officials on the state level on whom it relies for its financial support [54].

Two important research opportunities are afforded in studying national-local relationships. The first pertains to learning the processes by which pressure is exerted on the local chapter by both the community and the national agency, and the types of accommodation achieved by the local unit in resolving these conflicting pressures [98]. The second involves ascertaining the impact of a change in agency function (e.g., a shift from research to direct service) on the total structure of an organization and the processes by which the organizational structure may evolve.

RELATIONS AMONG HEALTH AGENCIES

In highlighting the need to study the organization in relation to its environment, Etzioni specified the area of interorganizational relationships as one requiring further empirical study [27]. In 1967 and 1969 sessions of the American Sociological Association, on formal organizations, were devoted to the topic; a number of articles on the problem have also appeared [1, 13, 28, 59]. Several of these are investigations of the relationships among health and welfare organizations. Aiken and Hage, for example, studied the "joint cooperative programs" of these agencies; Litwak and Hylton considered the problems in coordinating social welfare programs; and Warren has studied community-planning organizations [1, 59, 100]. March and Simon suggest that interorganization conflict is very similar to intergroup conflict within organizations, but they present no supporting data [62]. White has studied the validity of beliefs underlying and supporting interagency conflict, finding that the agencies were in reality not in competition even though they believed they were struggling for the same resources [101]. Health and welfare agencies in the local community offer an excellent opportunity for exploring and locating the relationships among organizations. An appreciable number of organizations exist in any medium-sized American community.

Lefton and Rosengren have proposed a model of organizational behavior based on the relationships of the organizations to their clients. They classify organizational commitment to the clients as either "longitudinal," or long-term, interest or "latitudinal," or comprehensive, interest in the client, and point out the ramifications of these commitments in the control or compliance of the client, the staff agreement on organizational goals, and modes of collaboration among the staff. They further state that interorganizational relationships are also affected by these commitments:

> . . . the fact of a longitudinal interest in the client's future biography means that the organization must devise ways of establishing working relationships with other organizations which may ultimately be held responsible for the later careers of the client. Thus one is likely to find that the non-lateral/non-longitudinal organization (hospital or not) has not established linkages with the juvenile court, nursing homes, family welfare agencies, the probation office, and so forth, while the administrative personnel in the longitudinal institution are often intimately tied in with a wide range of other interested institutions [53].

Eichhorn and Wysong have studied agency interrelationships in relation to tuberculosis control in a metropolitan area and explain "the contacts between agencies and the expansion of the Lake County Tuberculosis Hospital . . . in terms of organization's orientations towards their clients." They also examine data from a "skeptical perspective," stating that:

> . . . scholars hold that there is a strong tendency for an organization to become an end-in-itself rather than simply means to an end . . . when such a goal displacement occurs, an unnecessary proportion of organizational activity is allocated to ensuring

the organization's survival, autonomy, and prosperity [22].

They conclude by rejecting that viewpoint because of its insufficiency in explaining important aspect of organizational behavior.

Johns and de Marche suggest the following dimensions around which interagency relationships may be classified: (1) those involving "furthering acquaintance with other agency leaders"; (2) those resulting in the exchange of information; (3) those which "in addition to furthering acquaintance and exchanging information, have resulted in specific consultation with representatives of other agencies"; (4) those which "in addition to those above, have resulted in definite planning with representatives of other agencies"; and (5) those which "have also resulted in definite operating responsibilities with representatives of other agencies" [49].

The typology set forth by Johns and de Marche centers largely on the cooperative process or the intensity of the relationship. Levine and White, on the other hand, focus largely on the goods or resources—i.e., clients, personnel, and nonhuman resources—which are exchanged. Even the fullfillment of realistically limited functions requires access to certain kinds of resources. An agency, therefore, may seek to obtain these through exchange with other organizations. "Theoretically, then, were all the essential elements in infinite supply there would be little need for organizational interaction and for subscription to cooperation as an ideal. Under actual conditions of scarcity, however, inter-organizational exchanges are essential for goal attainment" [54].

The interdependence of agencies within the health system and their exchanges with one another are seen as contingent upon three related factors: (1) the objectives of each agency and the particular functions it selects, which, in turn, determine the kinds and numbers of resources it requires; (2) the access which each organization has to necessary resources from outside the health system, which may determine the agency's dependence upon other parts of the health system; and (3) the degree to which there is agreement among the agencies about their domains. "Organizational domain," in the health field, refers to the area the organization stakes out for itself in terms of disease covered, population served, and services rendered. Before two organizations can exchange elements with one another, there must be at least minimal agreement about their respective domains. Obviously, there can be little exchange between two agencies that do not know of each other's existence or are completely unaware of each other's functions; on the other hand, intense competition may occur between two agencies offering similar services, especially when other agencies have no clear criteria for referring patients to one rather than the other. In some cases, the conflict may be resolved by having the two agencies handle the same category of patients, but at consecutive stages. For example, one agency may assume responsibility for patients when they are bedridden, and the other when they become ambulatory. Another means of removing conflict and achieving agreement is to divide the population among the agencies in question. In one case, where three agencies were involved in providing rehabilitation services, the conflict was resolved by having one agency serve preschool children, another school children, and the third, adults.

Although administrators have expressed considerable concern about reducing barriers to cooperation and achieving greater coordination among health and welfare agencies, the problem itself has received little systematic attention. There is little empirical evidence that interagency cooperation *per se* is necessarily related to organizational effectiveness, although there is good reason to believe—for various direct-service agencies, at least—that some organizational objectives would be furthered by greater cooperation with other agencies. The comparatively little research which has been done on interagency cooperation has relied largely on assessment by staff rather than on more objective data. Johns and de Marche compiled a long list of conditions presumed to be barriers to interagency cooperation. They include such factors as lack of knowledge of the work or objectives of other agencies, personality conflicts, differences in professional philosophy, "vested interests," lack of funds, and the influences of national agencies [49].

Attention should be drawn to the possible consequences of engaging in interorganizational exchange. It may affect future exchanges with the three main sources of elements—other agencies in the health system, parent bodies, and the general community. A dramatic illustration is the apprehension of a good number of agencies about developing relationships with Planned Parenthood, since they may be ostracized by other agencies or significant segments of community, and thereby forfeit access to necessary resources [75]. But while the community may at times intrude on the interaction within the health-agency world, such occurrences are rare and dramatic. There are indeed crucial points of articulation between the community and the agencies —such as the allocation of funds and other resources by the community which establish the limits within which the health system operates, and the role of boards as policy makers who legitimize specific agency functions and delineate organizational domains. Once the policy makers establish the objectives and the functions of the organization, however, these objectives and functions largely determine the organization's interaction with other agencies. Other organizational variables, in turn, appear to affect interaction within the limits established by the agency's functions. Much of the interaction within the health system appears to be relatively insulated from the surrounding community.

Miller's observations on interinstitutional conflict as a major impediment to delinquency prevention are most relevant for our understanding of barriers to interagency cooperation [65]. Although the institutions with which he is concerned—the courts, the police, correctional institutions, and psychiatric agencies—extend beyond the health and welfare system and are less bound by a unifying value system than the health and welfare agencies, the differences among their approaches to treatment throw light on the problem of conflicts of domain. Also, Teele and Levine, in a study of child guidance and court clinics, found that organizational priorities and professional interests had a considerable impact on delinquency-control programs—and that very difficult cases or those most needing help were often not accepted by the guidance clinics [94].

Miller found differences on such issues as: (1) the etiology of crime (morality vs. pathology and individual locus vs. social locus); (2) methods of dealing with offenders (restriction vs. rehabilitation); (3) approach (action vs. research); (4) methods of organizing preventive programs (localization vs. centralization); and (5) the appropriate status of personnel (lay vs. professional). Miller concludes that interinstitutional conflicts stem from the differing philosophies of the respective institutions and that these differences serve to impede concerted community action. He suggests that there is need to shift the focus of research from the relationship between the agencies and the recipient population to the relationships among the agencies themselves [65].

An interesting note on interagency cooperation is offered in Form and Nosow's study of a disaster situation. The authors report that whatever interaction did take place during the emergency period was spontaneous and fortuitous, and rested on informal and implicit arrangements. They observe that "organizational cooperation was facilitated among organizations with similar internal structure" and that smooth cooperation is dependent upon congruent expectations among organizations in the disaster system. The authors conclude that "first and foremost . . . a disaster system must rest upon a pre-disaster plan of coordinated organizations" [29].

The problem of rationalization and coordination of services has long been of concern to health professionals, both from the viewpoint of efficiency of operations, on the one hand, and of convenience and comprehensiveness of care of the patient, on the other. For some time, it was thought that mutual knowledge of agency services would be sufficient to induce coordination of those services. The financial backing of Health and Welfare Councils is by Community Chests and United Funds was an attempt to allocate services rationally, but it has not succeeded because of its pluralistic base and inability to apply sanctions. Reid, in considering problems of organizational coordination, has listed several conditions of organizational coexistence which are conducive to coordination or its lack. The conditions are: (1) "independence"; (2) "recognized interdependence of goals"; and (3) "conflict" of several types, which results when the goal of one organization is attained at the expense of the goal of another organization [74]. Strantz and Miller attempt to abstract "principles," some of which are derived from sociological studies, to explain the coordination of several health agencies in a comprehensive medical care program [93].

On a regional basis, Hill-Burton funds have had some success in consolidating hospital facilities. Two relatively new federal programs, Regional Medical Programs and Comprehensive Health Planning, are also directed toward rationalizing services on regional levels, Regional Medical Programs, engendered in 1965 (P.L. 89–239), provided for the organization of regional cooperative efforts primarily among medical schools and hospitals, for research, training, and demonstration. Comprehensive Health Planning came into being under the Partnerships for Health Act of 1966 (P.L. 89–749). Under the aegis of the state governments (its geographical boundaries usually correspond with state boundaries), its goals, as stated in the preamble to the law, pose a sociological dilemma: "to support the martialling of all health resources, national, state and local; to assure comprehensive health care of high quality for every person, but without interference with existing patterns of private practice of medicine, dentistry and related arts."

There are other basic problems with these programs. The geographical jurisdictions are not coextensive, and the programs do not possess sanctions or resources commensurate with their purposes. Furthermore, the respective functional domains of the two programs have not been clearly defined, with the result that their relative roles differ in various regions. The impact of both programs also appears to have been weakened by budget reductions.

Mott, in an intensive study of a coordinating council, has analyzed the sources of its weaknesses and the conditions under which its efficiency could be increased. In comparing the hypothetical advantages and disadvantages of coordination by a council of "equals" with coordination by a hierarchically structured group, he indicates the need for futher study of alternative organizational arrangements, and also study that will lead to greater specification of the coordination required in specific situations [68].

Hospitals have also become the foci of coordination on the community level, largely as a consequence of two factors: The Regional Medical Programs that are administered in most regions under the aegis of medical school and teaching hospitals, and the demand for outpatient services of inner-city populations. Another powerful stimulus to coordination (the success of which is also unknown) is the movement to create comprehensive neighborhood health centers. These centers reflect the current general interest in consumer control and decentralization. Both these trends have implications for the development of community health organizations.

Many public-health directors feel that they are coordinating the work of other community agencies, but there is little evidence that this is actually the case, nor is there any clear agreement in the rest of the health-agency system as to what types of coordination are desired or whether the responsibility for coordination should reside in the health officer. Given the diverse array of health agencies with varying goals and loci of authority, the task of achieving more effective coordination challenges the wisdom and skills of the public-health professional, the medical-care specialist, the community organizer, and the sociologist [67].

CONCLUSION

The problems and activities of community health and welfare agencies comprise one sector in the health field to which the sociologist should be able to make a clear and unmistakable contribution. In relating to other problems in the health field (e.g., the etiology of illness), the sociologist, regardless of the merit of his potential contribution, must take into account the special experience and competence of the physician. But in the area of health and welfare organizations, the physician usually has little expert knowledge; if anyone can lay claim to this particular province, it is the sociologist. The diversity of the health and welfare agency system is still a fertile and relatively untapped field, and its proper exploration would enrich the field of organizational sociology.

REFERENCES

1. Aiken, Michael and Jerald Hagen, "Organizational Interdependence and Intra-Organizational Structure," *American Sociological Review*, 33 (December, 1968), 912–30.
2. Albee, George W., *Mental Health Manpower Trends.* New York: Basic Books, Inc., Publishers, 1959.
3. Belknap, Ivan and John G. Steinle, *The Community and Its Hospital: A Comparative Analysis.* Syracuse, N.Y.: Syracuse University Press, 1963.
4. Bellin, Seymour S., "The Impact of a Neighborhood Health Center on the Use of and Satisfaction with Health Care Services: A Study of Low-Income Public Housing Community." Unpublished paper, Tufts School of Medicine, Boston, 1968.

5. BENNIS, WARREN G., NORMAN H. BERKOWITZ, M. AFFINITO, AND M. MALONE, "Reference Groups and Loyalties in the Out-Patient Department," *Administrative Science Quarterly*, 2 (March, 1958), 481–500.
6. BERKOWITZ, NORMAN H. AND WARREN G. BENNIS, "Interaction in Formal Service Orientated Organizations," *Administrative Science Quarterly*, 6 (June, 1961), 25–50.
7. BLANKENSHIP, L. VAUGHN, "Power Structure and Organizational Effectiveness," in Robert Presthus, ed., *Men at the Top: A Study in Community Power*. Fairlawn, N.J.: Oxford University Press, 1964, pp. 368–404.
8. BLAU, PETER, *The Dynamics of Bureaucracy*. Chicago: University of Chicago Press, 1955.
9. ———, "Formal Organization: Dimensions of Analysis," *American Journal of Sociology*, 63 (July, 1957), 58–69.
10. BOULDING, KENNETH E., *The Organizational Revolution*. New York: Harper & Row, Publishers, Inc., 1953.
11. BRIGGS, JEAN L. AND SOL LEVINE, "Control over Local Affiliates by National Health Agencies." Paper delivered at annual meeting of the American Sociological Association, St. Louis, September 1, 1961.
12. CARTER, RICHARD, *The Gentle Legions*. New York: Doubleday & Company, Inc., 1961.
13. CAUDILL, WILLIAM, *The Psychiatric Hospital as a Small Society*. Cambridge, Mass.: Harvard University Press, 1958, pp. 266–303.
14. ———, FREDERICK C. REDLICH, HELEN R. GILMORE AND E. B. BRODY, "Social Structure and Interaction Processes on a Psychiatric Ward," *American Journal of Orthopsychiatry*, 22 (April, 1952), 314–34.
15. CHAPIN, F. STUART AND JOHN E. TSOUDEROS, "The Formalization Process in Voluntary Associations," *Social Forces*, 34 (1956), 342–44.
16. CLARK, BURTON R., "Organizational Adaptation and Precarious Values," *American Sociological Review*, 21 (June, 1956), 327–36.
17. ———, "Interorganizational Patterns in Education," *Administrative Science Quarterly*, 10 (September, 1965), 224–37.
18. COVERT, C., "No 'Common Man' on Hospital Boards," *The Syracuse Herald-Journal*, October 20, 1959.
19. DAVIS, MILTON S. AND ROBERT E. TRANQUADA, "A Sociological Evaluation of the Watts Neighborhood Health Center," *Medical Care*, 7, No. 2 (March–April, 1969), 105–17.
20. DIMOCK, MARSHALL E., "Expanding Jurisdictions: A Case Study in Bureaucratic Conflict," in R. K. Merton et al., eds., *Reader in Bureaucracy*. New York: The Free Press, 1952, pp. 282–91.
21. DULLES, FOSTER R., *The American Red Cross: A History*. New York: Harper & Row, Publishers, Inc., 1950.
22. EICHHORN, ROBERT L. AND JERY A. WYSON, *Interagency Relations in the Provision of Health Services: Tuberculosis Control in a Metropolitan Region*. Lafayette, Ind.: Purdue University Research Foundation, 1968.
23. ELLING, RAY H., "The Hospital-Support Game in Urban Center," in Eliot Freidson, ed., *The Hospital in Modern Society*. New York: The Free Press, 1963.
24. ———, "The Shifting Power Structure in Health," *Milbank Memorial Fund Quarterly*, 66 (January, 1968), 119–43.
25. ——— AND OLLIE J. LEE, "Formal Connections of Community Leadership to the Health System." Paper presented at the annual meeting of the Society for the Study of Social Problems. Chicago, August 29, 1965, pp. 73–111.
26. ELLING, RAY H. AND SANDOR HALEBSKY, "Organizational Differentiation and Support: A Conceptual Framework," *Administrative Science Quarterly*, 6 (September, 1961), 185–209.
27. ETZIONI, AMITAI, "New Directions in the Study of Organizations and Society," *Social Research*, 27 (Summer, 1960), 223–28.
28. EVAN, WILLIAM M., "Toward a Theory of Interorganizational Relations," *Management Science*, 11 (August, 1965), 217–30.

29. Form, William H. and Sigmund Nosow, *Community in Disaster.* New York: Harper & Row, Publishers, Inc., 1958.
30. Fox, Sherwood D., "Voluntary Associations and Social Structure." Unpublished Ph.D. dissertation, Harvard University, 1953.
31. Freeman, Howard E. and Camille Lambert, Jr., "The Influence of Community Groups on Health Matters," *Human Organization*, 24, No. 4 (Winter, 1965), 353–57.
32. Geiger, H. J., "Of the Poor, By the Poor, Or for the Poor: The Mental Health Implications of Social Control of Poverty Programs," *Psychiatric Research* Reports No. 21, (April 1967), 55.
33. ———, "The Neighborhood Health Center," *Archives of Environmental Health*, 14 (1967), 912.
34. Goldberg, George A., Frederick L. Trowbridge, and Robert C. Buxbaum, "Issues in the Development of Neighborhood Health Centers," *Inquiry*, 6, No. 1 (March, 1969), 37–48.
35. Goldhamer, Herbert, "Voluntary Associations in the United States," in Paul K. Hatt and Albert J. Reiss, Jr., eds., *Reader in Urban Sociology.* New York: The Free Press, 1951, pp. 505–6.
36. Gordon, C. Wayne and Nicholas Babchuck, "A Typology of Voluntary Associations," *American Sociological Review*, 24 (February, 1959), 22–29.
37. Goss, Mary E. W., "Influence and Authority among Physicians in an Outpatient Clinic," *American Sociological Review*, 26 (February, 1961), 30–50.
38. Gouldner, Alvin W., "Reciprocity and Autonomy in Functional Theory," in Llewellyn Gross, ed., *Symposium on Sociologocal Theory.* New York: Harper & Row, Publishers, Inc., 1959.
39. Gurin, Gerald, Joseph Veroff, and Sheila Feld, *Americans View Their Mental Health.* New York: Basic Books, Inc., Publishers, 1960.
40. Hamlin, Robert H., "The Role of the Voluntary Agency in the United States: Present and Future." Address at the opening session of the 1961 annual meeting of the National Tuberculosis Association, Cincinnati, May 22, 1961.
41. ———, *Voluntary Health and Welfare Agencies in the United States.* New York: The Schoolmasters' Press, 1961.
42. ———, "The Role of Voluntary Agencies in Meeting the Health Needs of Americans," *Annals of the American Academy of Political and Social Science*, 337 (September, 1961), 93–102.
43. Hanlon, John J., *Principles of Public Health Administration,* 2nd ed. St. Louis: The C. V. Mosby Company, 1955.
44. Hollander, Sidney, *Toward Improved Chest-Council Agency Relations.* New York: Association Press, 1951.
45. Holloway, Robert G., Jay W. Artis, and Walter E. Freeman, "The Participation Patterns of 'Economic Influentials' and Their Control of a Hospital Board of Trustees," *Journal of Health and Human Behavior,* 4 (Summer, 1963), 88–99.
46. Homans, George C., "Social Behavior as Exchange," *American Journal of Sociology*, 63 (May, 1958), 597–606.
47. Hunter, Floyd, *Community Power Structure.* Chapel Hill: The University of North Carolina Press, 1953.
48. Johns, Ray E., *The Cooperative Process Among National Social Agencies.* New York: Association Press, 1946, p. 199.
49. ——— and David F. de Marche, *Community Organization and Agency Responsibility.* New York: Association Press, 1951.
50. Kaplan, Howard B., "Implementation of Program Change in Community Agencies," *Milbank Memorial Fund Quarterly*, 65 (July, 1966), 31–58.
51. King, C. Wendell, *Social Movements in the United States.* New York: Random House, Inc., 1956, p. 114.
52. Leavell, H. R. and E. Gurney Clark, *Textbook of Preventive Medicine.* New York: McGraw-Hill Book Company, 1953.
53. Lefton, Mark and William R. Rosengren, "Organizations and Clients:

Lateral and Longitudinal Dimensions," *American Sociological Review*, 31 (1966), 802–10.
54. LEVINE, SOL AND PAUL WHITE, "Exchange as a Conceptual Framework for the Study of Interorganizational Relationships," *Administrative Science Quarterly*, 5 (March, 1961), 583–601.
55. ———, "Characteristics of Board Members of Voluntary Health and Welfare Agencies." Mimeographed. 1963.
56. ——— AND BENJAMIN D. PAUL, "Community Interorganizational Problems in Providing Medical Care and Social Services," *American Journal of Public Health*, 53, 8 (August, 1963), 1183–95.
57. LEVINE, SOL AND PAUL E. WHITE, "Differential Prestige of Health and Welfare Agencies." Mimeographed. 1963.
58. ———, "Board Overlap and Agency Interaction." Johns Hopkins University, School of Hygiene and Public Health, mimeographed. 1964.
59. LITWAK, EUGENE AND LYDIA F. HYLTON, "Interorganizational Analysis: A Hypothesis of Coordinating Agencies," *Administrative Science Quarterly*, 6 (March, 1962), 395–420.
60. LITWAK, EUGENE AND HENRY J. MEYER, "A Balance Theory of Coordination Between Bureaucratic Organizations and Community Primary Groups," *Administrative Science Quarterly*, 11 (June, 1966), 31–58.
61. LONG, NORTON, "Local Community as a System of Competing Games," *American Journal of Sociology*, 64 (November, 1958), 251–61.
62. MARCH, JAMES G. AND H. A. SIMON, *Organizations*. New York: John Wiley & Sons, Inc., 1958.
63. MESSINGER, SHELDON L., "Organizational Transformation: A Case Study of a Declining Social Movement," *American Sociological Review*, 20 (February, 1955), 3–10.
64. MILLER, PAUL A. et al., *Community Health Action*. East Lansing: Michigan State University Press, 1953.
65. MILLER, WALTER B., "Inter-Institutional Conflict as a Major Impediment to Delinquency Prevention," *Human Organization*, 17 (Fall, 1958), 20–23.
66. MOHR, LAWRENCE B., "Determinants of Innovation in Organizations," *American Political Science Review*, 43 (March, 1969), 111–26.
67. MORRIS, ROBERT, "Basic Factors in Planning for Coordination of Hospitals and Institutions for Long-Term Care." Mimeographed.
68. MOTT, BASIL J. F., *Anatomy of a Coordinating Council*. Pittsburgh: University of Pittsburgh Press, 1968.
69. MYTINGER, ROBERT E., "Innovation in Public Health: A Study of the Adaption of New Public Health Programs by Local Health Departments in California, and of Factors which Enhance or Inhibit Adaption of New Health Programs." Unpublished Ph.D. dissertation, University of California, Los Angeles, 1965, pp. 29–59.
70. NEW, KONG-MING AND J. THOMAS MAY, "Organization Under Stress: An Analysis of the Local Board of Health," *Journal of Health and Human Behavior*, 6 (Winter, 1965), 226–34.
71. PARSONS, TALCOTT, "Suggestions for a Sociological Approach to the Theory of Organizations: 1," *Administrative Science Quarterly*, 1 (June, 1956), 63–85.
72. PERROW, CHARLES, "Organizational Prestige: Some Functions and Dysfunctions," *American Journal of Sociology*, 66 (January, 1961), 335–41.
73. ———, "Goals and Power Structures," in Eliot Freidson, ed., *The Hospital in Modern Society*. New York: The Free Press, 1963.
74. REID, WILLIAM J., "Interorganizational Coordination in Social Welfare: A Theoretical Approach to Analysis and Intervention," in Ralph M. Kramer and Harry Specht, eds., *Readings in Community Organization Practice*. Englewood Cliffs, N.J.: Prentice Hall, Inc., 1969, pp. 176–88.
75. REIN, MARTIN, "An Organizational Analysis of a National Agency's Local Affiliates in Their Community Contexts: A Study of the Planned Parenthood Federation of America." Unpublished

Ph.D. dissertation, Brandeis University, 1961.

76. Reissman, Leonard and John H. Rohrer, eds., *Change and Dilemma in the Nursing Profession.* New York: G. P. Putnam's Sons, 1957.

77. Roemer, Milton I. and Rodney F. White, "Community Attitudes toward the Hospital," *Hospital Management,* 89, Part 1, (January, 1960); Part 2, (February, 1960).

78. Rogatz, Peter and Guido M. Crocetti, "Home Care Programs; Their Impact on the Hospital's Role in Medical Care," *American Journal of Public Health,* 48 (September, 1958), 1125–33.

79. Rosen, George and Edward Wellin, "A Bookshelf on the Social Sciences and Public Health," *American Journal of Public Health,* 49 (April, 1959), 441–54.

80. Sanders, Irwin T., *The Community: An Introduction to a Social System.* New York: The Ronald Press Company, 1958.

81. ———, "The Community Social Profile," *American Sociological Review,* 25 (February, 1960), 75–77.

82. Saunders, J. V. D. and J. H. Bruening, "Hospital-Community Relations in Mississippi," *Rural Sociology,* 24 (March, 1959), 48–51.

83. Seeley, John R., R. Alexander Sim, and E. W. Loosley, *Crestwood Heights.* New York: Basic Books, Inc., Publishers, 1956.

84. Selznick, Philip, "An Approach to a Theory of Bureaucracy," *American Sociological Review,* 8 (February, 1943), 47–54.

85. ———, *TVA and the Grass Roots.* Berkeley: University of California Press, 1949, pp. 258–59.

86. ———, *The Organizational Weapon.* New York: McGraw-Hill Book Company, 1952.

87. Sills, David L., *The Volunteers: Means and Ends in a National Organization.* New York: The Free Press, 1957.

88. Silver, George A., "Social Medicine at the Montefiore Hospital: A Practical Approach to Community Health Problems," *American Journal of Public Health,* 48 (June, 1958), 724–31.

89. Smith, Harvey L., "Two Lines of Authority: The Hospital's Dilemma," in E. Gartley Jaco, ed., *Patients, Physicians, and Illness.* New York: The Free Press, 1958, pp. 468–77.

90. Solon, Jerry, Cecil G. Sheps, Sidney S. Lee, and Maeda Jackowitz, "Staff Perceptions of Patients' Use of a Hospital Out-Patient Department," *Journal of Medical Education,* 33 (January, 1958), 10–21.

91. Sower, Christopher, John Holland, Kenneth Tridke, and Walter Freeman, *Community Involvement.* New York: The Free Press, 1957.

92. Stanton, Alfred H. and Morris S. Schwartz, *The Mental Hospital: A Study of Institutional Participation in Psychiatric Illness and Treatment.* New York: Basic Books, Inc., Publishers, 1954, 192–243.

93. Strantz, Irma and Winston R. Miller, "Development of Interagency Coordination in a Program of Comprehensive Medical Care," *American Journal of Public Health,* 56 (May, 1966), 785–96.

94. Teele, James and Sol Levine, "The Acceptance of Emotionally Disturbed Children by Psychiatric Agencies in Stanton Wheeler, ed., *Controlling Delinquents.* New York: John Wiley & Sons, Inc., 1967.

95. Thompson, James D. and William McEwan, "Organizational Goals and Environment: Goal Settings as an Interaction Process," *American Sociological Review,* 20 (April, 1955), 206–10.

96. Truman, David B., *The Governmental Process.* New York: Alfred A. Knopf, Inc., 1951, p. 118.

97. Tsouderos, John E., "Organizational Change in Terms of a Series of Selected Variables," *American Sociological Review,* 20 (April, 1955), 209.

98. Warren, Roland L., "Toward a Typology of Extra-Community Control Limiting Local Community Autonomy," *Social Forces,* 34 (May, 1956), 338–41.

99. ———, *Social Research Consultation: An Experiment in Health and Welfare Planning.* New York: Russell Sage Foundation, 1963.

100. ———, "The Interorganizational

Field as a Focus for Investigation," *Administrative Science Quarterly*, 12 (December, 1967), 396–419.

101. WHITE, PAUL E., "Myth and Reality In Interorganizational Behavior: A Study of Competition between Two National Voluntary Health Agencies," *American Journal of Public Health*, 58 (February, 1968), 289–304.

102. ——— AND SOL LEVINE, "Cost as a Factor in Interorganizational Exchange." Mimeographed. 1962.

103. WILLIE, CHARLES V., "Community Leadership in the Voluntary Health and Welfare System," in Alvin Gouldner and S. M. Miller, eds., *Applied Sociology: Problems and Possibilities.* New York: The Free Press, 1965.

104. ——— AND HERBERT NOTKIN, "Community Organization for Health: A Case Study," in E. Gartley Jaco, ed., *Patients, Physicians, and Illness.* New York: The Free Press, 1958, pp. 148–58.

16

PATTERNS OF USE OF HEALTH SERVICES

Odin W. Anderson and Ronald M. Andersen

Varying patterns of use of health services are of significance to a wide range of interests. For sociology, statistics on the use of health services are indices of certain types of behavior of people in certain contexts; for medical care, they are indices of the extent to which people receive health services. It is axiomatic that patterns of use are not quixotic; in different contexts there are patterns of use related to such factors as age and sex composition of the population, incidence of illness, proximity of health care facilities, family income, residence, and the perceptions of both the providers and recipients of health services. All of these factors are relevant, but some have more bearing on use than others in different contexts.

Since the previous edition of this book, studies on the use of health services have broadened in scope and have become more sophisticated in design. Still, as Greenlick observed recently:

> It is beyond the scope of any single study to develop a general theory of medical care utilization, and at this stage in the

development of the field such a general theory doesn't exist [24].

This chapter corroborates Greenlick's observations but suggests that progress has been made.

One example of the broader scope of current thinking, showing the kind of problems involved in successful implementation, is the application of systems analysis to the health services [6, 9, 30, 37, 44, 60][1] A basic indicator useful for the systems approach is an analysis of patterns of use of health services. There is considerable debate, however, whether rates of use of health services are a measure of what is put into the system or a measure of its results, i.e., in economic terminology, "input" or "output."[2] While it seems most logical to consider health services as input and health level of the population as output, such an approach is extremely difficult to implement. The problem is measuring the output of a health system in terms of its effect on the general health level of a population in developed societies, where the scourges of fifty years ago are now minor killers. The major killers today are chronic illnesses, which are largely intractable to procedures of current health services. There are, of course, exceptions such as diabetes where medical science has significantly reduced the death rate.

Regardless of whether health services are defined as input or output of the system, their use has been an important concern of policy makers, practitioners, administrators, and the public alike. For many years the general public was exhorted to avail itself of health services and particularly urged to see a physician at the first sign of illness. In recent times, however, there has been increasing concern about "overutilization" and "unnecessary" use. Implicitly, if not explicitly, this represents an attempt to coordinate the health needs of people and the health services resources in a more efficient and rational manner.

The difficulty continues to be the nebulous definitions of "need," "efficient," and "rational" in a health services system. The problems, at least, are now better understood than they were at the time of the first edition of this book. We hope that this chapter on the use of health services will help to shed light on some of these issues, because use is so central to both "proper" exposures of people to services and the rapidly rising expenditures for these services.

In the following sections we will first briefly describe what are commonly considered the *health services.* We will then consider the utilization of various kinds of these services and factors associated with this utilization. Finally, we will consider more general, conceptual approaches, which attempt to integrate the disparate findings.

COMPONENTS OF HEALTH SERVICES

Health services are usually divided into two broad categories: public and personal. Public health services traditionally are those provided for the population as a group without special regard for individual differences and initiative. The better-known public programs are those established to as-

[1] It should be noted that systems analysis as used here refers mainly to "large" systems approaches rather than to the "small" systems, or operations research, approach. A basic theoretical underpinning for the large systems approach is exemplified in the work of Daniel Katz and Robert Kahn [29].

[2] Melvin Reder discusses in some detail various economic approaches which might be employed to measure the output of a health services system [49].

sure a sanitary environment—pure water, food, and atmosphere. Others control communicable disease through mass immunization.

By far the larger category is that of personal health services. These are normally sought and received by people as individuals. The essential difference between personal and public health services is that the former services must be initiated by individuals, while the latter services can be carried out with only the passive participation of the population, without its knowledge, or even—if necessary—with enforced compliance. The remainder of this chapter is primarily concerned with personal health services.

The components of the health services differ greatly according to level of use, expenditures, and factors that influence their distribution. For example, the general hospital is a very different entity from the mental hospital; the use of dental services reveals a pattern quite different from that of physicians' services, and use of drugs shows variations not similar to those of other health goods and services.

Personal health services can be divided into the components which are listed below. These make up the usual units for the reporting of expenditures and the gross measures of utilization.

A. Hospital Services
  1. Days
     (a) Number of admissions
     (b) Number of days per stay
  2. Type of case
     (a) Medical
     (b) Surgical
     (c) Obstetrical
     (d) Diagnostic
     (e) Psychiatric
  3. Type of accommodation
     (a) Private
     (b) Semiprivate
     (c) Ward
  4. Ancillary services
     (a) Operating room
     (b) Delivery room
     (c) Drugs and medications
     (d) Laboratory
     (e) Radiology

B. Physicians' Services
  1. Site of services and number of contacts—home, office, hospital, clinic; proportion of population seeing a physician
  2. Type of service
     (a) Surgical
     (b) Medical
     (c) Obstetrical
     (d) Psychiatric
  3. Specialization
     (a) General practice
     (b) Range of specialties
  4. Type of practice
     (a) Solo
     (b) Partnership
     (c) Various types of groups

C. Drugs and Medications
  1. Number of prescriptions
  2. Prescription and nonprescription drugs

D. Dentists' Services
  1. Number of visits to dentist and proportion of population seeing a dentist
  2. General practice and various specialties
  3. Types of services
     (a) Extractions
     (b) Fillings
     (c) Crowns, bridges, dentures
     (d) Prophylaxis

E. Nursing Home Services
  1. Number of admissions
  2. Number of days per stay

F. Other
  1. Appliances—glasses, hearing aids, trusses
  2. Private duty nursing
  3. Other home care services

The foregoing units are the services and goods recognized as *professional* and *official*. It is also necessary to realize that there are considerable services and goods which are not recognized professionally, such as chiropractic. There are also services and goods which are part of the usual stock of informal health helps and devices. These undoubtedly shade into the professional helping services in various ways. We refer to such helping services as those given by family members to their kin, friends to friends, and so on.

There is hardly another enterprise which touches as large a proportion of the population in all age groups so much or with so much intensity and emotion as the personal health services. A recent nationwide survey of expenditures and use reveals this exposure in the United States. During 1963, 65 percent of the population saw a physician at least once; over 8 percent were admitted to a short-term general hospital at least once; 4 percent had surgery in the hospital, 38 percent saw a dentist at least once; 43 percent purchased prescribed drugs; and 20 percent had eye care. Estimating the population of the United States at approximately 200 million, it can be seen, for example, that 130 million people had contact with a physician during the year [4].

Use of General Hospitals

There is some logic in starting out with the use of the general hospital, because institutional care has probably been the fastest-growing component of health care use since the turn of the century, particularly since the thirties. The general hospital has increasingly replaced the home and the doctor's office as the locus for physicians' treatment and for nursing care.[3]

Not only has the general hospital been the fastest-changing component in the last forty years, it also shows tremendous variations in use between areas and countries which are generally similar as to economic and social development. This variation implies that the general hospital is a highly volatile component of the health services. It suggests that the general hospital could be subjected to a great deal of manipulation if the criteria of admissions and length of stay were systematically applied.

These observations are borne out by a few illustrative statistics on hospital use over time and space. In 1935, the admission rate of general hospitals in the United States was 59 per 1,000 population; in recent years it has been somewhat over 130 [19, 39]. Admission rates have been increasing

[3] There are contrasting views of the family role vis-à-vis the hospital and physician in performing sick-care functions for the patient. Parsons and Fox suggest that the stability and harmony of the family are endangered by the presence in the home of old, sick, retarded, or handicapped family members. The social organization of the modern, urban nuclear family makes it increasingly necessary, as well as convenient, for the family to surrender its traditional sick-care functions to the hospital [45].

Conversely, Vincent argues, "the notion that the sick-care functions are incompatible with the organization if not the goals and interests of the modern family is contradictory to a number of current developments and trends." These trends include specialization in medicine and the demise of the family doctor with his intimate knowledge of family members, increased awareness of the potentially detrimental results of the patient's long-term separation from home and community life, and increased use of family and community treatment settings [59].

Thus, while Parsons is concerned with the needs of the family, Vincent concentrates on the needs of the patient. If the underlying assumptions of both are correct, it appears that a basic dilemma may be present, with the modern family becoming increasingly unable to provide the support indicated by current trends in medical care.

throughout the Western world (and presumably in other parts of the world with developed and developing economies). In England and Wales the current admission rate is around 88 per 1,000 population; in Sweden it is very much the same as in the United States, 130; and in the Province of Saskatchewan, Canada, it is over 200 [27, 48]. This last, incidentally, is the highest-recorded general hospital admission rate anywhere.

There are also great differences *within* areas. In Canada and the United States admission rates for short-term hospitalization in the states and provinces having the highest utilization are more than double the rates for those with the least utilization [25]. Correction for age and sex composition, and even diagnostic mix, does not eliminate such variations. For example, Lerner made a pertinent comparison of hospital admissions by diagnosis between members of the Blue Cross Plan in Indiana and in the Province of Saskatchewan for 1956–57 [35]. The admission rate per 1,000 persons per years was 116 in Indiana and 202 in Saskatchewan, but the proportion of all admissions accounted for by the major diagnoses in the two areas were reasonably similar. The chief difference was the higher admission rate in Saskatchewan for each diagnosis.

Other studies show differences between admission rates for specific diagnoses, after taking into account overall differences in admission rates. For example, a study of hospital case loads in Liverpool, England, the New England section of the United States, and the county of Uppsala, Sweden (near Stockholm), revealed great differences [46]. The authors found (excluding psychiatric, maternity, and special-care infant cases) that the Liverpool region discharged fewer patients than the other two regions, despite having more discharges of adults than any other hospital region in England and Wales. The rate of surgical operations performed in New England was considerably higher than in the other two regions. Uppsala and Liverpool had similar surgical operation rates, but within these rates, Uppsala had significantly more gallbladder and gynecological operations.

Given the relatively high unit cost of general hospital care—now approaching $75 a day in the United States—and the increasing share of the "medical dollar" allocated to this component, it is understandable why these great variations are of interest to the health field. Over the course of time, a very high proportion of the population is admitted to this relatively expensive facility. One nationwide population survey revealed that 75 percent of the adults in the United States had been in a general hospital within ten years prior to the interview [23].

Admission rates to general hospitals are crude measures for comparative analysis of health systems. This is because the effects of the use of health services are related to age and sex, which, in turn, are determinants of morbidity and mortality rates. Hence, the patterns of use of health services are rooted in the biology of man. In Western industrialized countries similar general patterns are found despite differences in medical care organization. Table 16–1 can be considered almost a prototype of the general relationship between age and sex and hospital utilization in Western countries [2, 5]. Further, the nature of the relationship tends to be similar for other types of health services, including physician services and drugs.[4]

By age, the usual pattern is U-

[4] See Tables 16-4 and 16-5.

TABLE 16-1 Use of Short-Term Hospitals in the United States, 1963

Age and Sex	Admissions per 100 Person-Years
Age	
0– 5	8
6–17	6
18–34	19*
35–54	14
55–65	17
65 and over	18
Sex	
Male	10
Female	15
Total	13

* This rate reveals the maternity component; if it were removed, the admission rate would show a smooth upward gradation.

Source: Ronald Andersen and Odin W. Anderson, *A Decade of Health Services: Social Survey Trends in Use and Expenditures,* Chicago: University of Chicago Press, 1967, Table 16, p. 36.

TABLE 16-2 Use of Short-Term Hospitals in the United States by Income, 1953, 1958, and 1963

Income	Admissions per 100 Person-Years		
	1953	*1958*	*1963*
Under $2,000	12	14	16
2,000–3,499	12	12	12
3,500–4,999	12	14	12
5,000–7,499	12	12	14
7,500 and over	11	10	12
Total	12	12	13

Source: Ronald Andersen and Odin W. Anderson, *A Decade of Health Services: Social Survey Trends in Use and Expenditures,* Chicago: University of Chicago Press, 1967, Table 17, p. 38.

shaped, with older children receiving the least medical care. By sex one can usually expect a higher use of services by females than by males, even after correcting for maternity. The male-female differences seem to stem largely from a higher incidence of morbidity in the female, though, in seeming contradiction, the female lives longer than the male.

Past admission rates to the general hospital in the United States were generally lower for the lower-income groups than for higher-income groups [19]. For a variety of reasons—presumably mainly more generous financing of hospital care for the poor and the spread of hospital insurance—the admission rates are now largely independent of income, as seen in Table 16–2. Given the now official U.S. public policy of equalizing access to health services regardless of income, these trends are important indicators for the country as a whole.[5]

There are differences in admission rates by residence, as shown in Table 16–3. People living in large cities and the suburbs of these cities had the lowest admission rates. At the other extreme, people living in rural areas but not on farms had the highest rates. In between these extremes are the "other urban" and rural farm populations. That the populations by type of residence have considerably different age distribution might be a factor in narrowing these differences (or enlarging them). In the same study, however, by age groups, the admission rates appeared generally lower for the

[5] Similar admission rates do not necessarily mean that hospitals are being used in similar fashion by higher- and lower-income persons. For one thing, to a wage earner illness can reduce income so that use by low-income persons appears artificially high. Further, if we look at hospital utilization, attempting to hold constant the level of illness, the adjusted utilization of low-income persons drops considerably because they report more illness than higher income groups [3].

TABLE 16-3 USE OF SHORT-TERM HOSPITAL SERVICES BY RESIDENCE IN THE UNITED STATES, 1963

Residence	*Admissions per 100 Person-Years*
Large urban	10
Other urban	13
Rural nonfarm	15
Rural farm	11
Total	13

Source: Ronald Andersen and Odin W. Anderson, *A Decade of Health Services; Social Survey Trends in Use and Expenditures,* Chicago: University of Chicago Press, 1967, Table 19, p. 40.

large urban and rural farm populations than for the other urban and rural nonfarm population [4].

One constant influence on admission to hospitals is the presence of hospital insurance. Regardless of age, sex, family income, and residence, people covered by hospital insurance are admitted to hospitals more often than those without insurance. In 1963, there were 15 admissions per 1,000 population among those with hospital insurance, and 9 among those without insurance. The possession of hospital insurance had the greatest impact on the low-income groups, in that the insured group with under $2,000 annual family income had an admission rate of 25 per 1,000 population, compared with a rate of 12 for those without insurance [4].

In Western countries there seems to be an inverse relationship between admission rate and average length of stay. When the admission rate is relatively high, the length of stay tends to be relatively short. During the 1930's in this country the admission rate per 1,000 population was 59, and the average length of stay was between 15 and 16 days [19]. Currently, the general hospital admission rate is 123, and the length of stay is 8.5 days [40]. A commonsense reason for this shorter stay is the increase in the admission of patients with relatively minor conditions. In addition, surgical and obstetrical cases have a shorter stay than formerly because of changing concepts of medical practice.[6]

Use of Physicians' Services

Americans are seeking physicians' services much more frequently than they did a generation ago. During 1928–31, 2.6 out-of-hospital annual physician visits per person were reported [19]. During a twelve-month period in 1966–67, there were 4.3 physician visits per person per year [43].

Physician visits by age and sex reflect morbidity patterns. Those of younger people reveal a relatively high rate of acute disease episodes (chiefly respiratory and infectious), and upper-age groups have a high rate of long-term and chronic diseases—hence a U-shaped curve as suggested by Table 16–4.

Several years after the establishment of the National Health Service, Great Britain showed a rate of use of physicians' services similar to that in the United States, which has never had a universal health insurance system. But, in Sweden—with a near-universal health insurance scheme—physicians are seen only two-thirds as often as

[6] For comparative purposes, we might consider England and Sweden. England has a longer length of stay but a *lower* admission rate than the United States, thus supporting our generalization. Sweden, however, has a longer length of stay with a similar admission rate [48]. One apparent reason why the generalization is not supported in this instance is that Sweden has a much higher general hospital bed/population ratio than does the United States [5].

TABLE 16-4 PHYSICIAN VISITS BY AGE AND SEX IN THE UNITED STATES, 1963

Age and Sex	*Mean Number of Physician Visits per Person-Year*
Age	
1– 5	4.0
6–17	2.5
18–34	5.0
35–54	4.9
55–64	5.7
65 and over	8.2
Sex	
Male	4.1
Female	5.0
Total	4.6

Source: Andersen and Anderson *Decade of Health Services,* Table 10, p. 27.

TABLE 16-5 PERCENT OF PERSONS IN THE UNITED STATES SEEING PHYSICIAN IN 1963, BY AGE AND SEX

Age and Sex	*Percent of Total*
Age	
1– 5	75
6–17	58
18–34	67
35–54	65
55–64	68
65 and over	68
Sex	
Male	62
Female	68
Total	65

Source: Andersen and Anderson, *Decade of Health Services,* Table 10, p. 27.

in the United States or Great Britain [48].

Perhaps as significant a measure of use of physicians' services as the number of per person visits is the percentage of those in a population who see a physician during a year. It is the clearest measure of gross exposure of the public to physician decisions. Obviously, a physician cannot prescribe care until he encounters a patient. This percentage has increased considerably over the past few decades in the United States. During the period from 1928 to 1931, approximately 40 percent of the population in the United States sought physicians' services during a year; in 1963, 65 percent of the population did so [4, 19].

Variations by age and sex for the year 1963 in the United States can be seen in Table 16–5. Those in the age group under 6 are most likely to see physicians at least once during a year, and the age group from 6 to 17 is least likely to do so. It is of interest that those under 6 are more likely to see physicians than those 65 and over, even though the mean number of visits is much higher for old people. The proportion of people who see a physician at least once during the year under different methods of health care delivery is quite similar. Data from England and Wales, Sweden, and the Health Insurance Plan of Greater New York (HIP) and from the comprehensive fee-for-service medical insurance plans in the state of Washington and Windsor, Ontario, Canada, indicate that from two-thirds to three-quarters of the population sees a physician at least once [7, 11, 14, 56].

Utilization of physicians' services by family income shows that the higher the income, the greater is the number of physician visits per person, although the disparity between number of physician visits per person and family income, for the country as a whole, is not as great now as it was a generation ago [36]. Currently, the number of visits per person by family income is remarkably uniform on a nationwide basis when not corrected for age. When comparions are made by age and family income, the income differences are largest for young children, and they disappear for the aged [43].

As expressed earlier, a more important indication of use may be the proportion of people who see physicians at least once during a year. The lower one's income, the less likely he is to have seen a physician. In 1963, 56 percent of the people having a family income of under $4,000 saw a physician, compared with 71 percent in the income group $7,000 and over [4].

As with the number of visits, the older the age group, the smaller the discrepancy according to income. It may be reasonable to assume that older people seek physicians' services mainly because of acute and severe conditions. The incidence of such conditions is quite similar, being a function of age rather than income. The greater use of physicians' services by children in upper-income families can probably be explained by greater use of preventive services among upper-income groups and the tendency of such groups to seek early diagnosis.

A type of physicians' service that receives extraordinary attention from the public as well as from the health service system is surgery. Reasons for this attention are its dramatic, costly, and irrevocable characteristics. As a result, it was the first type of physicians' service to be covered by insurance. Surgical procedures accounted for 24 percent of all expenditures for private physicians' services in 1963, or over $1.5 billion out of a total for all physicians' services of $6.4 billion [4].

The hospitalized-surgical-procedure rate has remained reasonably stable in recent years, 5 per 100 person-years, although the mix of surgery has changed with new developments in surgical techniques. This rate has also remained roughly a third or slightly more of all general hospital admissions. In Table 16–6 it is seen that the rate of surgical procedures tends to increase with age and that for females is higher than for males. Turning now to Table 16–7, you will see that people with the lowest incomes have the lowest surgery rate—3 per 100 person-years. The rate then rises to a maximum of 6 for those with incomes of $7,500 and over.

TABLE 16-6 IN-HOSPITAL SURGICAL PROCEDURES PER 100 PERSON-YEARS BY AGE AND SEX, UNITED STATES, 1963

Age and Sex	*Surgical Procedures per 100 Person-Years*
Age	
0– 5	3
6–17	4
18–34	5
35–54	6
55–64	6
65 and over	5
Sex	
Male	4
Female	6
Total	5

Source: Andersen and Anderson, *Decade of Health Services,* Table 13, p. 32.

Use of Dental Services

Considering the overwhelming unmet need for dental care in the population, the utilization of dental services is low.[7] It is also low relative to other personal health services and goods. This is true even for upper-income groups. Still, during the last generation there has been a considerable increase in use of dental services, as measured by the proportion of people who see a dentist at least once during a year. In

[7] At the end of 1962, dental examinations indicated that the 111 million adults in the United States at that time had a total of 2 1/4 billion decayed, missing, and filled teeth. The average adult had 13.5 missing teeth, 5.7 filled teeth, and 1.2 decayed teeth [41].

TABLE 16-7 IN-HOSPITAL SURGICAL PROCEDURES PER 100 PERSON-YEARS BY FAMILY INCOME, UNITED STATES, 1963

Family Income	*Surgical Procedures per 100 Person-Years*
Under $2,000	3
$2,000–3,499	4
3,500–4,999	4
5,000–7,499	6
7,500 and over	6
Total	5

Source: Andersen and Anderson, *Decade of Health Services,* Table 13, p. 32.

TABLE 16-8 PERCENT OF PEOPLE RECEIVING DENTAL CARE IN THE UNITED STATES, BY AGE AND SEX, 1963

Age and Sex	*Percent*
Age	
1– 5	12
6–17	47
18–34	46
35–54	43
55–64	32
65 and over	19
Sex	
Male	36
Female	40
Total	38

Source: Andersen and Anderson, *Decade of Health Services,* Table 24, p. 46.

1930, 21 percent of the population saw a dentist at least once [19]. The percent is currently close to twice that figure. The dental profession has long had a standard that all people over three years of age should see a dentist at least once every year for prophylaxis and examination.

According to Table 16–8, the familiar sex differentials persist in dental care, i.e., higher utilization by females than by males. The age relationships are not common to other types of health services, however; children 6 to 17 are most likely to see a dentist, while there is a precipitous drop-off among those 65 and over. Hence, the familiar U-shape of use by age for physicians' services is completely reversed for dental care.

The proportion of persons in each income group who saw a dentist at least once during 1963 is reported in Table 16–9. This proportion rises rapidly as income rises. Thus, children in the 6 to 17 age group, from families

TABLE 16-9 PERCENT OF PEOPLE RECEIVING DENTAL CARE IN THE UNITED STATES, BY AGE AND FAMILY INCOME, 1963

	INCOME			
	Percent $0–1,999	*Percent $2,000–4,999*	*Percent $5,000–9,999*	*Percent $10,000 and over*
Age				
1– 5	0	4	13	23
6–17	11	30	48	71
18–34	31	33	49	57
35–54	23	28	42	58
55–64	16	25	32	52
65 and over	12	18	24	39
Total	16	25	40	58

Source: Andersen and Anderson, *Decade of Health Services,* Table 25, p. 47

making $10,000 or more, were about six times as likely to see a dentist as were children from the lowest-income families. Still, in the highest-income group—$10,000 and over—42 percent of the people did not consult a dentist at all.

Looking at the mean number of dental visits per person per year, we also find the inverted U-shape of use by age and the steep progression of the number of visits with rising income. The mean number of visits for all persons was 1.6, and there was a threefold increase in use, from 0.8 visits per person in the income class under $2,000 to 2.3 visits per person in the income class $7,000 and over [42].

Data on use of dental services have been presented in some detail, because among the major components of service, they show more variation by family income than any other service. Moreover, given the prevailing professional standard that everyone should see a dentist at least once a year, the data presented here suggest that actual utilization may be further from the accepted norm than for any of the other major types of health services.

Use of Preventive Services

The use of preventive services is regarded as an indicator of the level of sophistication at which the public and the health services interact in order to prevent, cure, and palliate disability. The concept of prevention is a very woolly and complicated one. Most of the time, it is used as a cliché and form of incantation because of the lack of an operational definition. It would seem that a classification presented by the Commission of Chronic Illness might be useful [13]. The Commission suggested three levels of prevention:

1. Primary prevention, i.e., stopping a disease from starting, such as vaccination against smallpox.
2. Secondary prevention—checking the development of a disease which is essentially not preventable but is curable, such as middle ear infections.
3. Tertiary prevention—managing a disease which is neither preventable nor curable, in order to stabilize it, such as diabetes.

Data on the use of preventive services, however defined, are not abundant. For this chapter we will use two common and gross measures of use of preventive services: the health checkup or physical examination, when the person seeks a physician's services although he feels free of symptoms, and prenatal visits to physicians, on a routine basis, to monitor the stages of a pregnancy.

Over one-half of a nationally representative sample reported having had a "physical examination or checkup" within one year of the time of a social survey interview in 1964, and one-third reported the elapsed time as six months or less. Young children and persons from the higher-income groups were most likely to have had a recent examination [4].

For every person reporting an examination the reasons for the last physical examination were elicited. They were

1. Symptoms: "Wasn't feeling good, was bothered by some symptom or condition."
2. Required: "Examination was required for a job, school, insurance, armed forces, or something like that."
3. Preventive exam: "There is nothing particularly wrong, and the examination wasn't required—it was just time for a checkup or physical examination."

The responses were fairly equally distributed over these three alternatives. Thirty-nine percent reported "symptoms" as the factor initiating their last physical examination. For 32 percent the examination was "required," and 29 percent of those having a checkup were symptom free. The latter is problaby the best measure of "pure" prevention, in that the person seeing a doctor did not have anything wrong and was not required to have a checkup for employment reasons, life insurance, or school. Preventive examinations are most common for young children to the age of five, females, persons with high incomes, and whites. They are least likely for males in the labor force, persons with low incomes, and nonwhites [4].

One of the cornerstones of preventive medicine is health services for expectant mothers, before, during, and shortly after delivery. Professional judgment has it that obstetrical care requires a visit to a physician during the first trimester of the pregnancy period and regularly thereafter. Another prevailing judgment in the United States is that all births should be attended by a physician and should take place in a hospital.

During 1963 the proportion of expectant mothers first seeing a physician by the end of their third month was 65 percent [4]. By the end of six months, 96 percent had consulted a physician. Fifty-eight percent of the expectant mothers in the lowest-income group saw a physician by the end of the first trimester, compared to 88 percent in the highest. As for the median number of prenatal visits, the lower-income mothers visited a physician 6.5 times, while mothers in the upper-income group has 11.1 visits. Virtually all live births were attended by a physician and took place in a hospital.

EXPENDITURES AS A MEASURE OF USE OF HEALTH SERVICES

From World War II to present time, prices for medical care have increased at a more rapid rate than prices for goods and services in general. Recent inflationary pressures in the economy as a whole, however, have changed this long-term relationship between the Consumer Price Index (CPI) and its medical care component. During 1969 the CPI increased 6.1 percent, and the medical care component moved at nearly the same 6.0 percent.[8] The combination of increases in use and increases in price has, of course, resulted in rapidly rising gross expenditures. Expenditures are changing more rapidly than patterns of use so that the dollar amounts reported are out of date in a year or two.

The average person in the United States had a personal health care bill of $256 in fiscal year 1969. The bill for persons sixty-five and over is about three and a half times that of people under sixty-five—$692 compared with $210. Medicare and other public programs subsidize much of this high

[8] From 1946 to 1960 the average annual increase in the Consumer Price Index for all items was 3.0 percent, compared to 4.2 percent for the medical care component. From 1960 to 1965 the rate of increase decelerated to 1.3 percent for the former and 2.5 for the latter. From 1965 through 1968 there was an increase in the annual rate of change of 3.3 percent for all items and a precipitous 7.1 percent for medical care [26, 26a].

[9] Barbara S. Cooper, "Medical Outlays for Aged and Non-Aged Persons, 1966–1969," *Social Security Bulletin*, 33:3–12, July, 1970.

medical bill of the aged person. Nevertheless, the amount paid directly by the aged remains higher per capita ($163) than for the non-aged ($98).[9] These expenditures for personal health services amount to almost 6 percent of the gross national product. The allocation of the dollar for personal health services provides one index of the relative importance of the various health services. In fiscal year 1969 the distribution was as follows:[10]

Hospital care	43%
Physicians' services	23%
Dentists' and other professional services	10%
Drugs	12%
Nursing home care	5%
Eye glasses, appliances, and other health services	8%
Total	101%

The most important shift in these components over the past twenty years has been the increasing proportion of the total devoted to hospital and nursing home care and the decreasing proportion for dentists and drugs. The component for physicians' services has remained relatively stable in the period since 1950 [50].

There continues to be an unresolved issue whether health care should be regarded as a service and "provided" or as a risk and insured against. The first implies a comprehensive program furnishing all services—including preventive—without charge at the time of service; the latter implies that, in the main, the need for personal health services is a contingency as are fires, accidents, and premature death, and hence costs incurred are reimbursed to the patient.

It can be shown that the use of any health services falls unevenly over families and individuals during a year, introducing a predictable element of contingency for the group but not, of course, for the individual. For example, Table 16–10, shows about 18 percent of the families having expenditures of under $50 for all health services (less than 2 percent incurred no expenditures) and about 8 percent having expenditures of $1,000 and over. This was in 1963, or at the present writing, eight years ago. A current survey would reveal higher over-all expenditure levels but a similarly shaped distribution.

TABLE 16-10 PERCENT DISTRIBUTION OF FAMILIES BY LEVEL OF TOTAL EXPENDITURES FOR PERSONAL HEALTH SERVICES, UNITED STATES, 1963

Total Family Expenditures	*Percent*	
None	1.8	17.8
Under $50	16.0	
$50– 99	11.7	
100– 199	18.7	
200– 299	12.8	
300– 399	9.5	
400– 499	6.3	
500– 749	10.0	
750– 999	5.1	
1,000–1,999	6.5	
2,000 and over	1.6	
Total	100.0	

Source: Andersen and Anderson, *Decade of Health Services*, Table 31, p. 57.

Still, there are particular services which fall naturally into a noncontingency or regular use category, such as maternity services for expectant mothers, well-baby clinics, periodic checkups for physicians' services, and dental services. Further, it is possible that a relatively small proportion of people suffer disproportionately from illness and disability over time compared with other people so that there is, in a sense, a continuously "sick" population core. This hypothesis has not been examined

[10] *Ibid.*, derived from Table 1. Total of percents exceeds 100 because of rounding-off error.

systematically because it requires a rather long longitudinal study. Health Insurance Plan of Greater New York maintains detailed records of the use of physicians' services on the part of its members, and a study was made some years ago of what were called "high" and "low" utilizers. The investigators examined the persistence of utilization levels by the same patients over a three-year period. It was found that 12 percent of the members received half of the services in a year, and 4 percent received one-fourth of the services. Using 1953 as the starting year, it was found that 46 percent of the non-utilizers remained such in 1955, and 33.2 percent of the utilizers were still utilizers in 1955 [16]. For this short time span there was, then, some indication that a core of "well" and "sick" persons persists over time.[11]

Leaving aside the extent to which the need for medical care is a contingency, public policy has directed that increasing portions of the total costs of medical care be paid for by third parties. Thus, we see in Table 16–11 that the proportion of total expenditures for personal health services paid for directly by the consumer has decreased consistently from about 68 percent in fiscal year 1950 to 41 percent in fiscal year 1969. In the early part of this period, insurance benefits made up most of the difference. Since 1966, with the advent of Medicaid and Medicare, public expenditures have increased sharply.

[11] Two other studies of aged populations have emphasized the persistent nature of illness and need for medical care for a considerable portion of older persons [22, 51, 55].

USE OF SERVICES IN SELECTED CONTEXTS

While our knowledge of why utilization rates differ according to basic demographic, social, and economic variables is far from certain, there is even more uncertainty as to why there are great differences in the volume of use in different medical care settings. Research has, so far, elucidated only that differences do exist. There is now, however, a sufficient volume and variety of utilization data to permit the formulation of research aimed at explaining these variations.

In this country interest has been chiefly directed to the short-term general hospital because of its relative costliness. That is, in the absence of a systems concept of personal health services, the tendency has been to pick out individual aspects, such as use of hospitals, which are disturbing to the

TABLE 16-11 SOURCE OF PAYMENT FOR PERSONAL HEALTH CARE EXPENDITURES, SELECT FISCAL YEARS 1950–1969

Source	*Percent of Total Expenditure*				
	1950	*1955*	*1960*	*1966*	*1969*
Direct consumer payment	67.7	59.6	56.3	51.8	40.6
Insurance benefits	8.3	14.8	20.2	24.5	22.3
Philanthropy and other	4.0	3.8	2.2	2.0	1.5
Public expenditure	19.9	21.9	21.2	21.7	35.6
Total	99.9	100.1	99.9	100.0	100.0

Source: Barbara S. Cooper, "National Health Expenditures, Fiscal Years 1929–1969 and Calender Years 1929–1968," *Research and Statistics* Note 18, Social Security Administration, November 2, 1969, p. 6.

policy makers, without any consideration of the effect on the whole spectrum of services. Thus, when hospital use is discovered as being relatively low in a group-practice prepayment context compared with a solo-practice and fee-for-service context, group practice is suggested as "the solution" for reducing medical costs, this without giving consideration to other factors such as patient preference, physician preference, presence or absence of substitute services, and so on.

More often than not, studies show lower hospital utilization under group-practice prepayment plans than under prevailing methods of delivering personal health services [7, 17, 18, 33, 47].[12] Studies showing lower utilization under prepaid group practice estimate the difference to be as much as 20 percent.[13]

What is particularly interesting is that there are no similar wide differences in the proportion of people who see a physician at least once in either context, pointing to the physician as the crucial decision maker in any context. While the hospital has received the greatest amount of scrutiny because it is the most visible and expensive component of the range of health services, it might be argued that emphasis should be shifted to the physician as the gatekeeper to the hospital.

In the absence of an over-all systems theory of use of health services, concern has been directed at the unit cost of hospitals and the inpatient population, i.e., *after* the patient is in, rather than before. Hence, most of the studies have been done on the inpatient population, and particularly on the variable of length of stay, to determine whether the patient "really needs to be in the hospital."[14] Two studies, however, have been conducted in attempts to study the decision-making process leading to hospital admission and discharge. While the findings are quite revealing, they offer no panacea to control the use of hospitals. A Massachusetts survey studied the necessity of hospitalization of a representative sample of patients and their physicians [8]. Some 2,000 patients were interviewed a few weeks after their discharge from general hospitals, as were their referring and attending physicians. Criteria of appropriateness of admission were then established *a posteriori,* as seen by the attending and referring physicians. Table 16–12 suggests that physicians exercise a great deal of discretionary judgment concerning whether to admit a patient to the hospital. Eleven percent of the surgical admissions, 17 percent of the medical admissions, and 23 percent of the diagnostic admissions could have been managed without hospitalization in the judgment of the admitting physician. If all admissions in these categories were in fact eliminated, an over-all reduction of hospital admissions of 15 percent would result.

In a second study, done in Michigan, eighteen diagnoses which were relatively clear-cut disease entities were selected [21]. For the diagnoses, criteria established *a priori* by appropriate board-certified specialists in private practice and in medical schools were applied. A sample of over 5,000 records representative of discharged hospital patients in Michigan were reviewed by medical review committees. Where there appeared to be deviations from the criteria set by those committees, the at-

12 Two studies showed no significant differences in the rate of use of hospitals [12, 15].

13 Klarman has questioned the magnitude of this difference. His calculations reduced the difference to 10 percent, no small difference still but "much smaller than 20 percent," as he put it [31].

14 The literature on this aspect of hospital use has been examined in some detail in Chap. 1 of Anderson and Sheatsley [8].

TABLE 16-12 ADMITTING PHYSICIAN'S JUDGMENT ABOUT SUBSTITUTING OUTPATIENT CARE FOR HOSPITAL ADMISSION, MASSACHUSETTS, 12 MONTHS, 1960–1961

Judgment	*Surgical Admissions*	*Medical Admissions*	*Diagnostic Admissions*
Impossible except in hospital	74%	46%	45%
Extremely difficult except in hospital	15%	37%	32%
Possible but less satisfactory outside of hospital	7%	14%	15%
Could be done as well outside hospital	4%	3%	8%
Total	100%	100%	100%

Source: Odin W. Anderson and Paul B. Sheatsley, *Hospital Use—A Survey of Patient and Physician Decisions,* Chicago: Center for Health Administrative, Studies Research Series, No. 24, 1967, p. 90.

tending physicians were interviewed to determine what other medical and "extra-medical" factors were present to account for the apparent deviation. From the record plus the interviews, a final decision was made on the basis of medical factors alone. For the eighteen diagnoses studied, "overuse" represented 2.3 percent of the admissions and 6.8 percent of the days [21].

The investigators in Michigan were well aware of the significance of extra-medical factors in determining hospital utilization [21].[15] Yet in their final evaluation of hospital stays, they attempted to restrict the criteria to medical factors. In contrast, it was assumed in the Massachusetts study that, because medical and extra-medical factors are exceedingly difficult to disentangle, the decision to see a physician and the decision of a physician to recommend the use of hospital care must be studied in relationship to time, place, and circumstance which embrace both medical and extra-medical factors. The great range of utilization patterns in industrialized countries supports these observations. Perhaps a fusion of the Massachusetts and Michigan approaches would be the most valid study method, i.e., the measurement of the variation between actual practice and perceptions and predetermined criteria established by a medical elite.[16]

[15] They write: "The use of the term "extra-medical" in no sense indicates that the factor does not adequately explain the hospital use in question, nor is it equated with any judgment that use was "unjustified." This judgment was not attempted. To divide all factors influencing use of the hospital into "justified" and "not justified" and to further class all "justified" factors as "medical" as is the tendency would completely obscure the causative factors relating to the use of the hospital.

[16] Although the Michigan and Massachusetts studies use different criteria, "inappropriateness" in the Michigan study might be compared with the category "could be done as well outside of hospital" for surgical, medical, and diagnostic admissions in Massachusetts. The proportion of all admissions in Massachusetts which "could be done as well outside" was 4.2 percent (computed from Anderson and Sheatsley [8]) or somewhat higher than the 2.3 percent "inappropriate" admissions estimated in Michigan.

A pilot study in Nassau County, New York, conducted in five hospitals and including seven diagnoses, using the same method as in the Michigan study and with the consultation of its research personnel,

The Massachusetts data do reveal that an appreciable proportion of hospital use can be reduced if circumstances demand it. The function of hospitals at this time is far beyond life saving. Hospital care now adds comfort, safety, and convenience. It is possible, however, that the hospital could be redefined as a place for acute, emergency care to reduce its volume of use.

The determinants of use of services are so open-ended that no system has yet had so large a supply of resources that physicians' offices or hospitals lack patients.[17] This has led some observers to generalize that demand rises to meet resources [52]. The conclusion that follows for hospitals is to control use by limiting beds and thereby force adjustments within these limits. Indeed, as pointed out by Klarman, this becomes the usual response of a health system in a context of third-party payment or certainly when government becomes the chief source of funds. Attempts are then made to fit demand to the supply rather than supply to the demand [31].

CURRENT TRENDS

Since the first edition of this handbook, a number of works have appeared using a general behavioral model, or "systems approach," for viewing peoples' use of and expenditures for health services.[18] These approaches can be roughly divided according to their emphasis on economic or social-psychological factors. The economic models stress means through which people can attain services or can translate their perceived need into economic demand for medical care. Thus, these models stress such variables as family income, health insurance coverage, and the prices of health services.[19]

In contrast, the social-psychological models are more likely to concentrate on variables which explain differential perceptions of need for health services. They emphasize factors referred to by economists as tastes and preferences. While tastes and preferences are generally included in the economic models, their role tends to be less well defined than that of the economic variables.

Within the realm of the economists' tastes and preferences, the social-psychologist is likely to make additional distinctions. First, he is interested in distinguishing social definitions of "illness" from "disease," as it might be clinically defined. Moreover, within the realm of the social variables, the social-psychologist sees further need to differentiate the sociodemographic classifications such as education and class from social-psychological measures including perception of illness and values and attitudes toward health and illness. Such differentiation is viewed as one path toward understanding why people of different social classes have different patterns of utilization.[20]

estimated that 3.9 percent of the admissions were "inappropriate." Although the patient records evaluated were not assumed to be a representative sample, this figure is of interest [38].

17 It should be noted, however, that there was talk of an oversupply in the United States during the Depression of the thirties.

18 The concept of "model" refers to a logical specification of anticipated relationships between certain characteristics of an individual, family, or geographical areas and utilization of health services. The adjectives "general behavioral" suggest models which attempt to incorporate economic and social as well as biological variables into an overall scheme to explain health service use.

19 A general overview of the economic approach will be found in [32]. For examples of empirical studies, see [20, 34, 54, 61].

20 For examples of models emphasizing the social-psychological approach see [10, 24, 28, 53, 57, 58].

One effort to combine elements of each of these approaches is found in an analysis of differences in families' use of health services [1].[21] The model employed in this study suggested that use of medical care was dependent upon

1. predisposition to use services,
2. enabling means to secure services,
3. perceived need for such services.

Further, it was postulated that the importance of the model components would vary among hospital, physician, and dental services according to the varying amounts of discretion exercised by the family in procuring each type of care. While the model proved helpful in understanding observed differences in utilization, the results also pointed to the need for further elaboration and specification of such models [1].

CONCLUSION

Does a theory of use of health services emerge from the foregoing review? The answer will have to be no. However, we are moving toward conceptual clarity which, in turn, can lead to increasingly sophisticated model building. Such models will recognize the interdependent nature of biological, sociological, epidemiological, and social-psychological variables and will strive to determine the relative weight of these variables. What may be reasonably predicted is that the classic medical model, which is biologically based, and the classic sociological model, where man and his group are by definition pure social entities and divorced analytically from the common clay of biology, may be fused into a sociomedical model.

[21] This study was an attempt to provide a more detailed analysis of differences in utilization patterns found in a nationwide social survey of families, as originally reported in [4].

More specifically, this review shows that since the original edition of this handbook, there has been a shift from disparate studies to area and cross-national comparision and comparisons in different medical care contexts. Further, inroads are being made toward the understanding of the essential characteristics of a health service:

1. Patient perception and discretion to act;
2. Physician discretion and prerogatives to prescribe.

These are reciprocals that profoundly permeate the operation of the health services system in any time, place, and organizational structure.

By the foregoing, we hope that we can lay to rest the concept of "proper" use. We would hope rather that as the field moves more into a systems approach, health service utilization will be understood as relative to a range of complex situational factors. Further, this suggests that a health services system should be flexible enough to devise delivery methods coincident with these changing factors. Ideally, such flexibility will maximize the fit between the health service system and the needs of the people it serves.

REFERENCES

1. Andersen, Ronald, *A Behavioral Model of Families' Use of Health Services*, Center for Health Administration Studies Research Series, No. 25. Chicago, 1968.
2. ——— and John T. Hull, "Hospital Utilization and Cost Trends in Canada and the United States," *Health Services Research*, 4 (Fall, 1969), 198–222, Table 3.
3. Andersen, Ronald and Lee Benham, "Family Income and Medical Care Consumption," in Herbert Klarman, ed.,

Empirical Studies in Health Economics. Baltimore: The Johns Hopkins Press, 1970.
4. Andersen, Ronald and Odin W. Anderson, *A Decade of Health Services: Social Survey Trends in Use and Expenditures.* Chicago: University of Chicago Press, 1967.
5. Andersen, Ronald et al., *Medical Care Use in Sweden and the United States—A Comparative Analysis of Systems and Behavior*, Center for Health Administration Studies Research Series, No. 27. Chicago, 1970, Tables 2, 17.
6. Anderson, Odin W. and Joanna Kravits, *Health Services in the Chicago Area—A Framework for Use of Data*, Center for Health Administration Studies Research Series, No. 26. Chicago, 1968.
7. Anderson, Odin and Paul B. Sheatsley, *Comprehensive Medical Insurance —A Study of Costs, Use and Attitudes under Two Plans*, Health Information Foundation Research Series, No. 9. New York, 1959.
8. ———, *Hospital Use—A Survey of Patient and Physician Decisions*, Center for Health Administration Studies Research Series, No. 24. Chicago, 1967.
9. Brackett, E. Maurice, "Community Medicine and the Improvement of Health Services: A Model for the University Contribution to Innovation," *Lancet*, 2 (July 5, 1969), 39–41.
10. Bice, Thomas and Kerr L. White, "Factors Related to the Use of Health Services, An International Comparative Study," *Medical Care*, 7 (March–April, 1969), 124–133.
11. Cartwright, Ann, *Patients and Their Doctors: A Study of General Practice.* New York: Atherton Press, 1967, p. 25.
12. Columbia University, School of Public Health and Administrative Medicine, with the Cooperation of the National Opinion Research Center, University of Chicago, *Family Medical Care Under Three Types of Health Insurance.* New York: Foundation of Employee Health, Medical Care and Welfare, Inc., 1965.
13. Commission on Chronic Illness, *Chronic Illness in the United States, Vol. 1, Prevention of Chronic Illness.* Cambridge: Harvard University Press, 1957.
14. Darsky, Benjamin J., Nathan Sinai, and Solomon J. Axelrod, *Comprehensive Medical Services under Voluntary Health Insurance: A Study of Windsor Medical Services.* Cambridge: Harvard University Press, 1958.
15. Densen, Paul M. and Sam Shapiro, "Comparisons of a Group Practice and a Self-insurance Situation," *Hospitals*, 36 (November 16, 1962), 63–65.
16. Densen, Paul, Sam Shapiro, and Marilyn Einhorn, "Concerning High and Low Utilization of Service in a Medical Care Plan and the Persistence of Utilization Levels over a Three Year Period," *Milbank Memorial Fund Quarterly*, 37 (July, 1959), 217–50.
17. Densen, Paul M. et al., "Prepaid Medical Care and Hospital Utilization in a Dual Choice Situation," *American Journal of Public Health*, 50 (November, 1960), 1710–26.
18. Falk, Isadore S. and J. Sentura, *Medical Care Programs for Steelworkers and Their Families.* Pittsburgh: United Steelworkers of America, 1960.
19. Falk, Isadore S., Margaret C. Klem, and Nathan Sinai, *The Incidence of Illness and the Receipt and Costs of Medical Care Among Representative Families: Experiences in Twenty Consecutive Months during 1928–31*, Committee on the Cost of Medical Care Report, No. 26. Chicago, 1933.
20. Feldstein, Paul, "Demand for Medical Care," in *The Cost of Medical Care*, Vol. 1. American Medical Association, 1964, pp. 57–76.
21. Fitzpatrick, Thomas B. et al., "Character and Effectiveness of Hospital Use," in Walter J. McNerney, ed., *Hospital and Medical Economics.* Chicago: Hospital Research and Educational Trust, 1962, pp. 361–591.
22. Freeman, Howard E. et al., "Use of Medical Resources by Spancos, I: Extent and Sources of Medical Care in a Very Old Population," *American Journal of Public Health*, 56 (September, 1966), pp. 1530–39.
23. Freidson, Eliot and Jacob J. Feldman, *The Public Looks at Hospitals,*

Health Information Foundation Research Series, No. 4. New York, 1958.
24. GREENLICK, MERWYN R. et al., "Determinants of Medical Care Utilization," *Journal of Health Services Research*, 3 (Winter, 1968), 296–315.
25. Health Resources Statistics 1968, Public Health Service Publication No. 1509. Washington, D.C.: Government Printing Office, p. 230.
26. HOROWITZ, LOUCELE A., "Medical Care Price Fact Sheet," *Research and Statistics Note 9*, Social Security Administration (May 9, 1969).
26a. ———, "Medical Care Price Fact Sheet," *Research and Statistics Note 2*, Social Security Administration (February 23, 1970).
27. *Hospital Statistics, Vol. 1, Hospital Beds, 1966*. Ottawa: Dominion Bureau of Statistics, 1968, p. 46.
28. KALIMO, ESKO, *Determinants of Medical Care Utilization*, Research Institute for Social Security, Series E. Helsinki: 11/1969.
29. KATZ, DANIEL AND ROBERT L. KAHN, *The Social Psychology of Organizations*. New York: John Wiley & Sons, Inc., 1966.
30. KISSICK, WILLIAM L., "Health Manpower in Transition," *Milbank Memorial Fund Quarterly*, 46, Pt. 2 (January, 1968), 53–90.
31. KLARMAN, HERBERT E., "Approaches to Moderating the Increases in Medical Care Costs," *Medical Care*, 7 (May–June, 1969), 175–90.
32. ———, *The Economics of Health*. New York: Columbia University Press, 1965, pp. 20–40.
33. ———, "Effect of Prepaid Group Practice on Hospital Use," *Public Health Reports*, 17 (November, 1963), 955–65.
34. ———, ed., *Empirical Studies in Health Economics*. Baltimore: The Johns Hopkins Press, 1970.
35. LERNER, MONROE, *Hospital Use by Diagnosis: A Comparison of Two Experiences*, Health Information Foundation Research Series, No. 19. New York, 1961.
36. LERNER, MONROE AND ODIN W. ANDERSON, *Health Progress in the United States, 1900–1960*. Chicago: University of Chicago Press, 1963, p. 91.
37. MAY, JOEL, *Health Planning, Its Past and Potential*, Center for Health Administration Studies, Perspective A-5. Chicago, 1967.
38. Nassau County Medical Society Voluntary Health Insurance Committee, *Pilot Study of Hospital Use in Nassau County*. November, 1965.
39. National Center for Health Statistics, *Age Patterns in Medical Care, Illness and Disability, United States—July 1963–June 1965*, Series 10, No. 32. Washington, D.C.: Government Printing Office, 1966.
40. ———, *Current Estimates*, Series 10, No. 52. Washington, D.C.: Government Printing Office, May, 1969, p. 19.
41. ———, *Selected Dental Findings in Adults*, Series 11, No. 7. Washington, D.C.: Government Printing Office, 1965, p. 8.
42. ———, *Volume of Dental Visits, U.S., July 1963–June 1964*, Series 10, No. 23. Washington, D.C.: Government Printing Office, 1965, p. 1.
43. ———, *Volume of Physicians' Visits, United States, July 1966–June 1967*, Series 10, No. 49. Washington, D.C.: Government Printing Office, 1968.
44. NAVARO, VICENTE, "Planning Personal Health Services: A Markovian Model," *Medical Care*, 7 (May–June, 1969), 242–49.
45. PARSONS, TALCOTT AND RENEE FOX, "Illness, Therapy and the Modern Urban American Family," *Journal of Social Issues*, 8 (1952), 2–3, 31–44.
46. PEARSON, R. JOHN C. et al., "Hospital Caseloads in Liverpool, New England, and Uppsala," *Lancet*, 564 (September 7, 1968), 559–66.
47. PERROTT, GEORGE S. AND J. R. CHASE, "The Federal Employee's Health Benefits Program," *Group Health and Welfare News*, Special Supplement (October, 1968).
48. PETERSON, O. L. et al., "What Is Value for Money in Medical Care?" *Lancet*, 1 (1967), 777.
49. REDER, MELVIN, "Some Problems in Measurement of Productivity in the Medical Care Industry," in Victor

Fuchs, ed., *Production and Productivity in the Service Industry.* New York: National Bureau of Economic Research, 1969, pp. 96–153.

50. RICE, DOROTHY P. AND BARBARA S. COOPER, "National Health Expenditures, 1950–1966," *Research and Statistics Note 3* (February 1, 1968).
51. RICHARDSON, ARTHUR H. et al., "Use of Medical Resources by Spancos, II: Social Factors and Medical Care Experience," *Milbank Memorial Fund Quarterly,* 45 (January, 1967), 61–75.
52. ROEMER, MILTON H. AND MAX SHAIN, Hospital *Utilization Under Insurance.* American Hospital Association Hospital Monograph Series, No. 6, 1959.
53. ROSENSTOCK, IRWIN, "Why People Use Health Services," *Milbank Memorial Fund Quarterly,* 44 (July, 1966), 94–124.
54. ROSENTHAL, GERALD, *The Demand for General Hospital Facilities,* American Hospital Association Monograph, No. 14, 1964.
55. SHANAS, ETHEL, *The Health of Older People: A Social Survey.* Cambridge: Harvard University Press, 1962, p. 36.
56. SHIPMAN, GEORGE A., ROBERT J. LAMPMAN, AND FRANK MIYAMOTO, *Medical Service Corporations in the State of Washington.* Cambridge: Harvard University Press, 1962.
57. STOECKLE, JOHN et al., "On Going to See the Doctor: The Contribution of the Patient to the Decision to Seek Medical Aid," *Journal of Chronic Diseases,* 16 (September, 1963), 975–85,
58. SUCHMAN, EDWARD, "Health Orientation and Medical Care," *American Journal of Public Health,* 56 (January, 1966), 97–105.
59. VINCENT, CLARK EDWARD, "The Family Health and Illness: Some Neglected Areas," *Annals of the American Academy of Political and Social Science,* 346 (March, 1963), 109–16.
60. WAGNER, CARRUTH J., "Program Planning: A Process of Health Program Planning and Implementation," *Archives of Environmental Health,* 12 (May, 1966), 660–69.
61. WIRICK, GROVER, "A Multiple Equation Model of Demand," *Journal of Health Services Research,* 1 (Winter, 1966), 301–46.

17

PUBLIC HEALTH IN THE COMMUNITY

Irwin T. Sanders

Within recent years the importance of the community in health concerns has greatly increased. The belief in the importance of citizen participation, so prominent in the antipoverty programs, has begun to influence programs in the health field also. "Community groups" are demanding better services and more control over those that do come into existence. In many cases, the authority of the medical personnel—based on the mystique of science—is questioned by those with political goals in mind. More and more, the community is the arena where the professional health worker and the lay public interact. New rules are being made and new forms of service are being created. Expectations which may or may not be fulfilled are rising. The most strident voices for reform come from the less privileged areas of the community, but the discontent is also spreading among the more affluent members of society who are confronted with rising medical costs beyond their financial means even

The author of this chapter wishes to acknowledge the valuable assistance of Ann Brownlee.

with conventional insurance coverage. And the economic dominants, who have much to say about what goes on in the community, exercise increasingly tight control over the additional tax dollars channeled into the health field.

Obviously, then, those responsible for health programs should not only be fully aware of the community dimension of these programs; they should also have a clear understanding of the community as a whole if they are to understand how the health subsystem functions within it. As a minimum they must be aware of three dimensions of the community: as a place, as a collection of people, and particularly as a social system.

THREE-DIMENSIONAL VIEW OF THE COMMUNITY

The Community as a Place

"Place" is important to health for at least three reasons. It is important in epidemiological study because such study partially relies upon mapping to locate and explain the incidence and spread of various types of illness—an important topic but not within the purview of this discussion [29, 55]. Place is important secondly because it is often used to reveal the availability and utilization of health services [64]. The location of the community, whether near to or distant from urban centers, can be a factor. Andersen and Anderson have shown that the hospital surgical rate for rural farm people was lower than for people with other types of residence, an important factor being the lack of insurance among the rural farm population. (In 1963, 10 percent were insured compared to 26 percent of the urban people and 19 percent of the rural nonfarm population. Also, rural nonfarm people have higher hospital admission rates than either urban or rural farm people, although they spend less money per family on personal health services than urban people [5].) Some studies show that such services as nursing homes may provide better care in rural than urban areas because they are owned by physicians resident in the community who take charge of the facility [99]. Numerous studies have dealt with the unequal distribution of physicians and hospital beds in the city and countryside, thus stressing the importance of location, or the community as a place. But even within the same community, people may find the health center inaccessible because of its location rather than for social or economic reasons [22].

But place is also important because it refers to the physical environment in which man lives, some of it natural and some of it manmade, but all of it part of the visible community—the tangible signs of communal living. The physical community is the arena in which one must deal with, among other things, the problems of traffic flow, sewage disposal, stream and air pollution, as well as the question of safe and adequate housing. In fact, the attention now being given to the ecosystem underlines the increasing awareness of the connection between the physical and social environment [75, 95].

Housing, whether attractive or deteriorated, stands as a physical symbol of certain assumed social traits of the community [105]. Through the years many programs have been devised to eliminate or renovate deteriorated housing in the slums. A slum is defined as an "area containing housing which is in an advanced stage of physical decay or which, because of poor planning, disagreeable surroundings, or bad sanitary facilities, is likely to produce diseased physical or social lives for its inhabitants" [65]. But not all studies would claim this much of a cause-effect relationship between housing and other social ills. It is clear that even very ambitious programs of slum clearance or urban renewal have not solved many of the social problems attributed to bad housing [18, 27, 133]. Frequently, public health authorities are empowered and directed to try to halt urban blight by requiring that landlords bring their property up to certain standards or face court action. An interesting example of a program of this type is the Neighborhood Improvement Program [124].

Loring, after examining the relationship between residential environment and type of personal interaction, points out that the "well" people may have an "immunity" which enables them to tolerate quite a range of differences in "arrangements of physical phenomena" without adverse results. Others, predisposed to ill health, may be adversely affected by extremes of either isolation or "overcrowded social activity" [74].

Pollution, in its various forms, has moved to the center of the stage which housing formerly occupied as a community concern. Though a given source of pollution is located in a particular community and must be subject to controls exercised within that community, the overall reduction of pollution usually calls for intercommunity or regional cooperation. The community as a place, in itself or as part of a larger area, whether in itself or as part of a larger area, cannot be ignored.

The Community as a Collection of People

A community can be viewed as a population, as a collection of people. Health authorities conduct demographic analyses in order to determine the extent of maternity, morbidity, and mortality within a community. Density of population is thought to be positively associated with sociological stress through studies dealing with Ohio farmers [84], rural counties in North Carolina [123], and the rural Zulu women of South Africa who moved to the city. [40, 110].

Communities differ in the types of people who inhabit them. Population composition, whether viewed in terms of sex, age, occupation, or marital status, is related to many health factors. Wechsler and Pugh conclude from a study in Massachusetts that individuals with a personal characteristic (age, marital status, place of birth, occupation) who are living in communities where that characteristic is less common have a higher rate of psychiatric hospitalization than people with the characteristic living in communities where it is more common [128].

Communities also differ in size of population. The problems of a city health department, which works primarily with the lower socioeconomic groups in the downtown population, may be of a different order from those in smaller suburban communities, where living standards and incomes are higher. Furthermore, the people in one community may move much more frequently than do those in another community, either changing houses within the community or leaving it, to be replaced by newcomers. A study in England reports that there is a logical explanation for the fact that community mental health service is most fully developed up to now in medium-sized county boroughs. These communities have populations sufficiently large to support a complete range of facilities, except for the most specialized, and the services can be located within fairly easy reach of the whole community. Rural areas have neither of these advantages, and the cities face concentrations of intractable social problems and large immigrant groups [38].

Communities may double in size over a ten- or fifteen-year period and develop a marked "oldtimer-newcomer" cleavage that is reflected in their disagreements about the value of innovative public health and medical programs. Rate of growth has also been shown to be associated with various factors. "Rapidly growing communities tend to to produce significantly higher rates of hospitalized depressive disorders and suicide, but not of schizophrenia, alcoholism, or other mental disorders" [127].

Those viewing the community as a collection of people are also interested in statistics which show the quality of the population as measured by its educational attainment, occupational skills, and physical fitness.

But people are more than statistics; they are carriers of traditions and cultural values, as Paul [92] and Straus [119] point out. The importance of these differences in traditions and values are emphasized in studies of the response of various ethnic groupings to health programs [25, 96]. Some ethnic groupings hold on to their traditional values more effectively and for a longer period of time than do others. And a comparison of three small, neighboring, ethnically different communities in eastern Pennsylvania showed that stable cultures have a lower frequency of coronary heart disease than cultures undergoing rapid change [16, 17]. Jenkins found that differences in perceptions of tuberculosis were associated with educational level and social class, but most markedly with *ethnic group* membership [58]. Suchman found in a study of a representative cross-section of adults in the Washington Heights area of New York City marked differences between Puerto Ricans and Protestants and Jews. He hypothesized that "the more ethnocentric and cohesive the social group, the more isolated and alienated it will be from the larger society and the less likely it will be to accept the objectives and methods of the formal medical care system." But when he utilized a social organization index, varying from cosmopolitanism to parochialism, he found this generally more important than either ethnicity or social class [120].

Lieberson has shown that ethnic identification of physicians significantly influences their pattern of medical practice [71]. Wellin finds that local culture affects public health in three ways: It affects the objective profile, or the ecology, of health and disease; it creates its own, or subjective, picture of health and disease; and it influences the progress of health programs [129]. Certainly, it is not stretching Wellin's analysis to point out that these same effects apply to subcultures within the communities as well as to the composite local culture.

The collectivity of people we call a community also reveals differences in social class. In some communities these classes may be so amorphous that only those at the extremes of top and bottom can be pointed out by the average citizen; in other communities the social distinctions may be so clearly drawn that most people know just where they stand in the social scale. Many studies of social stratification have shown that classes differ in educational opportunities, patterns of recreation, employment, religious affiliation, and political behavior. Thus, it is not surprising to find social class associated with utilization of health services or the incidence, prevalence, and treatment of mental disease [60]. Reeder has shown a connection between perception of community status and blood pressure groups [97], Freeman and

Simmons have presented data on social class and posthospital performance levels of the mentally ill [37], but other studies claim an indirect rather than direct relationship here [69]. A pioneering study by Koos found statistically significant differences in the symptoms reported by members of different social classes of a small rural community [67]. More recent studies take issue with each other on the significance of class, but some of the differences hinge on definitions of class and the health factors which are being measured [6, 14, 59, 81, 83, 100, 103].

The Community as a Social System

A third way to view a community is as a social system. This assumes that every community has a variety of patterns of action which have grown up around the satisfaction of important local needs, through specialization of function and of personnel. The community as a system, therefore, may be viewed as the totality of the interaction among these major systems, of which health is one.

The economy, for example, can be broken down into component social networks (or subsystems), which consist in large part of the formal groups and associations clustered together around a significant common interest: finance, industry, commerce, agriculture, transportation. Such groups, when studied individually, are seen to be sets of social relationships—among officers, among members, between officers and members, or between different subgroups. Relationships, in turn, can be reduced to the persons or units who fill the appropriate statuses in a given situation and carry out the expected roles. In such a way, the economy—a major system—is an abstraction which can be traced to the patterned behavior of the individuals in a community who, during part of the day at least, are filling economic statuses as opposed to familial or recreational statuses. Whether one studies the community at the analytical level of organizations, of subsystems, or even of major systems will depend upon the purposes the study is to serve and the appropriateness of a given level for that kind of study [106].

Many efforts are currently being made to define a community in such a way as to describe its communal properties so as to distinguish them from just any behavior which happens to occur within the community's geographical area. Sutton and Kolaja [122], Reiss [98], Parsons [91], Mercer [76], and Nelson, Ramsey, and Verner [89] have tried to put this problem in clearer focus. Kaufman and Wilkinson view the community as a social field [62, 131]. Arensberg has taken a fresh look at community studies from the anthropological point of view [7], and the present writer [106] and others (such as Summers, Scott, and Folse [121], and Loomis [73]) have elaborated the concept of social system, applying it to a local community. Warren [126], Sills [114], and Levine and White [70] have called attention to the conflict between the vertical and horizontal axes of health organizations which must serve national purposes and yet receive local support. Anyone seeking to view the community as a social system and attempting to fit the health system into such a context, must be aware of the developing theory and the clarification of concepts currently taking place.

HEALTH AS A MAJOR COMMUNITY SYSTEM

A major community system, whether it be education or the economy, has identifiable characteristics such as (1) a structure, or related series of agencies, organizations or establishments; (2) a set of functions, both manifest and latent; (3) functionaries, or persons charged with the responsibility of promoting the interest of the system or major segments of it; (4) ideology or rationale, which provides the justification for the continuation of the system; (5) paraphernalia, or the necessary equipment and material resources for carrying out the expected activities; and (6) linkages with other systems within and without the community.

The Organization or Structure of the Health System

Everyone connected with health has certain roles he is supposed to carry out. This applies not only to the physician, dentist, sanitary engineer, and public health educator but also to the hospital orderly, the patient, and even the patient's family.[1] Health services are provided through a definite network of social relationships which have been built up over many years but which survive because the members of each new generation learn to perform the roles expected of them in situations involving health. And the concept of "social situation" is very important, for social roles can be performed only in the presence of other people. This calls for activities in groups, whether in the small group (patient-doctor-nurse in an office visit) or in the large associations which range from organizations such as the local medical association to the entire bureaucracy of a hospital.

The concept of major system provides a means of taking all these diverse patterns and organizing them into a theoretical scheme, similar to but not necessarily exactly like that which one finds in any given community. In American communities, for instance, there are five types of health structures or subsystems, closely intertwined, but nevertheless distinct enough to be analyzed separately.[2] First, there is the private office practice of professional health persons, which would include small clinics where specialists work in proximity to take advantage of laboratories, X-ray equipment, and joint consultation on troublesome cases. Private practice traditionally has included home visits, but increasingly the patient is asked to come to the better-equipped doctor's office wherever possible, or even to the hospital when the physician deems the case to be too serious for home care. Embedded in this subsystem is the almost sacred belief that the doctor-patient relationship should be personal and inviolable.

A second subsystem might be termed group health care. People, by virtue of employment or membership rights, have access to medical and other health services in facilities set up by factories, stores, business or governmental agencies, schools, labor unions, and the like [33, 34, 86].

A third subsystem is the "world" of large hospitals, clinics, and health agencies. Although medical professionals can move easily from office to hospital and back again in the performance of any day's duties, the shift by a patient from his job or home to the hospital represents a tremendous reorganization of roles for him and his family. Community support of these hospitals and agencies has become much more crucial than in the past, and more effective ways of bridging the communication gap between the health professionals and the citizenry need to be devised [12, 15, 78, 111].

[1] See Chaps. 8, 9, 12, 13 for specific discussions of these parties.

[2] See Chap. 16 for a detail discussion of the organization of health services.

A fourth subsystem is public health. In general, its personnel do not "practice" in the customary sense of the word. They protect, administer, and perform services. Public health people detect but most often do not treat; they refer those who are ill to other medical personnel; they immunize to reduce incidence of disease, they inspect to prevent epidemics, they educate so as to raise the patient's understanding of health care for himself and his family, they make home visits to check on communicable disease, and they visit work sites to enforce standards protecting the workers' health. The structure of public health, then, consists of a set of roles different from those found in the other subsystems, and its personnel usually find themselves in social situations different from those in the doctor's office, the hospital operating room, or the emergency room of a factory [8]. These health workers are truly public, in the sense that they are at the contact points between local people and the health system and frequently work in a nonmedical setting. In fact, a local board of health has been described as "symbolic of a way of life in a community . . . it represents many things—a part of the town, individualism, self-rule" [90].

A fifth subsystem, peripheral but necessary, is that of the pharmacists and others who sell materials and appliances required by and usually purchased individually by the patient. In the United States the health system uses the free enterprise system as the mechanism through which such drugs and appliances are provided to the individual. The pharmacist who owns and presides over a mercantile emporium, with stock ranging from antibiotics and aspirin to school supplies and ice cream, is essential to both the economic system and the health system. As a registered pharmacist, his health role is supposedly limited to filling doctor's prescriptions and selling nonprescription remedies. And communities differ in the extent to which those in the private practice subsystem tolerate the offer of medical advice by pharmacists. In some communities, pharmacists remove from the doctors' shoulders the responsibility for prescribing for a cold, a backache, or constipation; in other communities, pharmacists carefully advise patients to give their doctor a ring. But since many people in American communities do not have "doctors of their own," they often purchase remedies on the basis of hearsay, advertisement, packaging, or price.

One could very well argue that another subsystem is emerging which deals with the financial aspects of medical care. At first, it was made up of various private insurance schemes but now also involves government-sponsored programs such as Medicaid and Medicare.

The structure of each of these subsystems differs because the requisite group situations vary. Obviously, the drugstore is no place for a physician's diagnosis, nor is the office of the public health director a suitable place for an operation. Each requires a different network or organized activity which constitutes the structure of the subsystem. One begins to understand the nature of the health system, then, as one examines these important components—individually and in relation to each other. It is the totality of their roles, social relationships, and groups that constitutes the major health system of any community.

A Set of Functions

The health system has certain functions which distinguish it from the other systems—education, local government, religion, economy, recreation, welfare—which the community supports. Some of these are what Merton calls *manifest*, or stated and obvious; others are *latent*, not so readily discerned. Two manifest functions are readily apparent. The first is to cure the sick. Within the United States the concept of illness differs among regions, communities, and social classes within the communities. This, of course, can lead to variations in what is meant by "curing the sick." Illness, however, is always a crisis experience for any individual and for his immediate kin and close associates; widespread illness, whether endemic or epidemic, is a crisis experience for a community. To take care of these individual and community crises, the health system has developed.

A second manifest function of the health system is to keep people well. It is significant that this is usually considered a less important function than curing the sick, when from a logical point of view it should be more important. In American communities health is taken for granted; the tendency is to accentuate the curative rather than the preventive. Again, there is great debate throughout the United States over just how much effort should go into keeping people well. Is this a personal or a community responsibility? Is a commmunity approach an invasion of the sphere of the private practitioner? To what extent should people be forced to adopt measures that research has shown to be in the interests of better health? Should all efforts at keeping people well be delegated to local, state, and national governments with only occasional assistance from the private practitioner? Although answers to all of these questions are not always available, there is general agreement that some community-wide efforts at keeping people well should be made.

Latent functions are also performed by the health system. One of these is the offsetting of the impersonality of mass society by giving people a chance to talk intimately with health personnel about matters that trouble them [113]. Psychiatrists are those most readily thought of in this connection, but anyone familiar with the health field realizes that health personnel of all types are viewed by those in need as possible confidants who are competent to give advice. Although recent studies show that there is more neighborliness and informal activity in urban areas than previous writers had supposed, people in these communities often do need the safety valve of talk. Most Americans consider health personnel the appropriate people to talk to, even if they must pay for it.

Another latent function of the health system is the introduction of some degree of rationality into everyday life. Health practitioners supposedly deal with cause-effect relationships, many of which are subject to empirical test. As people become better educated about health, to that extent do they accept scientific explanation in place of erroneous folk beliefs. The health system can often confront individuals with scientific facts to which they must respond in terms of personal choice. The fact that the health system has not always been successful in introducing rationality into everyday life (witness the flouridation battles) does not minimize the importance of this latent function.

The health system is also charged with a third task that is more often latent than manifest: that of preserving an efficient labor force. In the opinion of some, workers are to be kept well not for the sake of health alone but for the sake of the economy. It is considered a national scandal when a large proportion of draftees are rejected because of failure to meet the physical standards [43]. Perhaps one reason why recent attempts at national programs of physical fitness have not excited more popular support is that they are not being channeled through the health system, where they would seem to belong, but through the educational system and its peripheral personnel of football coaches and calisthenics experts.

The members of a community tend to have a picture of how specific tasks related to the various functions should be distributed among the subsystems previously described. Brower, in his study of Cortland County, New York, identified those specific tasks that the private doctor, the county health department, and the school were each most frequently expected to perform. Interestingly enough, methods of payments were expected to differ: direct reimbursement for the doctor and payments from taxes for the public health department and the school—although the school (representing the group health care subsystem) was frequently expected to render its services without being reimbursed [15].

Functionaries

Just as the other community systems have their functionaries (the economy, the Secretary of the Chamber of Commerce; religion, the clergymen; education, the school superintendent; local government, the mayor or party leader), so also does the health system have its functionaries. These are distributed throughout the health subsystems: the officers of the local medical or dental association; the executives of the group health arrangements supported by insurance company officials concerned with actuarial details; the hospital managers and the presidents of their boards of directors; the public health officer; and the spokesmen for the local pharmacists; and the public relations personnel of the drug companies. This listing of functionaries, partial though it is, shows that the health system—as is true of most major systems in American communities—has no single functionary who can speak for the entire field; instead, there are different functionaries and organizations for each subsystem [4]. To understand public health and the community, therefore, one must identify these functionaries and determine the degree to which their roles complement or conflict with each other.

A growing body of literature discusses the changing roles of these functionaries [20, 135]. Many studies deal with relationships among different functionaries—such as that between physician and nurse—or with the division of labor among the professionals in a public health department. In contrast to these roles related to the internal workings of the health system are some with marked community implications. Hassinger and McNamara have studied the relationships of the public to physicians in a rural setting in Missouri [49], and Saunders and Bruening have described hospital-community relations in Mississippi. The latter study found that the hospital administrator is the key to the hospital's community relations [108]. Because many of the roles are still ill-defined, the functionaries representing competing health interests occasionally make contradictory pronouncements about the same topic. In such cases many citizens become badly confused and tend to downgrade all health agencies or programs.

Ideology and Rationale

One of the difficulties those in the health field face is the lack of widespread acceptance of the rationale behind their efforts. What can the health functionaries present as their chief reason for existence? In the case of private practitioners, those presiding over large clinics and hospitals, or even with pharmacists, the problem is not very acute. Direct services are rendered upon the demand of individuals or groups. But public health work usually involves some intervention in the lives of people, often against their will. To date, those in public health have not succeeded in developing for themselves or conveying to the general public an ideology of intervention which jibes with the more widely accepted beliefs about individual rights and the general distrust of government involvement in daily affairs. Not unexpectedly, the need for public health services is outstripping the development of a rationale justifying the existence of its interventionist policies. The fact that many needed public health measures do not seem justifiable to a number of citizens—because of the loss of parental autonomy their adoption would entail—has prevented steady progress toward stated public health goals.

Paraphernalia

Every occupation uses tools which come to be identified symbolically as well as practically with that trade. The paraphernalia of health, from the relatively simple equipment for diagnosis to the much more complex laboratory equipment for running difficult tests, is expensive. Hospitals are expensive to build, furnish, and operate; public health programs involving large populations are also costly. The paraphernalia of the health system, designed to render specific services, is not as extensive as that of the economy, which concentrates upon many kinds of services, and yet some visitors from abroad stress the dependence of American physicians upon their paraphernalia. It is true that the health system, like other major systems in our society, is intricately linked with the technological side of our culture, many times producing almost miraculous results because of the aid of some specialized instrument.

The identification of the medical man with his paraphernalia distinguishes him from the old country doctor who was judged according to his performance as a person as well as a physician, and not as a specialist highly trained in the manipulation of equipment. The public image of the doctor, therefore, is undergoing a change; perhaps it is becoming less sympathetic and less favorable—just at the time when one disease after another is being brought under control.

Hospitals, too, gain status with the community and the medical profession according to the amount of paraphernalia they possess. In Rochester, New York, a citizens' advisory group fought a losing battle in its effort to limit the acquisition of a very expensive "cobalt bomb" to only one hospital in the community. Other hospitals felt compelled to have this, too, even though purchase of it did not represent the most rational use of local resources available for hospital support [23].

Linkages with Other Systems

The very nature of community life dictates that no major system can exist in isolation—each is inextricably tied in with most of the other systems. Whereas the subsystem of private practice is most closely connected with the ideology and folkways of the economy, the public health subsystem is most closely allied with the ideology and folkways of local government. The former stresses the rights of the individual, the latter is directed toward collective needs. Although a service motif, on the surface at least, runs throughout all our major systems, it is particularly emphasized by many in the health field.

The links between the health system and other systems in a given community must be traced if the full picture of the health field is to be obtained [47, 101]. An analysis of indigent disability, for example, indicates the close coordination required between the health and welfare systems if this problem or any similar problem is to be dealt with effectively by the community [31]. San Mateo County, California, is often cited as one place where these two systems work effectively together [23].

SOME COMMUNITY FACTORS AFFECTING THE HEALTH SYSTEM

A discussion of health and the community, necessarily limited in space, must be suggestive rather than definitive in scope. Its main contribution lies in presenting a relatively simple scheme for the analysis of social phenomena which relate to health and its community context. In applying such a scheme, however, there are at least two factors of community life which need to be taken into account. The first of these has to do with community power, leadership, and decision making; the second with citizen participation in community health programs.

Community Power, Leadership, and Decision Making

The American's yen for gimmicks has implications for the complex field of social relationships. One of comparatively recent vintage is the "power clique" gimmick, which has been given much attention in education, social welfare, public health, and many other fields where the community is the base of operations [3, 19, 39, 102]. In its naïvest, simplest terms this blandly states that (1) every community has an identifiable power clique and (2) that if you get the members of this clique on your side, all of your problems will be solved. There is, of course, a considerable element of truth in these two points, but they give no idea of the usual complexity of the power structure in the community.

The first difficulty frequently lies in an unrealistic view of power in the community. One can agree on a general definition of "power" as referring "to the ability or authority of individuals or organizations to control, effectively guide, or influence other individuals or groups" [45], but such definitions give scant clues to the actual structuring of power. There goes on in the community, as Long has pointed out, an ecology of "games"—banking, newspaper publishing, and so on—and he claims that these games give structure, goals, roles, strategies, tactics, and publics to the players. Players in each game make use of the players in the other games for their own particular purposes, and the totality of their interaction produces unintended but systematically functional results for the community. Long sees an overall leadership and social frame as providing a vague set of community-shared values that promote cooperation in the system, though not providing a government [72].

This picture of community interaction shows that there is a distribution of power throughout the whole system, with each game possessing power, in that players in other games must depend upon it to accomplish their own goals. This introduces the idea of functional necessity as an element in power; you have power if you are needed—a fact which labor unions discovered long ago. Though we often think of power as absolute or relative, it is perhaps more correct, at the community level, to think of it as *relevant* or *irrelevant*. Some players who are powerful in their own game or subsystem have no power in other games, for what they have to offer has no relevance to that other game. This is an important distinction for health workers wishing to enlist the support of "power figures" in behalf of a program. Some of these figures are relevant, and should be approached; others are irrelevant, and will turn down requests for assistance on several grounds, but the fundamental reason is their irrelevance.

The power clique gimmick fallaciously assumes that if one is powerful, he can do whatever he would personally like to do to help a cause. In fact, power is often circumscribed. The health official who dabbles in politics, the clergyman who tries to tell businessmen how to conduct their affairs, the school superintendent who poses as an authority on welfare problems—all are examples of functionaries who are moving beyond their circumscribed sphere. These functionaries, and others identified with only one system, will have no influence beyond their own sphere, unless they have in the past developed a wider base of power.

In one respect, however, the gimmick is realistic: there is an unequal distribution of power in the community, though it is probably not as concentrated as is implied. After all, the ordinary citizen with no pretense to power does have more than is often realized: He can vote on many issues, he can buy or not buy a product, he can watch or not watch a television program, and he can participate or not participate in a host of community activities. His choices may be somewhat predetermined by those with more power than he, but he is not altogether powerless.

To understand the distribution of power in American communities, it is necessary to draw up a typology of leadership, recognizing that each leadership type has certain power attributes that are identified with its structural position. Such a typology may have some "power slippage"; that is, it may not account for all conceivable types of control, effective guidance, or influence over other individuals or groups

PARADIGM I. A TYPOLOGY OF COMMUNITY LEADERSHIP

Type of leader	*System frame of reference*	*Range*	*Duration*
Key leaders	Two or more major systems	Diffuse	Indeterminate
Dominants	One major system	Specific	Indeterminate
Functionaries (primarily professionals)	One major system	Specific	Indeterminate
Organizational	One formal association	Specific-diffuse	Determinate
Issue leaders	One community realignment	Specific	Determinate
Spokesmen	A grouping or locality	Diffuse	Indeterminate

as set forth in the earlier definition of power. But such a typology is operational in that it traces the usual flow of influence and can be used practically in planning for and conducting various kinds of action programs. The paradigm presented here relates the type of leader to the total community system in terms of the number of systems or analytical levels at which he is concerned; it indicates the range of his power as well as its duration. Some leaders have a broader range of power than others, and some have fixed terms of office, while others occupy indeterminate positions which are not so limited.

Such a paradigm becomes more useful if it is related to some illustrative studies of comunity power and examined in terms of the health system. Each study cited will provide information about some but not all of the types. Long views the key leaders —or "top leadership," as he calls them —as largely confined to ritual and ceremonial roles and usually identified with status positions rather than with specifiable roles in social action. "The role of a top leader is ill-defined and to a large degree unstructured. It is in most cases a secondary role derived from a primary role as corporation executive, wealthy man, powerful ecclesiastic, holder of high social position, and the like" [72]. In terms of the paradigm and according to Long, key leadership is largely a derivative of dominant leadership. By typing such leadership in with what he calls the "social game," he gives it cross-system character, for "the custodians of the symbols of top social standing provide goals that in a sense give all the individual games some common denominator of achievement. While the holders of top social prestige do not necessarily hold either top political or economic power, they do provide meaningful goals for the rest" [72]. Of course, Long does not in this statement exclude the dominants from movement into key leadership, but he allows for other community variables, such as family background, to play their part. The conclusion to be drawn from such a statement is that key leadership is supported by a strange mixture of prestige, as well as certain kinds of major system power (economic, religious, political). This proves disturbing again to those looking for neat operational definitions, but it is the way communities seem to allocate this type of power.

Miller views the community power structure as "composed of key influentials, top influentials, the community power complex, and those parts of the institutionalized power structure of the community that have come into play when activated by a community issue." In his comparison of a Pacific Northwest city and an English city, he deals only with the key influentials, who are the sociometric leaders among the top influentials, or with those drawn from various systems of power relations according to the issue at stake [79]. If one thinks of the power grid as represented by the typology in Paradigm I, it can be observed that the key influentials compare with the key leaders and, as sociometric leaders, tend to have some permanence in that position, whereas the top influentials, or dominants in the typology, move into leadership as their relevance to issues increases. Contrary to Hunter's finding for a southern city (that "crowds" of influentials exist, with top leaders of each crowd clearing with leaders of other crowds), Miller does not find that key influentials repeatedly act in concert, although such leaders do seek the cooperation of other influentials when they are responsible for carrying out civic projects. On the other hand, relatively stable groups of leaders (the dominants) are identified with certain institutional sectors of the community through which they express common interests—i.e., business, labor, political party, education, and religion. (In the terminology used here these sectors are "community systems"; in Long's terminology, they are "games" [79].)

It is common for the key leaders and dominants to work through other types of leaders. The key leaders in finance or commerce may ask a functionary (the Secretary of the Chamber of Commerce) to make contact with political dominants about some matter of concern, or they may work through organizational leaders in the hope of extending their support through the associational network of the formal groups in the community. On certain questions, those issue leaders who have previously come out publicly on one side of the issue may be consulted and asked for help; also, contact of key leaders with the spokesmen (who know what is going on within a particular ethnic grouping, occupational segment, or local area) is usually considered essential at some point. But Freeman and Mayo [36] have shown that in a small North Carolina open-country community this use of intermediate leaders does not occur because (1) there are not enough intermediate leaders around and (2) the local emphasis upon neighborliness and equalitarianism promotes direct contact between what they call "upper lay leaders" and people at other levels of the leadership structure.

Agger, unlike Freeman and Mayo, stresses the importance of all levels of the power grid in his report of a study of a small Oregon town.

> In this small community, it was expected that the informal face-to-face relationships of the top leadership and "constituents" would constitute a primary, if not the most important, channel for the exercise of influence. The data hint at the importance of formal organizations as influence channels in the community, as well as the possible importance of the roles played by people who resemble the top leadership and who are sought out for advice in the generation or maintenance of legitimacy relationships between the masses and the top leadership. The secondary leaders who are the most active politically probably have the most influence on others. The passive advisers are less likely to reinforce the influence relationships between their advisees and the top leadership because of their own unawareness of or antipathy to that leadership [1].

White, in studying the formal and informal roles of organized leadership in a rural New York community, found among other things that "the more independent from control by higher authorities these organizations are, the more likely they are to be staffed by informally influential formal leaders" [130]. Williams noted that in a small farming community informal leaders served to integrate the system [132].

The assumption is sometimes made, particularly by those looking for a quick way of dealing with power, that there is invariably a power hierarchy. The more we learn about the comparative study of communities, the more we find that their power structures vary widely from the rigidly hierarchical to the nearly amorphous, fleeting coalitions of people with some measure of power. This is illustrated in another study by Agger and Goldrich [2], who reported that in the two far western communities studied, one —Boomtown—had a polynucleated set of leadership groups at the top of the power structure, whereas the other—Valley City—had a hierarchical power structure, whose top leaders (or key leaders) frequently conferred with each other. Form and D'Antonio [35] investigated the degree of integration among the influentials in Juarez, Mexico, and El Paso, Texas. They found that in neither community was there a single power system, but in El Paso conflicts arose between groups overlapping institutional boundaries (the major systems), whereas in Juarez conflicts arose between institutions.

Many of the points already mentioned about the power structure of a community give some insight into decision making there. Janowitz, in his introduction to a series of essays by other writers on aspects of community political systems, reaffirmed the importance of the community as the locus of power [57]. On the whole, however, as Polsby pointed out [94], most of our studies are concerned with the identification and description of the power holders of the community; relatively few have actually described the behavior of leaders involved in specific issues [26]. Perhaps Banfield's study of several major issues in Chicago comes closest to describing the dynamics of decision making [9]. What we do know, however, indicates that there will be no easy formulation which will explain this complicated process. Schulze, in his study of economic dominants in a midwestern industrial community of 20,000, found that they increasingly took a "hands-off" position with regard to local political decision making [109]; whereas Pellegrin and Coates [93], in their study of a southern industrial city, discovered a "power vacuum"—for no one group there seemingly had the power.

It does seem clear that communities differ in their styles of decision making. Merton has shown how some communities consist of local and cosmopolitan influentials, with the latter sensitive to issues and opinions outside the community [77]. Miller, in his study of 218 small hospital projects, found that the projects in the southeast developed amidst arrangements made through constituted governmental authority, while in the Northeast, private community organizational arrangements seemed related to the social-psychological components of influence [82]. One aspect of decision making is veto power, which means that a proposal can be stopped by a person with authority to say no at some point in the leadership structure. For some kinds of issues, the spokesman who can prove that the idea will not work with his "constituents" has veto power; for other issues involving the raising of much money from private contributions, organizational leaders may be in a position to give the "stop and go" sign. Or, if the proposal calls for a significant modification of existing institutionalized arrangements, the functionaries and dominants swing into action to protect their own. This would imply that much clearance has to be obtained at various stages in the proceedings, from several types of leaders. The key leaders, whose power is diffused across system lines, also have veto power. Their decisions, however, are not based on any absolute criteria of what is "good" or "bad" for the community, but upon their assessment of how the other types of leaders (dominants, for instance) and the general public are apt to react.

One might well ask how this excursion into community power structures and types of community leaders bears upon the system of health [32, 134]. It is necessary to derive propositions since little direct research on the health system has been undertaken. Several propositions may be advanced:

1. Communities differ widely in their power structure, so any health worker must be careful about automatically

transferring the analysis of one community to another.

2. The health system has its own assortment of leaders who have varying degrees of power: dominants (usually nonprofessionals), functionaries (usually professionals), organizational officers, issue leaders, and spokesmen. Some of the key leaders include health within their province.
3. These health leaders are frequently in touch with their counterparts in other major systems and often work out technical or strategy details at this level, thus avoiding the necessity of involving key leaders in many routine or technical matters.
4. Power does not necessarily flow through the formal bureaucratic structure of any subsystem (health department, hospital complex, and so on) but may move through other parts of the power grid, depending upon the participants' definition of whose power is relevant to the decision to be made.
5. The leaders of one health subsystem may try to speak for the whole health system, but when their pronouncements are of broader compass than their power, their influence is limited. By the same token, health leaders who step outside their circumscribed spheres in an effort to wield power are apt to meet discouragement unless they have developed the attributes of key leaders, to whom is granted the right to speak on matters relating to more than one major system.
6. It can happen that certain leaders of the health system move into positions of key leadership in the community because of a number of qualities: high social status, competence outside the health system which has earned them the respect of dominants in other systems, personal prestige built up through an outstanding job as leader of several important local organizations, or such success as issue leaders that they have been catapulted into public notice and accepted as capable leaders on several matters. Therefore, the fact that one is a health leader need not rule out the possibility that he will attain a larger sphere of influence.
7. It is necessary to distinguish between economic, political, and social power and to decide which combination of these is most important for promoting the interests of the health subsystem with which one is concerned [54]. When the major concern is political, there is little point in enlisting the support of businessmen who may have no standing with those making the political decisions; when the major concern is fund raising, the help of political leaders—who may be prevented by law from using public funds for the cause—may be less important than one might at first imagine.
8. Should there be a well-recognized power clique in the community, getting the approval and tacit support of its members is not the full answer. Studies show that, at the most, they are willing to lend their names, make a few phone calls to intimates, or pass the word along to their following. This is all very helpful, but it in no way gets done the organizational job which any health program requires. Nor does it inform and educate enough people at various levels to guarantee success. Key leaders can be of great help, but their contribution is limited by the time at their disposal, the competition for their sponsorship, and the extent to which they feel they can involve their followers in many disparate activities.
9. Participation in the decision-making process connected with a health program should extend, where appropriate, to all levels of the power grid. It is important to remember that the ordinary citizen more often than not has power to withhold the support he might render to the program through making financial contributions, being a client, serving as a volunteer worker, reelecting officials responsible for aspects of the program, or shifting (or reinforcing) his opinion about the merits of those responsible for the program. Where there is public apathy, and this does exist in many communities, power does become more highly concentrated and less responsive to the general community welfare.
10. Leaders of whatever rank have at best limited information about some major

systems. They are not omniscient. Often, therefore, an educational job needs to be done with them as much as with less influential persons [28]. Those promoting a health program, therefore, should have a clear-cut set of goals, a supporting rationale, and a description of expected gains worked out before contacting leaders who are not intimately involved with the broad spectrum of health. Even health personnel of one subsystem may be woefully ignorant of what goes on in other health subsystems. Health workers usually make a mistake in strategy when they contact key leaders prior to thinking through the implications of their program (its costs, effect on other programs, long-range benefits, allocation of responsibility, and the like).

Such considerations about community power and the health system give only one part of the picture of local health action and the kinds of controversies which arise. We need now to put matters in broader perspective.

Citizen Participation in Community Health Programs

An analysis of the leadership structure and an understanding of the power wielders is useful if related to the involvement and participation of their followers. In more comfortable, leisurely, and less-harried times health action programs were designed by the professionals, promoted and implemented through the efforts of a segment of the local leadership *for* the benefit of another segment of the community in need of help. Many of these programs involved the community only in their financial aspects. There were "drives" to reach certain budgetary goals: the local hospital sought funds for construction of a new wing, a voluntary agency campaigned for funds which would help launch a prenatal clinic. Some programs were primarily educational, as they sought to persuade local citizens to do certain things in the interest of better health: take immunization shots, stop smoking, have a chest X-ray, or learn the symptoms of cancer, heart disease, or mental illness, so that medical advice could be sought in time.

These more traditional approaches have been studied by sociologists [21, 104, 136], even to the point of delineating stages through which such action programs go [10, 11, 30, 44, 50, 53, 63, 117]. Robert Wilson related community structure to the community's efforts to deal with its perceived health problems [134] while Smolensky and Haar viewed community organization as a means toward solving community health problems [116]. Studies, too, have been made of attempted innovations which become controversial and are thus lively community issues.

The Miller-Form theory of issue outcome [80] has been summarized and tested successfully in Denver, Colorado, by Hanson.

> The theory is based on the proposition that the combined social force of three factors brings about a community decision on a general issue. These factors are: (1) the critically activated parts of the institutional power structure, which are aligned for or against the issue proposition; (2) the power arrangement of the community power complex, which may be unstructured, semi-structured, or unified on either side of the issue; and (3) top influential solidarity and activity. If the top influentials are a single, exclusive, elite of autonomous power, the outcome may be forecast by an analysis of their stand on the issue. If the top influentials are not the exclusive elite type, their degree of activity on either side of the issue becomes a relevant variable [46].

Barth and Johnson have given leads for developing a typology of social issues [10]. They have sought to pick dimensions generic to all issues and to relate theoretically variations in each dimension to variations in patterns of influencing behavior. Their five dimensions are:

1. *Unique-recurrent*, with unique issues handled by emergent leadership and recurrent issues handled by constituted community agencies having access to regularly allocated resources.
2. *Salient-nonsalient to leadership*, with some issues being central to the interests of community leaders and the organizational structures in which they hold positions, and some being peripheral to their interests.
3. *Salient-nonsalient to community publics*, with issues thought to be highly salient to the public involving the potential decision makers in the "public relations" aspect of the decision, and nonsalient issues not involving them in this respect.
4. *Effective action possible—effective action impossible*, with some issues, even though highly salient, perceived as necessitating impossible decisions or requiring inaccessible resources and other issues perceived as amenable to action.
5. *Local-cosmopolitan*, with issues having regional or national implications thought to require guidance and direction from outside experts, and local issues not requiring this type of aid.

One very colorful community issue is fluoridation. In connection with a study of this issue the present author has developed a typology of issue stages which differ in part from the social action stages mentioned earlier [107]. A key to the application of this typology is the realization that these stages repeat themselves in a sequence as the issue is reopened and has to be dealt with by the community a second, third, or fourth time. Many useful leads for dealing with health issues can be gained from the growing body of literature dealing with fluoridation as a community issue [41].

But the community action programs of ten or twelve years ago lacked some of the qualities of the most vital programs of today, particularly those in central cities across the United States. There is now less emphasis upon doing things for people and more of a desire to work with the people of a local area—not with the favored elite, but with the type of ordinary citizens who have a broad range of ethnic and socioeconomic backgrounds. In many of the health programs supported by war on poverty funds through the Community Action Program, there has been an insistence upon participation by local citizens in the areas to be serviced. The focus of community action has shifted noticeably from working with and through community leaders to achieve health objectives for the community—though this is still important—to working directly with the consumers. In some cases, the local citizen groups insist upon control over the actions of the professional medical and public health personnel. This insistence on control challenges the belief that professional authority is not to be questioned; it also affirms that health programs which use community resources and are supposed to serve the community are part of the political process in which use and control of power is to be recognized. It recognizes, too, that many pressures to change and control local practices and programs come from outside the community.

Another characteristic of the present health action programs is their tendency to move out to the areas of the city most in need of help rather than expecting the public of these areas to come into the long-established centers outside their neighborhoods and residential areas. Of course, the neighborhood health center is not a new concept. This type of health center was experimented with in the 1930s and 1940s [118] but did not succeed as well as had been expected. But it is now being revived as a type of community action program. A report on community health services in Boston notes:

> The biggest experiment in the history of American medicine is attracting thousands of city dwellers to neighborhood health centers for the care that used to be provided by the family doctor.
>
> Boston, with 24 neighborhood centers in operation and another half-dozen on the drawing boards, is at the forefront of this new trend in the delivery of medical care.
>
> The community clinic is emerging to fill the vacuum left by the disappearance of the general practitioner—only a handful of whom are left in Boston, and half of those are over 65. The neighborhood center experiment has been given impetus by the painful realization that hospital outpatient departments and emergency wards cannot cope with the overwhelming demand for medical care.
>
> The neighborhood clinic is designed to do things that the emergency room was never intended to do:
>
> —Treat whole people and whole families rather than isolated ailments on a one-shot basis.
>
> —Provide continuous care in an effort to prevent illness and reduce costly hospitalization.
>
> —Build lasting relationships between a medical team and its patients in an effort to eliminate the impersonality of the big city hospital.
>
> —Bring medical care to the neighborhoods where people live and encourage them to think of health care as a routine, not a service to be used only in time of crisis. The hope is that the centers will not only provide better care, but do it far more economically. Hospitals are designed to care for seriously sick patients; using them to treat sore throats and cut fingers is one more drain on expensive hospital resources that should be devoted to acute care.[3]

But despite these ambitious innovative efforts, those surveying the Boston scene conclude that only a fraction of the population is being served, that coherent planning is almost totally lacking, and that the financial problems are unsolved. The administrators of the less well-endowed centers are actively competing with each other for quite meager public support and funds. Those programs that are fairly well funded are quite highly dependent upon foundations or government agencies, distant from the community, whose policies may change from year to year. Some of the neighborhood centers welcome the participation of people in the immediate local area, even postponing the opening of the center until a director agreeable to both the medical authorities and the local residents can be found. Other centers insist that complete control will be kept in the hands of the professional personnel. Thus, in one community various experimental efforts are under way. Hopefully, lessons can be drawn from these multifaceted approaches leading to a well-devised, coordinated, and adequately funded system that can serve the needs of the entire community. Experiments of this type should teach us much about the relationship between the health system and the rest of the community.

Robert N. Wilson [134] has concluded a study of health action in twenty-one cities. Many of his observations reinforce points already made:

> What do our 21 cities identify as their chief health concerns? The most promi-

[3] *Boston Sunday Globe*, October 11, 1970, p. 2-A. Reprinted by permission of the publisher.

nent issue appears to involve not a specific disease entity, but rather the coordination of facilities to provide care for a variety of illnesses. Nearly all the communities exhibit capacity, or potential capacity, to provide a level of population-wide medical care higher than that now prevailing. Yet the application of service to those populations most in need of it often seems haphazard and irrational against a pattern of overlapping functions and less than optimal use of extant capacities, and the proliferation of agencies for preventive and therapeutic efforts. Study after study reveals the necessity of tying the network of local services together more logically and planning in concert to meet the health imperatives of the next several decades.

Related to the need for coordination is the developing cluster of problems associated with a growing, urbanizing population. These include especially the provision of care to the medically indigent, chronically ill, and aged, including the mentally ill, and the environmental health problems exemplified by sewage and water pollution in rapidly expanding communities.

At least two general impressions emerge from the analysis of perceived local problems thus far:

1. We are confirmed in our belief that health problems do not ordinarily command the intense concern of a cross-section of community leaders. They are on the whole less tangible, less dramatic, and perhaps appear less central to economic interests than do the gross features of the urban-industrial setting. Hence, it seems likely that health action can only occur if a technique is found to raise health concerns to a level of salience that they do not commonly possess. Increase in saliency has clearly been one of the major goals of the community self-studies, and has been partially realized by several of the cities we surveyed.

2. Our investigation of several facets of community life (perception of problems, perception of conflicts between leaders and interest groups, predictions of local action) tends to indicate that U.S. leaders are in general optimistic, conciliatory, and quite well satisfied with the current complexion of community affairs. . . . To generate health action may require that complacency be jarred and extant local resources utilized, rather than that rooted opposition be overcome.

. . . the chief hazard to effective local action would appear to be inertia: the task for the health planner—or any other community organizer—appears to be one of mobilizing community resources and finding mechanisms to couple existing favorable motivations to concrete steps to an action pattern.

Self-study, as a social technique for meeting community health needs, rests on the premise that local action will be more effective if substantial numbers of persons —especially leaders in other community affairs—can be involved in assessing health conditions and setting strategies for attack upon critical problems. There is good reason to believe that widespread voluntary efforts are essential to improved levels of public health. This belief is based on the fact that the prominent public health problems of today—chronic diseases and social organization of medical care—do not lend themselves to easy solution by administrative fiat or by police power traditionally used to combat the clear and present danger of infectious epidemics. Further, evidence from social psychological research indicates quite persuasively that people are more likely to sympathize with actions they have had some part in devising than with actions imposed arbitrarily from without.

U.S. communities appear to be moving, much too rapidly for some and much too slowly for others, towards a form of social organization distinguished by planning, a mixed pattern of public and voluntary institutions, and concern for protecting and cultivating human resources. Perhaps these have always been characteristic of our society, but are becoming more emphatically present in the contemporary situation of urban size and complexity.

Acceptance of planning as a continuing function within the community is increasing with the realization that many of our problems do not lend themselves to dramatic crisis-geared solution. . . . Today the community may be said to embrace the ideology of localism paired with the behavior of federalism.

Closely tied to our emphasis on the virtues of action is a faith, sometimes naïve, that men can through energetic effort master any obstacle they encounter. Again we may note that the belief in human dominion over both the physical and the social universe has been on the whole efficacious in our society. [But] . . . there may be some areas of community health concern that can only resolve themselves in a natural sequence of development, an imminent or intrinsic process of change that cannot be hastened and may be thwarted by a too-energetic application of rational will.

Another assumption, not seriously questioned in the Commission's total effort or in our community research, is that identification of health problems and ability to act upon them are centered in the most influential local leaders. This is a perfectly natural orientation, since people at the top of the prestige and power hierarchy may be considered to have the most general view of local affairs and the most advantageous position for encouraging action. It nevertheless contradicts two postulates of community mobilization currently employed by, for example, the war on poverty. The first of these is that problems can be best identified by persons most intimately affected. . . . Yet we have not asked the poor in our study localities about their health needs. . . . A second postulate . . . is that change in behavior can be induced best if the targets of that change themselves decide upon a course of action. If a specific change in health practices is necessary to meet a community problem, will the poor who have had no role in decision-making during a self-study be strongly motivated to accomplish this change? [134]

This brief discussion of action programs and social issues has indicated the need for a systematic approach, whether in terms of the analysis of social power or type of issue or of the ability to view the program as an overall sequence of interaction from its initiation to its resolution and aftermath. This stresses the primary importance of an overall theoretical framework into which the details of technique and tactics can appropriately be fitted.

Health systems not only operate within a system of power, but they also exist in a community constantly experiencing change. For one thing, the physical community is always changing. The built-up area expands, older residential areas deteriorate, population shifts, new transportation routes are opened up, and the economic base expands or contracts, as the physical city undergoes this change. Health personnel are constantly caught up in problems attendant upon these changes but are much less frequently called upon for advice with respect to measures for planned change.

The population of a community changes as well: not only in numbers, but in composition, in skills, in quality. New ethnic groupings make their appearance, while older ethnic groupings "disappear" through absorption into the general population. Local attitudes and values toward health shift, as cultural traditions associated with ethnic groupings change.

But even more important to those responsible for a community's health is what happens to the domain [68] of the health system *vis-à-vis* the other major systems in the community. Here one must be aware of the extracommunity pressures which invade to exert changes of many kinds. Federal funds for health or schooling alter respective systemic domains; religious action on birth control, parochial schools, or perhaps fluoridation abets or hinders various health programs; economic trends, both in the organization of the economic system and in the contribution by corporations and labor unions to health and welfare, figure prominently in today's civic life. The whole health system has to be set into the social action field—the arena of interaction that is the community. Again, Long's analogy of the ecology of games is pertinent here. Every move that is made has some impact upon subsequent moves, and there is seldom any reversal of the process. Thus, change is built into community life, although much of it is greatly accelerated by the impact of outside forces.

Finally there are changes going on within the health system itself. The subsystems, which have been described earlier, are in interaction with each other. As new statuses are created, old ones must give way or adjust; as new demands are made, the responses of some subsystems are quicker and more effective than others; as some subsystems become more institutionalized, the importance of the functionary rises and that of the layman declines—perhaps along with that of the general medical man whose training fails to prepare him for the complex of roles required of those administering and providing the specialties now called for in our health system. Geiger has indicated the degree to which the physician is faced with new medical problems and new concepts of health and illness, and he speaks of binding medicine to the rest of the changing social fabrics [42]. Any health professional who fails to accept social change as a normal part of the dynamic society in which we live cannot relate himself or his work to the changing community. Furthermore, unless he tries to develop some theory of social change as it affects health [41], he misses much of the rich panorama of community life. If health personnel would spend a fraction of the time they devote to the detailed, laboratory-oriented, time-consuming, but necessary, medical and scientific techniques of their profession to studying their community, they and their communities would be much the richer.

REFERENCES

1. Agger, Robert E., "Power Attributions in the Local Community: Theoretical and Research Considerations," *Social Forces*, 34 (May, 1956), 331.
2. ——— and Daniel Goldrich, "Community Power Structures and Partisanship," *American Sociological Review*, 23 (August, 1958), 383–92.
3. ——— and Bert Swanson, *The Rulers and the Ruled: Political Power and Impotence in American Communities.* New York: John Wiley & Sons, Inc., 1964.
4. Akers, Ronald L. and Richard Quinney, "Differentiation Organization of Health Professions: A Comparative Analysis," *American Sociological Review*, 33 (February, 1968), 104–22.
5. Andersen, Ronald and Odin W. Anderson, *A Decade of Health Services: Social Survey Trends in Use and Expenditures.* Chicago: University of Chicago Press, 1968.
6. Antonovsky, Aaron, "Social Class and Illness: A Reconsideration," *Sociological Inquiry*, 37 (Spring, 1967), 331–22.
7. Arensberg, Conrad, "The Community as Object and as Sample," *American Sociological Review*, 63 (April, 1961), 241–64.
8. Back, Kurt W., Robert E. Coker, Jr., Thomas G. Donnelly, and Bernard S. Phillips, "Public Health as a Career of Medicine: Secondary Choice within a Profession," *American Sociological Review*, 23 (October, 1958), 533–41.
9. Banfield, Edward E., *Political Influence.* New York: The Free Press, 1961.
10. Barth, Ernest A. T. and Stuart D. Johnson, "Community Power and a Typology of Social Issues," *Social Forces*, 38 (October, 1959), 29–32.
11. Beal, George M. with Ross C.

BLOUNT, RONALD C. POWERS, AND W. JOHN JOHNSON, *Social Action and Interaction in Program Planning.* Ames, Iowa: Iowa State University Press, 1966.
12. BELKNAP, IVAN AND JOHN G. STEINLE, *The Community and Its Hospitals: A Comparative Analysis.* Syracuse, N.Y.: Syracuse University Press, 1963.
13. BERRY, MILDRED C., "A Theoretical Framework for Community Organization," *Health Education Monographs*, 3 (1959), 8–17.
14. BLACKWELL, BARBARA LOUISE, "Upper Middle Class Expectations about Entering the Sick Role for Physical and Psychiatric Dysfunctions," *Journal of Health and Social Behavior*, 8 (June, 1967), 83–95.
15. BLANKENSHIP, L. VAUGHN AND RAY H. ELLING, "Organizational Support and Community Power Structure: The Hospital," *Journal of Health and Human Behavior*, 3 (Winter, 1962), 257–69.
16. BRUHN, JOHN G., "An Epidemiological Study of Myocardial Infarctions in an Italian-American Community," *Journal of Chronic Diseases*, 18 (April, 1965), 353–65.
17. ——— et al., "Social Aspects of Coronary Heart Disease in a Pennsylvania German Community," *Social Science and Medicine*, 2 (June, 1968), 201–13.
18. CHAPIN, F. STUART, CLARENCE A. JOHANSON, AND ARTHUR L. JOHNSON, "Rental Rates and Crowding in Dwelling Units in Manhattan," *American Sociological Review*, 15 (February, 1950), 97.
19. CLARK, TERRY N., *Community Structure and Decision-Making: Comparative Analyses.* San Francisco, Calif.: Chandler Publishing Company, 1968.
20. COHN, WERNER, "Social Status and the Ambivalence Hypothesis: Some Critical Notes and A Suggestion," *American Sociological Review*, 25 (August, 1960), 508–13.
21. COLEMAN, JAMES S., *Community Conflicts.* New York: The Free Press, 1957.
22. COLLVER, ANDREW, RALPH TEN HAVE, AND MARY C. SPEARE, "Factors Influencing Use of Maternal Health Services," *Social Science and Medicine*, 1 (September, 1967), 293–308.
23. CONANT, RALPH W., *The Politics of Community Health*, Report of the Community Action Studies Project, National Commission on Community Health Services. Washington, D.C.: Public Affairs Press, 1967.
24. CONFREY, EUGENE A., *Administration of Community Health Services.* Chicago: The International City Managers' Association, 1961.
25. CROOG, SYDNEY H., "Ethnic Origins, Educational Level, and Responses to a Health Questionnaire," *Human Organization*, 20 (Summer, 1961), 65–69.
26. CURTIS, JAMES E. AND JOHN W. PETRAS, "Community Power, Power Studies and the Sociology of Knowledge," *Human Organization*, 29 (Fall, 1970), 204–18.
27. DEAN, JOHN P., "The Myths of Housing Reform," *American Sociological Review*, 14 (April, 1949), 281–88.
28. DOHRENWEND, BRUCE P., VIOLA W. BERNARD, AND LAWRENCE C. KOLB, "The Orientation of Leaders in an Urban Area Towards Problems of Mental Illness," *American Journal of Psychiatry*, 118 (February, 1962), 683–91.
29. DUNHAM, H. WARREN, *Community and Schizophrenia: An Epidemiological Analysis.* Detroit, Mich.: Wayne State University Press, 1965.
30. ELDRIDGE, S., *The Dynamics of Social Action.* Washington, D.C.: Public Affairs Press, 1952.
31. ELLER, C. HOWE, GORDON M. HATCHER, AND BRADLEY BUELL, "Health and Welfare Issues in Community Planning for the Problem of Indigent Disability," Part II, *American Journal of Public Health*, 48 (1958), 49.
32. ELLING, RAY H. AND OLLIE J. LEE, "Formal Connections of Community Leadership to the Health System," *Milbank Memorial Fund Quarterly*, 44 (July, 1966), 294–307.
33. FALK, LESLIE A., "Group Health Plans in Coal Mining Communities," *Journal of Health and Human Behavior*, 4 (Spring, 1963), 4–14.
34. FIELD, MARK G., "The Doctor-Patient

Relationship in the Perspectives of 'Fee-for-Service' and 'Third-Party Medicine,'" *Journal of Health and Human Behavior*, 2 (Winter, 1961), 252–62.

35. FORM, WILLIAM H. AND WILLIAM V. D'ANTONIO, "Integration and Cleavage and Community Influentials in Two Border Cities," *American Sociological Review*, 24 (December, 1959), 804–14.

36. FREEMAN, CHARLES AND SELZ C. MAYO, "Decision-Makers in Rural Community Action," *Social Forces*, 35 (May, 1957), 319–22.

37. FREEMAN, HOWARD E. AND OZZIE G. SIMMONS, "Social Class and Posthospital Performance Levels," *American Sociological Review*, 24 (June, 1959), 345–51.

38. FREEMAN, HUGH AND GEORGE MOUNTNEY, "Towards a Community Mental Health Service, 1954–65," in Hugh Freeman and James Farndole, eds., *New Aspects of the Mental Health Services.* London: Pergamon Press, 1967.

39. FREEMAN, LINTON C., *Patterns of Local Community Leadership.* Indianapolis: The Bobbs-Merrill Company, Inc., 1967.

40. GAMPEL, B. et al., "Urbanization and Hypertension among Zulu Adults," *Journal of Chronic Diseases*, 15 (January, 1962), 67–70.

41. GAMSON, WILLIAM A. AND CAROLYN G. LINDBERG, "An Annotated Bibliography of Social Science Aspects of Fluoridation," *Health Education Journal*, 19 (November, 1961), 209–30.

42. GEIGER, H. JACK, "Social Responsibility of the Physician," *The Scientific American*, 85 (August, 1957), 89–94.

43. GINZBERG, ELI, JAMES K. ANDERSON, SOL W. GINSBURG, AND JOHN L. HERMA, *The Ineffective Soldier: Patterns of Performance.* New York: Columbia University Press, 1959.

44. GREEN, JAMES W. AND SELZ C. MAYO, "A Framework for Research in the Actions of Community Groups," *Social Forces*, 31 (May, 1953), 320–27.

45. HAER, JOHN L., "Social Stratification in Relation to Attitude toward Sources of Power in a Community," *Social Forces*, 35 (December, 1956), 137.

46. HANSON, ROBERT C., "Predicting a Community Decision: A Test of the Miller-Form Theory," *American Sociological Review*, 24 (October, 1959), 662–63.

47. ———, "The Systemic Linkage Hypothesis: Role Consensus Patterns in Hospital-Community Relations," *American Sociological Review*, 27 (June, 1962), 304–13.

48. HARDEN, WARREN R., "Social and Economic Effects of Community Size," *Rural Sociology*, 25 (June, 1960), 207.

49. HASSINGER, EDWARD W. AND ROBERT L. MCNAMARA, *Relationships of the Public to Physicians in a Rural Setting*, University of Missouri Agricultural Experiment Station Research Bulletin, 653 (January, 1958), 36.

50. HOFFER, CHARLES R., "Social Action in Community Development," *Rural Sociology*, 23 (March, 1958), 43–51.

51. ———, "Social Aspects of Health and Welfare in Rural Areas," in Alvin L. Bertrand, ed., *Rural Sociology.* New York: McGraw-Hill Book Company, 1958, p. 285.

52. ——— AND EDGAR A. SCHULER, "Measurement of Health Needs and Health Care," *American Sociological Review*, 13 (December, 1948), 719–24.

53. HOLLAND, JOHN B., KENNETH E. TIEDKE, AND PAUL A. MILLER, "A Theoretical Model for Health Action," *Rural Sociology*, 22 (June, 1957), 149–55.

54. HOLLOWAY, ROBERT G., JAY W. ARTIS, AND WALTER E. FREEMAN, "The Participation Patterns of 'Economic Influence' and Their Control of a Hospital Board of Trustees," *Journal of Health and Human Behavior*, 4 (Summer, 1963), 88–99.

55. JACO, E. GARTLY, *The Social Epidemiology of Mental Disorders.* New York: Russell Sage Foundation, 1960.

56. JACOBS, JANE, *The Death and Life of Great American Cities.* New York: Random House, Inc., 1961.

57. JANOWITZ, MORRIS, ed., *Community Political Systems, Vol. I, International Yearbook of Political Behavior Research.* New York: The Free Press, 1961.

58. JENKINS, C. DAVID, "Group Differences in Perception: A Study of Community Belief and Feelings about Tuberculosis," *American Journal of Sociology*, 71 (January, 1966), 417–30.
59. KADUSHIN, CHARLES, "Social Class and the Experience of Ill Health," *Sociological Inquiry*, 34 (Winter, 1964), 67–80.
60. KANTER, MILDRED B. et al., "Socio-Economic Level and Material Attitudes toward Parent-Child Relationships," *Human Organization*, 16 (Winter, 1958), 44–48.
61. KATZ, ALFRED H. AND JEAN SPENCER FELTON, eds., *Health and the Community: Readings in the Philosophy and Science of Public Health.* New York: The Free Press, 1965.
62. KAUFMAN, HAROLD F., "Toward an Interactional Conception of the Community," *Social Forces*, 38 (October, 1959), 8–17.
63. KAUFMAN, HAROLD F., WILLIS A. SUTTON, JR., FRANK D. ALEXANDER, AND ALLEN D. EDWARDS, *Toward A Delineation of Community Research*, Mississippi State College Bulletin (May, 1954).
64. KEYES, FENTON, "The Correlation of Social Phenomena with Community Size," *Social Forces*, 36 (May, 1958), 311–15.
65. KLABER, EUGENE H. AND HAROLD S. BUTTENHEIM, "Housing," *The Encyclopedia Americana*, 14 (1947), p. 488.
66. KNUTSON, ANDRE L., *The Individual, Society, and Health Behavior.* New York: Russell Sage Foundation, 1965.
67. KOOS, E. L., *The Health of Regionville.* New York: Columbia University Press, 1954, pp. 32 ff.
68. LARSON, OLAF F. AND DONALD G. HAY, "Hypotheses for Sociological Research in the Field of Rural Health," *Rural Sociology*, 16 (September, 1951), 225–37.
69. LEFTON, MARK et al., "Social Class, Expectations, and Performance of Mental Patients," *American Journal of Sociology*, 68 (July, 1962), 79–87.
70. LEVINE, SOL AND PAUL E. WHITE, "Exchange as a Conceptual Framework for the Study of Interorganizational Relationships," *Administrative Science Quarterly*, 5 (March, 1961), 583–601.
71. LIEBERSON, STANLEY, "Ethnic Groups and the Practice of Medicine," *American Sociological Review*, 23 (October, 1958), 542–49.
72. LONG, NORTON E., "The Local Community as an Ecology of Games," *American Journal of Sociology*, 64 (November, 1958), 251–61.
73. LOOMIS, CHARLES E., *Social Systems: Essays on Their Persistence and Change.* New York: D. Van Nostrand Company, Inc., 1960.
74. LORING, WILLIAM C., "Residential Environment: Nexus of Personal Interactions and Healthful Development," *Journal of Health and Human Behavior*, 5 (Winter, 1964), 166–69.
75. MEDALIA, NAHUM Z., "Air Pollution as a Socio-Environmental Health Problem: A Survey Report," *Journal of Health and Human Behavior*, 5 (Winter, 1964), 154–66.
76. MERCER, BLAINE E., *The American Community.* New York: Random House, Inc., 1956.
77. MERTON, ROBERT K., "Patterns of Influence: Local and Cosmopolitan Influentials," *Social Theory and Social Structures.* New York: The Free Press, 1957, pp. 387–420.
78. MILBANK MEMORIAL FUND, "Mental Hospitals Join the Community," Part 2, *Milbank Memorial Fund Quarterly*, 42 (July, 1964), entire issue.
79. MILLER, DELBERT C., "Decision-Making Cliques in Community Power Structure: A Comparative Study of an American and an English City," *American Journal of Sociology*, 64 (November, 1958), 299–310.
80. ———, "The Prediction of Issue Outcome in Community Decision-Making," *Proceedings of the Pacific Sociological Society (Research Studies of the State College of Washington)*, 25 (1957), 137–47.
81. MILLER, KENT S. AND CHARLES M. GRIGG, *Mental Health and the Lower Social Classes.* Tallahassee, Fla.: Florida State University, 1966.

82. MILLER, PAUL A., "The Process of Decision-Making within the Context of Community Organization," *Rural Sociology*, 17 (June, 1952), 153–61.
83. MYERS, JEROME K., LEE L. BEAN, AND MAX P. PEPPER, "Social Class and Psychiatric Disorders: A Ten Year Follow-up," *Journal of Health and Human Behavior*, 6 (Summer, 1965), 74–79.
84. NAGI, SAAD Z., *Factors Related to Heart Disease among Ohio Farmers*, Ohio Agricultural Experiment Station Research Bulletin, 842 (October, 1959), p. 27.
85. National Commission on Community Health Services, *Action-Planning for Community Health Services*. Washington, D.C.: Public Affairs Press, 1967.
86. ———, *Comprehensive Health Care: A Challenge to American Communities*. Washington, D.C.: Public Affairs Press, 1967.
87. ———, *Health Administration and Organization in the Decade Ahead*. Washington, D.C.: Public Affairs Press, 1967.
88. ———, *Health Care Facilities: The Community Bridge to Effective Health Services*. Washington, D.C.: Public Affairs Press, 1967.
89. NELSON, LOWRY, CHARLES E. RAMSEY, AND COOLIE VERNER, *Community Structure and Change*. New York: The Macmillan Company, 1960.
90. NEW, PETER KONG-MING AND J. THOMAS MAY, "Organization Under Stress: An Analysis of the Local Board of Health," *Journal of Health and Human Behavior*, 6 (Winter, 1965), 226–34.
91. PARSONS, TALCOTT, *Essays in Sociological Theory*, rev. ed. New York: The Free Press, 1954.
92. PAUL, BENJAMIN D., "The Role of Beliefs and Customs in Sanitation Programs," *American Journal of Public Health*, 48 (November, 1958), 1502–6.
93. PELLEGRIN, ROLAND J. AND CHARLES H. COATES, "Absentee-Owned Corporation and Community Power Structure," *American Journal of Sociology*, 61 (March, 1956), 413–19.
94. POLSBY, NELSON W., "The Sociology of Community Power: A Reassessment," *Social Forces*, 37 (March, 1959), 232–36.
95. PURDOM, P. W., "The Environmental Health Challenge: Environmental Health in the Metropolitan Setting," *Journal of Health and Human Behavior*, 5 (Winter, 1964), 136–41. Also see whole issue.
96. READ, MARGARET, *Culture, Health and Disease: Social and Cultural Influences on Health Programmes in Developing Countries*. London: Tavistock Publications, 1966.
97. REEDER, LEO G., "Social Factors in Heart Disease: A Preliminary Research Report on the Relationship of Certain Social Factors to Blood Pressure in Males," *Social Forces*, 34 (May, 1956), 367–71.
98. REISS, ALBERT J., JR., "The Sociological Study of Communities," *Rural Sociology*, 24 (June, 1959), 118–30.
99. ROBINSON, IRA E., HAROLD BRONFIN, AND JACK O. BALSWICK, "Nursing Home Resources and Rural and Urban Needs," *Journal of Health and Social Behavior*, 11 (June, 1970), 146–51.
100. ROEMER, MILTON I., "Medical Care and Social Class in Latin America," *Milbank Memorial Fund Quarterly*, 42 (July, 1964), 54–65.
101. ROEMER, RUTH, "Legal Systems Regulating Health Personnel: A Comparative Analysis," *Milbank Memorial Fund Quarterly*, 46 (October, 1968), 432–73.
102. ROSE, ARNOLD M., *The Power Structure: Political Process in American Society*. New York: Oxford University Press, Inc., 1967.
103. ROSS, JOHN A., "Social Class and Medical Care," *Journal of Health and Human Behavior*, 3 (Spring, 1962), 35–40.
104. ROSSI, PETER H., "Community Decision-Making," *Administrative Science Quarterly*, 1 (March, 1957), 415–43.
105. RUMNEY, JAY, "The Social Costs of Slums," *Journal of Social Issues*, 7 (1951), 69–85.
106. SANDERS, IRWIN T., *The Community: An Introduction to a Social System*, rev.

ed. New York: The Ronald Press Company, 1966.

107. ———, "The Stages of a Community Controversy: The Case of Fluoridation," *The Journal of Social Issues*, 17 (1961), 55–65.

108. SAUNDERS, J. V. D. AND H. BRUENING, "Hospital-Community Relations in Mississippi," *Rural Sociology*, 24 (March, 1959), 48–51.

109. SCHULZE, ROBERT O., "The Role of Economic Dominants in Community Power Structure," *American Sociological Review*, 23 (February, 1958), 3–9.

110. SCOTCH, NORMAN A., "A Preliminary Report of the Relations of Sociocultural Factors to Hypertension among the Zulu," *Annals of the New York Academy of Science*, 84 (1960), 1000–1009.

111. SCOTT, W. RICHARD AND EDMUND H. VOLKART, *Medical Care: Readings in the Sociology of Medical Institutions.* New York: John Wiley & Sons, Inc., 1966.

112. SHOSTAK, ARTHUR B., *Sociology in Action: Case Studies in Social Problems and Directed Social Change.* Homewood, Ill.: Dorsey Press, 1966.

113. SHUVAL, JUDITH T., AARAON ANTONOVSKY, AND A. MICHAEL DAVIES, "The Doctor-Patient Relationship in an Ethnically Heterogeneous Society," *Social Science and Medicine*, 1 (July, 1967), 141–54.

114. SILLS, DAVID L., *The Volunteers: Means and Ends in a National Organization.* New York: The Free Press, 1958.

115. SMITH, HARVEY L., *Society and Health in a Mountain Community: A Working Paper.* Chapel Hill: University of North Carolina Institute for Research in Social Science, 1961, p. 25. (Multilith.) See the treatment of "stressor" and "stress."

116. SMOLENSKY, JACK AND FRANKLIN B. HAAR, *Principles of Community Health.* Philadelphia: W. B. Saunders Company, 1961.

117. SOWER, CHRISTOPHER, JOHN HOLLAND, KENNETH TIEDKE, AND WALTER FREEMAN, *Community Involvement: The Webs of Formal and Informal Ties That Make for Action.* New York: The Free Press, 1957.

118. STOECKLE, JOHN D., "The Future of Health Care," in John Kosa, Aaron Antonovsky, and Irving Kenneth Zola, eds., *Poverty and Health: A Sociological Analysis.* Cambridge: Harvard University Press, 1969.

119. STRAUS, ROBERT, "Sociological Determinants of Health Beliefs and Behavior: A Generic Approach," *American Journal of Public Health*, 51 (October, 1961), 1547–51.

120. SUCHMAN, EDWARD A., "Sociomedical Variations among Ethnic Groups," *American Journal of Sociology*, 70 (November, 1964), 319–31.

121. SUMMERS, GENE F., JOHN T. SCOTT, JR., AND C. L. FOLSE, *Before Industrialization: A Rural Social System Base Study.* College of Agriculture, Agricultural Experiment Station Bulletin 736. University of Illinois at Urbana-Champaign, 1969.

122. SUTTON, WILLIS A., JR., AND JIRI KOLAJA, "The Concept of Community," *Rural Sociology*, 25 (June, 1960), 197–203.

123. TYROLER, H. A. AND JOHN CASSEL, "Health Consequences of Culture Change. II. The Effect of Urbanization on Coronary Heart Mortality in Rural Residents," *Journal of Chronic Diseases*, 17 (February, 1964), 167–77.

124. U.S. Housing and Home Finance Agency, Urban Renewal Administration, *Cleveland's Neighborhood Improvement Program*, Urban Renewal Service Bulletin 3. Washington, D.C.: U.S. Government Printing Office, June, 1961.

125. The Urban Coalition, *Rx for Action.* Report of the Health Task Force, Washington, D.C., n.d.

126. WARREN, ROLAND L., "Toward a Reformulation of Community Theory," *Human Organization*, 15 (Summer, 1956), 8–11.

127. WECHSLER, HENRY, "Community Growth, Depressive Disorders, and Suicide," *American Journal of Sociology*, 67 (July, 1961), 9–16.

128. ——— AND T. F. PUGH, "Fit of Individual and Community Characteristics and Rates of Psychiatric Hospitalization," *American Journal of Sociology*, 73 (November, 1967), 331–39.

129. WELLIN, EDWARD, "Implications of Local Culture for Public Health," *Human Organization*, 16 (Winter, 1958), 16–18.

130. WHITE, JAMES E., "Theory and Method for Research in Community Leadership," *American Sociological Review*, 15 (February, 1950), 50–60.

131. WILKINSON, KENNETH P., "The Community as a Social Field," *Social Forces*, 48 (March, 1970), 311–22.

132. WILLIAMS, VIRGIL, "Leadership Types, Role Differentiation and Systems Problems," *Social Forces*, 43 (March, 1965), 380–89.

133. WILNER, DANIEL M. et al., *The Housing Environment and Family Life*. Baltimore: The Johns Hopkins Press, 1962.

134. WILSON, ROBERT N., Community *Structure and Health Action: A Report on the Process Analysis*. Washington, D.C.: Public Affairs Press, 1968.

135. ———, "The Physician's Changing Hospital Role," *Human Organization*, 18 (Winter, 1959–60), 177–83.

136. YOUNG, JAMES N. AND SELZ C. MAYO, "Manifest and Latent Participators in a Rural Community Action Program," *Social Forces*, 38 (December, 1959), 140–45.

18

THE POLITICS OF HEALTH

Bert E. Swanson

Politics, in its broadest sense, is that activity wherein some people attempt to maintain or shift the pattern of action of government and its public officials. The politics of health then is the effort to have the commonwealth and public officials assume certain specific responsibilities for the health care of the people. In America this has come to mean almost all aspects of planning for community health services, directly or indirectly and comprehensively or in fragmented approaches. The process of sorting out which aspects of health concern should be public, which should be purely private, and which should be a mixture of public and private is one of the classic unresolved problems of our day.

Yet decisions and policies are made which imply that some answers have been found. From a national perspective, health care expenditures have increased from some 4 billion to 50 billion dollars during the period from 1940 to 1968. While most of these expenditures are primarily private, Table 18–1 illustrates the overwhelming reliance on public funds for health research. And legislation passed during

TABLE 18-1 Percentage Distribution of National Health Expenditures by Source of Funds and Type of Expenditures—1966

Source of Funds	*Total*	*Health Services*	*Research*	*Construction*
1966, total	100.0	100.0	100.0	100.0
Private	71.6	74.4	10.5	63.3
Consumers	66.2	71.9	—	—
Philanthropic	3.2	1.6	10.5	31.7
Other	2.1	0.8	—	31.7
Public	28.4	25.6	89.5	36.7
Federal	16.0	13.2	85.6	18.5
State and local	12.4	12.4	3.9	18.2

Source: Dorothy P. Rice and Barbara S. Dooper, " National Health Expenditures, 1950–66," U.S. Department of Health, Education, and Welfare, *Social Security Bulletin,* April, 1968, p. 6.

the 1960s has brought the federal government into the health arena in financing services; this is in addition to its previous commitment to construct health facilities.

At the local level, where most of the health care actually takes place, there is a growing recognition of the need to clarify the public-private coordinated base of community health facilities, services, and programs. For example, in hospital facilities and including their professional manpower, there is an expressed need to reorder and redistribute better care for a wider spectrum of health demands. In addition, providing health care for the medically indigent, the chronically ill, the aged, and the mentally ill and tackling the environmental problems of sewage and air and water pollution involve large expenditures of money and energy, by diverse and competing organizations and agencies, as well as several governmental jurisdictions. The political consequences are easy to see, as Robert Wilson describes the situation:

Compounding the difficulty of gaining all of these is the fact that health and non-health issues merge in the urban pattern; adequate sewerage for instance, may rest upon annexing suburban areas to the central city, calling forth a range of economic and political interests. Overcoming water and air pollution may imply the regulation of powerful local enterprises, business central to sustaining the flourishing economy of the community. Delivering improved care to the indigent population may stir up a series of non-health controversies, from tax rates and tax inequalities to the local situation in race relations [15].

THE SCOPE OF GOVERNMENT

It is important, therefore, to understand the role of government and how people decide to shift or maintain the scope—the ways of functioning—of government. Government not only produces and distributes or redistributes goods and services but regulates the production, distribution, and consumption patterns of other institutions [10]. In addition, it alone has the the right to use legitimate and physical force to deprive of their life, liberty, or property those within its jurisdiction who violate the government's rules and regulations. The health care area is no exception to governmental activity, as it is not only distributive but regulative also. Ralph Conant suggests, for example, that "community health planning on a scale calculated to meet the health needs of all population sectors may ultimately require the financial and legal security of a governmental base" [3].

Political development is the rather constant transformation in the roles and functions of government in man's attempt to control his environment. These roles and functions appear to change as the conditions of life vary in making a livelihood and sharing in the amenities of civilization. These changes can be analyzed in terms of their effect upon the economic condition, the social or human relations, and the welfare of citizens. The history of politics can, therefore, be viewed as a dynamic movement between efforts to have an active, interventionist government, a passive, laissez-faire government, or one that maintains minimal housekeeping-type functions. The New Deal, for example, generally expanded the scope of government, while the Eisenhower administration merely maintained it. The Johnson administration expanded it again, especially in the health realm. The Nixon administration maintains it but shifts some federal responsibilities to local government in the "new federalism" approaches.

Figure 18–1 illustrates the core of politics in terms of the expansion-contraction of the scope of government [1]. The two extremes of this continuum are point *A*, where there is no government activity or intervention and Line *B-B′*, which represents a situation where government activity is total. Thus, the boundaries of public space are curves *A-B* and *A-B′*; this represents the extent to which government functions in the day-to-day lives of people. The private space is the shaded portion. In the public space are the currents, forces, and pressures directed toward moving government in directions of expansion or contraction to increase or decrease its scope. The ratio of public to private space is defined as the net scope of government.

In housing, education, health, and welfare, we generally find a mix of public and private activities. Each of these areas has clearly defined public programs, for example, public housing authorities, public health departments, public school systems, and public welfare agencies. Similarly, each has some purely private programs such as private physicians and hospitals. There are those programs which are carrying out cooperative, coordinated or regulated activities as well. In America, government is far from either having total responsibility or no responsibility at all.

The action units in this model are the people, along with political activists and leaders, who make demands and counterdemands for a shift in government or who attempt to maintain the government's scope. They represent a vast array of interests, interests that are often competitive and seldom cooperative in providing an enduring consensus. However, it is through public officials' decisions and actions that the actual scope of government is determined and implemented. In recent years we have witnessed an expansionist-interventionist pressure to increase the scope of government in the health field at the national, state, regional, metropolitan, and local level. Yet the forces who prefer the *status quo* have not capitulated; electoral changes, however, can and have supported them, as have laissez-faire pressures to contract the scope of government.

It is extremely difficult to describe the particular public-private admixture

FIGURE 18-1 EXPANSION-CONTRACTION CONTINUUM OF THE LOCAL SCOPE OF GOVERNMENT

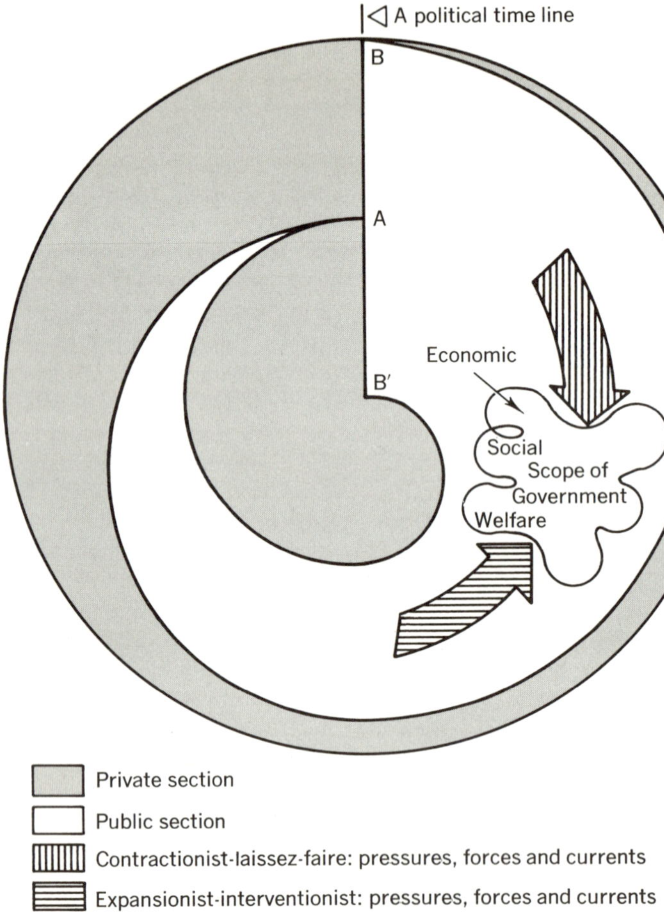

Source: Reprinted from Agger, Goldrich, and Swanson, *The Rulers and the Ruled.* New York: John Wiley & Sons, 1964. Fig. 1–1, p. 7. By permission of the publisher.

of the American health care system. The accounting system has not been well developed conceptually, nor have the tools of measurement. The relation of the public-private delivery system has not been sufficiently stable and unchanging to allow for an accurate and reliable picture of "who gets what, when, and how." Nonetheless, some rather rough approximations of sorting out who is responsible for what type health phenomena or problems are suggested in Fig. 18–2 to encourage a discussion of better conceptualization and more valid measurements and accurate measuring techniques.

In addition to who is responsible for health care—public or private—is the factor of who is affected by this health care. Those who are affected can be divided into two segments—the community and the individual client or patient. For instance, when an epidemic is caused by a polluted water supply, the health program to combat it is believed to affect and benefit most, if not all, residents of the community. In such a situation as well as with other health programs, public officials are often put in charge as a responsibility toward the whole community.

Most community health programs are viewed, however, as providing for special clients—the aged, emotionally disturbed, chronically ill, and so forth. Any list of community health agencies reveals how specialized most of them are. These organizations are designed to attend to the special needs of population groupings. The people who support such programs wish to express their concern for the problems of the particular group. For various reasons they are apt to regard one category as more important, or they are more sympathetic to one group because of personal experiences in the immediate family.

These special clienteles have become so well established that some communities have found it necessary to develop support for noncategoric health programs. Health leaders have proceeded without much regard, certainly at the explicit level, for whether the relative effectiveness of community action may depend on the nature of the health phenomena studied. In other words, the unstated assumption is that all aspects of health can be treated alike, with the possible exception that the questions asked or the measures used may differ from one health subject matter to another. Yet it is implicitly recognized that some health practitioners receive more public support than others or at least that their programs are more adequately staffed. Those in the mental health field, for example, look with envy at the past accomplishments of the public health officer. The Joint Commission on Mental Illness and Health was torn between the desire and need to be optimistic and the reality of being pessimistic when they confronted the key questions: "Why have our efforts to provide effective treatment for the mentally ill lagged (1) behind our own professional objectives, (2) behind the public demand for mental health services, and (3) behind programs staged against other major health problems?" [8].

Thus, the four major kinds of health programs can be placed in the typology of health systems in Figure 18–2. *Environmental* programs affect the whole community, and there is general agreement that they constitute a public responsibility over which public health officials have almost complete authority. The area of environmental

FIGURE 18-2 TYPOLOGY OF HEALTH SYSTEMS

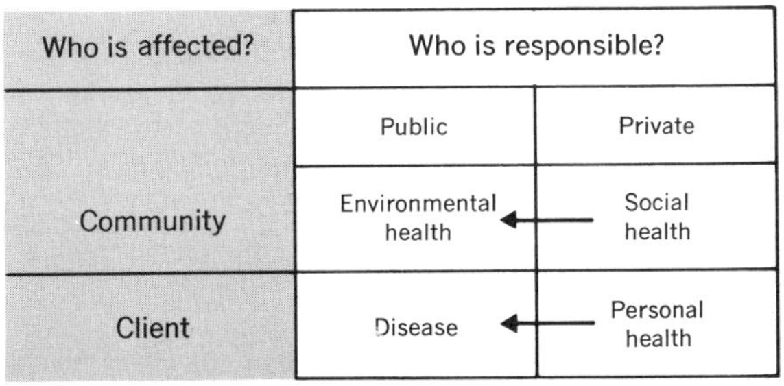

health includes problems in the community at large that constitute a threat to personal and/or social health: accidents, water pollution, floods and other natural disasters, drug and food contamination, slums and inadequate housing, radiation, and vectors and pests.

There has also been wide agreement that *personal health* problems requiring medical services essentially affect the individual client, and treatment should be private in nature. Personal health problems include blindness, speech and hearing defects, chronic and long-term illness, dental problems, physical handicaps, emotional disturbances, retardation, and poor nutrition. In recent years there have been efforts to develop a public responsibility for some of these personal health problems, particularly for those of the poor, the aged, and the young. When such a policy is proposed, it is generally couched in terms indicating that this is no longer the problem of an individual client but one that affects the whole community. Nonetheless, with few exceptions, the families affected are expected to consult their own physicians and dentists when they are in need of personal medical care.

By the same token, there is a growing recognition that *social health* problems—including alcoholism, child neglect, juvenile delinquency, narcotics—affect the whole community and not just the individual and his immediate family. Such problems however have been the traditional concern of private or voluntary health agencies. (This is not to say that there has been no public concern nor programs to regulate such problems as the use of narcotics.) But health leaders increasingly advocate the gradual—and sometimes not so gradual—transfer of these problems into the public sphere. Within the past decade and a half, for example, mental health has become a primary concern of local agencies at the community level and has been given some public support.

Yet *disease*, while it affects specific clients, is to a considerable extent a public responsibility, since it can potentially affect the whole community. Presently, however, most clients suffering from such diseases as arthritis and rheumatism, cancer, cerebral palsy, cystic fibrosis, diabetes, epilepsy, multiple sclerosis, polio, and tuberculosis depend substantially upon aid from private voluntary agencies.

It should be noted that the general tendency is to move most categories of health phenomena into the public realm (note the directional arrows in Figure 18–2). As they are moved, however, the character of public health begins to change to an interesting admixture of exercise of public responsibility through private contractual arrangements, making public-private distinctions all the more difficult to discern. Certainly, current health programs and services in most American communities are highly mixed systems involving complex operational relationships between public and private agencies.

HEALTH DECISIONS IN FOUR COMMUNITIES

Before proceeding to factor out some key concepts on the politics of health, it will be useful to gain comparative perspective on a few health decisions in their political context. Several years ago the author engaged in a comparative community study, *The Rulers and the Ruled*, which investigated a wide range of political decision-making processes in four American communities. This study not only evolved the scope of government concept but has elaborated on a number of other key concepts such as political ideologies and conflicts, as well as power structures which affect policy outputs. We will use this study in addition to other experiences and insights on urban politics to formulate a paradigm on the politics of health.

Health issues were present in all four communities during the one-year period of measurement. It is worth noting that the demands for action on these issues generally were not representative of all other demands for action in three of the four communities. Table 18–2 indicates that the implementation scores in Farmdale and Petropolis were zero on health demands, as compared to 14 and 44 percent respectively for all demands. Yet in Oretown health demands fared twice as well as all demands, and in Metroville health demands received greater acceptance than all demands.

The differences in outcomes in the patterns of political discussion is complex and involves many factors. In developing the paradigm, let me explore some of them. There were relatively few political demands in Oretown and, consequently, few political decisions. This may have been due to group conflict that channeled citizen attentions and energies away from potential decisional matters, or the city administration may have deliberately attempted to avoid political conflict on the grounds that it paralyzes the decision-making process. In Farmdale, demands to have a more active government, to strengthen the industrial base,

TABLE 18-2 IMPLEMENTATION SCORES FOR HEALTH-RELATED DEMANDS AS COMPARED TO ALL DEMANDS [1]

Farmdale (Western—population 2,500)
1. Establish garbage collection: rejected
2. Expand and improve water supply: substantially rejected
3. Establish municipal swimming pool: rejected

Implementation Score:	3 health demands	00 percent
	14 total demands	14 percent

Oretown (Western—population 15,000)
1. Establish sewage disposal plant: accepted
2. Establish a municipal hospital: rejected

Implementation Score:	2 health demands	50 percent
	8 total demands	25 percent

Petropolis (Southern—population 85,000)
1. Flan urban renewal program for Negro slum: rejected
2. Fluoridate the water supply: rejected

Implementation Score:	2 health demands	00 percent
	18 total demands	44 percent

Metroville (Southern—population 110,000)
1. Improve water system: accepted
2. Improve sewer system: accepted
3. Build additional public housing for Negroes: rejected
4. Plan urban renewal program for Negro slum: accepted
5. Build municipal swimming pool: rejected
6. Expand white mental hospital: rejected

Implementation Score:	6 health demands	50 percent
	23 total demands	39 percent

to stimulate business, to improve the amenities in civic life, and to extend the benefits of government to the rural-urban fringe were defeated by advocates of the *status quo*. In Oretown, on the other hand, the city administration engaged in consolidating, rationalizing, and preparing for new shifts in the scope of local government in order to boost the city and achieve more efficient municipal government. The mayor in Farmdale actively worked against future shifts in the scope of government.

The decisional preferences of the businessmen of Oretown were satisfied by a major shift in the scope of government which included the building of a municipal parking lot in the central business district and a modern sewage disposal plant. The rejection of the demand for a municipal hospital was turned into a victory for those preferring a quasi-public community hospital.

Oretown experienced intense community controversy and conflict, but Farmdale's political decisions were quietly made. In Oretown the merchants' association, as well as the unions, participated openly and actively, while in Farmdale there were only informal associations of merchants, and organized labor as such was not politically active.

There were striking similarities in the patterns of political decision making of small Farmdale and much larger Metroville and between Oretown and Petropolis. In Metroville, organized labor was not active, while in Petropolis it was very active. In Petropolis, as in Oretown, organizations of merchants were active and also successful participants in stimulating the business sectors of the local economy. The mayors of both cities were concerned with the vitality of the mercantile interests. In Petropolis the mayor improved the community through the planning and redevelopment functions of local government. The mayor of Metroville gave high priority to the interests of the major industries, which were often opposed to the interests of the merchants.

Petropolis and Metroville, both southern, differed sharply on the role of the Negro in local politics. Negroes were not only active but also successful in nearly half of their political preferences in Petropolis. They were effective in nonrace-related community issues; they were not effective, however, in such race-related issues as desegregation. In Metroville, on the other hand, Negroes received token desegregation of the schools but were frustrated on the outcomes of all other relevant issues. And although top leaders of Metroville sought a progressive image as a southern community, they rejected all Negro demands that municipal government help them acquire increased status relative to white citizens. This posture contributed to the decisional defeats for white citizens who were trying to improve the recreational, educational, and hospital facilities.

This picture of mixed response to demands poses a number of important questions about the relationship of communities and health decisions that should be examined further. These patterns may reflect differences in political interests. The following quotation discusses the variety of political interests which may be expected to influence health decisions.

To what extent were the following a reflection of differences in political interests: the apparent lack of participation in decision-making by organized labor in Farmdale and Metroville and the powerlessness of merchants in Farmdale and of both merchants and Negroes in Metroville, when compared to their visibility and power in Oretown and Petropolis? Or were the political interests of these groups comparable? Was the need to participate or have power weaker in Farmdale and Metroville than in Oretown and Petropolis? If the latter alternative is the case, did the political leaders of Farmdale and Metroville take the political interests of such groups of citizens into account—that is, accord them positive political status—more than in Oretown and Petropolis? To what extent was the political support organized behind the demands of merchants in Farmdale, and both merchants and Negroes in Metroville, less adequate than in Oretown and Petropolis? Were illegitimate sanctions being used against, or feared by, labor, merchants, or Negroes in Farmdale and Metroville more than in Oretown and Petropolis? If so, was this associated with a greater repression of or more poorly organized support for political demands in Farmdale and Metroville than in Oretown and Petropolis? Was there, in other words, a difference in types of regimes between Farmdale and Metroville on the one hand, and Oretown and Petropolis on the other? Was the difference in the character of decision-making conflict associated with a difference in regimes? [1]

A PARADIGM ON THE POLITICS OF HEALTH

The paradigm on the politics of health (Table 18–3) summarizes the interrelationships between and among seven factors involved in the political process.[1] The factors were gleaned not only from the decision-making processes discovered in the theoretical study of the four communities, but also from the process analysis of projects for the National Commission on Community Health Services and political prototyping experiences on mobilizing leadership for more effective community action in the New York metropolitan area. In addition, the operation of some were discerned in a participant-observation study on decentralizing decision making by instituting community control of public education in New York City.

The paradigm constitutes an analytic first approximation on how the scope of government in health is developed politically. It also provides clues and important considerations for participants involved in the politics of health, whether they be advocates of change or maintainers of the present health system. These factors appear to be operating at all levels—local, state, and national—of authoritative decision making. Each of the factors is itself subject to modification, subclassification, and refinement. And power structures can be changed from elite to mass systems and vice versa for example.

The seven factors affecting and shaping health systems are (1) system output, (2) levels of stress, (3) system inputs, (4) power structures, (5) political ideologies, (6) political focuses, and (7) system change processes. The last four factors should be considered intervening. We shall describe each factor and its variations and provide the linkage of factors as the efforts to shift the scope of government in health is developed.

System Outputs

We have classified the efforts to shift the scope of government as *increase*, *maintain*, and *decrease*. We have further subdivided the efforts to increase the scope into *incremental* and *comprehensive* [4]. Those who wish

[1] For a paradigm of political change in small communities, see Bert E. Swanson [14].

FIGURE 18-3 A Paradigm on the Politics of Health

	System Factors				*Intervening Factors*	
System Outputs	*System Stress*	*System Inputs*	*Power Structure*	*Political Ideology*	*Political Focus*	*System Processes*
Increase Scope						
Incremental	moderate	specific supports/demands	competitive mass	liberal	public policy	reform
Comprehen-sive	severe	demands/diffuse supports	consensual mass	progressive to radical left	decision-making arrangements	politicization/ creative tension
Maintain Present Scope	low	balance demands/supports	competitive elite	community con-servationist	process/ personnel	professionalization/ mediation
Decrease Scope	moderate	supports	consensual elite	conservative to radical right	financial resources	managerial

incremental change support a gradual change in policies which results from negotiating, bargaining, and mediating among the spokesmen of contending groups whose comparative influence is more-or-less stable. Incremental change is the normal pattern in the political life of America. Those who wish comprehensive change seek sweeping innovations and/or significant reversals of established policies; in addition, they advocate major shifts in the relative influence of contending groups or a dramatic redistribution of power and influence in the system. Robert Dahl points to revolution as a third magnitude of change. While many commentators point to the urban riots of the 1960s as revolutionary, this movement has not made revolutionary demands upon the health system as yet. Careful scrutiny reveals that advocates of community control of health programs and facilities are seeking comprehensive change; not only do they demand sweeping innovations in health care but a significant shift in the distribution and exercise of power and influence in reformulating new health policies. A recent example is the position of the Health Policy Advisory Center when it proposed:

> Encourage directly more action by neighborhood residents in shaping the decisions of community health institutions that affect their lives by (a) establishing broad-based, consumer-controlled community health boards in all areas of the city to develop comprehensive plans and to make basic program decisions as part of a public comprehensive health planning and HSA administrative regulation process, and (b) by creating broad-based, consumer-controlled boards with real policy and program powers for municipal hospitals and health centers, as well as requiring that all public-fund-receiving private health institutions and agencies (this means practically all of them) must be directed by broad-based community boards reflecting a membership of those persons actually served [8].

It is for this reason that we have subdivided the efforts to increase the scope of government. No comparable advocacy of comprehensive change has been articulated by those who wish to maintain or decrease the scope of government in health.

System Stress

David Easton suggests that there are two distinctive features or *essential* variables of political life—"the allocation of values for a society and the relative frequency of compliance with them" [5]. If these conditions cannot be met, there must be serious disturbances threatening the viability of the system by placing so much stress on it that it is pushed beyond a *critical range*. Such a situation can happen through defeat by an external enemy and also by widespread internal disorganization and disaffection from the system, which makes it difficult for the authorities to consistently formulate and implement policies.

For the most part, the American system seldom reaches its critical range, but the experience of urban unrest and increased dissatisfaction by select groups with the delivery of public services including health has given some analysts pause for thought. This phenomenon is, as E. E. Schattschneider points out, the contagiousness of conflict which is "the basic pattern to all politics" [12].

The degree of stress on the system can be measured by the degree of political contention, controversy, and conflict where the problems and issues may be (1) invisible, (2) potential, (3) routine, or (4) controversial. A problem that is not visible to the public may be disposed of solely by the top leadership or administrators. A potential issue is one in which there is public concern, but the dialogue through which policy is made has not yet been activated, either because the citizens have not translated their policy preferences into political demands, because the leadership has not deemed it necessary to respond to the demands, or because they fail to sense the particular problem and its need for some resolution. A routine issue involves a more-or-less habitual response, following the pattern of behavior where citizen preferences are managed administratively. A controversial issue develops when there is a lack of agreement among the major participants and they have decided to contend openly against one another in the expectation of implementing their own policy preferences, often at the expense of others.

Robert Dahl has identified a number of factors that affect the intensity of political conflict and stress on the system: (1) the convergence or divergence among the citizens and between the leaders and the citizens; (2) the pattern of social cleavages; (3) how much is at stake for the privileged and aspiring groups; and (4) the ability of political institutions to arrive at decisions and negotiate consent [4]. We have used these factors that affect the level of stress on the system, since the scope of government in health is subject to political contention and conflict.

To maintain the present scope of government generally implies a rather low level of stress upon the political system and that there is widespread agreement on the procedures and processes both for negotiating consent and arriving at decisions. A decrease in the scope of government is most likely under conditions of moderate stress when the attitudes among citizens and between the leaders and the citizens are convergently conservative to reactionary. The legislators of New York recently interpreted growing dissatisfaction in public opinion with the welfare system as allowing a cut in the state welfare recipients' budget. An incremental increase in the scope of government is more likely when system stress is moderate and when the privileged groups have a sense of security so that they can more generously entertain expanding the scope.

Securing a comprehensive increase in the scope of government is associated with severe conflict; it is also complex and seldom achieved. The most prevalent conditions include a frustrated, if not hostile, aspiring group whose attitudes are divergent from those of the political and civic leaders and which questions the credibility and legitimacy of the leadership [7]. In addition, the line of caste and class cleavages are no longer overlapping, with tensions and stress *close* to tearing the very social fabric apart. Yet the stress cannot go beyond the critical range into revolutionary activities or into movements that are committed to profound and radical alterations in the operating structure and functions of government. The quest for community control of health facilities and services could be viewed as an effort to secure a comprehensive increase in the scope of government, in that the movements advocate a significant shift in the relative influence of the disadvantaged clients of the medical profession.

System Inputs

Both inputs into the system—demands and supports—are potential sources of stress on the persistence of any system. Demands made by constituents and clients produce stress when they require excessive time for processing, either because of their quantity and/or their substantive quality—asking for more than can be granted or fulfilled. In the case of supports, the degree to which constitutents and clients tender their support or withhold it also determines the stress placed upon the system. Demands are made upon the authorities to either take action, or be removed. Demands may be determined by expectations, opinions, motivations, wants, felt needs, hopes, desires, and ideologies, but do not become demands until they are politicized through articulation by spokesmen.

Supports may be overt or covert. An accurate measurement of overt support involves knowing the number of constituents and clients who support or reject a particular set of authorities, policies output, rules of the game, or the sense of the political system itself. More specifically, support involves the regularity with which citizens perform legal obligations or, inversely, the number of breaches of the law, the number and intensity of riots, and the amount of emigration. Measurements of covert support, on the other hand, involve the intensity of feelings and attitudes of faith and/or hostility toward the system.

The puzzle for many political participants—both authorities and constituents—is knowing how many and what kinds of demands can and must be responded to; this simultaneously affects the levels of support among the citizenry for the policy, public officials, and the system. A new or expanded health program in response to an expressed need or demand may either increase or decrease political support. The effective political administrator accurately assesses the effect of any successful change in the scope of government upon the necessary ratio of supports to demands. As they decide what action to take, those in power must spend considerable energy using rational information or "pure instinct" to calculate many of the factors or corollary components of this paradigm.

The system input of those who are maintaining the *status quo* is to delicately balance the flow of demands against any possible change in supports. They sort among the array of competing demands, providing minimal policy outputs to maintain a minimal balance of support. Their period of governing is marked by "stand-patism" and apparent unresponsiveness while they allow their competitors to struggle among themselves. They will accede to minimal changes when the competitors have arrived at some consensus.

Those who seek an incremental increase in the scope of government also balance demands and supports, but they do so with a sense of quite specific sets of supports being effected by specific sets of demands. They use an operational political map where vested interests are known. They are also more responsive to a wider range of the health needs even of excluded minorities and disadvantaged populations.

The advocates of a comprehensive increase concentrate on placing many and varied demands upon the system. They often do so by making an appeal for diffused support of the common interest or general good around a charismatic political leader or authority.

Those who seek a decrease in the scope of government generally shut off or ignore demands for an increase in scope. Instead they concentrate on supports from selective segments of the citizenry, often the politically relevant who finance governmental services. They are willing to allow system stress to build up to at least moderate level.

They are willing to use coercion to hold stress within moderate limits and to be able to shut off or ignore demands from excluded, disadvantaged segments of the population.

Power Structure

A key factor in the politics of health is the distribution and exercise of power.[2] A useful typology of power structure has been developed on the basis of two dimensions: the extent to which political power is distributed broadly or narrowly throughout the citizenry and the extent to which the ideology in regard to the scope of government of the political leadership is convergent or compatible, on the one hand, or divergent and conflicting on the other [1]. By dichotomizing each variable, four types of power structures are delineated.

It is obvious that if there were but one political leadership group sharing a single ideology, the type of power structure, whether mass or elite, would be consensual. There may be two or more political leadership groups, though, in which case they may have either convergent, compatible ideologies or divergent ideologies. An example of the former would be two sets of political leaders who represent different socioeconomic interests but adhere to a compromise-bargaining-trading perspective. An example of the latter would be two sets of political leaders with such firm emotional commitments to an overall program relating to the scope of government in all areas of life that the loss of a single decisional battle or the prospects of compromise would be intolerable.

The most propitious types of power structure for increasing the scope of government are mass systems. Both Oretown and Petropolis in the comparative study (Table 18–2) were competitive mass power systems. Those who wish for incremental increase in the scope of government are a competitive mass in which power is quite broadly shared, allowing for the articulation of unmet health needs of the masses. Authorities are more inclined to respond and take seriously the expressed needs of those who participate in the political processes. In addition, the competitive nature of the power structure among contending ideological groupings provides improved opportunities both for those who have needs

[2] See Chapter 17 for additional discussion of community power structure.

FIGURE 18-4 Types of Power Structures

Political Leadership's Ideology	Distribution of Political Power Among Citizens	
	Broad	Narrow
Convergent	Consensual mass	Consensual elite
Divergent	Competitive mass	Competitive elite

Source: Reprinted from Agger, Goldrich, and Swanson, *The Rulers and the Ruled.* New York: John Wiley & Sons, 1964. Fig. 3–1, p. 73. By permission of the publisher.

to satisfy through public programs and leaders who are seeking to be responsive to these needs and also to develop issues around specific needs and demands to build support among selective audiences and clients.

The advocates of a comprehensive increase in the scope of government are most successful in a consensual mass, where power is broadly shared and leadership ideologies are relatively convergent. This kind of system generally insures acceptance of comprehensive increases in the scope of government in health care if the masses influence the leaders concerning their needs. If the leaders dominate the masses, they can popularize the need for a comprehensive shift in the scope. If the leaders refuse to make a shift in the power relationships to include disadvantaged groups, those who demand a comprehensive shift can make a mass appeal for change, threatening to place great stress on the system.

A competitive elite power structure is more likely to maintain the *status quo*. Much of the energies of the competing groups, leaders, and advocates for change are consumed in struggles to determine who shall govern. The narrow, or elite, base of power combined with competing groups with differing ideologies and policy preferences slows down the demands for increase, if not holds constant, the scope and level of the health delivery system. It takes enormous political energy to shift the scope when the competing elites veto the proposals of others or insist on their own decisional preferences.

The optimum power structure for a retraction in health care programs is a consensual elite. Here not only is the base of power narrow but the convergence of noncompeting ideologies makes a retraction of given levels of health services a simple matter that is decided upon by the governing elite. It should be noted that there are few communities with consensual elite power structures, nor are there many instances in which the contractionists have been successful in any substantial fashion.

Political Ideologies

Political ideologies are present in national and local politics [1, 2, 9]. Even though they may range from well-integrated doctrines to inarticulate or even unconscious operating premises, they all affect decisional preferences concerning the appropriate scope of government. Ideologies are a way of perceiving and reacting to the events occurring around the individual. They, in turn, help shape the attitudes of a person's political behavior. Ideologies are broader than vested political interests, which are concerned with the cost-benefits to particular policies. Furthermore, ideology takes into account the appropriate net scope of government in general, if not in particular. It should be pointed out that all or even most citizens have well-developed ideologies rather than more particularized political interests. However, it is the set of operational ideologies of the political and civil leaders of enduring groups and organizations having extraordinary political status and influence that are important and must be closely studied. These activists who often operate in small "inner cliques" filter decision preferences through their "proper" ideological sieve.

In American politics any close analysis reveals a rather wide range of articulated and operational ideologies. Liberals are generally associated with efforts to increase the scope of government incrementally. This becomes increasingly apparent when more radical comprehensive change movements suspect that the liberals are ill-prepared to support or are unable to use their influence to deliver on their comprehensive objectives. Yet liberals believe that the disadvantaged should provide their own leadership as one set of interests in the complex of competing interest groups. Liberals are sympathetic to labor, racial minorities, and even small businessmen. They ask that public officials recognize and respond to the needs of the disadvantaged, as defined by their leaders or spokesmen. They believe in the principle that resources should be distributed according to the ability of individuals to compete in the distribution processes. They seek the passive, if not active, cooperation of government to encourage counterorganizations to correct the unfair advantages of the affluent over the dispossessed.

The ideologies of those advocating a comprehensive expansion in the scope of government range from progressive to radical left. They differ from the liberals in that they see the community as collectivity sharing a national interest in the collective good of the masses. Political leadership is most frequently implemented through a cadre, more or less, of "true believers" who act in the name of, or in concert with, the relatively large disadvantaged population. They believe in the principle, "From each according to acquired abilities (skills), to each on the basis of equal distribution or on the basis of need, so that mercy and charity are unnecessary." Government is viewed as a key distributive or redistributive institution. While the progressive may be seeking a comprehensive change to redistribute power among the population, the radical leftist tends to use this movement to enhance his present relatively powerless position—and to bring it more under his own guidance and control—in oligarchies or pseudodemocracies run by his enemies.

Community conservationists, operating primarily at the local level and preferring maintenance of the present scope of government, are also collectivists in viewing the polity as a complex set of mutually interdependent parts where the individual good and the common good are compatible. They support programs for increasing the equality of opportunity to acquire skills, but they recognize and reward skills based on biological factors. They proclaim private capital and personal charity as vital principles but recognize that certain areas may require public and governmental supervision. Therefore, they will support though seldom initiate or create, efforts to use government to eliminate dirt, decay, and delinquency, as the poor are a blot on the city and their presence violates feelings of social justice. Community conservationists see public officials and professionals as the appropriate guardians, as well as the architects and builders, of the public interest and long-range plans.

Efforts to decrease the scope of government generally come from the conservative to reactionary radical rightists, who believe the good community is a national product of governmental noninterference, depending upon the private allocations of social and economic goods and services according to an individual's ability to compete for them, tempered by mercy and charity. Radical rightists adhere to this belief in a most uncompromising fashion and advocate restoration to a past condition, while "Jeffersonian" conservatives are less rigid, holding a preservationist outlook. "Progressive" conservatives, on the other hand, are less opposed to the use of government when private institutions and resources are unable and unlikely to act effectively. They, however, generally work out partnership arrangements whereby they play a prominent part in governing. For conservatives in general, government is necessary to provide regulation and services which affect their standard of living—for example, sewers instead of outhouses and a public water supply rather than private wells. They stand for an apolitical housekeeping government whose scope would be set by tradition and changed only by consultation between public officials, whom they generally influence, and the business community, whose spokesmen and organizations they dominate.

Political Focus

The decisional preferences of the political leaders do not focus solely on health in general but on equally important aspects of decision-making structures and processes, public policies, financial resources, and who shall administer the policies. Marmor has pointed out that

> Since the Second World War, most of these concerns have become politicized, whether the government should enact national health insurance, who should receive the benefits of governmental programs, how those programs should be administered and financed, and the effects of those programs on the costs of hospital and physician services have all been questions that have been widely publicized by the mass media, aroused group activity, and provoked Congressional debate and action [11].

The general preferences of the expansionists and contractionists on these aspects are summarized in Fig. 18–5. The entries are speculative; they are based on the observation of logical sets of possibilities, given the preferences of the two quite different net scopes of government. The expansionists prefer a decision-making *structure* which will be inclusive of all segments, with as much direct participation as possible. They assume that the more open and easily accessible is the policy-making arrangement, the more likely are the health needs of the whole populace to be met, including those of the disadvantaged. The contractionists, on the other hand, prefer a more exclusive decision-making structure, one that

FIGURE 18-5 TYPOLOGY OF POLITICAL FOCUSES OF EXPANSIONISTS AND CONTRACTIONISTS OF SCOPE OF GOVERNMENT

Political Focus	Political Advocates	
	Expansionists	Contractionists
Decision making: a. structure	Inclusive—direct participation	Exclusive—representative
b. process	Open, swift—use of public hearings	Closed, slow and deliberate
Public Policy	Comprehensive coverage	Private individual attention
Financial Resources	Massive	Selectively conservative
Personnel	Political administrators	Health professionals

relies on representative agents and technical health experts who are better informed and who are expected to proceed more cautiously with a thorough concern not only for the effect on cost-benefit ratio but on future consequences of the net scope of government. The contractionists assume that the less open is the system to the articulation of needs and demands, especially of the disadvantaged, the less likely will the scope of government be expanded to service them.

The contractionists and those who wish to maintain the *status quo* prefer a closed, slow, and deliberate decision-making *process*. The key policies should be made by a small group that governs. They rely on consensus arrived at by a small committee of influentials or an executive session of public officials behind closed doors. The expansionists, in sharp contrast, advocate open and swift processes. They encourage the use of open public hearings and may even risk the use of nonchanneled communication such as street demonstrations, boycotts, and sit-ins.

The expansionists seek comprehensive health care coverage, while the contractionsts, for the most part, limit health care to individual attention unless there is an overwhelming demonstrable need for the performance of a public function, for example, with communicable diseases. Much of the energies of both antagonists are concentrated on achieving legislative policy changes that authorize or reject an expanded scope of government. The expansionists often appear more successful in the formulation of policy that increases the scope of government than on the other focuses.

If there is an expansion, then the struggle centers on the later appropriation and designation of administrators to implement the policy outputs. The expansionists may win on policy output only to discover they have lost on securing sufficient appropriations; and/or they may face a conservative or restrictive implementation of policies.

The expansionists advocate massive expenditures for health care, not only competing with other governmental agencies but often attempting to tap additional tax resources. The contractionists are selectively conservative and often prevail on financial matters. Once a specific program has been stabilized, neither proponent is able to change the health budget by any substantial amount. Seldom has any massive amount of resources been made available and then only in the midst of or following a disaster or epidemic.

Perhaps the key aspect of health care programming is who is in authority over the health delivery system. Witness the struggle over the appointment of the U.S. Surgeon General with the advent of the Nixon administration. The expansionists generally prefer those with political-administrative skills who are sufficiently accessible and responsive to a wide spectrum of the populace, especially the disadvantaged. Those who would contract the scope of government in health rely on health professionals who can be counted upon to provide the necessary expertise of an orderly and rational approach for resolving the extent of health care.

Therefore, those who prefer an incremental increase in the scope tend to concentrate their efforts on shaping and reshaping public policy. Those advocating comprehensive change set as their target the distribution of political influence, preferring mass power systems. To maintain the *status quo* requires a focus upon the processes of policymaking and seeing to it that the procedural aspects, such as due process, are carefully adhered to. The concern over adequate levels of financial resources is the mainstay of those who wish to decrease the scope of government. They not only complain about high levels of taxation but believe it is a wasteful and inequitable way to purchase facilities and services.[3]

The Process of Change

The politics of health involves a number of processes for change. These processes include change agents who operationalize general objectives and strategies. They are often found to be operating in urban systems undergoing some stress [13].

Reform is the most prevalent process in making and securing an incremental increase in the scope of government. Reformers, frustrated and righteously indignant about health conditions, generally launch an intensive crusade-like movement to secure a change in public policy. They have been most successful not only in obtaining shifts in policies that affect the middle class but also in restructuring public services, such as establishing public health agencies to provide for more enduring governmental responsibilities.

Comprehensive increase in the scope of government can be associated with two change processes. The first is *politicization* of the populace, the objective being the acquisition of power. Generally, mutually exclusive and ever-widening cleavages have developed in the social system. The strident voices of the ideologues as change agents arouse the public to a threshold of awareness and, in addition, dominate the political dialogue, as their advocacy polarizes the issue. Under these circumstances it is extremely difficult for authorities to formulate and adopt appropriate policy outputs to satisfy the majority. As the controversy grows, the issue becomes depersonalized into support of abstract, doctrinaire, and often dogmatic positions. The ensuing conflict becomes contagious and imminently threatening. The authorities generally find themselves desperately seeking a way out, either by applying measures which repress the disturbances to "normal" processes or by finding ways to include and/or co-opt the dissenters and excluded population.

The second process for achieving a comprehensive change is *creative tension* and the innovative use of a variety of processes to discover and evolve superordinate goals for all segments of the polity. This includes the problem-solving methods of *professionalization*, *management*, *politicization*, and *mediation*, as well as methods to maximize sensitivity experiences which take into account human emotions and probe in depth the realistic power bases. The change agents can be either status leaders within the polity, catalytic agents from outside, or both, seeking to work on common tasks within the health arena.

Two processes are most often associated with maintaining the present scope of government. The first is *professionalization*, a traditional process by which the best medically trained talent and experts assume the role of change agents to make the staff and personnel more effective and skillful in present levels of health care services. This strategy generally insulates the professional from political forces and "keeps politics out of medicine" through high-quality programs, developed in a very rational way, which rely almost completely on the professionals' sense of health care needs. The second process, widely used to maintain the present scope of government, is *mediation*, which attempts to ameliorate widely held differences and rising tensions between the significant parties to the

[3] See Conant's case study of San Mateo, California [3].

dispute. Specially skilled mediators are brought in to negotiate *ad hoc* agreements—piecemeal, last minute efforts to avert a crisis. Mediation generally deals with the symptoms of the dispute and not the causal factors that eventually must be resolved.

Finally, those who wish to contract the scope of government can use many of the above processes but usually rely on the *managerial* process. The bureaucracy is expected to make the most efficient utilization of a fixed resource, too; it can be given the direction to quietly reallocate resources and to shift programs and services away from previously accepted target populations, with the net effect of contracting the scope of government. This is not to say that the managerial process cannot be used to expand or maintain the scope of government; but contractionists rely heavily on this strategy, as cost accounting on scarce public resources is the most effective way to reduce the scope of government, and it is certainly less troublesome than confrontation politics, as management depoliticizes the decision-making process, generally reducing the number and kinds of participants in the political process.

The Political Process

The interrelationship of the seven factors in the paradigm on the politics of health can be illustrated by briefly discussing the circumstances and courses of action that should be taken to increase the scope of government—incrementally or comprehensively. The former involves a policy pronouncement that would add another health responsibility or function to those already assumed by government. The latter involves a restructuring of the power arrangements to include in the decision-making processes disadvantaged populations who would share in formulating future policy.

Incremental expansionists feel disposed to discover additional ways to remedy the frustration over the unmet health needs of citizens which often place moderate stress on the system. Their general approach is to develop specific programmatic demands with accompanying promises of support. Their political focus is upon specific public policy changes in that their greatest effectiveness is in developing and articulating issues since they are one of the significant ideological groups (liberals) in the competitive mass. Their liberal rhetoric is cast in a reform mode with considerable mass appeal. The incrementalists have come under severe attack not only from the radical right but from the more militant spokesmen in the disadvantaged community, who are seeking their just share of political power and direct access to the authorities. This attack by the militants has challenged many assumptions of who speaks for whom, what kinds of and how much change is really required, and what are the immediate and long-range consequences on the distribution or redistribution of power and influence in the polity.

This paradox has tended to divide the expansionists. While some still prefer incremental increases in the scope of government in health, many are determined to move more cautiously and, therefore, prefer to maintain present levels of governmental responsibilities. A few are determined that a more comprehensive change is necessary not only in the relative influence of presently contending groups but through the mobilization of the disadvantaged community as a politically relevant contender seeking a dramatic redistribution of power and influence in the health system.

The sentiments in behalf of comprehensive change become most operational when there is severe system stress.

Here many and quite significant sets of demands are placed on the authorities. However, the key to success in being able to achieve a comprehensive change is to develop diffuse support around a charismatic personality or a unifying ideal or principle. Most often the authorities are more able to secure such support by an appeal to the common interest or general good of the established order. The political focus on decision-making arrangements is enhanced by processes of politicization and creative tension, strategies that progressive and radical leftists feel comfortable with. The politicization strategy mobilizes the citizens in a mass power structure, and the creative tension strategy can both attack and confront the harmony of a consensual system and provide innovative alternatives to replace the Establishment.

The question is no longer whether there is a "politics of health" but how better to understand the political process. Theoreticians and those responsible for formulating and implementing health care systems for the nation, state, and local communities have come to realize the importance of both public and private interests as they consider system stress, inputs and outputs. The effect of the intervening factors on the system—factors suggested here—requires further conceptual elaboration and refinement as well as political prototyping with the principle of configurative analysis of goals, trends, conditions, projections, and alternatives, in a specific health arena or context.

REFERENCES

1. AGGER, ROBERT E., DANIEL GOLDRICH, AND BERT E. SWANSON, *The Rulers and the Ruled: Political Power and Impotence in American Communities.* New York: John Wiley & Sons, Inc., 1964, pp. 8, 14–32, 73.
2. APTER, DAVID E., *Ideology and Discontent.* New York: The Free Press, 1964.
3. CONANT, RALPH W., *The Politics of Community Health.* Washington, D.C.: Public Affairs Press, 1968, pp. 18, 19–33.
4. DAHL, ROBERT A., *Pluralist Democracy in the United States.* Chicago: Rand McNally & Company, 1967, pp. 264, 270–81.
5. EASTON, DAVID, *A Systems Analysis of Political Life.* New York: John Wiley & Sons, Inc., 1965, p. 24.
6. HAMILTON, CHARLES, "Race and Education: A Search for Legitimacy," *Harvard Educational Review,* 38 (Fall, 1968), 669–84.
7. *Health-Pac Bulletin No. 1, June, 1968.* New York: Health Policy Advisory Center, Institute for Policy Studies, p. 3.
8. Joint Commission on Mental Illness and Health, *Action for Mental Health,* Final Report. New York: Science Editions, Inc., 1961, pp. 4, 195–259.
9. LANE, ROBERT E., *Political Ideology.* New York: The Free Press 1962.
10. LOWI, THEODORE, "American Business, Public Policy, Case Studies and Political Theory," *World Politics,* 16 (1963–64), 690.
11. MARMOR, THEODORE R., "The Politicizations of Personal Health Services." Paper delivered at the Symposium on Political Science and Public Health, April, 1969, pp. 18–19.
12. SCHATTSCHNEIDER, E. E., *The Semi-Sovereign People.* New York: Holt, Rinehart & Winston, Inc., 1960, p. 2.
13. SWANSON, BERT E., *Decision-Making in the School Desegregation-Decentralization Controversies.* Bronxville, N.Y.: Institute for Community Studies, Sarah Lawrence College, 1969.
14. ———, "Political Change in the Small Community," in William J. Gore and Leroy C. Hodapp, eds., *Change in the Small Community.* New York: Friendship Press, 1967, p. 151.
15. WILSON, ROBERT N., *Community Structure and Health Action.* Washington, D.C.: Public Affairs Press, 1968, p. 39.

part four

STRATEGY, METHOD, AND STATUS OF MEDICAL SOCIOLOGY

19

THE STRATEGY OF SOCIOMEDICAL RESEARCH

Richard H. Williams

The strategy of sociomedical research can be understood in two distinctly different contexts. On the one hand, it might be concerned with sociomedical research as an emerging body of systematic science, with crucial gaps in the system and, hence, with various strategies for furthering the systematics of this body of knowledge. On the other hand, it could be directed at identifying the institutional and other arrangements for getting sociomedical research done and, hence, to the strategy for using present resources and developing new ones. This chapter is concerned primarily with the second perspective. Ideally, a large research operation would have preceded its writing: one needs data from intensive interviews, participant observation, and operations research on the relative productivity of differing arrangements. No such research has been undertaken; therefore, the data for this chapter are of necessity relatively meager. There are, however, several useful surveys of the field, including recent monographs by Suchman [22] and Wellin [23]. They both focus on the uses of sociology and related sciences in public health but do not attempt to survey the entire range of sociomedical research. There are no comparable studies of the settings, requirements, problems, and sources of support for sociomedical research as a whole. The survey of the situation as it was in 1956 by Anderson and Seacat is useful [2]. And for the period from 1954 to 1959 [24], Wellin and Seacat reviewed research in this field. Apple collected a series of sociological studies of health and sickness done in the 1950s [3], while Freidson has reviewed the sociology of the medical profession. [6].

In July, 1967, *Social Science and Medicine* appeared as an international journal. A perusal of the various issues is valuable for seeing the broad scope of the field. However, none of the articles in the first two volumes attempts to give an overview or to draw implications for strategy.

David Mechanic has constructed a point of view to give perspective to the field of medical sociology [13]. In the introduction, he cites several syntheses of the field, and his bibliography, which contains 468 items, indicates its broad scope.

An important conclusion of this chapter, which seems fitting to be drawn at the outset, is that there is need for research on the sociology of this obviously expanding and important field. Such research would contribute to the sociology of knowledge, as well as provide an empirical basis for evaluating alternative arrangements for developing the field of medical sociology.

DELINEATION OF THE FIELD

It is necessary to delineate the field under discussion, for it is a broad one with many facets. The categorization of the field by Kendall and Merton into the four areas of etiology and ecology, variations in response to illness and maintenance of health, organization of health facilities, and professional education and training is quite useful [11]. Particularly useful for the present discussion is the distinction proposed by Straus, which cuts across these four areas, between the sociology *of* medicine and sociology *in* medicine [21]. The sociology of medicine is a facet of sociology qua sociology, which happens to take medicine and related medical activities as its subject matter. The latter is enmeshed in the medical field on a collaborative basis.[1]

There is another distinction which is useful in order to avoid considerable confusion, especially in relation to the organization and funding of sociomedical research. It may best be illustrated by reference to the field of mental health. There has been a tendency within the health field to view the behavioral sciences, including sociology, as coterminous with mental health. This tendency has been somewhat less pronounced within sociology due in part to the work of such people as Merton, Reader, and Kendall on the student physician [14] and of several studies of hospitals and other health facilities unrelated to mental illness as such. By some lines of reasoning, they too can be presumed to be related to mental *health*. There are understandable historical reasons for this view. The subject matter of mental health is immediately and directly related to behavior. Whatever the etiology of mental disorders may be, their manifestations are primarily behavioral on levels of direct concern to psychology, sociology, and social or cultural anthropology. They involve deviant behavior that affects the general stance of the individu-

[1] See chapter 1 for a discussion of the distinction between the sociology of medicine and sociology in medicine.

al and has an impact on those around him. The program of the National Institute of Mental Health and other mental health programs have drawn heavily on the behavioral sciences and have recognized the urgent need for their further development and support. Indeed, some aspects of psychiatry itself have taken on many of the characteristics of a behavioral science.

More recently there has been a growing and proper recognition that the behavioral sciences are an integral and necessary part of the *armamentarium* of research in public health and in health generally. On the basic side, the work of Dubos and others points to psychological, social, and cultural factors in the epidemiology of many communicable and chronic diseases. On the more applied side, the major question of relevance to service programs which behavioral scientists are especially qualified to provide an answer to is: What are the conditions under which people will take action to control a health problem or improve a health situation? Knowledge of the nature of channels of communication in various types of organizations or of patterns of influence within segments of a community has relevance to the design of programs intended to affect behavior within such organizations or population segments. Knowledge of this type can be useful in deciding where the energies should go in a particular program.

The primary concern of research in mental health (hence in training for it) is with behavioral or psychological functioning as such; put in somewhat more sociological terms, it is concerned with the viability of the action systems of individual actors. This view is similar to one developed recently in psychology by Smith [19]. Such functioning is viewed on a broad continuum, from extreme behavioral incapacitation to optimal ability to act. Factors affecting status and movement on this continuum range from the physical environment through the biological to the social and cultural. Some of them are conditional to behavior, others inherently part of the behavioral system itself. Mental health is not directly concerned with the former but is with the latter. For example, the National Institute of Mental Health would not consider it part of its mission to support research on paraplegia as such but would certainly sponsor a good research project on the ways in which paraplegics cope with life, mentally and emotionally. To take a somewhat more subtle example, research on the behavioral factors producing or reducing dental disorders (e.g., acceptance of fluoridation) would not fall within the province of the NIMH, but research on the impact of dental disorders on ego functioning would.

The conceptual difficulties arise from the fact that in significant (although not precisely known) part, the "disease entity" in the field of mental health involves behavioral functioning as such in a direct sense. On these grounds, both the independent and the dependent variables can be conceptualized as variables within action systems (e.g., impact of the action system of the mother on the action system of the child). There is a double incidence of social (and psychological) factors in much of the field of mental health. The independent variables may be sought for outside the action system as such, for example, the search for biochemical variables relating to schizophrenia. The population of schizophrenics under study has been defined by its behavioral manifestations, and in this sense, the dependent variables in research in mental health always are part of the action system. In other health and disease areas, one is looking for new independent variables of a social, social-psychological, or sociocultural nature which might explain at least part of the variance of dependent variables that are not themselves part of the action system (in the Parsonian sense), although they may be conditional to it as, for example, in the studies of social factors in chronic illness (see Chapter 3). Or, one may be studying the structure and functioning of organizations or institutions (e.g., hospitals, medical schools, the medical profession, and so forth) as such, without particular concern with the viability, i.e., mental health, of the individual actors.

Table 17-1 gives a few illustrations of these rather abstract distinctions. They are not meant to be rigid. There can be perfectly valid research efforts which cut across rows, down columns, or both. We believe, however, that they are analytically valid, and sociomedical research tends, in fact, to be organized in such a way as to fall primarily, if not exclusively, in one or another of these boxes. Furthermore, the predominant characteristic of a research project or program which would lead one to classify it one way or another according to this scheme will have considerable bearing on the types of setting and requirements appropriate to the research, the types of problems likely to arise in medical settings, and, quite clearly, the sources of support, to all of which we shall turn in subsequent sections.

SETTINGS FOR SOCIOMEDICAL RESEARCH

The most relevant features of the settings for sociomedical research in relation to the problems of doing such research and to the problems of being a researcher in such settings relate to the characteristics of the social systems of these settings.

Organized courses of action require cooperative action, the interaction of persons, a pattern of interpersonal relations, and, hence, a social system. Social systems themselves have certain basic requirements which must be met if they are to function adequately at a minimum of social cost. Relatively little is known about the requirements of social systems, and it must be stressed that greater relative gains can be expected from research directed at that question than at questions pertaining to the economic and technological systems. The present discussion suggests some of the general types of requirements which social systems have. They may be summarized as follows:

1. The requirement of optimal structuring—too much structure blocks the entire action system and inhibits the decision-making process. Too much structure also involves too great an investment of action energy in maintaining the structure, at the expense of getting things done—too little structure leads to general confusion, faulty insulation, duplication of effort, and not enough meaningful pattern to provide adequate motivation.

2. The requirement of maximal institutionalization—the amount of institutionalization is not equivalent to the amount of structure. A social system only operates by virtue of being institutionalized, and in the sense in which that concept has been developed here, there cannot be too much of it. It should also be stressed that as the requirements of the situation of action change, institutional patterns must change. Otherwise, in the new situation these patterns exist as ossified elements of structure rather than full-fledged institutions.

3. The requirement of minimal friction, but optimal tension—friction tends to develop when the density of interaction is too great and when too many actions are originated for persons occupying certain positions. Friction can be reduced by proper insulation and by changes in the

TABLE 17-1

Studies of	*Focused on*	
	Behavioral or psychological function as such ("basic") and viability of the action system of individual actors ("applied")	Social, social-psychological, and socio-cultural factors in other aspects of health and disease ("basic") and their management ("applied")
Etiology and ecology of diseases and health	1. Ecology of mental disorders; production and reproduction of successful or unsuccessful coping behavior in families; basic studies of motivation, learning perception, etc.	2. Social factors in the epidemiology of cancer, rheumatoid arthritis, etc.
Responses to health and disease	3. Communication of mental health concepts; social and social-psychological careers of mental patients during and after hospitalization; emotional factors and coping behavior in relation to leukemia, death, or other stressful situations	4. Factors affecting acceptance of fluoridation or other public health programs; the impact of influenza on a community
Organization of medical facilities and other groups affecting health	5. Social structure and functioning of a mental hospital; mental health in schools and industry (i.e., impact of schools or industries as sociocultural systems on the viability of the action systems of their members)	6. Social structure and functioning of the general hospital, health departments, group practice of medicine, etc.
Education, career development, and professionalization as a social process	7. Career development in all the "mental health" professions (i. e., all those whose primary concern is with helping others achieve a more viable action system); development of new roles in the field of mental health (e.g., the mental health worker)	8. The development of student physicians; choice of public health as a career; social factors in revising education

distribution of decisions and originations. 4. The requirement of optimal frustration and anxiety but maximal motivation—frustration and anxiety tend to produce aggressive behavior up to a point, beyond which they may result in a blocked action system, i.e., neurosis. Furthermore, the optimal amount of aggressive behavior is itself a variable, dependent in part on the requirements of the situation of action; the problem is a complex but highly important one. The ratios representing satisfaction and self-esteem should be neither too large nor too small.

5. The requirement of optimal distribution—of satisfactions, power, risks and responsibilities [25].

An Hypothesis Concerning Social Distance from Medical Settings

In the present stage of sociomedical research one can hypothesize with considerable assurance that the degree of difficulty in fulfilling the requirements of optimally functioning social systems varies inversely with the social distance between the research base and the medical setting itself, unless certain devices, such as institutionalized insulation, are evolved. Sociology as a science has grown and established traditional ways of procedure, primarily, indeed almost exclusively, within the academic setting of the college or university department. As sociological researchers move out from these settings, the new settings are likely to appear to contain more structure than these researchers readily tolerate. In large measure this is caused by the presence of elements of structure which are institutionalized in the view of medical practitioners and others accustomed to working in these settings but which appear as roadblocks to the sociologist. Considerable friction can develop through interaction with persons whose roles, goals, and requirements are quite different and through origination of many actions by these persons, actions which do, in fact, affect the work of the sociologist. For example, the apparently simple matter of access to medical records or other sources of data burdened with the norm of confidentiality—a norm to which the sociologist is quite accustomed but which he has institutionalized and internalized in ways different from those in the medical profession—can absorb a tremendous amount of time which to the sociologist may seem a waste of effort and a hindrance to his research. There is danger that the social researcher will become so frustrated and anxious that he will either behave in an overly aggressive way or be blocked into apathy, either of which can do much to retard the accomplishments and potential usefulness of sociomedical research.

Simultaneously, there is another very important aspect to this problem. The presence of a sociologist, especially of a behavioral science research team, in a medical setting based as part of the medical setting's social system alters the system itself. The "native" inhabitants of the system may well view the newcomer as a "foreigner," the more so because he is there to perform tasks they may not understand. He is viewed as a new element of noninstitutionalized structure, which easily gives the impression of excess baggage. New issues will arise concerning optimum distribution of satisfactions (e.g., in relation to office space, salary levels, job satisfactions, and the like), power ("What *is* the relation of these researchers to the power hierarchy?"), risks (e.g., tenure or the consequences of failure or success in research), and responsibilities.

Types of Settings

According to this hypothesis, then, the home-based social scientist, with a tenured position in a sociology department should have the least degree of difficulty in meeting social system requirements doing sociomedical research. Unless he is doing a survey of the literature or using readily accessible documentary sources, he will be faced with problems of social system requirements relating to access to data. He will have to obtain entrée, establish rapport with subjects, and be careful not to get himself thrown out once he has gotten in. But these problems are faced in any sociological research—in industry, school systems, community organization, or whatnot. Social researchers are generally trained to cope with such problems, and certainly they expect them to arise.

A social science team can be formally located in a medical setting and yet be insulated from it in crucial ways. For example, a team with which the writer had close connections for several years was administratively housed in a school of public health. The school provided certain housekeeping and bookkeeping services to the research project. One of the more "inside" members of the school's faculty, himself a social scientist, provided liaison with the research team and acted in a consultative capacity to it. The research team was physically housed in donated space, in a building belonging to a local public health unit (not part of the school), physically at a perceptible but "convenient" distance from the school. Members of the research team informally—occasionally officially—could and did participate in regular activities of the school, taking part in a seminar or giving a lecture. But the insulation of the team was sufficiently great that the social system problems with which they were faced had almost exclusively to do with interdisciplinary research and very little, if at all, with their relations to the setting (the school).

An independent researcher based in a more or less permanent way in a medical setting—a situation which, to the knowledge of this author, is relatively rare—would more likely be faced with problems relating to the social system requirements of his setting than would a team. For him, insulation would be tantamount to social isolation, and unless he is of the type that flourishes in isolation, he would be in trouble. On the other hand, his problems would be less than those of a noninsulated team, largely because his presence would constitute less of a change in the system, and, hence, be less of a threat to it. The researcher may, of course, be frustrated by the system, but the system is not likely to be much frustrated by him.

A very special case of a nonuniversity, medically oriented setting is the National Institute of Mental Health. In a crude sense, it could be said that all of the social scientists on its staff are in a medical setting, have no distance from it, and, hence, would be open to the full range of problems created by social system requirements as suggested by the general hypothesis formulated above. However, there are important variations within the Institute illustrative of the subtle complexities of such relationships. The Institute has the diversified functions of research, both intramural and—through grants—training and consultation for both hospital and community mental health programs. Social scientists are involved in all these functions.

Researchers in the intramural program are in an institutionalized setting which is virtually indistinguishable from that of scientists doing research in a university. The major boundary of their social system is the laboratory, and the bulk of their interactions are within it. Their research, in turn, may be done in a medical setting (for example, Saint Elizabeth's Hospital or the wards of the Clinical Center for the National Institutes of Health), or it may not be (e.g., studies of class difference in parent-child relationships conducted on "normal" populations living in the community). If it is done in a medical setting, the researchers are defined and perceived as coming *from* the laboratory, their base being there. This situation is essentially no different, in point of institutional structure, from that of a sociologist based in a university department doing research in a hospital. In the grant program the function is research administration, a specialized function which is beginning to appear in some universities, and the main interactions are with actual or prospective grantees or study section members, the great majority of whom are university based.

An intermediate position was occupied by members of the Professional Services Branch, which until 1964 was the focal point for long-range program development within the NIMH (its functions have subsequently been spread to many parts of the Institute, concommitant with its growth). The Branch was composed primarily of behavioral scientists. Its first chief was a social psychologist, and its second (the author), a sociologist. There were other sociologists, social psychologists (one of whom also had background in economics), and an anthropologist. At any one time out of a total professional staff of nine or ten there were no more than two psychiatrists. This composition reflected the basic position of the NIMH concerning the close relation between the behavioral sciences, with fairly heavy emphasis on sociology, and mental health programs. It was also the policy of the Institute to give members of this Branch much freedom to develop their own priorities and select the general directions of program development. They were given access to funds in the form of special grants with which they could develop collaborative studies with research groups across the country, subject to approval by the Special Grants Review Committee, a body of consultants outside of the federal government, and the National Advisory Mental Health Council. The Review Committee participated not only in a scientific review of projects, but also in consultation with the Branch, on strategy in terms of priorities and sources of research talent in particular fields. These arrangements proved so successful that from 1951 to 1964 only one proposal was disapproved by the Council. They did not, however, negate the basic policy of the Institute, from its inception to date, that the bulk of research grants should be made on a free competitive basis, with judgments made by peers from outside of government and a minimal administrative involvement of staff (special grants were never more than 3 percent to 5 percent of all research grants).

The members of this Branch were free to be as involved in or as insulated from the research teams with which they collaborated as they deemed appropriate. One member of the Branch (the author) tended to be quite heavily involved, and in one major instance he was considered "co-principal investigator." He wrote articles and a book from data collected by this team. Other members consulted only occasionally with their teams and spent the bulk of their time generating new projects in new areas of program development. In all instances, their base for salary, tenure, leave, and retirement was the NIMH.

Social scientists in the Division of Manpower and Training are not directly engaged in research, although they are involved in the promotion of research training; their interactions are primarily with staffs of training institutions, mostly universities. Within their own division they face problems of interdisciplinary collaboration, although minimally because each training specialist concentrates pretty much in his own field.

Social scientists in the Division of Mental Health Service Programs and the Regional Offices are in a quite different institutional setting. Within the group they are a small minority surrounded by psychiatrists, social workers, nurses, and clinical psychologists, yet all are concerned with the same types of programs. Their orientation must be of the sociology *in* medicine type, rather than the sociology *of* medicine. Outside the Institute, they act as consultants, sometimes to applied or evaluative research projects, sometimes directly to a program. Their interactions in those situations are very largely, but not exclusively, with people responsible for operating mental health programs.

No systematic analysis of these variations within the National Institute of Mental Health has been made in relation to the hypothesis formulated above. Such an analysis would be difficult because the number of social scientists directly involved in consultation for service programs is very small. However, on the basis of the writer's general experience over several years, it seems clear that the problems of meeting social system requirements are least in the intramural laboratory, greatest in the extramural consultation, and middling (but closer to the intramural) in the other programs. No judgment is implied that the problems which do exist are insoluble or create insuperable barriers, indeed; it is the writer's impression that those who have faced the greatest problems in this respect have handled them particularly well.

The social scientist anchored in a school of public health, medical school, or school of nursing enjoys a setting which retains the general institutional characteristics of the university. The orientation is primarily toward learning, rather than toward day-to-day responsibility for the operation of a health program. This is particularly true of schools of public health; medical schools of nursing are intertwined with the operational exigencies of a hospital. The extreme end of this continuum of degree of social distance from a medical setting (conversely, from a liberal arts department) is employment in a health department having no ties to a university.

As indicated by Wellin,

> . . . a number of state and local health departments have employed, or now employ, social scientists on a full-time basis. Among the state health departments are those of California, Colorado, Connecticut, Florida, Kentucky, Maryland, New Mexico, New York, Pennsylvania, and Washington. In addition, social scientists are employed full-time in the health departments of the cities of New York, Philadelphia, and Cambridge, and in the St. Louis County Health Department. The Los Angeles City and County Health Departments make use of the part-time services of social scientists, mainly on a contractual basis [23].

None of these positions existed prior to 1952, and several of them are very recent.

These instances represent the case which, according to the general hypothesis, should present the most problems in relation to meeting the requirements of the social system of the setting. Unfortunately, there is no systematic evidence to confirm or deny the theoretical expectation; certainly, such a study would be particularly interesting at this stage of the development of sociomedical research, because it represents a recent innovation and because, to date, the type of institutional arrangement and mode of participation of social scientists in health settings have been matters of opportunity and circumstance, not of planned development according to stated principles, as Suchman suggests [22]. It is the author's impression, however, based on talking with many people in the fields of mental and public health, that the hypothesis would hold.

The form of the hypothesis, hence the tenor of this section, might suggest the erroneous conclusion that sociomedical research should not be encouraged to decrease the social distance between the researchers and the medical settings. Both Suchman and Wellin have made a very good case for the functional value of social scientists engaging in research and other activities, especially consultation, within schools and state and local departments of public health. A similar case could probably be made for medical schools, schools of nursing, and other medical settings. Gouldner, among others, has indicated the potential value of applied research [7], and some kinds of applied medical research are very clearly better done based within a medical setting rather than conducted from outside. Thus, the question of strategy is one of facing problems created by the requirements of the social system, rather than retreating from such problems.

Solving the Problems

The best approach to these problems is a direct one—clear recognition of the nature of the problems and open discussion of them. Occasionally, formal techniques of group dynamics, familiar to many social scientists, might be used, although a researcher based in a medical setting is in a somewhat awkward situation if he initiates formal procedures that are primarily and expressly intended to better his own position. If such techniques are used, it is probably best to focus them on fairly specific operating problems of the agency and a develop clarifications and understandings of the social position of the social researcher indirectly as a by-product.

There are various institutional devices which are potentially helpful. One of them is insulation, but that would be functional only under certain special circumstances; it would be damaging in others. Another is to make part-time use of university-based social scientists for research on a contractual basis. At least one major local public health program follows that practice. It would be a better arrangement, in the opinion of the author, to employ social scientists within health settings (health department or other) as their primary base but, at the same time to permit them to hold appointments in a nearby university. This is done in the Saint Louis County Health Department. As a corollary, such social scientists should not engage exclusively in research; their position in the system will be strengthened and be more functional for the system if they also participate in university teaching, in-service training, and consultation.

A particularly important question when sociomedical research (and other activities) is based in a health setting is the position given such research within the formal organization. Various arrangements have been used, but there are no hard data on which to evaluate the relative merits of each. In principle, however, a social scientist or the head of a social science unit should be placed in a staff position and report directly to the head of the health agency. The functions that social scientists perform, whether in research, training, or consulation, tend to relate to general matters affecting the entire setting, its operation, and the accomplishment of its general mission. If social scientists are identified with one segment of the total organization, and if they must relate to more than one link in the chain of command, their activities can readily become both distorted and frustrated. Other arrangements have been used and appear to work relatively well, but they might work even better if changed to conform with this principle.

Finally, the placement of sociomedical research in various settings should take cognizance of the distinction drawn in the introductory section of this chapter and illustrated in Table 17-1. If the research is predominantly of a character which would place it in any of the boxes in the left-hand column, it should be based in an academic department in a university; or, if it is based in a medical setting, such a setting should be clearly identified as relating to mental health (e.g., a department of psychiatry in a medical school, a mental health unit in a school of public health, a state or local department or division of mental health, a mental hospital, or whatever). If its predominant characteristic places it somewhere in the right-hand column, it should either be based in an academic department of a university or in a health setting clearly *not* identified with mental health. The confusions arising from identification of the social and behavioral sciences in health with mental health are not likely to occur, in any event not to be of any particular consequence, in academic settings, but they do arise and are likely to be damaging in a service or teaching-oriented medical setting.

REQUIREMENTS FOR ADEQUATE PROFESSIONAL PERFORMANCE

Is Standardization Occurring and Is It Desirable?

It is clear that sociology *in* medicine is a very recent phenomenon, and it is also clear that it has grown relatively rapidly. The demand for qualified people currently exceeds the supply. As Wellin points out, "this, plus the fact that the health field is still nearer the margin than the center of employment acceptable to qualified people, increases the risk that marginal or poorly trained social scientists will be recruited" [23].

Theoretically, one possible safeguard would be formal standardization of qualifications, through use of such devices as competitive examinations. Wellin takes a cure from Sibley [17], who claims that the demand for formal criteria of qualifications is greater in applied fields where the employers are not themselves sociologists. Wellin takes the position that a trend toward standardization is inevitable, that those in the relevant behavioral sciences should take the leadership in this respect. He specifically recommends that "*standard examinations* be developed as part of the objective selection procedures for *social science personnel in official* (i.e., merit system) *agencies*. Inasmuch as such examinations would constitute concrete attempts to spell out the essential core(s) of knowledge required for social scientists, it is highly desirable that outstanding behavioral scientists be involved in the preparation of such materials" [23].

Such a development should be approached with considerable caution. There is as yet no consensus concerning what a sociologist should know to work in official health agencies—to say nothing of the various other fields of health or medicine—or what his particular skills should be. Standardized procedures could become uninstitutionalized and dysfunctional elements of structure, creating friction and noise in the system and impeding further, more imaginative development of the field.

The problem is much more complex for sociology *in* medicine than for sociology *of* medicine. In the latter field, the sociologist is most likely to be spending only some of his time on his research, the rest on his academic teaching. The fact that his research happens to be about something that utilizes data from the social fields of medicine or health does not in itself raise any special issues concerning his qualifications. The sociologist *in* medicine is likely to spend a great deal of his time on research, perhaps some in academic teaching, but he is also likely to put time into in-service training and consultation on programs. Even if most of his time is devoted to research, he must be concerned with feedback and utilization, or his utility to the agency which employs him will appear to it minimal or nil. Standardized screening devices to assure possession of the skills necessary to meet requirements of these other functions would be extraordinarily difficult, if not impossible, to devise.

If standardized selection procedures are to be used at all, beyond the well-established ones of meeting certain formal requirements such as academic degrees and years of experience, they could only serve to determine minimal qualifications in research competence and substantive knowledge of the discipline. Possibly such procedures would help to establish a "solid floor," as Sibley suggests, but it seems more likely that they would be redundant with the more usual types of formal requirements for jobs. Would it really be worth the effort to devise standard examinations which might possibly screen out a very small number of people who met the other formal requirements but could not pass the exams?

Another possible approach to formal standardization would be to follow the practice of the medical profession itself and subject applied medical sociologists (or applied sociologists generally) to licensing and for higher-level jobs, to board certification. To enter directly into the pros and cons of this issue, which has been debated for several years, would take us too far afield. Suffice it to say that there would be the serious danger, at this stage in the development of the field, of reinforcing a tendency to turn the medical sociologist into an unfortunate crossbreed, a matter which we will discuss further.

Alternatives to Formal Standardization

Since the problem of assuring that highly qualified people are involved in sociology in medicine, and since formal selection devices might be redundant or create more problems than they would solve, it seems important to consider the reinforcement of less formal, more fully institutionalized devices.

A relatively simple one, which could be reinforced through the usual channels of the American Sociological Association and the sociological journals, would be to emphasize the fact that the sociologist in medicine must be sufficiently qualified so that he could do sociological research and teaching in a college or university, and qualified also to meet the other demands of the setting into which he is going. The other demands require skills in interpersonal and group relations, which may not be quite so crucial in all academic settings. Dissemination of this concept would also do much to raise the prestige of sociologists who choose to work in applied settings.

Another device is to preserve the professional identity of the applied sociologist as a sociologist, and to make sure that there are opportunities for maintaining strong relations with his peers in sociology. This type of problem arises infrequently, if at all, in a setting such as the National Institute of Mental Health. There are sufficient numbers of sociologists and members of related disciplines to provide about as many peer relations as exist in most universities. In addition, there are seminars, consultant groups, study sections, and review committees which bring large numbers of peers in from the outside for varying periods of time. This type of problem is very apt to arise in the case of the lone social scientist in a medical school, school of public health, school of nursing, or health department. Various settings are intermediate between these two in this respect. But there are ways to offset this characteristic of the setting. The joint university appointment, for instance, has much to commend it from this point of view. The use of outside consultant groups can also be valuable and need not be on the scale used by the National Institute of Mental Health, which runs the risk of producing an overly rich diet. Certainly, ample provision should be made for travel to professional meetings.

CHARACTERISTIC PROBLEMS OF WORKING IN MEDICAL SETTINGS

There are no available data sufficiently exhaustive or systematic to say just what the range of problems facing sociological researchers based in medical settings is, or how "characteristic" they are. Many of these problems are probably found in varying degrees wherever research is based in an applied setting and done on a collaborative rather than independent basis. However, the well-known institutional characteristics of the medical profession and those in it (such as the role of the doctor and the sick role) and the high cultural value generally placed on the whole field undoubtedly heighten these problems in medical settings.

One study has faced this and related issues in one aspect of the field of mental health. Kandel and Williams [10] analyzed data furnished by project members in forty-nine projects in the field of psychiatric rehabilitation, broadly defined. The data were obtained in connection with a working conference attended by a member of each project. A guide for preparation of advance communications to the conference was prepared in the form of a focused interview.

A major focus of the analysis was on transactional problems faced by the project and personal problems associated with them; hence, the projects were viewed as social systems in a variety of settings. Manifestations of strain—including fantasy, anxiety, hostility, and defensive behavior—were analyzed. Personal, social, and cultural factors underlying the strains were sought. Attempted solutions were analyzed, including increasing structure, attempts to increase motivational commitment, minimizing disruption and training. Some of the more formal administrative problems relating to personnel policies, general institutional policies, and legal and financial problems were also studied.

A major conclusion was that there are "two requirements essential in maintaining the equilibrium of a social system: (1) the rules defining the obligations that interacting persons have toward one another should be sufficiently clear and generally agreed upon; and (2) persons in the system should be adequately motivated to fulfill these obligations. By introducing change, these projects affected one or both of these requirements. They did this by disrupting the personality system of the interacting members, the structure of the social situation, or the general cultural climate in which they were operating" [10]. There must be a dual concern—with the individual and the social situation—in the introduction of change. Sociomedical research almost invariably introduces change. Anticipation of these problems in the design of the project and frank discussion of them during its initial phase among the project staff and those persons with whom they will be working should prove very valuable. Anticipation of reactions to change requires an awareness of the total social organization in which the project is to be carried out. For this endeavor, social science concepts will continue to prove most helpful.

Interdisciplinary and Team Research

The inherently collaborative nature of research in the context of sociology in medicine gives rise to the full range of interdisciplinary problems, whether or not the research is organized as a formal interdisciplinary team. There is considerable literature discussing these problems, among which is the classic work of Luszki [12]. And Wellin includes sixteen items on team and interdisciplinary relations in his bibliography [23]. During the 1960's interdisciplinary and team research were taken more or less for granted, and there was less literature devoted specifically to the subject. But many of the basic problems persist.

These problems vary both with the type of medical setting and with the type of research. Probably the most inherently compatible medical setting for collaborative research in social science is public health, either in health departments or in schools of public health. Hanlon and others in public health maintain that this field is to a very significant extent an applied social science [8]. Within public health, the problems of ambiguity of roles and of communication are probably reduced to a minimum in research of a sort that would fall in Boxes 2 and 4 of Table 17–1—social factors in the epidemiology of various diseases and social factors in the acceptance of public health programs. They become more sensitive issues in Box 6, for example, in studies of the social structure and function of a health department or a school of public health. Such studies might better be done, in the present stage of development, in a context of the sociology of medicine from an outside base. Straus may well be right when he alleges that " the sociologist in medicine risks a good relation if he tries to study his colleagues" [21].

Research teams which are relatively well insulated within their settings, as illustrated earlier in the chapter, serve to highlight the problems of interdisciplinary team research as such, relatively uncontaminated by the characteristics of the setting. Simmons and Davis, operating in such a relatively insulated setting, found that major problems and issues were methodological rather than conceptual [18]. There tends to be cleavage between those oriented to more qualitative, clinical methods and those oriented to more quantitative methods. The two approaches can, it has been found, be combined. A major effort to clarify these problems is the report on controls in psychiatric research of the Research Committee of the Group for the Advancement of Psychiatry [20]. Applied social scientists and members of other disciplines or professions who intend to engage in research will find this small volume well worth studying. Simmons and Davis also indicate that they were not prepared for the amount of interaction in team research. There are "sustained and unremitting pressures" which can become quite wearing. This situation was probably heightened to some extent by the relative insulation but is probably an experience common to team research generally.

The problems of interdisciplinary collaboration are greatest in relation to all of the types of research on the left-hand side of Table 17–1, work done within a medical setting. The double incidence of social (or action system) factors; the subtle distinctions and considerable overlap between applied social science and mental health; the relative ignorance of the etiology of mental disorders; and the relatively high sensitivity to problems of differentiation of role within the mental health professions, a problem the author has recently analyzed [28], all serve to heighten and intensify the problems of interdisciplinary collaboration. It is in this area particularly that every effort must be made to maintain the professional identity of the sociologist as sociologist. If he tries to become a clinician, he is neither fish nor fowl, only a source of confusion.

At the present stage of development in medical sociology, it is probably wise to have the great bulk of sociomedical research proceed in areas falling within the odd-numbered boxes in Table 17–1, in a context of the sociology *of* medicine rather than of sociology *in* medicine. It should be emphasized, however, that this distinction, borrowed from Straus, does not imply (at least in this context) an equivalence to the distinction between "basic" and "applied" research. Research of all the types in the left-hand column can be done in such a way as to furnish the practitioner with the basis for sounder judgments about alternatives in the organization and conduct of mental health programs.

Communication

Discussions of interdisciplinary research frequently point up problems of communication. The impression is sometimes given that they are essentially intellectual problems of conceptualization and vocabulary. The experience reported by Simmons and Davis does not substantiate this view; methodological posture rather than conceptual difficulties was the core of the problem. Back of either type of problem lie subtle cultural differences associated with the social process of professionalization in a given discipline. Jackson has indicated that what are often called problems of communication are only symptomatic of other difficulties found generically in organizations. He indicates four problems which must be solved indirectly, but effectively, to overcome barriers to communication: "(1) the problem of trust or lack of trust; (2) the problem of creating interdependence among persons: common goals and agreement about means for achieving them; (3) the problem of distributing rewards fairly; and (4) the exceedingly important problem of understanding and coming to common agreement about the social structure of the organization" [9].

Cross-Disciplinary Collaboration

Both Wellin and Suchman call attention to two particularly valuable analyses made by the Russell Sage Foundation [15, 16] of problems of cross-disciplinary collaboration and of possible solutions to these problems. On the basis of these analyses the problems can be grouped essentially into cultural barriers, social position (role, status, and authority) within the social structure of the setting, and ambiguities in expectations. The solutions call for wider ranges of understanding. The analyses underline the importance of interpersonal skills in addition to research skills. They make the extremely significant point that caution should be exercised in attributing difficulties which do arise to "personality clashes"; the probabilities are that they relate more fundamentally to "cultural, social-structural, and role specification problems" and could be dealt with more effectively in that context.

Relation to Service Functions

The sociologist in medicine will, of course, be surrounded by and must take cognizance of the requirements of training and service. In general, he is least well prepared to cope with demands of this kind. He has been trained to think, to raise issues, and to do research, but not necessarily to find answers to practical questions, and least of all to carry out service functions.

There is essentially only one type of medical setting where there could be any thought of a sociologist assuming treatment function in the sense of direct therapeutic intervention with individuals or groups, namely, a setting where the primary responsibility is for mental health. The best approach to such a situation is to make it quite clear from the outset that sociologists are not therapists. They may, with proper experience and other qualifications, provide important consultation concerning programs of care, treatment, and rehabilitation of the mentally ill, but they will merely add to such confusion as may already exist if they permit themselves to enter into treatment relations with patients.

This position was taken by the author in 1962. He holds essentially the same position today if "therapist" and "treatment" are defined in the classical sense of entering into a contract with someone who chooses to be defined as a "patient," and who is seeking help for what is mutually defined as an "illness" or "disorder." Such a relationship requires special skills outside the province of sociology as such; if a sociologist acquires these skills, and some have, he is a sociologist and something else. In the field of mental health, there has been a growing tendency to give a broader definition to "treatment," in relation to social systems, and to change factors in social systems which lead toward behavioral incapacitation in a direction of optimal ability to act. In this sense, the sociologist could have much to contribute, essentially in the ways discussed below.

The major contributions sociologists can make apart from research are through the indirect services of consultation in program development and in-service training to the staffs of their agency or other related agencies.[1] It is by no means always necessary to "do research" from scratch in relation to every sociologically relevant problem that may arise in service programs. There is already a considerable body of applicable knowledge plus useful perspectives and approaches. The sociologist can be quite helpful to others in the program, assisting them to define their problems more sharply and systematically and bringing to their attention the documented experiences of other, similar programs. In-service training may take the form of general sociological orientation to sharpen awareness of a range of social factors influencing the service program, or it

[1] The author has made a special analysis of the relations between direct and indirect services [26].

may be training in specific research techniques. If the sociologist has a dual appointment in a nearby university, he may be able to arrange a valuable combination of academic work with practical experience, thus helping to prepare a better new generation of medical sociologists.

There are other, more direct, types of service functions which a sociologist may perform or in which he may share, in certain medical settings, notably public health. To do them well requires additional training or some "secondary professionalization" in public health. Also, in-service training can work both ways—the sociologist can learn much from his colleagues in other professions. Perhaps the most promising field for direct sociological contribution in both public health and public mental health is community organization and development, including questions of the logistics in utilization of services. A second promising field, one in which somewhat more work has been done, is in gaining acceptance of health programs.[2]

These service functions can be of strategic importance to research in an indirect way. If done well, they do much to validate the sociologist in the eyes of his colleagues from other disciplines in the medical setting. They help him "pay his freight" and legitimize the time he spends in the riskier ventures of research. Involvement in service functions can also have strategic importance for research in a somewhat more direct way. Such involvement helps to familiarize the sociologist with the laymen's hypotheses, which he can then test through research. As Gouldner indicates, "the latent function of such tests, however, is to document the inadequacy and breakdown of lay hypotheses, thus enlarging the area of intellectual discretion allowable to applied social scientists, and easing their introduction of independent variables that are novel to laymen" [7]. Finally, involvement in service functions can help to further in quite a direct way the detection and closure of those gaps between the basic and applied disciplines which, Gouldner points out, may "signalize, not only a handicap of the applied scientist, but also an unnecessary defect in pure theory itself" [7].

The major shift which is occurring within the health fields, notably within public health, from emphasis on communicable diseases to emphasis on chronic diseases and the "social diseases" or "social deviances" (alcoholism, drug addiction, juvenile delinquency, suicide) makes all of the problems of collaboration between social scientists and the health professions of crucial importance today.[3] The area of social deviances overlaps significantly with the field of mental health, hence, with matters that appear to involve the actor and his action system primarily and the organism secondarily. There are very prominent sociobehavioral facets in the chronic diseases (Chapters 3 and 5). It seems important to emphasize again that it would be good strategy to put larger pieces of the present resources of sociomedical research into research relating to service programs in the health field.

In a discussion of evaluative research the author concluded that, "There is the need to involve practitioners in the attitudes and understandings of evaluative research where they should all have the feeling that they are students. There should be the expectation that they will add self-development in the areas of observation, investigation and

[2] For a detailed discussion of utilization of health services and acceptance of health programs, see Chaps. 16 and 17.

[3] See Chap. 6 for a discussion of the addictive diseases.

critical thinking. Unfortunately, the mental health professions generally have three major lacks in their training: training in administration, training in the research approach, and specific training in the social and behavioral sciences, as contrasted with the clinical sciences. These lacks can be overcome in part by the development of a postgraduate climate in mental health programs." The same conclusion could apply in other health fields. Sociomedical research can be an important catalyst in the development of a postgraduate climate in service programs in the field of health.

SOURCES OF SUPPORT

Unfortunately, even in the relatively "simple" aspect of sources of financial support for sociomedical research, no systematic body of data has been collected for the entire field. In broad perspective, the federal government is the major single source of support, by way of grants and occasionally contracts. Various parts of the government give some support, such as Housing and Urban Development and the various antipoverty programs, depending on how broadly or narrowly one defines "sociomedical research." Within the Department of Health, Education, and Welfare, the Public Health Service gives by far the major share. There are currently three major components of the Public Health Service: Consumer Protection and Environmental Health Service, Health Services and Mental Health Administration, and the National Institutes of Health. The intramural program of the National Institute of Mental Health still has some administrative arrangements with NIH, but the professional direction is within the National Institute of Mental Health, one of the two major components of the Health Services and Mental Health Administration.

All parts of the Public Health Service support sociomedical research in varying ways and degrees, but over the years the NIMH has been and continues to be the focal point in government for the behavioral sciences and, hence, NIMH supports by far the largest share of sociomedical research. The Veterans Administration has a sizable program, especially in the psychiatric field, with a small amount of sociology and social anthropology involved. The Social Rehabilitation Service (including the former Office of Vocational Rehabilitation) has a small program of research and demonstration projects, some of which fall within the sociomedical field. Also some state governments are supporting sociomedical research, particularly in the field of mental health, as are a few city and county health programs.

Foundations support in varying degrees and ways; some of them have played a major role in determining the course of the development of this sociomedical research field. The voluntary health agencies have supported research in the social sciences only to a limited extent.

Other sources of support which seem to have assumed major proportions quite recently are the larger insurance companies and some labor unions—notably the United Mine Workers and the United Auto Workers—but their efforts are supported in part by federal grants, including those from the NIMH.

Federal Support Through the National Institute of Mental Health

More specifically, the National Institute of Mental Health awarded 38 research grants for a total of $373,226, a mean size of $9,822 in 1948. In

1961, there were 1,286 active grants for a total of $30,492,087, a mean size of $23,711.[4] A marked increase in the program began in 1957 when it rose from $3,890,631 to $7,326,311. This trend continued up until about 1967, at which time the Behavioral Sciences Research Branch of the Division of Extramural Research Programs supported $18,525,000 worth of grants, or 33.6 percent of the total research grants. Since that time there has been a leveling off process, in line with the general drive toward cuts in various aspects of federal spending. The comparable figures for 1968 were $18,116,000, or 31.3 percent; in 1969, $19,050,000, or 32.7 percent; and the projection for 1970 was $20,085,000, or 34 percent. Since many grants have commitments for five years and sometimes more, this process means that there is much less room for new projects, and many approved projects cannot be funded. It is important to note that in spite of an over-all reduction in growth of the program, the percentage of extramural grants in the behavioral sciences has not been reduced.

Figures are available for 1967 which give an indication of the number and amount of grants from the NIMH which fall rather clearly within the field of sociomedical research. Extramural grants in that fiscal year totaled 1,546, amounting to $61,975,811. Within psychology there were 61 active grants in the child and developmental field, amounting to $2,593,068, or 4 percent of total grants. Social psychology had 65 grants, which amounted to $2,237,327, also 4 percent of total grants. Within the social sciences, anthropology had 65 grants for 4 percent of total grants but $1,339,297, or 2 percent of total grant funds. Sociology had 77 grants for 5 percent of total grants in the amount of $5,109,906 and 6 percent of total funds. It should be emphasized that these grants are classified by the discipline of the principal investigator, and there are undoubtedly many other social scientists on other teams, especially in psychiatry, which had 257 grants for 17 percent of total grants, in the amount of $15,907,951 and 26 percent of total funds.

Other types of figures were available in 1961 which are no longer available for more recent years. They are included for historical reasons and also because the proportions have not changed greatly. There were 113 principal investigators sustained by NIMH grants from the social sciences (50 in anthropology and 63 in sociology), 9 percent of the total. However, there were 574 psychologists, representing 45 percent of the total, a significant number of whom are social psychologists. In terms of all investigators (actually listed by discipline in grant applications), there were 228 social scientists (84 in anthropology and 144 in sociology), 10 percent of the total, and 783 psychologists, 37 percent of the total. Social scientists who are principal investigators are not evenly distributed on a regional basis. They represent only 2 percent of the total in the South and Southwest, 15 percent in the Middle Atlantic states, and 14 percent on the West Coast. Psychologists, on the other hand, are fairly evenly distributed in terms of percentage of the total number of principal investigators. No cross-tabulations are available by sponsoring institution and discipline,

[4] All of the earlier data for the National Institute of Mental Health is taken from two documents prepared by the Program Analysis Section of the Research Grants and Fellowships Branch, NIMH, under the direction of Dr. Julius Segal, "Summary Data NIMH Research Grants and Fellowships, Fiscal 1961," and "Research in Social Psychology and the Social Sciences Supported by the National Institute of Mental Health—Fiscal Year 1960." Mimeo.

but in 67 percent of all grants (in the fiscal year 1961) the sponsoring institution was a college or university. It is safe to assume that this percentage is even higher for social scientists, as they are less likely to be found in hospitals, clinics, or service organizations than are representatives of the other disciplines involved. Thus, it seems clear that as far as NIMH grants represent a large share of the support of sociomedical research, the research is very largely university based.

In the social science area, regardless of whether the principal investigator is listed as a social scientist or in some other discipline, there were 363 grants in fiscal year 1961, 28 percent of all grants. Among these grants were 136 in group interaction, 53 in culture and personality, and 57 in social change, and a few others not categorized or tabulated.

The majority of all grants fall on the "basic" side. On a seven-point scale from the totally basic (11 percent of the total) to the totally applied (16 percent of the total), 61 percent fall on the basic side of the midpoint, 35 percent on the applied side, and the remainder are equally basic and applied. There is no cross-tabulation by discipline, but in view of the range of disciplines involved (including 21 percent in psychiatry and a goodly number in clinical psychology), it may be assumed that the social sciences would fall even more heavily on the basic side.

An analysis has been made to indicate the general scope of sociopsychological research in the grants program of the NIMH during fiscal year 1960. One hundred sixty grants were supported during that year, 15 percent of the total. They are grouped by areas of research interest. There were large numbers in such areas as social roles, social perception, cross-cultural studies, and social behavior in animals—all of which tend to be fairly basic. But there were perceptible numbers relating to schizophrenia [7], juvenile delinquency and the mental hospital [9], and a substantial number relating to community mental health [14], mostly in the mental health project grants rather than the regular research grant program. There were 21 grants in the area of marriage and the family, of which 12 were based in universities, and 9 in service organizations. They ranged from a project to restructure family theory to a family care demonstration project. There has undoubtedly been a significant increase in the area of community mental health on which there has been heavy emphasis in recent years, especially with the development across the country of community mental health centers.

There are no hard data to show that the above patterns are typical or modal for all sociomedical research. However, the NIMH program is obviously a large one. Also, it follows a pattern of free competition for support, judged by peers of the grantees in their discipline, who, in turn, are drawn from a broad segment of these disciplines. The NIMH staff exercise relatively little specific influence, through "programming," on the type of research or the direction it should take, although they do exercise leadership in certain special areas. It seems probable that the NIMH pattern is fairly typical of the general pattern of sociomedical research. If so, it is largely the sociology or related social science *of* medicine rather than *in* medicine, although a significantly perceptible segment is clearly in medicine. It is largely of a basic character, at one or more removes from application to medical problems; yet, again, a significant segment is concerned rather directly with applications.

Private Support

In 1960–61 Brand made a detailed survey of sources of private support for mental health, including research in this field [4]. (This material is currently being updated on a contract from the NIMH to John E. Hinkle, University Counselling Center, Colorado State University, Fort Collins, Colorado 80521.) Much of Brand's research involved the behavioral sciences, including sociology. In a survey of 1,182 philanthropic and other tax-exempt granting agencies, all of whom made grants on a national basis, Brand provided material which is still relevant today. Of the 122 organizations that replied that they do support research, training, or service in mental health, 21 (17 percent) said they supported "sociology and anthropology as related to mental health." This number ranks very close to the 27 (22 percent) who said they support psychology. Seven, one-third of the 21 organizations contributing to mental health at an annual average rate of 100,000 dollars or more support "sociology and anthropology as related to mental health," and an equal number support "psychology." Research is overall the most richly supported category (56 percent), both for the 122 organizations and for the 21 larger ones. It may be presumed that research is even more predominantly the type of support in sociology and anthropology.

Wellin calls attention to three groups that have made particularly strategic contributions to collaboration between the health field and the behavioral sciences: the Russell Sage Foundation, the Social Science Research Council, and the Health Information Foundation [23]. Russell Sage has emphasized relations between behavioral scientists and the practicing professions, including health but not exclusively health. The Social Science Research Council, through its Committee on Preventive Medicine in Social Science Research, stimulated systematic development of the field. The Health Information Foundation has done much not only to sponsor research directly but to disseminate knowledge of the field through its annual *Inventory of Social and Economic Research in Health.*

Wellin makes the important suggestion that "the Russell Sage Foundation's residency and training program for social scientists in health sorely needs a counterpart program to enable selected medical and paramedical personnel to work in and deepen their understanding of the social sciences" [23].

Is the General Pattern of Support Sound?

It is clear that sociomedical research depends largely on grants. A congressional Committee of Consultants on Medical Research reported that 47 percent of total national medical research was supported by the federal government in 1957 [5]. The federal share, which has been about three-fifths for several years, was 62 percent in 1970. A large share of nonfederal support is given in the form of grants. This situation gives rise to two somewhat related problems. On the one hand, many people in this field are dependent on "soft" money, with its real or fancied insecurities. On the other hand, granting agencies may potentially exercise extraneous influences on the development of the scientific fields related to medicine. There is a resulting danger that a special culture known as "grantsmanship" will develop, characterized by fads, fashions, and other qualities which are not only extraneous to the needs and requirements of scientific development as such but which may actually impede it.

We believe there are certain counterbalancing tendencies. By no means are all sociomedical researchers dependent on grants for their own salaries, although they generally are for supportive staff and equipment, at least if a perusal of NIMH grant applications is a fair indication. Also, there is a marked tendency to develop broad, long-term program support through grants. The grant-giving pattern of the National Institutes of Health, which is also followed by the NIMH, and similar patterns, with varying modifications, followed by many other grant-giving agencies in the field of health, have certain very important built-in safeguards, which, it is fair to say, have become quite well established and institutionalized and which guard against whimsy in any form. A study section or review committee composed of highly qualified experts in the relevant fields of research, and brought in from outside the granting agency, has the crucial role in determining the fate of the grant application. The major criteria relate to the qualifications of the investigator, the adequacy of his design in relation to his aims, and the realistic characteristics of the aims. They relate only secondarily or occasionally to judgments about the "importance of the field."

There is danger of course, that institutionalization can lead to elements of ossified structures which cramp the development of research. However, there are constant proddings to approve high-risk or maverick applications and to encourage young investigators.

The review pattern has one especially important by-product. Persons who participate in study sections and review committees have an opportunity for extensive interaction with key people in their fields in an intensely focused way not generally possible through professional meetings or otherwise, and they are exposed to a very large range of research ideas. It is the writer's opinion, based on discussions with many people who have been involved in the review pattern, that it has exercised a positive and equilibrating influence in the total development of sociomedical research.

The Proper Level of Support

What is the proper range and scope of support? This question is extraordinarily difficult, if not impossible, to answer with any precision. The congressional Committee of Consultants on Medical Research (in general) concluded, "the funds appropriated by the Congress for the support of medical research, although substantial, are still not sufficient to assure the full utilization of the Nation's potential for an attack on the dread diseases, and the present level of support is far from adequate to permit the great advances essential for the future." They recommended that "the Federal Government should supplement private, industrial, and State funds, as may be necessary, to support medical research on the scale required to carry out a determined attack on major health problems. The magnitude of Federal support should be neither limited by nor paced by the rate of increase of non-Federal sources of support." Research in this field expanded at rapid rates from 1957 to 1967. From all appearances it did so without undue growing pains. Rather, pains are being felt now with the leveling off process.

Certain major social events suggest the need for the continued expansion of sociomedical research. The report of the Joint Commission on Mental Illness and Health, issued in 1961 [1], gave considerable impetus in that field. It was followed by the Act,[5] establishing grants for the construction and staffing of comprehensive community mental health centers. Again in the field of mental health there was much activity in the area of planning, beginning with "plans for planning" and continuing with the planning itself, state by state. A great deal of this work was done by volunteers and "lay" people as far as the social sciences are concerned. There is need for much more sociomedical research in this field. A current major need is for evaluative research on the functioning of community mental health centers. As the book edited by the author and Ozarin [29] indicates, a few good evaluative studies of various aspects of community mental health exist, but there is a dearth of such research on the centers in the United States [27]. Similarly, the emphasis now on total health planning, the "partnership for health," and the development of multipurpose human service centers point to the need for expanded sociomedical research.

In the original chapter (1962) the author stated, "In the light of these considerations, it would seem safe to conclude that as a minimum the expansion should continue at the same rate for the next five years as it has in the past five years. Less rapid expansion would be inadequate, and more rapid expansion might be unfeasible in terms of manpower." That expansion did occur and proved valuable. That type of expansion is badly needed today. It is to be hoped that the current leveling off process will be temporary and of short duration.

There are three areas, in particular, where increased research efforts are needed: (1) longitudinal studies; (2) studies of community organization, development, and the logistics of health services; and (3) the development of population laboratories for a variety of studies in the field of health. All three areas require relatively large-scale and expensive research operations.

In the light of these considerations, it would seem safe to conclude that as a minimum the expansion should continue at the same rate for the next five years as it has in the past five years. Less rapid expansion would be inadequate, and more rapid expansion might be unfeasible in terms of manpower.

[5] The Mental Retardation Facilities and Community Mental Health Center Construction Act of 1963, amended in 1965, 1967, 1968, and 1970.

REFERENCES

1. *Action for Mental Health*, Final Report of the Joint Commission on Mental Illness and Health. New York: Basic Books, Inc., Publishers, 1961.
2. ANDERSON, ODIN W. AND MILVOY S. SEACAT, *The Behavioral Scientists and Research in the Health Field*. Research Series No. 1. New York: Health Information Foundation, May, 1957.
3. APPLE, DORIAN, *Sociological Studies of Health and Sickness*. New York: McGraw-Hill Book Company, 1960.
4. BRAND, JEANNE L., *Private Support for Mental Health*. Public Health Service Publication No. 838. Washington, D.C.: Government Printing Office, 1961.
5. Committee of Consultants on Medical Research, *Federal Support of Medical Research*. A Report to the Subcommittee on Departments of Labor and Health, Education, and Welfare of the Committee on Appropriations, U.S. Senate, 86th Cong. 2nd sess. Wacshington, D.C., May, 1960.
6. FREIDSON, ELIOT, *Professor of Medicine: A Study of the Sociology of Applied Knowledge*. New York: Dodd, Mead & Co., 1970.
7. GOULDNER, ALVIN W., "Theoretical Requirements of the Applied Social Sci-

ences," *American Sociological Review*, 22 (February, 1957), 92–102.

8. HANLON, JOHN J., *Principles of Public Health Administration*. St. Louis, Mo.: The C.V. Mosby Company, 1960.
9. JACKSON, J. M., "The Organization and Its Communications Problem," *Advanced Management* (February, 1959), 17–20.
10. KANDEL, DENISE BYSTRYN AND RICHARD HAYS WILLIAMS, *Psychiatric Rehabilitation: Some Problems of Research*. New York: Atherton Press, 1964.
11. KENDALL, PATRICIA L. AND ROBERT K. MERTON, "Medical Education as a Social Process," in E. Gartley Jaco, ed., *Patients, Physicians and Illness*. New York: The Free Press, 1958, pp. 321–50.
12. LUSZKI, MARGARET B., *Interdisciplinary Team Research, Methods and Problems*. New York: New York University Press, 1958.
13. MECHANIC, DAVID, *Medical Sociology: A Selective View*. New York: The Free Press, 1968.
14. MERTON, ROBERT K., GEORGE G. READER, AND PATRICIA L. KENDALL, eds., *The Student-Physician*, Cambridge: Harvard University Press, 1957.
15. Russell Sage Foundation, "Direction to Solutions of Collaboration," *Russell Sage Foundation Annual Report, 1958–1959*. New York, pp. 7–17.
16. ———, "An Appraisal of the Problems of Collaboration," *Russell Sage Foundation Annual Report, 1958–1959*. New York, pp. 8–16.
17. SIBLEY, ELBRIDGE, "The Objectives of Sociological Training," *American Sociological Review*, 25 (August, 1960), 571–75.
18. SIMMONS, OZZIE G. AND JAMES A. DAVIS, "Interdisciplinary Collaboration in Mental Illness Research," *American Journal of Sociology*, 63 (November, 1957), 297–303.
19. SMITH, BREWSTER, "'Mental Health' Reconsidered: A Special Case of the Problem of Values in Psychology," *American Psychologist*, 16 (June, 1961), 299–306.
20. *Some Observations on Controls in Psychiatric Research*, Report No. 42. New York: Group for the Advancement of Psychiatry, May, 1959.
21. STRAUS, ROBERT, "The Nature and Status of Medical Sociology," *American Sociological Review*, 22 (April, 1957), 200–204.
22. SUCHMAN, EDWARD A., "Sociology and the Field of Public Health." Manuscript prepared for the American Sociological Association under the sponsorship of the Russell Sage Foundation, September, 1960. (Mimeo.)
23. WELLIN, EDWARD, "Uses of the Behavioral (Social) Sciences in Public Health." Prepared under contract and Submitted to the National Institute of Mental Health, July, 1961. (Mimeo.)
24. ——— AND MILVOY S. SEACAT, "Social Science in the Health Field," *American Journal of Public Health*, 52 (September, 1962), 1465–72.
25. WILLIAMS, RICHARD H., ed., *Human Factors in Military Operations: Some Applications of the Social Sciences to Operations Research*. Washington, D.C.: Operations Research Office, September, 1954.
26. ———, "Trends in Community Psychiatry: Indirect Services and the Problem of Balance in Mental Health Programs," in Leopold Bellak, ed., *Community Psychiatry and Community Mental Health*. New York: Grune & Stratton, Inc., 1964, pp. 343–57.
27. ———, "Differential Evaluation: Channeling Our Satisfactions and Dissatisfactions," in Fritz Redlich, ed., *Social Psychiatry*. Baltimore: Waverly Press, 1970.
28. ———, "The Mental Health Professions: Who, What and Whither?" Paper presented at the 1968 meeting of the American Orthopsychiatric Association, Chicago. To appear in Morton Levitt, ed., *The Mental Health Field: A Critical Appraisal*. Detroit: Wayne State University Press (forthcoming).
29. ——— AND LUCY D. OZARIN, *Community Mental Health: An International Perspective*. San Francisco: Jossey-Bass, Inc., Publishers, 1968.

20

METHODS OF SOCIOMEDICAL RESEARCH

Jack Elinson

An analysis of advances in social science indicates "... that practical demands or conflicts stimulated about three-fourths of all [major] contributions between 1900 and 1965," and that "major social science advances were applied to social practice in about the same proportion as they were stimulated by it" [14].

There seems to be less introspection today than there was a decade ago as to whether social research is or is not valuable when applied to problems of health and health care. Psychiatry, nursing, and medical care administration are being joined by dentistry and pharmacy in concern about the social aspects of professional and scientific problems. Research and research training in the social sciences in relation to health and health care have been producing an increasing cadre of sociomedical researchers. As the contributions of social research in health are cumulated and systematized, we may yet zig-zag our way toward a more general science of "sociosalustics" [16].

It is probably too much to ask that legislators and administrators defer decision and action on important sociomedical problems until adequate evidence is available. In the first place, there is seldom consensus as to what is "adequate evidence." Second, some are more prone to take risks than others. Third, political pressures and humanitarian impulses force or trigger decision and action, even when outcomes are unpredictable. Nevertheless, a persistent rational faith asserts that messes, failures, and unanticipated consequences in general can be reduced if time, effort, and resources are devoted to the prior study, research, and evaluation of *proposed* solutions of sociomedical problems.

The exploration of problems of sociomedical concern, untouched by empirical investigation, has been made possible by applying systematic social research methods largely forged in the twentieth century. Reproducible methods of observation and data analysis have contributed to the cumulation of knowledge and the achievement of scientific consensus.

Clinical impressions by observers of varying acuity have lost none of their importance, but these are no longer the only source for understanding the social and psychological factors in illness and disease. Anecdotal accounts by both professional and nonprofessional observers continue to provide pictorial accompaniment and to promote dramatic interest, but they have become primarily supplemental or precursive to carefully developed quantitative studies, in tracing changes in the attitude of the medical student as he proceeds through the medical school curriculum. The secret feelings and unexpressed sentiments of significant participants in patient-practitioner relationships and in other medical settings are no longer entirely hidden and are beginning to become amenable to subtle techniques of observation of manifest behaviors, which in turn can be made to yield information on latent relationships when analyzed by imaginative, yet rigorous, mathematical methods. Aggregate, routinely collected economic statistics of medical care utilization and its cost have become background to household sample surveys which make possible—limited only by the creativity of the researcher, the computational facilities at his disposal, and the patience of patients—multivariate analyses of the intricate patterns of utilization of health services. Neatly drawn organization charts carry grossly superficial, and often mythical, information about patterns of medical practice, while sophisticated analysis guided by sociological theory reveals underlying order in the apparent hodgepodge of bureaucratic structure and function.

Not all problems of proper medical concern are equally suitable subjects for social research. It is unlikely that studies of cell metabolism or electrolytic balance will directly benefit in the near future from social research methods. On the other hand, the health problems that easily engage the efforts of the social researcher are those with prominent or dominant social and behavioral components: alcoholism, addiction (to narcotics or food), venereal disease, accidents, mental disorders, and certain chronic diseases. Social disability and rehabilitation are broad areas in which social researchers have also been especially active. Patterns of participation (and nonparticipation) in public health programs are particularly intriguing. The organization of medical care in its social aspects can be fruitfully explored as a sociological question. The choice and pattern of medical care are significant areas of application for students of social psychology. In general, any health behavior—including relevant behavior on the part of persons not yet patients—is a fit subject for social research.

Despite the existence of meritorious texts on social research, most advances in *sociomedical* research methodology remain uncodified and are described in a relatively small number of specialized publications, some sociomedical such as the *Journal of Health and Social Behavior, Social Science and Medicine, American Journal of Public Health, Medical Care,* and *HSMHA Health Reports.* General social research methods applicable to sociomedical problems can of course be found in the various established social science and statistical journals. Two major reference sources which became available during the late sixties are the *International Encyclopedia of the Social Sciences* [29] and the second edition of *The Handbook of Social Psychology* [36].

Of special interest is the series of methodological reports published by the U.S. National Center for Health Statistics. These reports, many based on specifically commissioned studies, deal with central and practical questions of the reliability and validity of health data collected by means of social surveys. The single most detailed overview of methodological studies in sociomedical research is contained in Haberman's chapter on the reliability and validity of morbidity data, in Kosa et al., *Poverty and Health* [21].

The U.S. National Center for Health Services Research and Development has had a great interest in supporting relevant methodological research, but there have been relatively few investigators devoting major efforts or even doing substantial studies in this area. Among the notable exceptions is Loewenstein's study "Two Approaches to Health Interview Surveys" [37], which settled in a rigorous manner a long-debated issue of questionnaire construction in health survey research. The studies of Cannell and Kahn [6], Hyman [28], and Sheatsley [52] have made major contributions to the understanding of the interviewing process. As Kish points out, however, "Nonresponse or resistance to social research deserves more attention than it has gotten to date" [33].

THEORY

Both medicine and sociology are fields of research characterized by a low degree of articulation. "The degree of articulation of a field is the extent to which the phenomena with which the field is concerned are potentially capable of being explained and predicted in terms of a small number of fundamental concepts and constants" [12]. Unlike physics, medicine and sociology require numerous concepts and theories to explain limited sets of phenomena. And in the history of both medicine and sociology are found "grand theorists," who sought to explain everything with one idea they believed to be fundamental. Thus, in the eighteenth century, Dr. Benjamin Rush advanced a theory of convulsive action now regarded as a medical fad [58]. An example from psychology early in the twentieth century is John B. Watson's theory of behaviorism. In sociology, the efforts of Parsons with his theory of action exemplify a struggle to "unify . . . scattered propositions" [44].

A hundred years ago, the physicist Helmholtz and some colleagues issued a scientific manifesto to the effect that all human activity—including consciousness—would ultimately be reducible to simple physical laws. Efforts along these lines persist today in sociology, where the prospect seems even dimmer than in medicine. It would be presumptuous to predict that the grand sociological theorists are doomed to the same fate that befell the early physicists. It is fitting, however, to observe that the terrain in sociology is qualitatively different and manifestly more variable than that in physics or chemistry. Is there not as much justification in the scientific exploration of a variable terrain as there is in the study of simpler concatenations of phenomena?

A more hopeful approach is the development of limited theories [39], which are testable [56]. Examples of limited theories are so commonplace in medicine and have been so productive that they need no iteration here. It is sufficient to cite three examples—(1) relationships between nutrition and atherosclerosis, (2) relationships between cigarette smoking and lung cancer and cardiovascular disease, and (3) relationships between social isolation and schizophrenia—to dramatize the stimulation to research afforded by viable but limited epidemiological theories of disease.

The linking of theories from both medicine and sociology is a relatively untouched area. Caudill [7] has suggested a chain of theoretical linkage between physiological and cultural phenomena. The testing of sociomedical theories by empirical research is even more virginal. Only rough efforts are beginning to be made in these areas in such settings as community health population laboratories. In *The Community as an Epidemiologic Laboratory: A Casebook of Community Studies*, Kessler and Levin [31] systematically bring together in one volume reports on fifteen "community" studies, with editorial commentary from an epidemiological point of view. Many of the studies reported therein could also be considered from a sociological point of view. All face the difficulty of explicitly formulating theories that embody both social and medical variables and of deciding which variables to emphasize as dependent or independent. All have the advantage of a community laboratory in which work is done by various combinations of medical and social scientists. A singular advantage of these community health population laboratories is that they provide unique opportunities for work in the interstices of academic disciplines, drawing on the health sciences and social sciences for hypotheses. It may well be that community laboratories will offer appropriate testing grounds for the linkage of theories from the various disciplines as suggested by Caudill. Still, very little progress has been made in such theoretical linkage. Part of the reason for this may be found in the degree of understanding possessed by investigators, prepared in one discipline, of the theoretical underpinning of another discipline—an understanding inadequate to accomplish the desired linkage [4, 16].

If the process of linkage is to be accepted, it may be useful to have investigators trained in the social sciences who are also knowledgeable in the health sciences. To some extent this is already happening; there are a number of adventurous individuals in a few centers. At the time of this writing, the American Sociological Association under contract with the U.S. National Center for Health Services Research and Development, is exploring, the teaching of behavioral sciences —i.e., anthropology, psychology, sociology—in schools of medicine.

CONCEPTS

Organizing concepts are expressed in technical language, created because ordinary words have too many meanings in everyday discourse, and thus lack clarity and may be misleading. Confusion arises when sociologists use ordinary words and endow them with technical meanings. Although the use of polysyllabic words is less prevalent in sociology than in medicine (e.g., atherosclerosis, carcinogenesis, bacteriology), sociomedical scientists should not shrink from the thought that their technical language may some day approach that of medicine in novelty and polysyllabicity. In time, physicians will accept technical sociological terminology as they have done with biochemistry and with the same equanimity now accorded medical terminology by sociologists.

Here reference should be made to the hold that the terms "medicine" and "physician" have had in the thinking and work of social scientists. Since the call by Dr. Rosen for the use of the broader concept of health (in the first edition of this book), some advances have taken place in terminology. For example, the naming of federal agencies—National Center for *Health* Statistics, National Center for *Health* Services Research and Development—and the establishment of *health* sciences campuses at various universities (such as the State University of New York at Stony Brook and the University of Connecticut) presage some changes. Another major force in the direction of change is the increasing convergence of interest of other health sciences and professions (notably dentistry and nursing, and even more recently, pharmacy) in the social sciences. While no term yet exists for the conjoint investigations in health and social sciences, one such as "sociosalustics" may someday be considered [16].

It is paradoxical, but the initial use of ordinary terms and vague concepts, such as "illness" and "disease," in research may stimulate research toward clearer concepts precisely because the use of ordinary terms is controversial and leads to different interpretations by different researchers. Statements like "Illness is related to poverty" or "Mental disorder is more prevalent among lower-class people" may be challenged by researchers because "illness" may be narrowly interpreted as and equated with "disease," and "mental disorder" may be narrowly interpreted as and equated with "psychosis." Similarly, what is meant by "poverty" and "lower-class"? Challenges of this sort, when accepted positivistically, lead to a refinement of concepts, with increasing precision and subtlety of understanding.

The central phenomena of medical sociology are health, illness, and disease, and the way society organizes to deal with these events. Empirical research and reflections thereon have served to clarify the overly simple notions about the prevalence of illness and disease in the population. Technical distinctions have been made among the various methods of measuring morbid conditions. If we designate **MM** as a general symbol for measures of morbidity, we can distinguish at least the following six types:

MM-1 Tissue alterations, viewed as such and judged by pathologists to be causes of death—e.g., "atherosclerosis," "carcinoma."

MM-2 Records produced by physiologic measuring equipment—e.g., the electrocardiogram; and the interpretations by specialists—e.g., cardiologists—of such records as the "right bundle branch block."

MM-3 Judgments rendered by clinicians in the form of a "diagnosis" after considering "all the evidence"—e.g., "coronary artery disease." There is an analogy here to a judge rendering a decision in a court of law, except that the clinician acts as prosecutor and defense attorney as well as judge. Sometimes he calls in other clinicians (i.e., judges) to help him in rendering a decision.

MM-4 Reports of people that they have a

given "disease"—e.g., "I have a bad heart." These reports have conventionally been put into two classes: (1) those in which the person reports that he has been so told by a physician (MM-4a) and (2) those in which he has not been so told (MM-4b).

MM-5 Reports of symptoms objectively observable (to other than the reporter) —e.g., rash, sweating, swelling, lumps, sores, rapid breathing, and so on.

MM-6 Reports of sensations, feelings, or thoughts not directly or readily observable by others—e.g., itch, headache, tiredness, anger, depression, guilt, fear, pain, discomfort, hallucinations, and so on. Again, although sensations, feelings, and thoughts are best known to the person who has them (MM-6a), useful inferences about them can often be made by objective observers (MM-6b)—i.e., physicians, psychologists, social workers.

In the interests of conceptual clarity, each of the above morbidity measures and submeasures deserves a separate name. In any case, it is useful to call attention to their distinctions. Note must be taken that conceptual muddles arising from failure to make these distinctions in studies of illness and disease result in misinterpretation and misunderstanding. These distinctions, in turn when properly perceived, can generate more fruitful research.

It is fair to say that social scientists dipping into epidemiology have tended to concentrate their observations on the last three measures of morbidity (MM 4–6); medical scientists, on the first three (MM 1–3). In other words, each has been speaking his own language under the general umbrella of "illness" or "disease" [10, 11, 17, 49, 65]. Recognizing these conceptual distinctions and separating them by distinct terms for which there can be consensus are necessities for research progress in the sociomedical field. It should be noted that each of the measures of morbidity is subject to reliability studies. In addition to such studies, empirical correlations among the various measures contribute to our understanding of each. The advantages and disadvantages of various concepts as a basis of assessing the health status of a population have been carefully discussed by Sullivan [61] and Moriyama [42].

The Five Ds

Another way of slicing the conceptual health pie is by taking more of a "medical care" or "health services" point of view than a strictly "disease" one. Epidemiologists are interested in disease; indeed, it is hard to find an authoritative definition of epidemiology which does not contain that word. Other sociomedical researchers may be interested in the "outcome" or effectiveness of health services. In assessing or evaluating the effectiveness of health services, a set of classes of outcome variables has been defined, conveniently referred to as the Five Ds. [50]. These are

death
disease
disability
discomfort
dissatisfaction

Death. While death is an obvious and necessary concept in assessing health services, with advances in biochemical tissue-preserving technology, its exact operational determination has in some cases become arbitrary; it is known now, for example, how to keep a human heart beating long after the brain has ceased to function detectably. Death rates are most readily and accurately determined for populations where they are least valuable in assessing the health of the population. In parts of the world where death rates are still high, it is difficult to attain accuracy in their measurement because of incomplete records, uncertain population base, etc. Where death rates are relatively low, they tend not to be very serviceable as indicators in the assessment of health services. For example, in any given year, in countries with low death rates, 99 percent of the population remains alive in markedly varied degrees of health. In such countries, death rates are insensitive indicators, except perhaps for special population subgroups that have higher than average mortality, as, for instance, people living in poverty areas of California [3, 25] or New York [64].

Disease. Restricting the meaning of the term "disease" to the judgments rendered by clinicians after examination of "all the evidence" (Morbidity Measure 3), we have a variable which is the basis for many if not most social epidemiological studies [20, 47]. Imposing this restriction on disease makes necessary the collaboration of medical scientists or clinicians, since usually skills for determining the presence of disease are outside the ken of social scientists.

Today preventing and curing disease occupies the attention of industrialized societies much less than in earlier days. Chronic disease control rather than cure appears to be a major objective of health services. Indeed one view, advanced by Dubos, in his *Mirage of Health* [15], is that more and more we shall come to look upon health as a functional balance of biological and environmental forces. Accordingly, we must seek meaningful variables other than disease alone.

Disability. One such variable is disability. Fine diagnostic distinctions among diseases as "entities" are lost upon nonmedically trained individuals. What is of consequence to everyone is the effect of a disease on a person's ability to function in normal social roles. Measures of disability have been developed [1] and can be used as a common denominator for all diseases, and, therefore, become useful as indicators of the effectiveness of community health programs. It has been argued, and rightly, that disability is a function of a person's social role, for instance, his usual occupation, and that a disease which may be disabling for one class of worker is not for another. A few biomedical researchers like Hinkle [24] have placed more emphasis on disabling episodes of disease than on the specific disease entities [23]. Further, measures of disability rates may be unrelated to disease, being instead measures of worker morale or reflections of labor-management disagreements (for example, when policemen, for whom it is illegal to strike, "call in sick" in the effort to enforce their demands). When this happens, the medical scientist or epidemiologist is more likely than the sociologist or economist to lose interest in the measure.

Discomfort. This concept is operationally definable as self-reports of feelings of aches, pains, tiredness, sadness, etc. The feelings may be said to arise out of illness when they can be clinically said to be part of or precursors to a diagnosable disease or identifiable injury. Again, as in the case of disability, discomfort may be produced by events other than disease or injury, in which case it may be of minimal professional concern to a physician, while it continues to be a substantial problem for his patient.

Dissastisfaction. This completely subjective state may or may not arise out of objective conditions. It is included as an important concept in sociomedical research since it is now well recognized that the use or nonuse of health services depends not only on the presence or absence of disease but also on feelings of acceptance or rejection of health services offered by professionals.

MEASUREMENT

Medical scientists, particularly epidemiologists, are fond of pointing out that it would be nice to be able to study the relationship between certain social variables—e.g., stress and disease—if only it were possible to "measure" such variables. A report of the World Health Organization states that: "Despite the great importance of these factors [mental, emotional and socio-economic], no adequate measuring techniques are available" [67]. The term "measure" in such comments undoubtedly refers to the higher order forms of measurement—i.e., interval and ratio scales—and neglects the more rudimentary but useful forms such as nominal and ordinal scales. Social scientists, on the other hand, are so delighted to have even these more limited measures to work with that the possibilities of achieving more elegant measures rarely enter their research frame of reference. It will be shown here, however, that both medical and social scientists use all forms of measurement—the more rudimentary as well as the more elegant—to some extent.

The situation would be clarified if a general definition of "measurement" was accepted. According to Stevens, "measurement is the assignment of numerals to objects or events according to rules" [55]. The sets of rules that are commonly employed by scientists have been classified as various types of scales: nominal, ordinal, interval, and ratio. Several of these have been further divided into subtypes, depending on whether or not they possess certain special properties. It will suffice for us here to review the four main types.

The Nominal Scale

A nominal scale is essentially no more than a nonoverlapping classification, with numbers assigned to the various classes. Any numbers at all can be assigned to classes in a nominal scale, provided that the same number is not assigned to two different classes. The numbers used in a nominal scale are then little more than names (hence, nominal) and have no advantage over names except as a kind of shorthand. A nominal scale is a primitive scale indeed, and hardly deserves other than a formal place in a discussion of measurement.

Much of the measurement in medical science has not passed beyond the primitive nominal scale stage—i.e., the distinctive naming of sets of phenomena in order to distinguish among them. Nosology—the naming of diseases—constitutes no more than nominal measurement, yet the classification of disease entities is the bedrock of medical science and has fostered much epidemiologic research. The *International Classification of Diseases* [68] and the *Standard Nomenclature of Diseases and Operations* [2] are prime examples of nominal scales in medicine. The use of numbers to identify disease entities is not quantification in any real sense, but simply the substitution of small sets of numerals (codes) for larger sets of letters (disease names) to facilitate recording, data processing, and tabulating operations. That there is difficulty even in naming is exemplified by the work of an international committee attempting to arrive at a consensus about criteria defining coronary artery disease [13, 67].

In social science, with few exceptions, variables of interest have not been classified, codified, and numbered in a way that makes them universally employable. The exceptions are the classifications of occupations and industries developed by the Census Bureau [8] and the *Dictionary of Occupational Titles* [63] developed by the U.S. Employment Service, both of which receive extensive use. Aside from such practically useful classifications, there is no universally accepted classification of either concept-terms or index-terms as used by social scientists. Sociologists are incurable conceptualizers, and among them the naming of social categories is a great sport. Such terms as "reference groups" have an important use, as Merton and Kitt have pointed out, "not because the term itself helps explain behavior, but because it does not easily allow us to overlook . . . components . . ." [40]. Perhaps most sociological measurement still takes place on a nominal level.

Most classifications and numbered codes both in medicine and the social sciences have been ad hoc—i.e., useful in a particular investigation—and have generally not survived the immediate use for which they have been constructed. Concept naming in sociology is particularly ephemeral, and psychological variables, for example, have an uncertain stability and a high evanescent rate (e.g., authoritarianism, permissiveness, apprehension, innerdirectedness) and rarely survive a single study by the same investigator or a flurry of subsequent studies. There are notable exceptions of course: Freudian terms have been remarkably tenacious, but even these may have had their day [18].

The Ordinal Scale

Ordinal scales are a step up the measurement ladder. In them numbers are assigned so that the order of the numbers corresponds to the order of magnitude of the instances of a property. The hardness scale of minerals and the pecking order of chickens in a barnyard are examples of ordinal scales. The concept of ranking as to more and less is a property of an ordinal scale, but nothing is implied as to the distances or intervals between ranks.

Ordinal scales are quite common in medicine. The patient is "cured," "improved," "unchanged," "worse." Using the adjectives constitutes an ordered set of meaningful relationships in terms of better or worse but says nothing quantitative about how much better "cured" is than "improved." Another example of an ordinal scale in medicine is the frequent classification of a condition along a dimension of severity, such as "severe," "moderate," "mild." In the field of medical care, an interesting ordinal scale was developed by Hassinger for characterizing the rank of a county within a state in terms of the availability of medical care services [22].

A large number of obvious ordinal scales come to mind from the domain of the social sciences—e.g., ratings of employee efficiency or conditions of housing. A large number also of less obvious ordinal scales have been demonstrated by Guttman's scalogram technique for sociological variables [59]. Among these is John Dollard's scale of a combat soldier's manifestations of fear in battle, and the various morale attitude scales developed by Stouffer and his associates in *Studies in Social Psychology in World War II* [58].

The Interval Scale

An interval scale has all the properties of nominal and ordinal scales (distinctiveness, order) but, in addition, has the property of operationally defined distance between ranks. Familiar examples of interval scales are the Centigrade and Fahrenheit temperature scales, in which the units between adjacent degrees are equal. In these scales the starting point is arbitrary (there is no absolute zero as in Kelvin), so that with them it is incorrect to say that 40 degrees is twice as hot as 20 degrees. Interval scales that are not also ratio scales are rare in medicine and practically nonexistent in the social sciences. Even standardized psychological tests—such as some aptitude and achievement tests which provide numerical scores for right answers—are pseudointerval, since the interval between scores is completely arbitrary, being dependent on the particular questions or items employed.

Attitude research has advanced to the use of ordinal measures (that is, cumulative noninterval scales), and efforts have been made to introduce equal-appearing intervals into attitude scales [62]. Attempts to do this have been seriously challenged on logical and empirical grounds. The so-called equal units were derived from averages of judges' ratings of attitudinal distances among items. The inadequacy of this approach derives from the empirical fact that the ratings vary with the judges who are doing the judging [53]. Under some conditions, however, assignments of numbers may be made to rank order categories as if they conform to interval scales [35].

The Ratio Scale

Ratio scales permit one to say that something exists in *x* times the amount of something else. This property of a scale is made possible by the existence of an absolute zero, as well as equal intervals, in the quantity being measured. Ratio scales are common in the physical sciences—e.g., length and mass—and find practical application in measures of height and weight. The pulse, and visual and auditory acuity are examples of measures that are ratio scales in medicine. In the social sciences, ratio scales are to be found primarily in that most highly quantitative field known as demography, or population research. The counting—of babies born, of persons who migrate, of persons who die—makes possible the use of the most advanced measuring scales and the performance of the greatest variety of mathematical manipulations with the fewest assumptions.

The examples of different types of scales used in medicine and the social sciences set forth here illustrate the analogy between measurement in medicine and measurement in the social sciences.

RELIABILITY AND VALIDITY

Perhaps no words have been used more in connection with measurement than "reliability" and "validity." Enough work has been done with these concepts so that they no longer serve as useful scientific terms in an unqualified sense. They have become differentiated into several operationally definable "reliabilities" and "validities." In keeping with an operational frame of reference, one can see that there are

Alpha Reliabilities, i.e., the correspondence between two observers or the same observer at different times, interobserver and intraobserver reliability; and

Beta Reliabilities, i.e., the correspondence between two measuring instruments or between briefer and lengthier versions of the same measuring instruments (e.g., short and long intelligence tests).

The time dimension introduces an interesting paradox with respect to the concept of reliability. If what one observes is highly variable by nature (blood pressure, a mood, the position of an electron), how can one tell whether differences in repeated measurements are caused by a change in the observed phenomenon or by the unreliability of the method of observation? This paradox has led to experiments with simultaneous observation of a given phenomenon by multiple observers—e.g., multiple stethoscopy. In such instances, the observer becomes an integral part of the measuring process, and the separation of the unreliability of the measuring instrument, for example, the stethoscope, from that of the observer becomes difficult if not impossible. Reliability studies of measures are not common in medicine; many more have been done in the behavioral and social sciences. It is as if to question the reliability of a medical measure is to interfere with the practice of medicine (have confidence in your doctor!). In one study it was shown that of two physicians with comparable training, one was able to find 50 percent more diagnosable diseases in equivalent random samples of patients [11].

The best-known reliability study of medical observations is Yerushalmy's study of X-ray readings [69]. Clark and his co-workers have shown how variable blood pressure readings are when taken under different conditions [9]. Other studies deal with the reliability of electrocardiogram readings and of cardiovascular and psychiatric diagnoses [10, 34]. There may well be an upsurge in studies of the reliability of medical measuring instruments to accompany research and development in automated multiphasic health testing [46].

In studies of reliability there is a danger of permitting the perfect to become the enemy of the good or committing the error of errorlessness. Some investigators give up the measurement of a phenomenon for scientific studies when they find any degree of unreliability. But the important question should be, how much unreliability is there in relation to the purpose of the measure?

"Validity" is a more emotionally charged term than "reliability," and clinicians usually regard validity as more important than reliability. "A dozen careless psychiatrists may all agree that a patient's marital adjustment is satisfactory solely because they have neglected to ask the important questions. In these instances reliability may be high, yet validity low . . ." [34].

On the other hand, statisticians and epidemiologists have a high regard for reliability, frequently leaving appraisals of validity to nonmethodologists, as in the definition of Validity A below. In a survey made of epidemiological research requirements, reliability studies were listed first [66].

Just as for reliability, the time has come to regard a single definition of validity as no longer scientifically useful. Operationally, there are at least four validities:

Validity A Construct validity is what the investigator says the measure is measuring: "Intelligence is what intelligence tests measure." What, with this concept of validity, is blood pressure [9]?

Validity B Consensual validity involves construct validity, but is assessed by the degree of consensus among investigators that a measure is measuring a certain quality. Should the investigators have a common background of training?

Validity C Criterion validity is the association between one measure and a measure of some other variable taken to be the criterion variable (i.e., the "more valid" measure).

Validity D Predictive validity is the association between one measure and a measure of some other variable taken to be the criterion variable (i.e., the "more valid" measure) over time—i.e., predictive of some criterion.

Of the four definitions cited, Validity C is the most common. It is usually not expressed in such abstract terms as defined here. Nor is it usually understood that Validity C necessarily implies either Validity B or, in some instances, Validity A. To illustrate by a mean example:

Suppose there was a roomful of men and women behind a closed door. And suppose from a position outside the room, you wished to identify the sex of its occupants by the sound of their voices. The question is, is the sound of a voice so heard a valid measure of sex? To answer this question one could, in an open-door situation, correlate his judgments made on the basis of the sound of the voices with another measure of sex which ranks high on Validity B. The degree of association obtained would be considered an assessment of Validity C.

The closed-door situation frequently obtains both in medicine and in the social sciences. An example from medicine is found in studies of diet and blood cholesterol. It has been shown that variations in diet are accompanied by variations in blood cholesterol [30]. Yerushalmy has dubbed this "the substitution game" [45a], since the interest in these studies is to learn what relationship there might be between diet and coronary heart disease. The question then is asked: is the blood cholesterol level a valid assessment of the likelihood of developing coronary heart disease? This question can be answered by investigations that have already been carried out [19, 32, 51] and by prospective studies. Thus far, the reasoning is straightforward and practically self-evident. What is missing is the recognition of the necessity for assessing the validity of the diagnosis of coronary heart disease. We are now back to consensual validity: Validity B. Efforts at establishing criteria for diagnosing coronary heart disease are actually being made [67]. The establishment of such criteria is an example of Validity B. If one investigator should decide that he prefers another set of criteria, or modifications of these criteria, we should then have an example of Validity A.

Validity D enters the picture when predictions about dying from coronary heart disease are made from a knowledge of the presence or absence of this disease in living persons. It should be clear that the presence or absence of the disease in question may be consensually determined (Validity B) and that the prediction of death from the disease may be more or less successful (Validity D). Yet there are many who would argue that the validity of any method of measuring a variable is in question if successful predictions (Validity D) cannot be made. This argument is most commonly used by psychometricians, and it takes the following form: A mathematical aptitude test cannot be considered valid until it can be shown to predict success in a job involving mathematics—e.g., actuary, computer programmer, teacher, and so on.

Validity D (predictive validity) is clearly not equivalent to Validity C (criterion validity) or to Validities B and A (consensual and construct validities). Prediction is only one operational definition of validity.

Research in medicine and the social sciences is often closed-door research. We cannot always measure directly what we wish to measure, and often have to content ourselves with some index. It is important, however, to distinguish between situations in which it is possible at times actually to get behind the closed door and situations in which we only imagine that if we could get behind the closed door, a reality might be there, which could be directly measured and correlated with our more indirect measure.

The latter situation may be exemplified by reference to struggles by social scientists with measures of socioeconomic status or social position. Numerous ingenious combinations of the education-income-occupation complex have been proposed [26], as if there were some underlying variable which one really wants to measure but cannot because of a closed door. So far no one has come up with a real measure of socioeconomic status. The indices are all we have; and they are real enough.

EXPERIMENT

> The greatest difference between modern times and the Middle Ages, in medicine as well as in all sciences, is the objective, the experimental method [48]. . . . [T]he thing that differentiates the modern method from either the ancient or the medieval method is that it definitely abandons all attempts at a complete synthesis of knowledge, built up with any philosophic system, and starts by trying to get at definite facts and thus allows these facts themselves, with their inevitable consequences, to determine the direction in which conclusions are formed [41].

Experimentation with a capital *E* has won a properly revered place in the scientific method. But too often the form is honored more than the substance. A carefully controlled experiment on a trivial variable which is manipulable makes a less significant contribution than a careful inferential analysis of the associations of nonmanipulable but nontrivial variables. The kind of evidence available for interpreting the association between smoking and lung cancer is a case in point.

The idea of experimentation is quite old and predates modern science. An example will be cited from the field of medical care. Petrarch, in a letter to Boccaccio, wrote that a famous physician once told him that

> . . . if 100 or 1000 individuals of the same age and the same constitution and mode of life at one and the same time were attacked by the same disease and half availed themselves of the physicians, the others acted without any medical advice, following their natural instincts and discretion, there could be no doubt whatsoever that the second half would happily recover [48].

A modern instance of this alleged phenomenon is contained in the results of an evaluation of rehabilitation in which an experimental group of patients in nursing homes receiving rehabilitative services had a slightly higher mortality rate than a control group of patients not receiving such services [43]!

The first point to be emphasized is that the variables studied are more important than the methods available to study them. Second, a different logic is not involved in capital *E* experiments and other types of investigation. Third, there is a set of experimental designs —i.e., E_1, E_2, E_3, and so on—and not one best way to design an experiment. And fourth, the classic experimental before/after design with control and experiment groups is not always the design of choice—especially in sociomedical research—even where the choice is a feasible one.

It is a common philosophic gambit to contrast experiment with observation. The similarities between these two scientific approaches (if they are, indeed, two) are greater than their differences. In the first place, no experiment is of any value unless observation is an integral part of it. One has to observe change or lack of change in the experimental group and control, if any. Next, inferences are made after experimental observation as to the existence of a relationship; similarly with the observational "method." There is then no difference in kind between "experimental" and "observational" methods. To quote Cornfield:

> If important alternative hypotheses are compatible with available evidence, then the question is unsettled, even if the evidence is experimental. But if only one hypothesis can explain all the evidence, then the question is settled even if the evidence is observational. The proposition that some inherent logical incompetence attaches to an inference based on observational, as distinguished from experimental, evidence seems to have little to commend it beyond the great positiveness with which it is sometimes asserted [12].

We call attention to the proposition that there is not one, but a set of experimental designs; that each has its advantages and disadvantages; and that no one experimental design is superior to all other designs in all instances. Support for this proposition is contained in the writings of the following social scientists: Hovland [27], Payne [45], Solomon [54], and Stouffer [57]. The most comprehensive and insightful treatment of this subject has been presented by Donald T. Campbell [5].

EVALUATION

This past decade has seen a burgeoning of systematic efforts to evaluate social action programs, including the sociomedical. These efforts have roots in a preoccupation with the failure of society to apply what is scientifically known to the amelioration of problems of human concern, and in the recognition, even among non-economists, that there is never enough to go around, with the resultant urgent emphasis upon making the most of what one has. The process of determining the effectiveness and efficiency of social action programs has been called evaluation.

Methods of evaluation ranging from decrees by self-proclaimed authorities to formal, systematic, painstaking efforts approaching scientific rigor have been subjected to analytic review from the point of view of social utility. Among the most comprehensive of these reviews is Suchman's *Evaluative Research* [60]. Other assessments more specifically targeted to a particular social action program are included in *Dilemmas of Social Reform*, by Peter Marris and Martin Rein [38]. Several other thoughtful appraisals of the process of evaluation have appeared.

The most sophisticated writing in the field of design of social experimentation continues to be that of Donald Campbell. If adopted, his imaginative idea of regarding *reforms as experiments* [5] may result in more equanimous relations between programmatic practitioners and evaluative researchers. Practitioners have called on researchers to be more interested in programs. What Campbell has done is to ask practitioners to think more like scientists than advocates.

CONCLUSIONS

Both medical and social science research are concerned with problems inherent in studying man and his behavior. Virtually all problems of method in sociomedical research have their analogues in other areas of inquiry, and the scientific issues that confront the medical sociologist are not endemic to his field. The problems are not solved simply, however; if anything, the methodological limitations in the two fields are often compounded in sociological investigations of health and illness. But a rigorous methodology is essential to the growth of systematic research in medical sociology. The available medical and behavioral science literature on method provides a basis for developing appropriate designs, instruments, and analytical procedures. This literature reveals that the power of research methods in medical sociology is a function of the development of appropriate statistical theory, particularly in sampling, experimental design, and multivariate data analysis. The confrontation of the statistician with scientific problems conceptualized by the medical sociologist should continue to produce innovation in method, more efficient research, and greater certainty of inference toward a better quality of evidence for entertaining scientific propositions.

The merger of social and medical scientists proliferated in the past decade. Their relationship is now an easier one; they are not likely to be found justifying themselves to each other, but are more likely to spend a higher proportion of their shared time listening to each other express fine points of conceptualization, measurement, and research design, and with more mutual understanding than ever before. National research grant review bodies in epidemiology and in health services research and development are now composed of equal parts of social and medical scientists along with statisticians who can tolerate both breeds.

Sensitivity to the problems of method has resulted in improved and more sophisticated research techniques in both the medical and behavioral sciences. Creativity and conceptual skill, as well as technical knowledge, are essential in the development of appropriate measures, in the assessment of their validity and reliability, and in the implementation of analysis procedures. The logic of science and the craftsmanship of research transcend the disciplines of medicine and sociology.

REFERENCES

1. ADAMS, M., T. D. DOWNS, A. B. FORD, AND S. KATZ, "Chronic-disease Classification in Evaluation of Medical Care Programs," *Medical Care*, 7 (March–April, 1969), 139–43.
2. American Medical Association, *Standard Nomenclature of Diseases and Operations*, 4th ed. New York: McGraw-Hill Book Company, 1952.
3. ATHANASOPOULOUS, D. A., J. R. HOCHSTIM, AND J. H. LARKINS, "Poverty Area Under The Microscope," *American Journal of Public Health*, 58 (October, 1968), 1815–27.
4. BORKMAN, T. S., "A Biosociological Problem: Blood Pressure and Sociocultural Incongruity." Ph.D. dissertation, Columbia University, Department of Sociology, 1968.
5. CAMPBELL, D. T., "Factors Relevant to Validity of Experiments in Social Settings," *Psychological Bulletin*, 54 (July, 1957), 297–312.
6. CANNELL, C. F. AND R. L. KAHN, "Interviewing," in G. Lindzey and E. Aronson, eds., *The Handbook of Social Psychology*, 2nd ed. Reading, Mass.: Addison-Wesley Publishing Company, Inc., 1968.
7. CAUDILL, W., *Effects of Social and Cultural Systems in Reactions to Stress*, Social Science Research Council, Pamphlet 14. New York, June, 1958.
8. CENSUS BUREAU, U.S. Department of Commerce, *Alphabetical Index of Occupations and Industries*, rev. ed. Washington, D.C.: U.S. Government Printing Office, 1960.

9. Clark, G. E., C. Y. Glock, and R. Vought, "Studies in Hypertension, I–VI," *Journal of Chronic Diseases*, 4 (September, 1956); 4 (November, 1956); 5 (February, 1957).

10. Commission on Chronic Illness, *Chronic Illness in a Large City: The Baltimore Study*, Vol. 4. Cambridge: Harvard University Press, 1957.

11. ———, *Chronic Illness in a Rural Area: The Hunterdon Study*, Vol. 3. R. E. Trussell and J. Elinson. Cambridge: Harvard University Press, 1959.

12. Cornfield, J., "Principles of Research," *American Journal of Mental Deficiency* (September, 1959), pp. 240–52.

13. Dawber, T. R., F. E. Moore, and G. V. Mann, "Coronary Heart Disease in the Framingham Study in Measuring Risk of Coronary Heart Disease in Adult Population Groups: A Symposium," *American Journal of Public Health*, 47 (April Supp., 1957), 4.

14. Deutsch, K. W. et al., "Conditions Favoring Advances in Social Science," *Science*, 171 (February 5, 1971), 450–59.

15. Dubos, R., *Mirage of Health*. New York: Harper & Row, Publishers, 1959.

16. Elinson, J. and C. E. Herr, "A Sociomedical Response to Edward S. Rogers: 'Public Health Asks of Sociology . . .'." Paper read at the American Sociological Association Annual Meeting, San Francisco, September, 1969. (Mimeographed.)

17. Feldman, J. J., "The Household Interview Survey as a Technique for the Collection of Morbidity Data," *Journal of Chronic Diseases*, 11 (May, 1960), 535–37.

18. Gilman, R., "The FemLib Case Against Sigmund Freud," *New York Times Magazine* (January 31, 1971), pp. 10 ff.

19. Gordon, T. and W. B. Kannel, "The Framingham, Massachusetts, Study Twenty Years Later," in I. I. Kessler and M. L. Levin, eds., *The Community as an Epidemiologic Laboratory*. Baltimore, Md.: The Johns Hopkins Press, 1970.

20. Graham, S., M. Levin, and A. M. Lilienfeld, "The Socio-Economic Distribution of Cancer at Various Sites in Buffalo, New York, 1948–52," *Cancer*, 13 (1960), 180.

21. Haberman, P. W., "The Reliability and Validity of the Data," in J. Kosa et al., eds., *Poverty and Health*. Cambridge: Harvard University Press, 1969.

22. Hassinger, E. and R. L. McNamara, "The Pattern of Medical Services for Incorporated Places of 500-or-More Population in Missouri, 1950," *Rural Sociology*, 21 (June, 1956), 175–77.

23. Hinkle, L. E., *Human Ecology and Health in Modern Society*. Philadelphia: Lea Febiger, 1970.

24. ——— and H. G. Wolff, "Ecologic Investigations of the Relationship between Illness, Life Experiences and the Social Environment," *Annals of Internal Medicine*, 49 (December, 1958), 1373–88.

25. Hochstim, J. R., "Conceptual and Methodological Problems in Developing a Measure of Health Status," *Proceedings of the Outcomes Conference 1*, California Center for Health Services Research, Pacific Grove, Calif., May, 1969, pp. 58–70.

26. Hollingshead, A. B. and F. C. Redlich, *Social Class and Mental Illness*. New York: John Wiley & Sons, Inc., 1958.

27. Hovland, C. I., A. A. Lumsdaine, and F. D. Sheffield, *Experiments in Mass Communication*. Princeton, N.J.: Princeton University Press, 1949.

28. Hyman, H. H. et al., *Interviewing in Social Research*. Chicago: University of Chicago Press, 1954.

29. *International Encyclopedia of the Social Sciences*, New York: Crowell Collier and Macmillan, Inc., 1968.

30. Inter-Society Commission for Heart Disease Resources, "Primary Prevention of Atherosclerotic Diseases," *Circulation*, 42 (December, 1970), A-55–A-95.

31. Kessler, I. I. and M. L. Levin, eds., *The Community as an Epidemiologic Laboratory*. Baltimore, Md.: The Johns Hopkins Press, 1970.

32. Kinch, S. H. et al., "Risk Factors in

Ischemic Heart Disease," *American Journal of Public Health*, 53 (March, 1963), 438–42.

33. KISH, L., *Survey Sampling*. New York: John Wiley & Sons, Inc., 1965.
34. KREITMAN, N., "The Reliability of Psychiatric Diagnoses," *Journal of Mental Science*, 107 (September, 1961), 876–86.
35. LABOVITZ, S., "The Assignment of Numbers to Rank Order Categories," *American Sociological Review*, 35 (June, 1970), 515–24.
36. LINDZEY, G. AND E. ARONSON, eds., *The Handbook of Social Psychology*, 2nd ed., Vols. 1–5. Reading, Mass.: Addison-Wesley Publishing Company, Inc., 1968–1969.
37. LOEWENSTEIN, R., *Two Approaches to Health Interview Surveys*. New York: Columbia University School of Public Health and Administrative Medicine, 1969.
38. MARRIS, P. AND M. REIN, *Dilemmas of Social Reform*. New York: Atherton Press, 1967.
39. MERTON, R. K., *Social Theory and Social Structure*. New York: The Free Press, 1957.
40. ———, AND A. S. KITT, "Contributions to the Theory of Reference Group Behavior," in R. K. Merton and P. F. Lazarsfeld, eds., *Continuities in Social Research*. New York: The Free Press, 1950.
41. MILLIKAN, R. A., "The Diffusion of Science," *The Scientific Monthly* (September, 1932), 203–8.
42. MORIYAMA, I. M., "Problems in the Measurement of Health Status," in W. Moore and E. Sheldon, eds., *Indicators of Social Change*. New York: Russell Sage Foundation, 1968.
43. MULLER, J. N., J. S. TOBIS, AND H. R. KELMAN, "The Rehabilitation Potential of Nursing Home Residents," *American Journal of Public Health*, 53 (February, 1963), 243–47.
44. PARSONS, T., E. SHILS, K. D. NAEGELE, AND J. R. PITTS, eds., *Theories of Society*, Vols. 1 and 2. New York: The Free Press, 1961.
45. PAYNE, S. L., "The Ideal Model for Controlled Experiment," *Public Opinion Quarterly*, 15 (1951), 557–62.

45a. POLLACK, H. AND D. E. KRUEGER, "Epidemiology of Cardiovascular Diseases Methodology—Hypertension and Arteriosclerosis," *American Journal of Public Health*, Supplement, 50 (October, 1960), 18.

46. *Provisional Guidelines for Automated Multiphasic Health Testing and Services*, Vol. 1. Washington, D.C.: National Center for Health Services Research and Development, 1970.
47. REEDER, L. G., "Social Epidemiology: An Appraisal," in E. G. Jaco, ed., *Patients, Physicians and Illness*, rev. ed. New York: The Free Press, 1971.
48. RIESMAN, D., *Medicine in the Middle Ages*. New York: Paul B. Hoeber, Inc., 1935.
49. ROSEN, G., *Specialization of Medicine*. New York: Froben Press, 1944.
50. SANAZARO, P. J., "Research in Patient Care," *Science*, 148 (June, 1965), 1489–90.
51. SHAPIRO, S. et al., "Social Factors in the Prognosis of Men Following First Myocardial Infarction," *Milbank Memorial Fund Quarterly*, 45 (January, 1970), 37–50.
52. SHEATSLEY, P. B., "The Art of Interviewing and a Guide to Interviewer Selection and Training," in M. Jahoda, M. Deutsch, and S. W. Cook, eds., *Research Methods in Social Relations*, Part 2. New York: The Dryden Press, 1951.
53. SHERIF, M. AND C. I. HOVLAND, "Judgmental Phenomenon and Scales of Attitude Measurement," *Journal of Abnormal and Social Psychology* (1953), 135–41.
54. SOLOMON, R. W., "An Extension of Control Group Design," *Psychological Bulletin*, 46 (1949), 137–50.
55. STEVENS, S. S., "Mathematics, Measurement and Psychophysics," in S. S. Stevens and H. Davis, eds., *Handbook of Experimental Psychology*. New York: John Wiley and Sons, Inc., 1951.
56. STOUFFER, S. A., *Social Research to Test Ideas*. New York: The Free Press, 1962.

57. ———, "Some Observations on Study Design," *American Journal of Sociology*, 55 (1949–50), 355–61.
58. ——— et al., *The American Soldier*, Vols. 1 and 2, *Studies of Social Psychology in World War II*. Princeton, N.J.: Princeton University Press, 1949.
59. ———, *Measurement and Prediction*, Vol. 4, *Studies in Social Psychology in World War II*. Princeton, N.J.: Princeton University Press, 1950.
60. SUCHMAN, E. A., *Evaluative Research*. New York: Russell Sage Foundation, 1967.
61. SULLIVAN, D. F., *Conceptual Problems in Development an Index of Health*, Public Health Service Publication No. 1000, Series 2, No. 17. Washington, D.C.: National Center for Health Statistics, 1966.
62. THURSTON, L. L. AND E. J. CHAVE, *The Measurement of Attitude*. Chicago: University of Chicago Press, 1929.
63. U.S. Employment Service, *Dictionary of Occupational Titles*. Washington, D.C.: Government Printing Office, 1944–49.
64. *Vital and Service Statistics, Health Center Districts, New York City*, New York City Department of Health, Bureau of Health Statistics and Analysis. Published annually.
65. WOOLSEY, T. D. AND H. NISSELSON, "Some Problems in the Statistical Measurement of Chronic Disease," in *Improving the Quality of Statistical Surveys*. Washington, D.C.: American Statistical Association, 1956.
66. World Health Organization, *Epidemiology of Mental Disorders*, Series 185. Geneva: World Health Organization, 1960.
67. ———, *Scientific Group on Comparable Methodology for the Epidemiological Study of Hypertension and Ischaemic Heart Disease—Report to the Director General*. Geneva: World Health Organization, 1962.
68. ———, *Manual of the International Classification of Diseases, Injuries, and Causes of Death*. Based on recommendations of the Eighth Revision Conference, 1965, and adopted by the Nineteenth World Health Assembly. Geneva: World Health Organization, 1967–69. 2 vols.
69. YERUSHALMY, J., "Reliability of Chest Roentgenography and Its Clinical Implications," *Diseases of the Chest*, 24 (August, 1953), 133–47.

21

PRESENT STATUS OF MEDICAL SOCIOLOGY

Howard E. Freeman, Sol Levine, and Leo G. Reeder

The growth of medical sociology and the direction of work in the field strongly support the view that the pace and scope of the scientific and intellectual enterprise is responsive to, if not determined by, the structure of the social order [3, 31]. As is the case with the organization of medical care and the provision of health services themselves [14], the current interests of medical sociologists reflect the social, political, and economic character of the community. Both the growth of the field and the marked shifts in emphasis can be documented most simply: In the final chapter of the first edition of this handbook, reference was made to the availability of a number of literature reviews. Today it would be foolhardy to attempt to cover the field in a few pages; the range of conceptual and substantive material and the prolific outpouring of monographs and articles makes such a task impossible. The matter of a shift in emphasis also can be supported by examining the earlier edition of the handbook. As remarkable as it may seem, neither the terms "poverty" nor "Negro," let alone "black," were employed frequently enough by contributors for the editors to include them in the Index!

It is more difficult to identify changes in the work roles of medical sociologists. The boundaries of the field remain elusive. Undoubtedly, conducting research investigations remains their major work role, and both government and foundation support for research activities is rather generous for the times, at least when compared with expenditures and opportunities for funds in other substantive specialties. Sociologists' participation in research-related activities in the health field —such as memberships on study sections and other committees that recommend grant support, and their roles in advising foundations on health programs, including consultation on studies that are biologically oriented—has increased markedly; so has their employment in comparatively high-level government positions, particularly in the various executive branches of the federal government.

Within academe the changes also have been pronounced, and several merit brief attention.

1. At the undergraduate level, courses in medical sociology have become quite common. Partly because of the impetus provided by federal and private foundation training grants, training programs are now found in most major graduate departments.

2. Medical, dental, public health, nursing, and other schools that train health practitioners and scientists have established faculty posts for sociologists, and a number of them have developed either separate behavioral science departments or relatively autonomous social science units. Perhaps most marked is the changed academic status of sociologists in these centers. Despite the competition for tenure posts that exist in professional schools, a large proportion of schools in medicine and public health have provided permanent posts for sociologists. It is no longer unusual for sociologists to occupy key administrative positions, to chair important academic committees, and to otherwise influence the programs and policies of education in the health field. Today sociologists in health settings often teach courses bearing the title Medical Sociology or provide the content of their field in such courses as Public Health Practice, Epidemiology, Preventive Medicine and the like. It was less than ten years ago, it should be recalled, that the first department of behavioral science under the chairmanship of a sociologist was established at the University of Kentucky; prior to 1960, the number of sociologists who held tenure appointments in health-related professional schools could be counted on the fingers of one hand.

3. Sociologists have become engaged heavily in graduate medical education. The teaching hospitals that provide the training of residents in the various medical specialties often have either staff members with sociological training or make use of those based in medical schools and sociology departments. In addition to offering formal seminars and lectures, sociologists serve as consultants to senior staff members responsible for the supervision of residents, interns, and postgraduate fellows.

4. It is not possible to count precisely the number of medical sociologists, for there are many more persons who either work in the field only part of the time, who "moonlight" occasionally, or who contribute to health research without having a formal identity with medical sociology. About the only statistic available is the membership list of the Medical Sociology Section of the American Sociological Association; the 700 to 800 persons who pay dues for Section membership make

it the largest Section devoted to a *substantive area* among the organized specialties in the Association.

5. The past decade has seen a significant increase in the number of journals that publish reports for sociological health research. While certain medical journals such as the *Journal of Chronic Diseases, American Journal of Public Health, Journal of the American Medical Association,* and *Psychiatry* have published papers authored by sociologists for a considerable time, the frequency of publication by sociologists in them has increased steadily. In 1965, the *Journal of Health and Social Behavior* became an official publication of the American Sociological Association; it began as an independent publication under the name of the *Journal of Health and Human Behavior* only in 1960. In the late 1960s, a second journal devoted to studies of a sociological character in the health field, *Social Science and Medicine,* began publication. In addition, a number of comparatively new journals specializing in the provision of health services and in mental health, such as *Social Psychiatry, Community Mental Health Journal,* and *Medical Care,* include frequent contributions of persons with sociological training.

6. Sociological studies have influenced the content and philosophy of medical education. Volumes published by Merton, Reader, and Kendall [32] and by Becker, Geer, Hughes, and Straus [5] called into question many aspects of existing programs of medical education and stimulated considerable curriculum revision in a large number of settings. In addition, there have been a number of assessments of innovative educational programs [21, 38], and such work continues. For example, Miller's [33] study of intern education can be considered a follow-up to the work of Becker and his associates on medical students. In addition to such works as those cited, sociologists are participating intensely in the ongoing efforts of the National Institutes of Health to improve medical education.

7. Perhaps the most striking role for medical sociologists—to a large extent a new one—is their participation in policy making at both the local and national levels. Sometimes this is done by research investigations directed at obtaining policy-relevant information. Increasingly, sociologists are involved in studies on the utilization of health services and the evaluation of different modes of delivery of health services [46]. A number of investigations are being undertaken of the impact of Medicare and industry-sponsored health benefit programs [39]. Sociologists have also contributed to the political process by which social policies on health are developed. Their activities range from testifying before congressional committees and advising such national groups as the Association of American Medical Colleges, to participating in decisions on the relocation of local hospitals and the modification of medical care programs [24]. In passing, it should be pointed out that some persons in the sociological discipline are skeptical of the appropriateness of direct involvement in policymaking. This matter will be discussed again later in this chapter.

It is intriguing to speculate on the various forces that have accelerated the growth of medical sociology and which have shaped work in the field. Although it is not possible to specify the relative importance of these various forces, clearly a combination of events in the medical world, in sociology, and in the community at large are responsible. As the chapters by Reader and Kendall (Chap. 1) and by Rosen (Chap. 2) inform us, concern with the relationship between social conditions and health is as old as documented accounts of medicine. Pronouncements of physicians such as Benjamin Rush in the eighteenth century on the relationship between social life and health could have been written at the present time. McIntire [29] in 1894 actually used the term "medical sociology" in the title of a paper that appeared in the *Bulletin of the American Academy of Medicine*.

Now, however, scientific and technical developments in medicine have reached the point where marked reductions in mortality and, to a lesser extent perhaps, morbidity are unlikely to be brought about by further biological and pharmacological discoveries. While it would be an exaggeration to claim that the era of the laboratory hero is at an end, his work certainly must be supplemented by studies of a sociological character.

Increased health for the population depends much more now on obtaining the cooperation and participation of community members in programs of prevention, on reducing the problems of poverty and social disorganization that directly or indirectly contribute to illness, on controlling the environmental hazards of social life, and on providing existing treatment modalities to the entire population. Naturally, new physiological discoveries will take place and technical innovations in practice will continue, but even here there is going to be an increase in the importance of the social component. The social consequences and social issues currently raised by programs of radical surgery, prolongation of life, artificial organs, and birth control illustrate this observation well [7]. Physicians and other health practitioners are increasingly aware of the growing interface between biology and the social sciences, and the importance of interpersonal and social factors in the provision and delivery of medical care.

Even if established medical practitioners were to remain insensitive to the contribution of the social sciences to health care, and senior educators and scientists in medicine failed to modify their teaching and research programs, increased concern with social behavior and social relations would still be expressed by the medical student and the young health worker. Their social science orientation is a consequence in part of their general socialization and the emphasis on the social sciences in undergraduate education today. A new breed of health professional is rapidly coming to the fore. This is evidenced in the pressures being exerted by medical students to force modification of curricula and to reorganize medical education so that it is more atuned to the needs and demands of contemporary community life. Interns and residents now press health administrators and senior hospital staff members to obtain rearrangements in services and to make the hospital and other medical settings more relevant to the patients' requirements.

Cadillacs and country club memberships undoubtedly remain within the aspirational set of today's student in the health field and the budding physician. But more and more, young persons in the health field see themselves as social-change agents. And medical establishment finds it increasingly necessary to be responsive to the demands of these Young Turks. The growth of the social sciences in professional education has occurred not merely because of the farsightedness of faculties but also because the knowledge and concerns of the social sciences are congruent with the interests and ambitions of students, interns, medical residents, and young faculty [18].

Then, too, at least brief notice should be made of the political climate. Conservative forces in medicine and the political area resist modifying the entrepreneurial structure of medical practice and are reluctant to provide the necessary economic resources for health care. But minority groups and the poor, as well as progressive community members, are insistent today that the organization of health care and the delivery of services be modified to provide quality medicine for all in the population. They demand that economic barriers do not prevent community members from enjoying optimal health and maximizing their life spans. The relevance of social science to these movements is apparent.

The current political ideology and the call for social action have influenced the work of sociologists in general and the programs of graduate departments of sociology. "Relevance" today is a term often bandied about to describe the orientation of a new cadre of academicians and the frame of reference of graduate students throughout the country. Relevance implies the application of scientific knowledge and intellectual ideas; it has probably had an influence on reducing the ivory tower posture of professors and has devalued simply accumulating and storing knowledge for its own sake. The evident failure in the American community to meet the health needs of its members has contributed to the growing interest in medical sociology. The indisputable link between the economic conditions of community members and their levels of health and illness and the relationship between inadequate and incompetent programs of general human services and the provision of health care have awakened interest in the field of medical sociology for students in our major centers of graduate training.

Finally, it should be noted that, in general, there has developed an emphasis on the use of social science in the development of social policies and the implementation of social action programs. Legislators and public administrators are more likely to have at least a passing acquaintance with social science concepts, theories, and methods, and the general public increasingly accepts the sociological enterprise, as Brim and his associates observed in their recent commission report [35]. As a consequence, economic support and both interpersonal and organizational cooperation have increased. The sociologist finds himself in a climate that facilititates his work. Perhaps because of the pressing concern for improved health care in the United States, the work situation now is one of cooperation for the medical sociologist.

Thus, there are vast differences in the status of the field of medical sociology now, compared to the 1960s, when the final chapter of the first edition of this volume was written. Unlike then, there is no reason today either to persuade persons of the importance and potential of social research in health or to be concerned with the prospects for growth and development in the field. Within sociology, among persons in the health field, and in the community at large there exists presently a considerable investment and commitment to medical sociology as a legitimate field of teaching and research. These introductory remarks, however, by no means should imply that the field is fully matured or that many of the conceptual and methodological problems that existed in its infantile period have been solved. Perhaps the first issue that merits attention is a consideration of the boundaries of the field of medical sociology.

THE FIELD OF MEDICAL SOCIOLOGY

Sociology is a broad academic discipline with diverse roots [19, 25, 36]. In many ways the development of medical sociology mirrors the diverse orientations and parallels the genesis of other sociological specialties. Medical sociology is distinctive only in its subject matter; its boundaries are phenotypic. It makes use of concepts, theories, and methods in sociology for the study of the health and illness of persons, the social relationships and social processes of individuals involved in the web of medical settings, and the provision and organization of medical care. These studies generally have not only a utilitarian focus but often contribute to sociological theory and methodology.

There are no reasons for the development of unique or special theories in medical sociology. Medical sociology, like all sociology, is concerned with social relationships and social processes, and its theoretical base must of necessity be that of general sociology. The activities of medical sociologists span the various areas of interest to the discipline: social organization, deviant behavior, social control, socialization, and the other subjects of generic sociological interest.

There is, of course, an interplay between the current concerns and fashions within the general field of sociology and the types of conceptual and theoretical frameworks that are employed in medical sociology. At the same time the work done in a specialty such as medical sociology influences the emphasis on different frameworks in other areas of sociology. It is, of course, not always feasible to select from the spectrum of sociological concepts and sociological concepts and frameworks in developing a particular investigation. Some orientations are more consistent with particular research problem areas than others. But not only is it often possible to choose between competing frameworks—let us say, the focusing of a study in terms of deviant behavior in comparison with organizational theory—but the selection and development of specific research investigations also may reflect current trends in the field.

There is no point here in attempting to unravel the mystique that surrounds why different conceptual and theoretical frameworks achieve popularity at one point in time and not at another within sociology. Undoubtedly, in part, this depends upon the recognition given the works of particular men at a point in time. In part, in all sociology, it is related to the social and political forces that influence the directions of scientific and intellectual thought. If one had to point to a single illustration, it would be to the growth of organizational theory and research in both general sociology and medical sociology. Without, perhaps, deemphasizing concerns of a more social-psychological character, both the general field and the specialty have increased their attention to social structural dimensions and the relations between organizations. It could be argued, of course, that the organizational frame of reference is most useful in dealing with problems of the provision and delivery of medical services and that the increased interest in organizational theory within the health field is a consequence of the attention being paid to the matter of health services. But it is equally reasonable to assert that the widespread interest of sociologists in organizations has led to an increased sensitivity of the relevance of the organizational frame of reference in dealing with problems in the health field.

The observation probably applies equally as well to the selection of particular research methods. Interest in experimental design of field studies probably has increased not only in medical sociology but in the entire spectrum of research endeavors in sociology. Again, it is possible to argue that such recent emphases are a result of the particular, variant policy questions in the health field; concern with evaluating alternative means of providing services and of reducing the psychological and interpersonal effects of hospitalization has led to a number of experimental studies [43].

Increased interest in field studies likewise stems from the useful policy-related work that has gone on. For example, there are few medical educators who do not know of and are unimpressed by the field study of Becker and his associates [5], noted earlier as one of the significant contributions of medical sociology to professional education. With the growth of a large number of innovative medical settings, such as comprehensive health centers in core cities, there is increased effort to document and understand what goes in them and how provision of services there differs from more traditional treatment facilities.

In the past, and even to some extent today, sociologists entered the medical world at the call of health professionals who wanted specific tasks undertaken —tasks that primarily exploited the technical craft of investigators rather than the central interests of sociologists. Thus, medical sociologists have had a continued concern with the legitimacy of their specialty. Straus [45] suggested some years ago that medical sociology can be divided into the sociology *of* medicine and sociology *in* medicine. This distinction has been the focal point of a large number of discussions of the work of medical sociology [23]. According to Straus' view, at one end of the continuum are those whose interest in medicine is solely exploitive—they regard medical settings and health and illness as possible phenomena which can be subjected to study and would permit the elaboration, refinement, and testing of general propositions about social behavior. At the other end are sociologically trained persons who become enmeshed in the specific problems of prevention and treatment of illness and the maximal allocation of health resources, and whose identification with medicine far overshadows their commitment to sociology. However, the distinction between the sociology of medicine and sociology in medicine has become less clear. This is so in part because the posture of sociologists has changed and action-oriented work has attained more legitimacy.

At the same time, it is foolish to dismiss the issue of whether or not the medical sociologist is engaged in work that contributes to his discipline, or is he merely a technician using a special set of skills to help solve the problems of health practitioners and of the settings in which they work? Medical sociologists who try to balance an interest in sociology and one in health often are concerned with the general status in applied sociology, a topic which has been the subject of considerable discussion [17, 48]. The question of the circumstances under which an individual is functioning as a sociologist when helping "men of action," such as medical practitioners, is not simple to answer. One guideline, perhaps, is that he is performing as a sociologist when the repertoire of skills and knowledge that he employs is not possessed by just any intelligent individual. The individual is not acting as a sociologist unless he utilizes available knowledge of social organization, social relationships, and social processes in his work. The notion that applied sociology consists of the application of principles of social relations to the field of action problems has been elaborated in considering the field of industrial relations.

It is clear that most of the sociology of medicine—study of organizational structures, role relationships, and belief systems—is a legitimate activity of the sociologist; they contribute to the general body of sociological knowledge [34]. It is more questionable whether the work of sociologists *in* medicine contributes to general sociological knowledge. For this reason the sociologist working in medicine, even today, may become defensive about his role. He is confronted by some of his sociological peers, like Hall, who insist that the applied sociologist must contribute to general sociology. As Hall states: "Medicine has no unique interest for sociology. The justification for its study lies in the light it throws on more general forms of social organization" [20].

Certainly in these times, in the eyes of most sociologists, however, a stringent position such as Hall's may be dismissed as puristic and unrealistic. Not only has a significant segment of the sociological profession traditionally had an interest in action fields, but public support for the sociological enterprise requires a commitment to the objectives of action agents and the needs of community members. It is unlikely that medical sociology would have flourished to the same extent without some attention to the goals of the medical community and the public concern with health care.

Under the most favorable circumstances, the sociologist is engaged at the same time in work which is regarded as useful to both his sociological peers and his medical colleagues. Some sociologists, such as Davis [9], have argued that the most intellectually stimulating and academically productive work in sociology is undertaken by persons who are addressing themselves to applied problems. Certainly in the field of mental health, for example, the studies on social class by Hollingshead and Redlich [22] and hospital structure by Stanton and Schwartz [44] are illustrations of research highly valued by both the medical and sociological worlds.

It is not always possible, of course, for the activities of medical sociologists to accommodate the diverse expectations of both groups. For this reason, despite the emphasis upon social action and the bringing to bear of a sociological acumen for social change, the medical sociologist who continually regards his work, or is regarded by others, as not contributing to the main theme of sociological knowledge is faced with problems of identity. The diverse interests, pressures, and expectations of persons in the discipline in which he was socialized, as opposed to those of individuals whose roots are in the practicing professions, may result in concomitant strain for the medical sociologist.

The current policy concerns of the health field have further complicated the role of the medical sociologist. As we noted at the outset of this chapter, scientific and intellectual development are responsive to the current political and social situation. Thus, the medical care system is heavily criticized for its slowness to adapt to the needs of community members, and sociologists indeed are often faced with a choice about "whose side we're on."

VALUES AND THE ROLE OF THE SOCIOLOGIST

Current discussions on the appropriate posture of the sociologist reflect the extent of concern with the stance of sociology on matters of social policy. Gouldner's [17] now classic paper on value-free sociology and subsequent discussions clearly indicate the breadth and depth of the issue. It is probably fair to say that the discipline of sociology is much more sympathetic today to engaging in work that has relevance for the immediate social scene [13], but merely acknowledging the sociologist's social responsibility is insufficient as a guide for individuals or as a beacon for the field.

Health, it would seem, is held in universal esteem, and consequently it may appear that the sociologist is subjected to either little strain or conflict about the appropriateness of his work. However, while health is an ultimate value, the means of realizing health objectives are pervaded by controversy. No one questions, for example, the desirability of reducing dental caries, but the technical expedience of fluoridating community water sources is not supported by all. Medical personnel clearly differ on the appropriateness of birth control devices in order to limit the population growth; indeed some even argue about whether or not population control is consistent with the desired ultimate objective of health. Moreover, it is clear that the controversy over means to achieve maximum health is overshadowed by the furor certain medical issues raise on the larger social scene, for example, the controversy on how to finance health services.

The medical sociologist, as a community member and as someone who is identified with the medical world or part of it, is confronted by value dilemmas. They occur particularly in connection with appropriate means for the realization of the ultimate goal and with the selection of certain intervention strategies. Two perspectives are advocated by some sociologists and challenged by others: One is that there is a moral responsibility on the part of sociologists to take the side of the disenfranchised underdog [4]; the second is that actions that undermine the social structure and upset the very underpinnings of the social order are acceptable tactics by community members and merit sympathy, if not encouragement.

There is no simple stance on such matters. On the one hand, sociologists not only are socialized within the Establishment but are dependent upon it as a place to work and for financial resources. It is difficult and impractical, if not impossible oftentimes, for the individual to carry on his activities without a continued integration within the existing social institutions. On the other hand, many, if not most, sociologists are hard put to defend either the extent or pace of social change occurring in the health field. The power of institutional interest groups is far from waning. Witness the control exerted on the Food and Drug Administration and the blocking in 1969 of the appointment of a particular physician to be the Assistant Secretary of HEW for Health and Scientific Affairs. If anything, health is going to increase as the salient concern within the general community and among groups disenfranchised economically and socially. The sociologist is bound to be pressed to take sides, and it is doubtful whether he is going to do so easily without developing for himself a consistent value framework.

It should be observed that the general notions of democratic society and of consent of the governed may be counted as some of the most expeditious and effective means of realizing health objectives. But this is not always the case. The fluoridation controversy is a good illustration [37]. In a number of communities, when given an opportunity to vote on the issue, the public has rejected this public health practice. Fluoridation is most likely to be implemented when the decision can be made at an executive or expert level. If he is consulted, a recommendation by the sociologist that the decision be left in the hands of authorities may be congruent with health objectives, but it is inimical to the democratic values which are typically harbored by him, for he is often an advocate of community participation, and he supports the right of individuals to manifest their choices on matters that affect them.

A related value conflict is the individual sociologist's choice in supporting and working for intermediate objectives which may have long-range negative consequences or which may impede other types of desirable social change. For example, successful efforts at controlling epidemics have mitigated a major mechanism of population control; particularly those engaged in disease control in underdeveloped areas must realize the potential consequences of their efforts on the long-term well-being of the world community. Another example is the social-science-oriented public health programs with impoverished groups, whereby the amelioration of certain health problems may dissipate the intensity of and fever for radical changes in the over-all social and political structure. A specific illustration of the possibility of an inverse relationship between health and political action can be drawn from reports of health care in South Africa. It can be suggested that there the provision of medical care acts as a brake on militant political activity [8].

The matter is most sharply illustrated, perhaps, by the need to decide on a strategy for the provision of health services to the neglected in the American population. On the one hand, it is argued that a variety of attitudinal and ecological differences demand that special types of health facilities be rushed into being for the poor and the ghetto resident—thus the development of various types of store-front clinics and multiservice health centers. On the other hand, as an ultimate objective, most individuals would agree that a single medical care system, one through which all individuals receive maximal care in the same settings, is a desired goal. To what extent does the development of special programs, however transitory they are labeled, impede and inhibit the objective of a single medical care system?

Even the sociologist with "hard facts" often will find that his data are not regarded as neutral, and the way he casts his reports of findings may reflect to some extent his own values, those of his sponsors, or his assessment of the community's climate (and often the three are not congruent). There are few facts on health and illness which can be communicated in a neutral and detached manner, and even if such were the case, the audience would be unlikely to assess the data in neutral terms. Current evaluations are being undertaken by sociologists on the impact of Medicaid and Medicare; the politically charged arena into which the results will be fed is only illustrative of the problems that confront the sociologist in the health field. Today when the political sector is so alert to, if not enamored with, the outcomes of social research, the pressures upon the medical sociologist in the social policy arena are intense.

The responsibility is a many-sided one. While anything but full and objective reporting is to be decried, there may be consequences for either the community or the medical world which are inconsistent with the value commitments of sociologists in the unrestricted issuance of research results. For example, a number of studies suggest the limited efficacy of mental health education efforts [41]. But there are few alternatives available, and there is a question of whether or not such studies serve any function except to undermine further the faith and confidence of the practitioner and, consequently, diminish his action role. While certain professional activities are ineffective, the social order may suffer more if community members are deprived of them.

Indeed, the sociologist often is discouraged from communicating with his medical colleagues because of tendencies on their part to accept his findings uncritically and to act on them even though he may plead that his results are incomplete and tentative. The same observation holds for his relationships with policy makers and politicians. Moreover, the sociologist—particularly when placed in the role of a consultant—is pressured to make "best guesses," which are then treated as scientific recommendations.

The different postures of medicine and sociology are related, to some extent at least, to the degree of acceptance of various styles and orders of data. Although sociologists vary among themselves in styles of research, few question the utility of probability statements and quantitative analysis. This obtains to a lesser degree among medical persons, at least among clinically-oriented physicians. It is a paradox that many of those in the medical field who are most sympathetic and supportive of social science—e.g., psychiatrists—are least enchanted with "hard" sociology. The sociologist is faced with the problem that the persons in medicine whom he is most likely to alienate by the implementation of certain research procedures are the ones most attuned to and appreciative of the social dimensions in health and illness.

Incompatibility in research styles is only one manifestation of the differences in orientation between sociology and medicine. Sometimes the sociologist's frame of reference and his body of knowledge challenge some of the basic assumptions of medicine. On the one hand, physicians are prone to link the technology and the culture of their profession [30]. The American physician, for example, does not distinguish between diagnosing the patient's illness and examining him privately rather than in the presence of his relatives. As Freidson has pointed out (see Chap. 14), contrary to the views of some, there seems to be little relationship between the efficacy of medical practice and the mode of organizing services. On the other hand, the sociologist, seeking to separate the technology from the culture of medicine, may be accused of usurping the role of practitioner [28]. Because the physician characteristically insists on mixing culture with technology, the sociologist may have no choice at times but to become involved in the study and evaluation of the technology of medicine, and the dilemma is that he is usually ill-equipped for this task.

There also are instances where sociologists maintain that the technology involved in the treatment of illnesses is not the exclusive domain of the medical practitioner. This view is held particularly by certain sociologists involved in the mental health field. Here, where manifestations of illness are essentially behavioral and interpersonal, the sociologist may feel he is as appropriate a person as the physician to make a judgment on the course of treatment. Moreover, there are clinicians who actually expect sociologists to participate in clinical judgments. Whether or not this is appropriate is one of the most controversial issues. In 1969, a conference on behavioral science and medical education was held under the aegis of the National Institute of Child Health and Human Development. In dealing with drug addiction, alcoholism, and certain types of mental illness, sociologists do become involved in therapeutic relationships which challenge the domain of the physician. There are also sociologists who hold that their field offers more relevant training for group psychotherapy, for example, than does medicine. Obviously, the guild-like structure of medical practice presents barriers to involvement of nonmedical people in any therapeutic relationships. Social scientists who lay claim to these somewhat marginal therapeutic areas run the risk of being rejected in their research roles as well. It is interesting that certain aspects of the technology of medicine, again mainly in psychiatry, have been more enthusiastically supported by social scientists than by physicians. For example, as a method of therapy, psychodrama probably has attracted proportionately more support from social scientists than from physicians.

The guild-like structure of the medical profession raises other problems for the sociologist, particularly in studies which involve contact between the social researcher and patients. Physicians legally (and perhaps morally) have the "ultimate" responsibility for the well-being of the patient. Sociologists usually do not question the ultimate responsibility of the physician in the treatment of patients, with the possible exception of those who suffer from certain behavior problems. In carrying out research projects, however, this authority may intrude on certain decisions which are really the province of the methodologically astute person, often the sociologist. The sociologist, in arguing for research integrity, may sometimes appear to be assailing the physician's human concern for the patient.

It is certainly true that some medical sociologists in clinical settings, along with physicians, are in conflict over the requirements of research design and the negative impact the research activity may have for the patient. This dilemma typically is most sharp in studies involving control groups which are deprived of potentially beneficial therapies. A dramatic study of this value conflict has been reported by Fox [12], who reports the strains in continuing an experiment when one group of patients is being mortally risked to a much greater extent. The more usual case, however, does not involve clinical settings but rather differences in views over the variables in field surveys and epidemiology investigations. Sociologists and physicians simply do not always agree on what are the important determinants of health and illness.

The medical sociologist also is beset with problems of a personal nature. For example, what is his line of action in those cases where he is not well received in the host setting, or even worse, where he finds that the objectives of his medical colleagues are unpalatable to his personal, social, and political outlooks? For example, can a sociologist who personally favors government financed medicine associate himself with groups actively opposed to such a program? These value problems are complex and pervasive, and it is impossible to offer a set of instructions and prescriptions which will resolve them. One would suspect that the more mature sociologist anticipates many of the potential sources of strain and avoids them by explicitly structuring and clarifying his role to his medical colleagues at the outset and by actively assessing the needs and expectations of his medical hosts. By virtue of his training, the sociologist has at his disposal an array of concepts and skills which are a potential source of strength in dealing with these problems.

THE MEDICAL SOCIOLOGIST AT WORK

The extensive literature on interdisciplinary research and the cocktail hour chatter on the difficulty of sociologists in getting along with physicians and other health personnel may give the impression that the sociologist has an unusually hard time in accomplishing his work. Even if this formerly was the general case, it certainly is not true any longer. Early in this chapter we recounted the extensive growth of sociology in academic medicine and the greater awareness of the social system, social processes, and interpersonal behavior by health practitioners and medical students. Certainly the concept that the sociologist must always be in a subordinate position to the physician in the direction of research activities or even in administrative structures is disappearing rapidly. There are still many institutional settings, however, where either the slowness of bureaucratic change or the meaninglessness of formal status symbols makes it appear that the sociologist is marginal and, to some extent, disfranchised. Public bodies employing sociologists may do so under other titles, and medical and other professional schools may indeed appoint a sociologist as a professor of preventive medicine, psychiatry, or epidemiology. To a large extent, it is probably fair to suggest, the conflicts that arise are related to temperamental differences and are probably no more extensive and severe than those that occur between a sociologist and his peers in settings in which they all belong to the same discipline.

The sociologist in medicine does find himself compelled at times to take on some of the trappings of his medical world—which range from wearing the proverbial "white coat" to occupying a post originally intended for an M.D. Some of these trappings are undoubtedly useful in facilitating entry into medical settings, in fostering communication with medical colleagues, and in expediting the learning of the medical culture. But some of them have concomitant liabilities—physical isolation, social distance from colleagues, and diversion from sociological preoccupations. Most serious, however, are the potential loss of identification, relinquishment of a critical stance, and separation from the mainstream of the sociological enterprise. The sociologist in medicine is often expected and tempted to play the "expert role" on matters beyond his sociological capacity, to assume consulting and administrative tasks in lieu of more scholarly roles, and to commit himself to a career course which impedes his reentry into more traditional sociological jobs.

In these circumstances, a number of rationalizations come to the fore. One is that a minimal concession and involvement in medicine is a necessary precondition to the conduct of valid sociological work. Admittedly, in some cases, this is a fact. For example, Anderson, in describing his research program at the Health Information Foundation, claimed that his early studies had to be directly relevant to the medical world before he could embark on more predominantly sociological research [1]. The problem, however, is that, in many cases, the "means" may indeed become "ends," and the earlier concessions may become irrevocable.

A second rationalization is that outside research support is most easily obtained if one is closer to and more accepted by the medical world. Here, too, there is some basis in fact. Frequently, grants by medical sociologists are reviewed by boards having heavy medical and life science representation. There is a danger, however, that research integrity may be sacrificed by opportunism.

A third rationalization is that a "good" sociologist can convert every problem into one of sociological import. Again, there is some truth to this proposition; sensitive social scientists can often perceive the sociological dimensions of narrow medical problems. But it is necessary to recognize that a considerable waste of time and effort may be involved in conjuring useless conceptual frameworks around mundane problems.

A fourth rationalization is that closeness to medical personnel permits the acquisition of most penetrating insights and understanding. As in the other cases, there is some truth here too; many sociologists are sympathetic to the research potential of participant and field observation. Often, however, their very identification with settings and people makes objective data collection difficult and limits their freedom of reporting.

Separation of medical sociology from sociology has disadvantages to the field as a whole, as well as to individual sociologists. Of continued concern is the possibility that medical sociology, if not all of sociological specialties, is likely to take on the structure of a guild-like occupation rather than a scholarly discipline [15]. While a trend toward a guild-like structure is not now evident among medical sociologists in their attitude toward certification, they do take a number of roles vis-à-vis medical personnel which have the earmarks of a narrow professionalism [2]. The more the medical sociologist becomes enmeshed in and subordinate to the "action system" he is serving, the more likely he is to assume a guild-like stance. His roles, especially as administrator and consultant in medical settings, make him most vulnerable to relinquishing his core identification as a sociologist. To the extent this pattern occurs, there is danger that the work of sociologists will feed back less and less to the dominant streams of sociology. It is highly problematic whether the quality of research by sociologists under these conditions would compare favorably with efforts in the main body of the field. On these grounds, Levine and Bennis warn against excessive involvement in the action system of the client: "the sociologist may increasingly make contributions which stem from whatever unique virtues or skills he may possess as an individual rather than from the data, concepts and skills of his discipline. As the contribution he makes is less and less sociological, a point may be reached where the man of action may do the job just as well" [27].

A solution suggested by some sociologists, such as Gouldner, is the articulation, elaboration, and refinement of a "new brand" of sociology and a special breed of sociologists devoted to effecting social change in their own right and not as a byproduct of particular institutional affiliation. Rather than serve as a handmaiden to the medical practitioner, the sociologist in medicine could become a new action specialist [16, 17]. The need and potential acceptance of a "clinical sociology" has been advanced [72]. It is doubtful whether most sociologists would concur with this projected development, but it is probably a more desirable alternative than the subjugation of sociologists into action roles without a systematic and explicit frame of reference. Probably the development of a clinical sociology is more palatable now than in the past.

In lieu of any marked departure from the present modes of conduct, it is dangerous for the sociologist to proceed without safeguarding his professional identity and even more his disciplinary orientation. For the individual involved, this can be accomplished in part by effective organizational arrangements and open channels of communication with other sociologists. It is clear that well-developed structural mechanisms influence the effective conduct of the medical sociologist. It also means that he should limit his participation as a sociologist in medicine, both in time and in intensity of interest. Given the problem, it seems to us that all medical sociologists must be oriented, at least in part, toward the larger sociological field. As a report from the Russell Sage Foundation concludes: "given a reasonable flexibility on the part of the host profession, a scientist who is competent and creative in his own discipline, and can maintain his professional identity, can continue to contribute basic scientific knowledge and win appropriate recognition in his own discipline, and at the same time be responsive to the needs of the field of application in which he works" [40]. We are not asking sociologists to relinquish their participation as sociologists in medicine or in social policy but rather to regard health settings, at least in part, as field stations for research on a wide variety of problems, in much the same way as such disciplines as genetics and physiology participate in the work of agricultural experiment stations.

THE DEVELOPMENT OF A BODY OF KNOWLEDGE

Certain problems endemic to the development of the general body of sociological knowledge and to that of other sociological specialties also confront the field of medical sociology. Here, too, it is easier to characterize the dilemmas than to formulate ready solutions to them. Many of the limitations of current research efforts are solely technical, related to the present level of methodological sophistication in sociology and to the uneven training with which sociologists are provided in graduate school, a point discussed in detail by Sibley [42]. A number of these technical problems have been alluded to by Elinson (see Chap. 20), and here we will concern ourselves with only a few of the broad issues, ones which really border more on the philosophy than the method of scientific inquiry.

In medical sociology, many worthwhile studies are solely descriptive, and one objective of research is to describe particular situations, settings, and social phenomena. But in most scientific fields, much of the research effort needs to be devoted to predictive and causal investigations. For example, measures of health, of quality of medical care, and of rates of hospitalization, are included in studies which utilize an independent-dependent variable frame of reference. One or more measures are looked upon as predictive or causative and others as outcome or criteria variables. In more complex investigations, variables are assigned other statuses, e.g., as intervening or control measures. There are, of course, clear-cut instances where studies adopt an explicit frame with respect to the ordering of variables. One well-known example is Hollingshead and Redlich's analysis of social class and mental illness, in which the former is clearly explicated as the independent variable and the latter as the dependent one [22]. Often, of course, the ordering of variables is purely arbitrary and "causal sequence" is not a relevant issue. Nevertheless, from the standpoint of the field of medicine, knowledge becomes relatively useless unless some ordering can be identified or at least assumed. Given the present status of knowledge, it is essential that careful explication of the actual or assumed ordering of variables be undertaken in all but solely descriptive studies. If it is not done, the practitioner does it instead, and the medical sociologist finds himself in the position of contending with false inferences for which, through omission, he is at least in part responsible. The problem of "as if it were causal" has always plagued sociology but takes on particular importance in a field where findings may potentially, no matter how tentatively they are noted, be put to immediate use.

An illustration of concern with this issue is the comments of Feldman regarding the use of health survey data in demographic analysis [10]. He illustrates, using research on the relationship between social-class measures and health status, that there is a tendency always to regard the former variable as the independent one and the latter as the dependent one. Admittedly, demographic variables are primarily governed by forces other than health. There is reasonably good evidence, by controlling for other influences in cross-sectional studies and by tracing the time sequence in longitudinal ones, to regard the usual ordering as the correct one. But this is not true in terms of other domains of variables, such as attitudinal measures. Consequently, it is poor science—and unfair to the practitioner—not to identify the time sequence or at least to estimate the plausibility of sequence among variables.

Moreover, as Feldman notes, the tendency of social scientists working in the health field is to devote almost all their energies to trying to explain medical phenomena in terms of social processes, when in reality many of these processes have not been rigorously defined, and so little is known about them. It is essential that the medical sociologist maximize his opportunities to investigate the bearing of physiological factors on the social environment—in other words, to view health measures as the independent variables. A provocative example of using health as an independent variable is the analysis of interpersonal competence by Foote and Cottrell, who specify a series of hypotheses in which health is regarded as a predictor of the competence of family members [11]. Admittedly, the interest of the medical profession is on health as the dependent variable, but the sociologist in the health field must recognize that his responsibility to his own field and his ultimate contribution to the medical field rest in being resistive to and circumspect about ordering which is most meaningful to his medical colleagues [cf. 47].

A more specific issue, but of no less importance, is the development of realistic operational definitions, i.e., those most appropriate and relevant to the needs of the action field. The medical sociologist is vulnerable to both barrels of a shotgun in this respect. The *medical variables* which often constitute part of his research are variously and differently defined by physicians, and so are the variables from his own realm of competence.

The problem of operationalizing medical variables can be illustrated most readily by looking at studies of the quality of medical care—a phenomenon defined variously as (1) the conduct of appropriate practices; (2) the fulfillment of certain obligations; (3) the attitudes of staff or patients; and (4) the actual illness or well-being of patients. Studies of medical efficacy may use as measures of quality such phenomena as how long an operation took, how the drug was dispensed, and how detailed was the medical record—

all on the assumption that these and other such variables reflect real differences in patient outcome. The medical sociologist must be most aware of the hazards of assessing operational measures which are only believed to reflect the actual phenomenon being studied. Here the medical sociologist is compelled to challenge the "expert" knowledge of his medical colleagues, and either to limit carefully the generalization or conceptualization potential of his variables or to demand the rigorous testing of the linkage between certain reflectors of major phenomena and the actual conditions. Another major problem lies in synthesizing the results of studies which make use of different operational measures of the same phenomenon. In both medicine and sociology, the operationalization of variables takes many forms. The different ways in which social class is measured is a sufficient illustration. Consequently, there are limits on the extent to which research results can be integrated. As the field continues to mature, hopefully there will be more consistent use of the same measures and thus a greater potential to build a body of knowledge.

Sociologists working on medical problems not only fail to take advantage of sociomedical studies to refine measures more precisely but often do not even utilize the sophistication developed in other areas of sociology. Accusations by sociologists about the naïveté of some medical persons such as epidemiologists are often unfair. More often than not, medically trained epidemiologists will make use of a single measure of class status—usually occupation—in their analyses of disease causation. One reason is that they feel they thus have a reliable scale. But it also happens that the medical epidemiologist can more easily understand what occupation is, while he may be confounded by social class measures predicated on notions of "style of life" or "social prestige"—and perhaps rightly so because such concepts lie within the diffuse sociological realm of discourse. The joint sharing of concepts, and particularly of operational measures, represents an indispensable key to the development of a systematized body of sociomedical knowledge. Particularly in epidemiological research, the sociologist contributes a broader conceptual framework, but its value is sometimes minimized because of the lack of uniform operational measures.

A wide range of methods is used within medical sociology, and it is clear that no one approach represents the most efficacious means for the development of the field. In a paper some years ago, Zelditch outlined the utility of various methods such as field observation and surveys [49]. The choice of the appropriate method rarely is made on the basis of logic alone. It depends also upon which approach, at a given point, the particular investigator feels he is most competent in and to which he has the greatest commitment.

Persons concerned with the development of a body of knowledge need to realize, however, the great difficulty and often impossibility of synthesizing findings obtained through vastly different methods. This is not to imply that one method is better than another or that several methods may not be appropriate for the study of the same problem, but that the probability of developing a body of knoweldge without recurring use of similar methods in various areas is rather unlikely. For example, two volumes on medical education (see Chap. 8) report findings of studies of two medical schools [5, 32]. Different frames of reference may account for the rather diverse findings, but so may the use of a field approach in one case and a questionnaire approach in the other. While the justification for diverse approaches is apparent, the development of a systematic and codified body of knowledge requires sustained efforts and conscious attempts at replicaton. At the same time, the practitioner must develop a patient outlook toward the process of knowledge building.

Not only do methods differ but so do the frames of reference of sociomedical research. A good illustration is the previously noted volumes on medical education. One study emphasizes an internal process of "becoming" and uses the approach of viewing a narrow scene as a "culture." The other does not consider "boys in white" as a discrete entity but rather places them within the perspective of a larger medical system. It is not possible to determine whether the findings differ because of variations in the two medical schools studied, in the methodological approaches, or in the frames of reference. All fields grow and prosper by diversity, and only continued research—particularly replicative investigations—can resolve differences in the findings of parallel efforts.

The problems discussed here are not unique to the field of medical sociology but pervade the entire discipline. The sociological literature is replete with discussions and considerations of these and related issues in much more detailed and sophisticated ways. But as specialists within a discipline, medical sociologists have a responsibility to contribute to the unraveling of these problems.

SOCIALIZATION OF MEDICAL SOCIOLOGISTS

If there is merit in our position that medical sociology is a specialty defined substantively and with theoretical and conceptual roots in general sociology, it follows that medical sociologists must be well trained and competent general sociologists. The diversity in the theoretical perspectives and emphases among sociologists are, of course, reflected in the orientations of various departments of sociology.

Virtually all departments, however, require certain minimal competencies today from their graduate students, such as a familiarity with the historical background of sociology, a grasp of contemporary theories, and a knowledge of research methods [42]. If medical sociology is to grow and prosper as part of general sociology, the training of the sociologist who turns to this field must be broad and comprehensive. But this does not mean that the sociologist can operate successfully in the medical field solely on the basis of his academic training. Sociologists vary in their opinions of the importance of field training to the educational process, but it is doubtful whether any would contest that familiarity with the settings in which they are to work is not useful. A familiarity with the medical field, in one way or another, is essential to the development of the medical sociologist [6].

There are, however, a number of alternative points of entry into medical sociology. The most formal route consists, of course, in obtaining further graduate training in medicine. But the number of sociologists who have subsequently completed medical school for the explicit purpose of becoming better medical sociologists is almost zero. A number of social scientists, however, have received training or degrees from schools of public health. A second formal route is through the various predoctoral and postdoctoral medical sociology programs in social science departments. Several of these programs recruit their students from medicine as well as sociology, and both the formal course work and field experiences are supplemented by informal contacts between physician and social scientist. In addition, postdoctoral fellowships and apprentice-type research positions are becoming relatively common in medical and public health schools, and they represent a valuable means of breaking into the field.

It is the informal contact system which has provided the immersion into medicine of most social scientists currently interested in health. As previously noted, many of the sociologists who work in the medical field hold teaching or research appointments at medical schools or schools of public health or in programs of research in hospital and clinic settings. Most recently, state and even local public health departments and voluntary health groups have been adding sociologists to their staffs, and some medical practitioners concerned with social science advocate some sort of "internship" program.

The type of socialization process is perhaps not as important as whether there are safeguards to assure that the sociologist in training does not become a hybrid but maintains an identity with his field. Realistically, there are a number of stimuli which threaten the identification of the sociologist with his discipline. Medicine is both an intriguing scientific field and a creative art; moreover, it is often pleasant to be identified with physicians—both as individuals and as a socioeconomic group. In many settings, such as schools of public health, there are other disciplines represented which also invite affiliation—biostatistics, medical epidemiology, and other "hard" health sciences. It is not a matter of faith in one's discipline which is important—although some of that is also useful to have—but a realization that orientations and tastes do differ and the guidelines appropriate in one field may not be as useful in another. Many of the choices in statistical procedure recommended by biostatisticians are not congruent with the necessary operations in social science research, and many of the ways in which public health practitioners approach the study of social structure and social organization are incongruent with those of social scientists. The temptation exists, particularly for the sociological novice, to adapt to the modal patterns of the medical settings. The medical profession, as well as the sociological professions, has a responsibility for training and developing both the competence and autonomy of medical sociologists.

In addition to the socialization of sociologists for work in the health field, it should be noted that two new professions—or disciplines, if you will—are emerging. One group is made up of persons who may be regarded as physician-sociologists; these are individuals whose interest in sociology and indeed whose conceptual and technical background qualify them for full participation in the sociological enterprise as well as in the medical one. To a large extent, many of these individuals are self-trained or have learned their sociology in a quasi-apprenticeship relationship with colleagues having sociological training. While still rare, it is becoming more common, however, for physicians to actually undertake graduate work—if not fully to the Ph.D.—in sociology. They are also being exposed to substantial amounts of the content of the field in behavioral science departments and in medical schools and schools of public health. With changing emphasis in medical education and the increased awareness of the contributions of social science in health, certainly many relatively young physicians and other health professionals will be reasonably, if not completely, qualified as sociologists. One can debate, of course, the possibility of serving two masters at the same time. It may result in the single individual's having the same levels of conflict and stress that occur in the interpersonal relationships between the sociologist and the person who identifies himself as a health professional.

There also is an emerging field known as health planning. Some of the individuals in it are drawn from medicine, others from social work and hospital administration. Some schools and departments within academe are training persons from the bachelor's to the Ph.D. level as specialists in health planning. In many of these cases social science, and particularly sociology, represents the basic science to which they are exposed. These individuals, like the physician-sociologist, may actually be equipped to participate fully in the sociological enterprise. Again, the matter of duality of roles should be noted.

Both of these emerging groups represent a potential strength for the development of medical sociology, despite the potential difficulties of bridging the field of practice and an academic discipline. In many cases they may indeed serve as provocateurs who stimulate and enocurage the application of sociological concepts and techniques to problems of concern in the health fields. In still other cases, they may serve a new role in communicating the findings and ideas of sociologists to health professionals who are less aware and equipped to handle sociological material. Finally, because of their greater sympathy and knowledge in the conduct of action-demonstration programs and other research, they may serve as the colleagues of sociologists. While it is doubtful, and perhaps undesirable, for individuals with such backgrounds to dominate the work of a sociological character in the health field, they are growing in importance and deserve notice.

CONCLUSIONS

The views and impressions recorded in this chapter are hardly an exhaustive analysis of the present status of medical sociology, although we have tried to span some of the important and critical areas and concerns. It should be noted that in general we know very little about the way persons in various academic fields work; sociologists have not been particularly conspicuous about studying themselves. Certainly a careful perusal of the various chapters in this volume would reveal statements at variance with some of the remarks made here. There continues to be considerable need for systematic study of the development of the field of medical sociology and the day-to-day work as sociologists in health.

It should be apparent, certainly, that the growth of the field has not been uniform and orderly and that neither when the first edition of this volume was published nor now does an enduring "homeostatic" balance exist between the medical sociologist and his peers in a sociological discipline or between the sociologist and medical practitioners and scientists. The issues elaborated in this chapter will continue to be matters of explicit and continued concern. Moreover, undoubtedly, additional ones cannot only be examined now but will arise in the future. But it is no longer a platitude to claim that the field of medicine has deep roots in the social sciences and that the future health of community members and the enhancement of their physical, psychological, and social well-being depends upon the fruits of an endeavor that bears the generic term "medical sociology."

REFERENCES

1. ANDERSON, ODIN W., "The Roads to Social Research," *American Behavioral Scientist*, 5 (March, 1962), 8–11.
2. ———, "Letter to Members of the Medical Sociology Section, American Sociological Association," 1962.
3. BARBER, BERNARD, *Social Stratification*. New York: Harcourt Brace Jovanovich, Inc., 1957.
4. BECKER, HOWARD S., "Whose Side Are We On?" *Social Problems*, 14 (Winter, 1967), 239–47.
5. ———, E. C. HUGHES, B. GEER, AND A. STRAUS, *Boys in White*. Chicago: University of Chiacgo Press, 1961.
6. BLOOM, SAMUEL W., "The Sociologist as Medical Educator," *American Sociological Review*, 25 (February, 1960), 95–102.
7. BRIM, ORVILLE G., HOWARD E. FREEMAN, SOL LEVINE, AND NORMAN SCOTCH, eds., *The Dying Patient*. New York: Russell Sage Foundation, 1970.
8. CASSEL, JOHN, "A Comprehensive Health Program among South African Zulus," in Benjamin D. Paul, ed., *Health, Culture, and Community*. New York: Russell Sage Foundation, 1955, pp. 15–41.
9. DAVIS, JAMES A., "Great Books and Small Groups," in Phillip E. Hammond, ed., *Sociologists at Work*. New York: Basic Books, Inc., Publishers, 1964, pp. 244–69.
10. FELDMAN, JACOB J., "Barriers to the Use of Health Survey Data in Demographic Analysis," *Milbank Memorial Fund Quarterly*, 36 (July, 1958), 203–19.
11. FOOTE, NELSON N. AND LEONARD S. COTRELL, *Identity and Interpersonal Competence*. Chicago: University of Chicago Press, 1955.
12. FOX, RENEE C., *Experiment Perilous*. New York: The Free Press, 1959.
13. FREEMAN, HOWARD E. AND CLARENCE C. SHERWOOD, *Social Research and Social Policy*. Englewood Cliffs, N.J.: Prentice-Hall, Inc., 1969.
14. GALDSTON, IAGO, "Doctor and Patient in Medical History," *Journal of Medical Education*, 37 (March, 1962), 222–32.
15. GOODE, WILLIAM J., "Community Within a Community: The Professions," *American Sociological Review*, 22 (April, 1957), 194–99.
16. GOULDNER, ALVIN W., "Explorations in Applied Social Science," *Social Problems*, 3 (January, 1956), 169–81.
17. ———, "Theoretical Requirements of the Applied Social Sciences," *American Sociological Review*, 22 (February, 1957), 92–102.
18. ———, "The Myth of a Value-Free Sociology," *Social Problems*, 9 (Winter, 1962), 199–213.
19. GREEN, ARNOLD W., *Sociology: An Analysis of Life in Modern Society*. New York: McGraw-Hill Book Company, 1952.
20. HALL, OSWALD, "Sociological Research in the Field of Medicine: Progress and Prospects," *American Sociological Review*, 16 (October, 1951), 639–49.
21. HAMMOND, KENNETH R. et al., *Teaching Comprehensive Medical Care: A Psychological Study of a Change in Medical Education*. Cambridge: Harvard University Press, 1959.
22. HOLLINGSHEAD, AUGUST B. AND FREDERICK C. REDLICH, *Social Class and Mental Illness*. New York: John Wiley & Sons, Inc., 1958.
23. HYMAN, MARTIN D., "Medicine," in Paul F. Lazarsfeld, William H. Sewell, and Harold L. Wilensky, eds., *The Uses of Sociology*. New York: Basic Books, Inc., Publishers, 1967, pp. 119–55.
24. LAMBERT, CAMILLE, JR., AND HOWARD E. FREEMAN, *The Clinic Habit*. New Haven, Conn.: College and University Press, 1967.
25. LEE, ALFRED M., "Sociologists in an Integrating Society," *Social Problems*, 2 (October, 1954), 57–66.

26. Lenski, Gerhard E., "Status Crystallization: A Nonvertical Dimension of Social Status," *American Sociological Review*, 19 (August, 1954), 405–13.
27. Levine, Sol and Warren G. Bennis, "The Action Role of the Sociologist," Paper read before American Sociological Association, New York, 1960.
28. Levine, Sol, Norman A. Scotch, and George J. Vlasak, "Unravelling Technology and Culture in Public Health," *American Journal of Public Health*, 59 (February, 1969), 237–44.
29. McIntire, Charles, "The Importance of the Study of Medical Sociology," *Bulletin American Academy of Medicine*, 1 (February, 1894), 425–34.
30. McKin, Marriott, "Western Medicine in a Village of Northern India," in Benjamin D. Paul, ed., *Health, Culture, and Community*. New York: Russell Sage Foundation, 1955, pp. 239–68.
31. Merton, Robert K., *On the Shoulders of Giants*. New York: Harcourt Brace Jovanovich, Inc., 1965.
32. ———, George Reader, and Patricia L. Kendall, eds., *The Student-Physician*. Cambridge: Harvard University Press, 1957.
33. Miller, Stephen J., *Prescription for Leadership*. Chicago: Aldine Press (forthcoming).
34. Moore, Wilbert E., *Industrial Relations and the Social Order*. New York: The Macmillan Company, 1947.
35. National Research Council, *The Behavioral Sciences and the Federal Government*. Washington, D.C.: National Academy of Sciences, 1968.
36. Odum, Howard W., *American Sociology*. New York: Longmans, Green, & Company, Inc., 1951.
37. Paul, Benjamin D., William A. Gamson, and Stephen Kageles, eds., "Trigger for Community Conflict: The Case of Fluoridation," *Journal of Social Issues*, 17 (1961).
38. Reader, George G. and Mary E. W. Goss, "The Sociology of Medicine," in R. K. Merton et al., eds., *Sociology Today*. New York: Basic Books, Inc., Publishers, 1959, pp. 229–46.
39. Richardson, Arthur H. and Howard E. Freeman, "Use of an Extended Health Benefit Program by Octogenarian U.A.W. Retirees," *Medical Care*, 7 (May–June, 1969), 225–34.
40. Russell Sage Foundation, *Annual Report, 1960–1961*. New York, 1961.
41. Scott, John F., "The Selective Influence of Social and Psychological Characteristics of Mothers on Information and Attitude Change in Mental Health Education Programs." Unpublished Ph.D. thesis, Brandeis University, 1961.
42. Sibley, Elbridge, "The Objectives of Sociological Training," *American Sociological Review*, 25 (August, 1960), 571–75.
43. Skipper, James A., Jr., and Robert C. Leonard, "Children's Stress in Hospitalization: A Field Experiment," *Journal of Health and Social Behavior*, 9 (December, 1968), 275–87.
44. Stanton, Alfred H. and Morris S. Schwartz, *The Mental Hospital*. New York: Basic Books, Inc., Publishers, 1954.
45. Straus, Robert, "The Nature and Status of Medical Sociology," *American Sociological Review*, 22 (April, 1957), 200–204.
46. Suchman, Edward A., *Evaluative Research: Principles and Practice in Public Service and Social Action Programs*. New York: Russell Sage Foundation, 1967.
47. Sussman, Marvin B., ed., *Sociology and Rehabilitation*, American Sociological Association. Washington, D.C.: Government Printing Office, 1965.
48. Williams, Robin M., "Application of Research to Practice and Intergroup Relations," *American Sociological Review*, 18 (February, 1953), 78–83.
49. Zelditch, Morris, "Methodological Problems of Field Studies," *American Journal of Sociology*, 7 (March, 1962), 566–76.

SOCIAL RESEARCH IN HEALTH AND MEDICINE: A BIBLIOGRAPHY

Ozzie G. Simmons and Emil Berkanovic

This selective bibliography is an overview of the literature in medical sociology. A number of areas peripheral to medical sociology, such as gerontology and fertility, have been excluded. The bulk of the literature referenced here has been published in the principal journals which serve as the major vehicles of communication within sociology. Other sources, such as the journals of the other behavioral sciences and of the health fields, were not systematically searched.

The steady increase in publications in medical sociology in the years since our bibliography was published (in the first edition of this book) has required substantial delections as well as a stringent selection of new inclusions, lest the length become unreasonable. To that end, we have favored reports of empirical research over historical, descriptive, and programmatic statements. Moreover, unlike the earlier version, this bibliography contains no papers originally published or reprinted in source books or other collections. Only the collections themselves have been listed.

One purpose of this chapter is to

provide the reader with the information he needs to keep abreast of developments in medical sociology. Thus, in the final section we list journals and periodical bibliographies which should be consulted regularly by the reader who wishes to stay currently informed about any aspect of medical sociology. While there are other possible sources of information about developments in the field, those listed should allow the reader to survey the medical sociological literature easily.

The bibliography is divided into nine parts, as follows, and within each part the publications are listed alphabetically.

I. General, Introductory, and Historical Statements
II. Health Behavior of the Individual
III. Knowledge, Attitudes, and Reactions of the Layman
IV. The Relationship Between Patients and Health Professionals
V. The Organization of the Delivery of Medical Care
VI. The Health Professions
VII. Social Epidemiology
VIII. Epidemiological and Etiological Aspects of Mental Problems
IX. Sources of Information About Medical Sociology

I. GENERAL, INTRODUCTORY, AND HISTORICAL STATEMENTS

ACKERKNECHT, ERWIN H., *A Short History of Medicine*. New York: The Ronald Press Company, 1955.

ANDERSON, ODIN W., "The Sociologist and Medicine," *Social Forces*, 31 (October, 1952), 38–42.

ANDERSON, ODIN W., AND MILVOY S. SEACAT, *The Behavioral Scientists and Research in the Health Field: A Questionnaire Survey*, Health Information Foundation Research Series No. 1. New York, 1957.

ANDERSON, ODIN W., AND MILVOY S. SEACAT, "Behavioral Science Research in the Health Field: A Statement of Problems and Priorities," *Social Problems*, 3 (Winter, 1959), 268–71.

APPLE, DORRIAN, ed., *Sociological Studies of Health and Sickness*. New York: McGraw-Hill Book Company, 1960.

BACKETT, E. MAURICE, "Preventive Medicine in Europe and in the United States," *Milbank Memorial Fund Quarterly*, 42 (October, 1964), 22–36.

BADGLEY, ROBIN F., ed., "Behavioral Science and Medical Education in Latin America," *Milbank Memorial Fund Quarterly*, 44 (April, 1966, Part 2), entire issue.

BULLOUGH, VERN L., "Status and Medieval Medicine," *Journal of Health and Human Behavior*, 2 (Fall, 1961), 204–10.

CAUDILL, WILLIAM, "Applied Anthropology in Medicine," in A. L. Kroeber, ed., *Anthropology Today*. Chicago: University of Chicago Press, 1953, pp. 771–806.

CAUDILL, WILLIAM, AND BERTRAM ROBERTS, "Pitfalls in the Organization of Interdisciplinary Research," *Human Organization*, 10 (Winter, 1951), 12–15.

CHEN, EDITH, AND SIDNEY COBB, "Family Structure in Relation to Health and Disease: A Review of the Literature," *Journal of Chronic Diseases*, 12 (November, 1960), 544–67.

CLAUSEN, JOHN A., *Sociology and the Field of Mental Health*. New York: Russell Sage Foundation, 1956.

Clausen, John, and Robert Straus, eds., *Medicine and Society.* Philadelphia: Annals of the American Academy of Political and Social Sciences, 1963.

Dain, Norman, *Concepts of Insanity in the United States: 1789–1865.* New Brunswick, N.J.: Rutgers University Press, 1964.

Davis, Michael M., "Social Medicine as a Field for Social Research," *American Journal of Sociology,* 44 (September, 1938), 274–79.

"Demography and Public Health in Latin America," Proceedings of the Fortieth Annual Conference of the Milbank Memorial Fund, *Milbank Memorial Fund Quarterly,* 42 (April, 1964, Part 2), entire issue.

Duff, Raymond S., and August B. Hollingshead, *Sickness and Society.* New York: Harper & Row, Publishers, Inc., 1968.

Eaton, Joseph W., "The Social Science Content of the Medical Curriculum," *American Sociological Review,* 21 (October, 1956), 614–17.

Foster, George M., *Problems in Intercultural Health Programs,* Social Science Research Council Pamphlet No. 12. New York, 1958.

Foster, George M., "Public Health and Behavioral Science: The Problem of Teamwork," *American Journal of Public Health,* 51 (September, 1961), 1286–93.

Foucault, Michel, *Madness and Civilization: A History of Insanity in the Age of Reason.* New York: Pantheon Books, Inc., 1965.

Frank, Lawrence K., *Society as the Patient.* New Brunswick, N.J.: Rutgers University Press, 1948.

Freeman, Howard E., and Leo G. Reeder, "Medical Sociology: A Review of the Literature," *American Sociological Review,* 22 (February, 1957), 73–81.

Freidson, Eliot, *The Sociology of Medicine.* New York University: Basil Blackwell Company, 1961–1962.

French, John R. P., Jr., Robert L. Kahn, and Floyd C. Mann, eds., "Work, Health and Satisfaction," *Journal of Social Issues,* 8 (July, 1962), entire issue.

Galdston, Iago, ed., *Medicine and Anthropology.* New York: International Universities Press, Inc., 1959.

Gertman, Samuel, "The Physician Views the Psychosocial Health of the American," *Journal of Health and Human Behavior,* 1 (Fall, 1960), 237–41.

Gordon, Gerald, et al, *Disease, The Individual, and Society.* New Haven, Conn.: College and University Press, 1968.

Goss, Mary E. W., and George G. Reader, "Collaboration Between Sociologists and Physicians," *Social Problems,* 4 (July, 1956), 82–89.

Graham, Saxon, "Sociological Aspects of Health and Illness," in R. E. L. Faris, ed., *Handbook of Modern Sociology.* Chicago: Rand McNally & Co., 1966, pp. 310–47.

Halmos, P., ed., *Sociology and Medicine: Studies Within the Framework of the British National Health Service.* Keele: University of Keele, 1962.

Hayes, Donald P., and Joan J. Jackson, "Teaching Social Science in the Medical School," *Journal of Health and Human Behavior,* 1 (Spring, 1960), 34–41.

Jaco, E. Gartly, "Areas for Research in Medical Sociology," *Sociology and Social Research,* 42 (July–August, 1958), 441–44.

Jaco, E. Gartly, "Problems and Prospects of the Social Sciences in Medical Education," *Journal of Health and Human Behavior,* 1 (Spring, 1960), 29–34.

Jaco, E. Gartley, ed., *Patients, Physicians, and Illness.* New York: The Free Press, 1958.

King, Stanley H., *Perceptions of Illness and Medical Practice.* New York: Russell Sage Foundation, 1962.

Klausner, Samuel Z., *Psychiatry and Religion.* New York: The Free Press, 1964.

KOOS, EARL L., *The Health of Regionville.* New York: Columbia University Press, 1954.

LEIGHTON, A. H., J. A. CLAUSEN, AND R. N. WILSON, eds., *Explorations in Social Psychiatry.* New York: Basic Books, Inc., Publishers, 1957.

MANGUS, A. R., "Medical Sociology: Study of the Social Components of Illness and of Health," *Sociology and Social Research*, 39 (January–February, 1955), 158–64.

MAY, JACQUES M., *Studies in Disease Ecology.* New York: Hafner Publishing Company, Inc., 1961.

MECHANIC, DAVID, "The Sociology of Medicine: Viewpoints and Perspectives," *Journal of Health and Human Behavior*, 7 (Winter, 1966), 237–48.

MECHANIC, DAVID, *Medical Sociology: A Selective View.* New York: The Free Press, 1968.

"Medical Sociology," *Social Problems*, 4 (July, 1956), entire issue.

Milbank Memorial Fund, *Research in Public Health.* New York, 1952.

OPLER, MARVIN K., *Culture, Psychiatry, and Human Values.* Springfield, Ill.: Charles C Thomas, Publisher, 1956.

PAUL, BENJAMIN D., ed., *Health, Culture, and Community.* New York: Russell Sage Foundation, 1955.

POLGAR, STEVEN, "Health and Human Behavior: Areas of Interest Common to the Social and Medical Sciences," *Current Anthropology*, 3 (April, 1962), 159–206.

READER, GEORGE C., AND MARY E. W. GOSS, "The Sociology of Medicine," in R. K. MERTON et al., *Sociology Today.* New York: Basic Books, Inc., Publishers, 1959, pp. 229–46.

ROEMER, MILTON I., "Medical Care and Social Class in Latin America," *Milbank Memorial Fund Quarterly*, 42 (July, 1964), 54–65.

ROEMER, MILTON I., AND JAMES M. MACKINTOSH, eds., *Henry E. Sigerist on the Sociology of Medicine.* New York: M.D. Publications, Inc., 1960.

RONEY, JAMES G., "Social Sciences in the Teaching of Public Health," *Journal of Health and Human Behavior*, 1 (Spring, 1960), 47–52.

ROSE, ARNOLD M., ed., *Mental Health and Mental Disorder: A Sociological Approach.* New York: W. W. Norton & Company, Inc., 1955.

ROSEN, GEORGE, "What is Social Medicine? A Genetic Analysis of the Concept," *Bulletin of the History of Medicine*, 21 (July–August, 1947), 674–733.

ROSEN, GEORGE, "Approaches to a Concept of Social Medicine: A Historical Survey," in *Backgrounds of Social Medicine.* New York: Milbank Memorial Fund, 1949, pp. 9–23.

ROSEN, GEORGE, "Social Stress and Mental Disease from the Eighteenth Century to the Present: Some Origins of Social Psychiatry," *Milbank Memorial Fund Quarterly*, 37 (January, 1959), 5–32.

ROSEN, GEORGE, *Madness in Society: Chapters in the Historical Sociology of Mental Illness.* Chicago: University of Chicago Press, 1968.

RUBIN, VERA, ed., "Culture, Society, and Health," *Annals of the New York Academy of Sciences*, 84 (December, 1960), 783–1060.

SAND, RENE, *The Advance to Social Medicine.* London: Staples Press, Ltd., 1952.

SAUNDERS, LYLE, *Cultural Difference and Medical Care.* New York: Russell Sage Foundation, 1954.

SCOTT, W. RICHARD, AND EDMUND H. VOLKART, eds., *Medical Care: Readings in the Sociology of Medical Institutions.* New York: John Wiley & Sons, Inc., 1966.

SHRYOCK, RICHARD H., *The Development of Modern Medicine: An Interpretation of the Social and Scientific Factors Involved.* New York: Alfred A. Knopf, Inc., 1947.

Shryock, Richard H., "The Interplay of Social and Internal Factors in the History of Modern Medicine," *Scientific Monthly*, 76 (1953), 221–30.

Sigerist, Henry E., *Civilization and Disease*. New York: Cornell University Press, 1943.

Simmons, Leo W., and Harold G. Wolff, *Social Science and Medicine*. New York: Russell Sage Foundation, 1954.

Simmons, Ozzie G., *Social Status and Public Health*, Social Science Research Council Pamphlet No. 13. New York, 1958.

Simmons, Ozzie G., and James A. Davis, "Interdisciplinary Collaboration in Mental Illness Research," *American Journal of Sociology*, 63 (November, 1957), 297–303.

Sokolowska, Magdalena, "Medical Sociology in Poland," *Milbank Memorial Fund Quarterly*, 44 (October, 1966), 426–37.

Straus, Robert, "The Nature and Status of Medical Sociology," *American Sociological Review*, 22 (April, 1957), 200–4.

Suchman, Edward A., *Sociology and the Field of Public Health*. New York: Russell Sage Foundation, 1964.

Sullivan, Harry Stack, *The Fusion of Psychiatry and Social Science*. New York: W. W. Norton & Company, Inc., 1964.

Tayback, Matthew, "Social Barriers to Optimal Health," *Milbank Memorial Fund Quarterly*, 35 (July, 1957), 245–57.

Winslow, Charles Edward A., *Man and Epidemics*. Princeton, N.J.: Princeton University Press, 1952.

Wolf, George A., Jr., "Preventive Medicine: 1952–1964," *Milbank Memorial Fund Quarterly*, 42 (October, 1964), 9–22.

Yamamoto, Mikio, and Susumu Sawaguchi, "The Development of the Social and Health Sciences in Japan," *Social Science and Medicine*, 3 (April, 1970), 639–52.

Zinsser, Hans, *Rats, Lice, and History*. New York: Bantam Books, Inc., 1960.

II. HEALTH BEHAVIOR OF THE INDIVIDUAL

Baker, A. A., et al., "Social Status after Five Years in a Mental Hospital," *British Journal of Medical Psychology*, 30 (1957), 113–18.

Barker, R. G., "The Social Psychology of Physical Disability," *Journal of Social Issues*, 4 (1958), 28–38.

Barker, R. G. et al., *Adjustment to Physical Handicap and Illness: A Survey of the Social Psychology of Physique and Disability*, Social Science Research Council, Bulletin No. 55. New York, 1953.

Baumann, Barbara, "Diversities in Conceptions of Health and Physical Fitness," *Journal of Health and Human Behavior*, 2 (Spring, 1961), 39–46.

Bean, Lee L., "Mental Illness and Occupational Adjustment: A 10 Year Follow-up Study," *Social Science and Medicine*, 2 (December, 1968), 435–47.

Bernstein, Basil, "Social Class, Speech Systems and Psychotherapy," *British Journal of Sociology*, 15 (March, 1964), 54–64.

Blackwell, Barbara Louis, "Upper Middle Class Adult Expectations about Entering the Sick Role for Physical and Psychiatric Dysfunctions," *Journal of Health and Social Behavior*, 8 (June, 1967), 83–95.

Blandford, Belvin R., "Peer Group Membership of Young Women with Cancer," *Journal of Chronic Diseases*, 21 (August, 1968), 315–22.

BLOOMBAUM, MILTON, AND TED GUGELYK, "Voluntary Confinement Among Lepers," *Journal of Health and Social Behavior*, 11 (March, 1970), 16–20.

BORN, DAVID OMAR, "Psychological Adaptation and Development Under Acculturative Stress: Toward a General Model," *Social Science and Medicine*, 3 (April, 1970), 529–47.

BORTNER, RAYMAN W., "A Short Rating Scale as a Potential Measure of Pattern *A* Behavior," *Journal of Chronic Diseases*, 22 (July, 1969), 87–91.

BORTNER, RAYMAN W., RAY H. ROSENMAN, AND MEYER FRIEDMAN, "Familial Similarity in Pattern *A* Behavior: Fathers and Sons," *Journal of Chronic Diseases*, 23 (June, 1970), 39–43.

BROWN, BARRY S., AND WILLIAM FLYNN, "Sociometric Choice in a Mental Hospital Population," *Journal of Health and Human Behavior*, 7 (Winter, 1966), 309–12.

BROWN, GEORGE W., "Experiences of Discharged Chronic Schizophrenic Patients in Various Types of Living Groups," *Milbank Memorial Fund Quarterly*, 37 (April, 1959), 105–31.

BROWN, G. W., G. M. CARSTAIRS, AND GILLIAN TOPPING, "Post-Hospital Adjustment of Chronic Mental Patients," *Lancet*, (September 27, 1958), 685–89.

CAFFREY, BERNARD, "Behavior Patterns and Personality Characteristics Related to Prevalence Rates of Coronary Heart Disease in American Monks," *Journal of Chronic Diseases*, 22 (July, 1969), 93–103.

CALDWELL, JOHN R., et al., "The Dropout Problem in Anti-hypertensive Treatment: A Pilot Study of Social and Emotional Factors Influencing a Patient's Ability to Follow Anti-hypertensive Treatment," *Journal of Chronic Diseases*, 22 (February, 1970), 579–92.

CALLAHAN, EILEEN M., et al., "The 'Sick Role' in Chronic Illness: Some Reactions," *Journal of Chronic Diseases*, 19 (August, 1966), 883–97.

CAMPBELL, ALISON C., "Attitudes of Mentally Disordered Adults to Community Care," *British Journal of Preventive and Social Medicine*, 22 (April, 1968), 94–99.

CASSEE, E. TH., "Deviant Illness Behaviour: Patients of Mesmerists," *Social Science and Medicine*, 3 (January, 1970), 389–96.

CAUDILL, WILLIAM, *Effects of Social and Cultural Systems in Reaction to Stress*, Social Science Research Council Pamphlet No. 14. New York, 1958.

CAUFFMAN, JOY, "Motivating University Women to Positive Health Behavior," *Journal of Health and Human Behavior*, 7 (Winter, 1966), 295–302.

CLAUSEN, JOHN A., "Adolescent Antecedents of Cigarette Smoking: Data from the Oakland Growth Study," *Social Science and Medicine*, 1 (January, 1968), 357–82.

COBB, SIDNEY, et al., "The Intrafamilial Transmission of Rheumatoid Arthritis: VII. Why do Wives with Rheumatoid Arthritis Have Husbands with Peptic Ulcers?," *Journal of Chronic Diseases*, 22 (September, 1969), 279–93.

CROOG, S. H., "Patient Government: Some Aspects of Participation and Social Background on Two Psychiatric Wards," *Psychiatry*, 19 (May, 1956), 203–7.

CROOG, SYDNEY H., SOL LEVINE, AND ZIFRE LURIE, "The Heart Patient and the Recovery Process: A Review of the Directions of Research on Social and Psychological Factors," *Social Science and Medicine*, 2 (June, 1968), 111–64.

DAVIS, FRED, "Definitions of Time and Recovery in Paralytic Polio Convalescence," *American Journal of Sociology*, 61 (May, 1956), 582–88.

DAVIS, FRED, *Passage Through Crisis: Polio Victims and Their Families*. New York: The Bobbs–Merrill Co., Inc., 1963.

DAVIS, JAMES A., HOWARD E. FREEMAN, AND OZZIE G. SIMMONS, "Rehospitalization and Performance Level Among Former Mental Patients," *Social Problems*, 5 (July, 1957), 37–44.

DAVIS, MILTON S., "Predicting Non-Compliant Behavior," *Journal of Health and Social Behavior*, 8 (December, 1967), 265–71.

DAVIS, MILTON S., AND ROBERT L. EICHHORN, "Compliance with Medical Regimens: A Panel Study," *Journal of Health and Human Behavior*, 4 (Winter, 1963), 240–50.

DELANGE, WALTER H., "Patient Role Conflict and Reactions to Hospitalization," *Journal of Health and Human Behavior*, 4 (Summer, 1963), 113–18.

DENZIN, NORMAN K., AND STEPHEN P. SPITZER, "Paths to the Mental Hospital and Staff Predictions of Patient Role Behavior," *Journal of Health and Human Behavior*, 7 (Winter, 1966), 265–72.

DINITZ, SIMON, et al., "The Ward Behavior of Psychiatric Patients," *Social Problems*, 6 (Fall, 1958), 107–15.

DINITZ, SIMON, et al., "Psychiatric and Social Attributes as Predictors of Case Outcome in Mental Hospitalization," *Social Problems*, 8 (Spring, 1961), 322–28.

DOW, THOMAS E., JR., "Optimism, Physique and Social Class in Reaction to Disability," *Journal of Health and Human Behavior*, 7 (Spring, 1966), 14–20.

EICHHORN, ROBERT L., AND RONALD M. ANDERSEN, "Changes in Personal Adjustment to Perceived and Medically Established Heart Disease," *Journal of Health and Human Behavior*, 3 (Winter, 1962), 242–49.

EIFRIG, DAVID E., et al., "Constrictive Pericarditis: Psychologic Aspects of Convalescence Following Pericardectomy," *Journal of Chronic Diseases*, 13 (January, 1961), 52–58.

ELLING, RAY H., RUTH WHITTEMORE, AND MORRIS GREEN, "Patient Participation in a Pediatric Program," *Journal of Health and Human Behavior*, 1 (Fall, 1960), 183–91.

ERIKSON, KAI T., "Patient Role and Social Uncertainty: A Dilemma of the Mentally Ill," *Psychiatry*, 20 (August, 1957), 263–74.

FIELD, MINNA, *Patients Are People: A Medico-Social Approach to Prolonged Illness*. New York: Columbia University Press, 1953.

FORDYCE, WILBERT E., et al., "Some Implications of Learning in Problems of Chronic Pain," *Journal of Chronic Diseases*, 21 (June, 1968), 179–90.

FREEMAN, HOWARD E., AND OZZIE G. SIMMONS, "Wives, Mothers, and the Posthospital Performance of Mental Patients," *Social Forces*, 37 (December, 1958), 153–59.

FREEMAN, HOWARD E., AND OZZIE G. SIMMONS, "Social Integration of Former Mental Patients," *International Journal of Social Psychiatry*, 4 (Spring, 1959), 264–71.

FREEMAN, HOWARD E., AND OZZIE G. SIMMONS, "Social Class and Posthospital Performance Levels," *American Sociological Review*, 24 (June, 1959), 345–51.

FREEMAN, HOWARD E., AND OZZIE G. SIMMONS, *The Mental Patient Comes Home*. New York: John Wiley & Sons, Inc., 1963.

FUNKENSTEIN, DANIEL H., STANLEY H. KING, AND MARGARET DROLETTE, *Mastery of Stress*. Cambridge, Mass.: Harvard University Press, 1957.

GAMBRILL, EILEEN, "Post Hospitalized Disabled Children," *Journal of Health and Human Behavior*, 4 (Fall, 1963), 206–10.

GIBBS, JACK P., AND WALTER T. MARTIN, "Mortality Rates and Participation in Sustenance Activities," *Journal of Health and Human Behavior*, 3 (Summer, 1962), 112–21.

GLASER, BARNEY G., "Disclosure of Terminal Illness," *Journal of Health and Human Behavior*, 7 (Summer, 1966), 83–91.

GLASER, BARNEY G., AND ANSELM L. STRAUSS, *Awareness of Dying*. Chicago: Aldine Publishing Company, 1965.

GLASSER, BARNEY G., AND A. L. STRAUSS, "Temporal Aspects of Dying as a Non-scheduled Status Passage," *American Journal of Sociology*, 71 (July, 1965), 48–60.

GOFFMAN, ERVING, *Asylums*. Chicago: Aldine Publishing Company, 1962.

GOLDSTEIN, B., AND P. DOMMERMUTH, "The Sick Role Cycle: An Approach to Medical Sociology," *Sociology and Social Research*, 47 (October, 1961), 1–12.

GORDON, GERALD, *Role Theory and Illness: A Sociological Perspective*. New Haven, Conn.: College University Press, 1966.

GRAYSON, MORRIS, et al., *Psychiatric Aspects of Rehabilitation*, Institute of Physical Medicine and Rehabilitation Monograph No. 2. New York, 1952.

GREENBLATT, M., D. J. LEVINSON, AND G. L. KLERMAN, *Mental Patients in Transition: Steps in Hospital-Community Rehabilitation*. Springfield, Ill.: Charles C Thomas, Publisher, 1961.

GUTERMAN, STANLEY S., "Social Isolation, Activeness, and Leisure Reading Among the Blind," *Social Science and Medicine*, 3 (January, 1970), 349–61.

HEINZELMAN, FRED, "Factors in Prophylaxis Behavior in Treating Rheumatic Fever: An Exploratory Study," *Journal of Health and Human Behavior*, 3 (Summer, 1962), 73–82.

HENLEY, BARBARA, AND MILTON S. DAVIS, "Satisfaction and Dissatisfaction: A Study of the Chronically Ill Aged Patient," *Journal of Health and Social Behavior*, 8 (March, 1967), 65–75.

HEYDEN, SIEGFRIED, ALBERT HEYMAN, AND LINDA CAMPLONG, "Mortality Patterns Among Parents of Patients with Atherosclerotic Cerebrovascular Disease," *Journal of Chronic Diseases*, 22 (July, 1969), 105–10.

ISHIYAMA, TOARU, AND ANN FOLEY BROWN, "Modifications in the Role-Image of the Chronic Psychotic Patient as a Function of Social Pressures," *Journal of Health and Human Behavior*, 7 (Fall, 1966), 203–11.

JANIS, IRVING L., *Psychological Stress: Psychoanalytic and Behavioral Studies of Surgical Patients*. New York: John Wiley & Sons, Inc., 1958.

KADUSHIN, C., "Individual Decisions to Undertake Psychotherapy," *Administrative Science Quarterly*, 3 (December, 1958), 379–411.

KALISH, RICHARD A., "The Aged and the Dying Process: The Inevitable Decisions," *Journal of Social Issues*, 21 (October, 1965), 87–96.

KARMEL, MADELINE, "Total Institution and Self-Mortification," *Journal of Health and Social Behavior*, 10 (June, 1969), 134–41.

KARMEL, MADELINE, "The Internalization of Social Roles in Institutionalized Chronic Mental Patients," *Journal of Health and Social Behavior*, 11 (September, 1970), 231–35.

KASL, STANISLAV V., AND SIDNEY COBB, "Some Psychological Factors Associated with Illness Behavior and Selected Illnesses," *Journal of Chronic Diseases*, 17 (April, 1964), 325–45.

KASL, STANISLAV V., AND SIDNEY COBB, "The Intrafamilial Transmission of Rheumatoid Arthritis: V. Differences between Rheumatoid Arthritics and Controls on Selected Personality Variables," *Journal of Chronic Diseases*, 22 (September, 1969), 239–58.

KASL, STANISLAV V., AND SIDNEY COBB, "The Intrafamilial Transmission of Rheumatoid Arthritis: VI. Association of Rheumatoid Arthritis with Several Types of Status Inconsistency," *Journal of Chronic Diseases*, 22 (September, 1969), 259–78.

KASSEBAUM, GENE G., AND BARBARA O. BAUMANN, "Dimensions of the Sick Role in Chronic Illness," *Journal of Health and Human Behavior*, 6 (Spring, 1965), 16–27.

KEDWARD, H. B., "Social Class of Consulting," *British Journal of Preventive and Social Medicine*, 16 (July, 1962), 147–52.

KEGELES, S. STEPHEN, "Why People Seek Dental Care: A Test of Conceptual Formulation," *Journal of Health and Human Behavior*, 4 (Fall, 1963), 166–73.

KELMAN, HOWARD R., JONAS N. MULLER, AND MILTON LOWENTHAL, "Post Hospital Adaptation of a Chronically Ill and Disabled Rehabilitation Population," *Journal of Health and Human Behavior*, 5 (Summer and Fall, 1964), 108–14.

KOENIG, RONALD, SAUL M. LEVIN, AND MICHAEL J. BRENNAN, "The Emotional Status of Cancer Patients as Measured by a Psychological Test," *Journal of Chronic Diseases*, 20 (November–December, 1967), 923–30.

KOOS, EARL L., *The Sociology of the Patient*. New York: McGraw-Hill Book Company, 1959.

KOSA, JOHN, JOEL J. ALPERT, AND ROBERT J. HAGGERTY, "On the Reliability of Family Health Information: A Comparative Study of Mothers' Reports on Illness and Related Behavior," *Social Science and Medicine*, 1 (July, 1967), 165–82.

KUTNER, BERNARD, AND GERALD GORDAN, "Seeking Care for Cancer," *Journal of Health and Human Behavior*, 2 (Fall, 1961), 171–78.

KUTNER, B., H. B. MAKOVER, AND A. OPPENHEIM, "Delay in the Diagnosis and Treatment of Cancer: A Critical Analysis of the Literature," *Journal of Chronic Diseases*, 7 (February, 1958), 95–120.

LECK, IAN, W. L. GORDON, AND THOMAS MCKEOWN, "Medical and Social Needs of Patients in Hospitals for the Mentally Subnormal," *British Journal of Preventive and Social Medicine*, 21 (July, 1967), 115–21.

LEFTON, MARK, et al., "Social Class, Expectations, and Performance of Mental Patients," *American Journal of Sociology*, 48 (July, 1962), 79–87.

LEFTON, MARK, et al., "Former Mental Patients and Their Neighbors: A Comparison of Performance Levels," *Journal of Health and Human Behavior*, 7 (Summer, 1966), 106–14.

LESHAN, LAWRENCE, "The World of the Patient in Severe Pain of Long Duration," *Journal of Chronic Diseases*, 17 (February, 1964), 119–26.

LEVENSON, BARBARA, AND JEROME GREEN, "Return to Work after Severe Disability," *Journal of Chronic Diseases*, 18 (February, 1965), 167–80.

LEVINE, GENE N., "Anxiety About Illness: Psychological and Social Bases," *Journal of Health and Human Behavior*, 3 (Spring, 1962), 30–34.

LEVINSON, DANIEL J., AND EUGENE B. GALLAGHER, *Patienthood in the Mental Hospital*. Boston: Houghton Mifflin Company, 1964.

LEWIS, LIONEL S., "Rational Behavior and the Treatment of Illness," *Journal of Health and Human Behavior*, 4 (Winter, 1963), 235–40.

LEWIS, LIONEL S., AND JOSEPH LOPREATO, "Arationality, Ignorance, and Perceived Danger in Medical Practices," *American Sociological Review*, 27 (August, 1962), 508–15.

LIBERMAN, ROBERT, "An Analysis of the Placebo Phenomenon," *Journal of Chronic Diseases*, 15 (August, 1962), 761–83.

LITMAN, THEODORE JAMES, "The Influence of Self Conception and Life Orientation Factors in the Rehabilitation of the Orthopedically Disabled," *Journal of Health and Human Behavior*, 3 (Winter, 1962), 249–57.

LITMAN, THEODORE JAMES, "The Family and Physical Rehabilitation," *Journal of Chronic Diseases*, 19 (February, 1966), 211–17.

LOWENTHAL, MARJORIE FISKE, AND CLAYTON HAVEN, "Interaction and Adaptation: Intimacy as a Critical Variable," *American Sociological Review*, 33 (February, 1968), 20–31.

LUDWIG, EDWARD G., AND SHIRLEY DAVIDSON ADAMS, "Patient Cooperation in a Rehabilitation Center: Assumption of the Client Role," *Journal of Health and Social Behavior*, 9 (December, 1968), 328–36.

LUDWIG, EDWARD G., AND GEOFFREY GIBSON, "Self Perception of Sickness and Seeking of Medical Care," *Journal of Health and Social Behavior*, 10 (June, 1969), 125–33.

MACGREGOR, GORDON, "Social Determinants of Health Practices," *American Journal of Public Health*, 51 (November, 1961), 1709–14.

MACKAY, JAMES R., DEREK L. PHILLIPS, AND FORBES O. BRYCE, "Drinking Behavior Among Teenagers: A Comparison of Institutionalized and Non-Institutionalized Youth," *Journal of Health and Social Behavior*, 8 (March, 1967), 46–54.

MADDOX, GEORGE L., KURT W. BACK, AND VERONICA R. LIEDERMAN, "Overweight as Social Deviance and Disability," *Journal of Health and Social Behavior*, 9 (December, 1968), 287–98.

MECHANIC, DAVID, "Illness and Social Disability: Some Problems in Analysis," *Pacific Sociological Review*, 2 (Spring, 1959), 37–41.

MECHANIC, DAVID, "The Concept of Illness Behavior," *Journal of Chronic Diseases*, 15 (March, 1960), 189–94.

MECHANIC, DAVID, AND EDMUND H. VOLKART, "Illness Behavior and Medical Diagnoses," *Journal of Health and Human Behavior*, 1 (Summer, 1960), 86–94.

MECHANIC, DAVID, AND EDMUND H. VOLKART, "Stress, Illness Behavior, and the Sick Role," *American Sociological Review*, 26 (February, 1961), 51–58.

MILLER, DOROTHY, "Retrospective Analysis of Posthospital Mental Patients' Worlds," *Journal of Health and Social Behavior*, 8 (June, 1967), 136–40.

MILLER, LEO, "Social Isolation and Role Performance Among Hospitalized Male Schizophrenics," *Social Science and Medicine*, 2 (September, 1968), 301–13.

MILLS, ENID, *Living With Mental Illness: A Study in East London*. London: Routledge & Kegan Paul, Ltd., 1962.

MORROW, WILLIAM R., AND ARTHUR J. ROBINS, "Family Relations and Social Recovery of Psychotic Mothers," *Journal of Health and Human Behavior*, 5 (Spring, 1964), 14–25.

NAGI, SAAD Z., RICHARD D. BURK, AND HARRY R. POTTER, "Back Disorders and Rehabilitation Achievement," *Journal of Chronic Diseases*, 18 (February, 1965), 181–97.

NAGI, SAAD Z., AND LAWRENCE E. RILEY, "Coping with Economic Crisis: The Disabled on Public Assistance," *Journal of Health and Social Behavior*, 9 (December, 1968), 317–27.

OAKES, THOMAS W., et al., "Family Expectations and Arthritis Patient Compliance to a Hand Resting Splint Regimen," *Journal of Chronic Diseases*, 22 (April, 1970), 757–64.

OPLER, MARVIN K., AND JEROME L. SINGER, "Ethnic Differences in Behavior and Psychopathology," *International Journal of Social Psychiatry*, 2 (Summer, 1956), 11–22.

OSSENBERG, RICHARD J., "The Experience of Deviance in the Patient-Role: A Study of Class Differences," *Journal of Health and Human Behavior*, 3 (Winter, 1962), 277–83.

PHILLIPS, DEREK L., "Mental Health Status, Social Participation, and Happiness," *Journal of Health and Social Behavior*, 8 (December, 1967), 285–91.

Picken, Bruce, and George Ireland, "Family Patterns of Medical Utilization: Possible Influences of Family Size, Role and Social Class," *Journal of Chronic Diseases*, 22 (August, 1969), 181–91.

Pittman, David J., and C. Wayne Gordon, *Revolving Door: A Study of the Chronic Police Case Inebriate*. New York: The Free Press, 1958.

Pratt, Lois, "How Do Patients Learn About Disease?" *Social Problems*, 4 (July, 1956), 29–40.

Ray, Marsh B., "The Cycle of Abstinence and Relapse Among Heroin Addicts," *Social Problems*, 9 (Fall, 1961), 132–40.

Reeder, Leo G., "Mailed Questionnaires in Longitudinal Health Studies: The Problem of Maintaining and Maximizing Response," *Journal of Health and Human Behavior*, 1 (Summer, 1960), 123–29.

Reeder, Sharon J., and Leo G. Reeder, "Some Correlates of Prenatal Care Among Low Income Wed and Unwed Women," *American Journal of Obstetrics and Gynecology*, 90 (December 15, 1964), 1304–14.

Rogler, Lloyd H., and August B. Hollingshead, "Class and Disordered Speech in the Mentally Ill," *Journal of Health and Human Behavior*, 2 (Fall, 1961), 178–84.

Rosenberg, Larry, and Jane Moosbruker, "The Participation of Working Class Mental Patients in a Mixed-Class Therapeutic Group," *Social Science and Medicine*, 1 (April, 1957), 85–96.

Rosengren, William R., "Social Sources of Pregnancy as Illness or Normality," *Social Forces*, 39 (February, 1961), 260–67.

Rosengren, William R., "The Sick Role in Pregnancy: A Note on Research in Progress," *Journal of Health and Human Behavior*, 3 (Fall, 1962), 213–19.

Roth, Harold P., and Herbert S. Caron, "Patients' Misconceptions About Their Peptic Ulcer Diets: Potential Obstacles to Cooperation," *Journal of Chronic Diseases*, 20 (January, 1967), 5–11.

Roth, Julius, *Timetables: Structuring the Passage of Time in Hospital Treatment and Other Careers*. New York: The Bobbs–Merrill Co., Inc., 1963.

Ruesch, Jurgen, et al., *Chronic Disease and Psychological Invalidism: A Psychosomatic Study*. Berkeley: University of California Press, 1951.

Sall, Joan, William W. Vosburgh, and Abby Silverman, "Psychiatric Patients and Extended Visit: A Survey of Research Findings," *Journal of Health and Human Behavior*, 7 (Spring, 1966), 20–28.

Samora, J., L. Saunders, and R. F. Larson, "Medical Vocabulary Knowledge Among Hospital Patients," *Journal of Health and Human Behavior*, 2 (Summer, 1961), 83–92.

Sampson, Harold, et al., *Schizophrenic Women: Studies in Marital Crisis*. New York: Atherton Press, 1964.

Sanua, Victor D., "Sociocultural Factors in Response to Stressful Life Situations: The Behavior of Aged Amputees as an Example," *Journal of Health and Human Behavior*, 1 (Spring, 1960), 17–24.

Savin, J. A., "Social Behaviour and the Use of Medical Services," *British Journal of Preventive and Social Medicine*, 23 (February, 1969), 53–55.

Scheff, Thomas J., "Users and Non-Users of a Student Psychiatric Clinic," *Journal of Health and Human Behavior*, 7 (Summer, 1966), 114–22.

Schlesinger, Lawrence E., "Disruptions in the Personal-Social System Resulting from Traumatic Disability," *Journal of Health and Human Behavior*, 6 (Summer, 1965), 91–98.

SCHNEIDER, DAVID M., "The Social Dynamics of Physical Disability in Army Basic Training," *Psychiatry*, 10 (August, 1947), 323–33.

SCHWAB, JOHN J., et al., "Evaluating Anxiety in Medical Patients," *Journal of Chronic Diseases*, 19 (October, 1966), 1049–57.

SCHWARTZ, JEROME L., "Participation of Consumers in Prepaid Health Plans," *Journal of Health and Human Behavior*, 5 (Summer and Fall, 1964), 74–84.

SEEMAN, MELVIN, AND JOHN W. EVANS, "Alienation and Learning in a Hospital Setting," *American Sociological Review*, 27 (December, 1962), 772–82.

SHANAS, ETHEL, *Medical Care Among Those Aged 65 and Over: Reported Illness and Utilization of Health Services by the "Sick" and the "Well,"* Health Information Foundation Research Series No. 16. New York, 1960.

SHATIN, LEO, PAULA BROWN, AND MARION LOIZEAUX, "Psychological Remotivation of the Chronically Ill Medical Patient: A Quantitative Study in Rehabilitation Methodology," *Journal of Chronic Diseases*, 14 (October, 1961), 452–68.

SHEKELLE, RICHARD B., et al., "Personality Traits and Coronary Heart Disease: A Reexamination of Ibrahim's Hypothesis Using Longitudinal Data," *Journal of Chronic Diseases*, 23 (June, 1970), 33–38.

SHERWIN, ALBERT C., AND ROBERT S. MCCULLY, "Reactions Observed in Boys of Various Ages (Ten to Fourteen) to a Crippling, Progressive, and Fatal Illness (Muscular Dystrophy)," *Journal of Chronic Diseases*, 13 (January, 1961), 59–68.

SHUVAL, JUDITH T., AARON ANTONOVSKY, AND A. MICHAEL DAVIES, *Social Functions of Medical Practice*. San Francisco: Jossey–Bass, Inc., 1970.

SILLS, D. L., AND R. E. GILL, "Young Adults' Use of the Salk Vaccine," *Social Problems*, 6 (Winter, 1958–59), 246–53.

SIMMEL, MARIANNE L., "The Body Percept in Physical Medicine and Rehabilitation," *Journal of Health and Social Behavior*, 8 (March, 1967), 60–64.

SIMMONS, OZZIE G., "Drinking Patterns and Interpersonal Performance in a Peruvian Mestizo Community," *Quarterly Journal of Studies on Alcohol*, 20 (March, 1959), 103–11.

SIMMONS, OZZIE G., *After Hospitalization: The Mental Patient and His Family*, Austin, Tex.: The Hogg Foundation for Mental Health, 1960.

SIMMONS, OZZIE G., AND HOWARD E. FREEMAN, "Familial Expectations and Posthospital Performance of Mental Patients," *Human Relations*, 12 (August, 1959), 233–42.

SOUTHARD, SAMUEL, *The Family and Mental Illness*, Philadelphia: The Westminster Press, 1957.

SPITZER, STEPHAN P., AND NORMAN K. DENZIN, *The Mental Patient: Studies in the Sociology of Deviance*. New York: McGraw-Hill Book Company, 1968.

STOECKLE, JOHN D., AND GERALD E. DAVIDSON, "Communicating Aggrieved Feelings in the Patient's Initial Visit to a Medical Clinic," *Journal of Health and Human Behavior*, 4 (Fall, 1963), 199–206.

STOECKLE, JOHN D., IRVING K. ZOLA, AND GERALD C. DAVIDSON, "On Going to See the Doctor: The Contributions of the Patient to the Decision to Seek Medical Aid," *Journal of Chronic Diseases*, 16 (September, 1963), 975–89.

STRAUS, ROBERT, "Sociological Determinants of Health Beliefs and Behavior," *American Journal of Public Health*, 51 (October, 1961), 1547–51.

SUCHMAN, EDWARD A., "Accidents and Social Deviance," *Journal of Health and Social Behavior*, 11 (March, 1970), 4–15.

SUCHMAN, EDWARD A., BERNARD S. PHILLIPS, AND GORDON F. STREIB, "An Analysis of the Validity of Health Questionnaires," *Social Forces*, 36 (March, 1958), 223–32.

SUSSMAN, MARVIN B., AND MARIE R. HAUG, "The Vicissitudes of Change," *Social Science and Medicine*, 3 (August, 1969), 179–89.

TAGLIACOZZO, DAISY M., AND KENJI IMA, "Knowledge of Illness as a Predictor of Patient Behavior," *Journal of Chronic Diseases*, 22 (April, 1970), 765–75.

TAYLOR, P. J., AND A. J. FAIRRIE, "Chronic Disabilities and Capacity for Work. A Study of 3,299 Men Aged 16–64 in a General Practice and an Oil Refinery," *British Journal of Preventive and Social Medicine*, 22 (April, 1968), 86–93.

THOMAS, EDWIN J., "Problems of Disability from the Perspective of Role Theory," *Journal of Health and Human Behavior*, 7 (Spring, 1966), 2–14.

TWADDLE, ANDREW C., "Health Decisions and Sick Role Variations: An Exploration," *Journal of Health and Social Behavior*, 10 (June, 1969), 105–15.

WALLACE, ANTHONY F. C., AND HAROLD A. RASHKIS, "The Relation of Staff Consensus to Patient Disturbance on Mental Hospital Wards," *American Sooiclogical Review*, 24 (December, 1959), 829–35.

WECHSLER, HENRY, et al., "Religious-Ethnic Differences in Alcohol Consumption," *Journal of Health and Social Behavior*, 11 (March, 1970), 21–29.

WERTS, CHARLES E., et al., "Factors Related to Behavior in Labor," *Journal of Health and Human Behavior*, 6 (Winter, 1965), 238–43.

WHATLEY, CHARLES D., JR., "Status, Role and Vocational Continuity of Discharged Mental Patients," *Journal of Health and Human Behavior*, 4 (Summer, 1963), 105–13.

WILLIAMS, RICHARD H., AND CLAUDE G. WIRTHS, "Apragmatism Among Youth. Case Studies of Some Hospitalized Young Adults," *Social Science and Medicine*, 1 (April, 1967), 31–44.

WILLIAMS, WARREN S., "Class Differences in the Attitudes of Psychiatric Patients," *Social Problems*, 4 (January, 1957), 240–44.

WINSBERG, B., AND M. GREENLICK, "Pain Responses in Negro and White Obstetrical Patients," *Journal of Health and Social Behavior*, 8 (September, 1967), 222–27.

WYLIE, CHARLES M., "Delay in Seeking Rehabilitation After Cerebrovascular Accidents," *Journal of Chronic Diseases*, 14 (October, 1961), 442–51.

ZOLA, IRVING KENNETH, "Culture and Symptoms: An Analysis of Patients Presenting Complaints," *American Sociological Review*, 31 (October, 1966), 615–31.

ZYZANSKI, STEPHEN J., AND C. DAVID JENKINS, "Basic Dimensions Within the Coronary Prone Behavior Pattern," *Journal of Chronic Diseases*, 22 (May, 1970), 781–95.

III. KNOWLEDGE, ATTITUDES, AND REACTIONS OF THE LAYMAN

ADAIR, JOHN, KURT DEUSCHLE, AND WALSH MCDERMOTT, "Patterns of Health and Disease Among the Navahos," *Annals of the American Academy of Political and Social Science*, 311 (May, 1957), 80–94.

APPLE, DORRIAN, "How Laymen Define Illness," *Journal of Health and Human Behavior*, 1 (Fall, 1960), 219–25.

BAUMANN, B., "Diversities in Conceptions of Health and Physical Fitness," *Journal of Health and Human Behavior*, 2 (Spring, 1961), 39–46.

BECKER, HOWARD S., "History, Culture and Subjective Experience: An Exploration of the Social Bases of Drug-Induced Experiences," *Journal of Health and Social Behavior*, 8 (September, 1967), 163–76.

Belcher, John C., "Background Norms of Patients and the Therapeutic Community," *Journal of Health and Human Behavior*, 6 (Spring, 1965), 27–35.

Berkman, Paul L., "Spouseless Motherhood, Psychological Stress, and Physical Morbidity," *Journal of Health and Social Behavior*, 10 (December, 1969), 323–34.

Bruun, Kettil, ed., *Drinking Behavior in Small Groups: An Experimental Study*, trans. Fred A. Fewster. Stockholm: Almqvist and Wiksell, 1959.

Chigier, E., and Miriam Chigier, "Attitudes to Disability of Children in the Multi-Cultural Society of Israel," *Journal of Health and Social Behavior*, 9 (December, 1968), 310–17.

Clark, Margaret, *Health in the Mexican–American Culture: A Community Study.* Berkeley: University of California Press, 1959.

Clausen, John A., and E. W. Linn, "Public Reaction to a Severe Polio Outbreak in Three Massachusetts Communities," *Social Problems*, 4 (July, 1956), 40–51.

Clausen, John A., and Marian Radke Yarrow, eds., "The Impact of Mental Illness on the Family," *Journal of Social Issues*, 11 (1955), entire issue.

Crain, Alan J., Marvin B. Sussman, and William B. Weil, "Effects of a Diabetic Child on Marital Integration and Related Measures of Family Functioning," *Journal of Health and Human Behavior*, 7 (Summer, 1966), 122–28.

Crawford, Fred R., Glen W. Rollins, and Robert L. Sutherland, "Variations in the Evaluations of the Mentally Ill," *Journal of Health and Human Behavior*, 1 (Fall, 1960), 211–19.

Crawford, Fred R., Glen W. Rollins, and Robert L. Sutherland, "Variations in the Evaluation of the Mentally Ill: Part II. The Viewpoint of the Rural Dweller," *Journal of Health and Human Behavior*, 2 (Winter, 1961), 267–75.

Croog, Sydney H., "Ethnic Origins, Educational Level, and Response to a Health Questionnaire," *Human Organization*, 20 (Summer, 1961), 65–69.

Cumming, Elaine, and John Cumming, *Closed Ranks: An Experiment in Mental Health Education.* Cambridge, Mass.: Harvard University Press, 1957.

Davis, James A., *Education for Positive Mental Health.* Chicago: Aldine Publishing Company, 1965.

Davis, Morris, "Community Attitudes Toward Fluoridation," *Public Opinion Quarterly*, 23 (Winter, 1959–1960), 474–82.

Dohrenwend, Bruce P., Viola W. Bernard, and Lawrence C. Kolb, "The Orientations of Leaders in an Urban Area Toward Problems of Mental Illness," *American Journal of Psychiatry*, 118 (February, 1962), 683–91.

Dohrenwend, Bruce P., and E. Chin-Shong, "Social Status and Attitudes Toward Psychological Disorder: The Problem of Tolerance of Deviance," *American Sociological Review*, 32 (June, 1967), 417–33.

Downey, Kenneth J., "Parents' Reasons for Institutionalizing Severely Mentally Retarded Children," *Journal of Health and Human Behavior*, 6 (Fall, 1965), 147–55.

Downey, Kenneth J., "Public Images of Mental Illness: A Factor Analytic Study of Causes and Symptoms," *Social Science and Medicine*, 1 (April, 1967), 45–66.

Eaton, Joseph, and Robert Weil, *Culture and Mental Disorders.* New York: The Free Press, 1955.

Evans, Robert R., and Edgar F. Borgatta, "An Experiment in Smoking Dissuasion among University Freshmen: A Followup," *Journal of Health and Social Behavior*, 11 (March, 1970), 30–36.

Fabrega, Horacio, Jr., Richard J. Moore, and John R. Strawn, "Low Income Medical Problem Patients: Some Medical and Behavioral Features," *Journal of Health and Social Behavior*, 10 (December, 1969), 334–43.

FELDMAN, JACOB J., *The Dissemination of Health Information: A Case Study in Adult Learning.* Chicago: Aldine Publishing Company, 1966.

FIELD, MARK G., *Doctor and Patient in Soviet Russia.* Cambridge, Mass.: Harvard University Press, 1957.

FLETCHER, C. RICHARD, "Attributing Responsibility to the Deviant: A Factor in Psychiatric Referrals by the General Public," *Journal of Health and Social Behavior,* 8 (September, 1967), 185–96.

FOLKARD, STEVEN, "Comparative Study of Attitudes to the Rehabilitation of Psychiatric Patients," *British Journal of Preventive and Social Medicine,* 14 (January, 1960), 23–27.

FREEMAN, HOWARD E., "Attitudes Toward Mental Illness Among Relatives of Former Patients," *American Sociological Review,* 26 (February, 1961), 59–66.

FREEMAN, HOWARD E., AND GENE G. KASSEBAUM, "Relationship of Education and Knowledge to Opinions about Mental Illness," *Mental Hygiene,* 44 (January, 1960), 43–47.

FREEMAN, HOWARD E., AND CAMILLE LAMBERT, JR., "Preventive Dental Behavior of Urban Mothers," *Journal of Health and Human Behavior,* 6 (Fall, 1965), 141–47.

FREEMAN, HOWARD E., AND OZZIE G. SIMMONS, "Feelings of Stigma among Relatives of Former Mental Patients," *Social Problems,* 8 (Spring, 1961), 312–21.

GAMSON, WILLIAM A., "Social Science Aspects of Fluoridation: A Summary of Research," *Health Education Journal,* 19 (September, 1961), 159–69.

GAMSON, WILLIAM A., AND HOWARD SCHUMAN, "Some Undercurrents in the Prestige of Physicians," *American Journal of Sociology,* 48 (January, 1963), 463–71.

GLASSER, M. A., "A Study of the Public's Acceptance of the Salk Vaccine Program," *American Journal of Public Health,* 48 (February, 1958), 141–46.

GOLDENBERG, MAURICIO, et al., "Attitudes Towards Alcohol, Alcoholism and the Alcoholic: An Exploratory Study," *Social Science and Medicine,* 2 (March, 1968), 29–40.

GOODENOUGH, WARD H., "Human Problems in the Conduct of Environmental Health Programs: The Role of Environment in Culture and Society," *Journal of Health and Human Behavior,* 5 (Winter, 1964), 141–44.

GOODMAN, NORMAN, et al., "Variant Reactions to Physical Disabilities," *American Sociological Review,* 28 (June, 1963), 429–36.

GOTTLIEB, LEON S., "In Search of Nepenthe," *Journal of Health and Human Behavior,* 3 (Winter, 1962), 288–93.

GREEN, ARNOLD L., "The Ideology of Anti-Fluoridation Leaders," *Journal of Social Issues,* 17 (1961), 13–25.

GURIN, G., J. VEROFF, AND S. FELD, *American View Their Mental Health.* New York: Basic Books, Inc., Publishers, 1960.

GURSSLIN, ORVILLE R., RAYMOND G. HUNT, AND JACK L. ROACH, "Social Class and the Mental Health Movement," *Social Problems,* 7 (Winter, 1959–1960), 210–18.

JAHODA, MARIE, *Current Concepts of Positive Mental Health.* New York: Basic Books, Inc., Publishers, 1958.

JENKINS, C. DAVID, "Group Differences in Perception: A Study of Community Beliefs and Feelings about Tuberculosis," *American Journal of Sociology,* 71 (January, 1966), 417–30.

JOHNSON, A. L., et al., *Epidemiology of Polio Vaccine Acceptance.* Chapel Hill: School of Public Health, Department of Epidemiology, University of North Carolina, 1962.

JOURNAL OF SOCIAL ISSUES, "Trigger for Community Conflict: The Case of Fluoridation," 17 (1961), entire issue.

JOYCE, C. R. B., AND R. M. C. WELLDON, "The Objective Efficacy of Prayer: A Double-Blind Clinical Trial," *Journal of Chronic Diseases*, 18 (April, 1965), 367–77.

KADUSHIN, CHARLES, "The Friends and Supporters of Psychotherapy: On Social Circles in Urban Life," *American Sociological Review*, 31 (December, 1966), 786–802.

KALUZNY, ARNOLD D., AND CHARLES A. METZNER, "Cognitive Balance in a Choice Situation Involving Two Health Care Plans," *Journal of Health and Social Behavior*, 11 (June, 1970), 104–15.

KEGELES, S. STEPHEN, "Attitudes and Behavior of the Public Regarding Cervical Cytology: Current Findings and New Directions for Research," *Journal of Chronic Diseases*, 20 (November–December, 1967), 911–22.

KEGELES, S. STEPHEN, "A Field Experimental Attempt to Change Beliefs and Behavior of Women in an Urban Ghetto," *Journal of Health and Social Behavior*, 10 (June, 1969), 115–24.

KIEV, ARI, "Psychotherapeutic Aspect of Pentecostal Sects among West Indian Immigrants to England," *British Journal of Sociology*, 15 (June, 1964), 129–38.

KIRSCHT, JOHN P., AND ANDIE L. KNUTSON, "Fluoridation and the 'Threat' of Science," *Journal of Health and Human Behavior*, 4 (Summer, 1963), 129–45.

KIRSCHT, JOHN P., et al., "A National Study of Health Beliefs," *Journal of Health and* Human Behavior, 7 (Winter, 1966), 248–55.

KLEIN, JULIUS, AND DEREK L. PHILLIPS, "From Hard to Soft Drugs: Temporal and Substantive Changes in Drug Usages among Gangs in a Working-Class Community," *Journal of Health and Social Behavior*, 9 (June, 1969), 139–45.

KLEIN, ROBERT F., ALFRED DEAN, AND MORTON D. BOGDONOFF, "The Impact of Illness upon the Spouse," *Journal of Chronic Diseases*, 20 (April, 1967), 241–47.

KURTZ, RICHARD A., AND WOLF WOLFENSBERGER, "Cultural Deprivation, Lower Class and Mental Retardation: Certain Terminological and Conceptual Confusions," *Social Science and Medicine*, 3 (August, 1969), 229–37.

LAWSON, ANNETT R. L., *The Recognition of Mental Illness in London*. Fairlawn, N.J.: Oxford University Press, 1966.

LAWTON, M. POWELL, "Psychosocial Aspects of Cigarette Smoking," *Journal of Health and Human Behavior*, 3 (Fall, 1962), 163–71.

LEMERT, EDWIN M., "Alcohol and the Northwest Coast Indians," *University of California Publications in Culture and Society*, 2 (1954), 303–406.

LEMERT, EDWIN M., "The Use of Alcohol in Three Salish Indian Tribes," *Quarterly Journal of Studies on Alcohol*, 19 (March, 1958), 90–107.

LEMKAU, PAUL V., AND GUIDO M. CROCETTI, "An Urban Population's Opinion and Knowledge about Mental Illness," *American Journal of Psychiatry*, 118 (February, 1962), 692–700.

LINN, ERWIN L., "Social Meanings of Dental Appearance," *Journal of Health and Human Behavior*, 7 (Winter, 1966), 289–95.

MABRY, JOHN H., "Lay Concepts of Etiology," *Journal of Chronic Diseases*, 17 (April, 1964), 371–86.

MACGREGOR, FRANCES C., "Social and Cultural Components in the Motivations of Persons Seeking Plastic Surgery of the Nose," *Journal of Health and Social Behavior*, 8 (June, 1967), 125–35.

MACLEAN, CATHERINE M. UNA, "Traditional Healers and Their Female Clients: An Aspect of Nigerian Sickness Behavior," *Journal of Health and Social Behavior*, 10 (September, 1969), 172–86.

MACLEAN, UNA, "Community Attitudes to Mental Illness in Edinburgh," *British Journal of Preventive and Social Medicine*, 23 (February, 1969), 45–52.

MADDOX, GEORGE L., "Self-Assessment of Health Status: A Longitudinal Study of Selected Elderly Subjects," *Journal of Chronic Diseases*, 17 (May, 1964), 449–60.

MADDOX, GEORGE L., "Drinking Among Negroes: Inferences from the Drinking Patterns of Selected Negro Male Collegians," *Journal of Health and Social Behavior*, 9 (June, 1968), 114–20.

MADSEN, WILLIAM, *Society and Health in the Lower Rio Grande Valley.* Austin, Tex.: The Hogg Foundation for Mental Health, 1961.

MANIS, JEROME G., et al., "Public and Psychiatric Conceptions of Mental Illness," *Journal of Health and Human Behavior*, 6 (Spring, 1965), 48–55.

MATTHEWS, VICTOR, AND CHARLES WESTIE, "A Preferred Method for Obtaining Rankings: Reactions to Physical Handicaps," *American Sociological Review*, 31 (December, 1966), 851–55.

MCNEIL, DONALD R., *The Fight for Fluoridation.* Fairlawn, N.J.: Oxford University Press, 1957.

MCPARTLAND, THOMAS S., AND JOHN H. CUMMING, "Self-Conception, Social Class and Mental Health," *Human Organization*, 17 (Fall, 1958), 24–29.

MEADOW, KATHRYN P., "Parental Response to the Medical Ambiguities of Congenital Deafness," *Journal of Health and Social Behavior*, 9 (December, 1968), 299–309.

MECHANIC, DAVID, "Perception of Parental Responses to Illness: A Research Note," *Journal of Health and Human Behavior*, 6 (Winter, 1965), 253–57.

METZ, A. STAFFORD, "The Relationship of Dental Care Practices to Attitude Toward Fluoridation," *Journal of Health and Social Behavior*, 8 (March, 1967), 55–59.

METZNER, CHARLES, A., AND RASHID L. BASHSHUR, "Factors Associated with Choice of Health Care Plans," *Journal of Health and Social Behavior*, 8 (December, 1967), 291–99.

MEYEROWITZ, JOSEPH H., AND HOWARD B. KAPLAN, "Familial Response to Stress: The Case of Cystic Fibrosis," *Social Science and Medicine*, 1 (September, 1967), 249–66.

MILNE, J. S., K. HOPE, AND J. WILLIAMSON, "Variability in Replies to a Questionnaire on Symptoms of Physical Illness," *Journal of Chronic Diseases*, 22 (May, 1970), 805–10.

MONEY, JOHN, REYNOLDS POTTER, AND CLARICE S. STOLL, "Sex Reannouncement in Hereditary Sex Deformity: Psychology and Sociology of Habilitation," *Social Science and Medicine*, 3 (August, 1969), 207–16.

MULFORD, HAROLD A., AND DONALD E. MILLER, "An Index of Alcoholic Drinking Behavior Related to the Meanings of Alcohol," *Journal of Health and Human Behavior*, 2 (Spring, 1961), 26–31.

NALL, FRANK C., II, AND JOSEPH SPEILBERG, "Social and Cultural Factors in the Responses of Mexican–Americans to Medical Treatment," *Journal of Health and Social Behavior*, 8 (December, 1967), 299–308.

NICKERSON, GIFFORD S., AND DONALD L. HOCHSTRASSER, "Factors Affecting Non-Participation in a County-Wide Tuberculin Testing Program in Southern Appalachia," *Social Science and Medicine*, 3 (April, 1970), 575–96.

NUNNALLY, JUM C., *Popular Conceptions of Mental Health.* New York: Holt, Rinehart & Winston, Inc., 1961.

O'SHEA, ROBERT M., AND S. STEPHEN KEGELES, "An Analysis of Anti-Fluoridation Letters," *Journal of Health and Human Behavior*, 4 (Summer, 1963), 135–41.

Overs, Robert P., and Elston L. Belknap, "Evaluating Stroke Patient Families," *Journal of Chronic Diseases*, 20 (January, 1967), 45–51.

Paul, Benjamin, "The Role of Beliefs and Customs in Sanitation Programs," *American Journal of Public Health*, 48 (November, 1958), 1502–06.

Petroni, Frank A., and Carol Griffin, "Labeling and Psychiatry: Perspectives in Need of Data," *Social Science and Medicine*, 3 (August, 1969), 239–47.

Pfautz, Harold W., "Christian Science: A Case Study of the Social Psychological Aspect of Secularization," *Social Forces*, 34 (March, 1956), 246–51.

Phillips, Derek L., "Rejection: A Possible Consequence of Seeking Help for Mental Disorders," *American Sociological Review*, 28 (December, 1963), 963–73.

Phillips, Derek L., "Rejection of the Mentally Ill: The Influence of Behavior and Sex," *American Sociological Review*, 29 (October, 1964), 679–88.

Pinard, Maurice, "Structural Attachments and Political Support in Urban Politics: The Case of Fluoridation Referendums," *American Journal of Sociology*, 68 (March, 1963), 513–27.

Pittman, David J., and Charles R. Snyder, *Society, Culture and Drinking Patterns.* New York: John Wiley & Sons, Inc., 1962.

Ramsey, Glenn V., and Melita Seipp, "Attitudes and Opinions Concerning Mental Illness," *Psychiatric Quarterly*, 22 (July, 1948), 428–44.

Rawnsley, J., J. B. Loudon, and H. L. Miles, "Attitudes of Relatives to Patients in Mental Hospitals," *British Journal of Preventive and Social Medicine*, 16 (January, 1962), 1–15.

Rlchardson, Stephen A., et al., "Cultural Uniformity in Reaction to Physical Disabilities," *American Sociological Review*, 26 (April, 1961), 241–47.

Riley, John W., and C. S. Marden, "The Social Patterns of Alcohol Drinking," *Quarterly Journal of Studies on Alcohol*, 8 (September, 1947), 265–73.

Robinson, David, "Mothers' Fear, Their Children's Well-Being in Hospital, and the Study of Illness Behaviour," *British Journal of Preventive and Social Medicine*, 22 (October, 1968), 228–33.

Rogler, Lloyd H., and August B. Hollingshead, *Trapped: Families and Schizophrenia.* New York: John Wiley & Sons, Inc., 1965.

Rose, Charles L., "Relatives' Attitudes and Mental Hospitalization," *Mental Hygiene*, 43 (April, 1959), 194–203.

Rosenstock, Irwin M., et al., "Public Knowledge, Opinion and Action Concerning Three Public Health Issues: Radioactive Fallout, Insect and Plant Sprays and Fatty Foods," *Journal of Health and Human Behavior*, 7 (Summer, 1966), 83–91.

Rothaus, Paul, and Robert Morton, "Problem Centered versus Mental Illness Self-Descriptions," *Journal of Health and Human Behavior*, 3 (Fall, 1962), 198–204.

Rubel, Arthur J., "Concepts of Disease in Mexican–American Culture," *American Anthropologist*, 62 (October, 1960), 795–814.

Salber, Eva J., B. Welsh, and S. V. Taylor, "Reasons for Smoking Given by Secondary School Children," *Journal of Health and Human Behavior*, 4 (Summer, 1963), 118–29.

Samora, Julian, Lyle Saunders, and Richard F. Larsen, "Medical Vocabulary Knowledge Among Hospital Patients," *Journal of Health and Human Behavior*, 2 (Summer, 1961), 83–92.

Samora, Julian, Lyle Saunders, and Richard F. Larsen, "Knowledge about Specific Diseases in Four Selected Samples," *Journal of Health and Human Behavior*, 3 (Fall, 1962), 176–85.

SAPOLSKY, HARVEY M., "Science, Voters and the Fluoridation Controversy," *Science*, 162 (October 25, 1968), 427–33.

SAYRES, WILLIAM C., "Ritual Drinking, Ethnic Status and Inebriety in Rural Colombia," *Quarterly Journal of Studies on Alcohol*, 17 (March, 1956), 53–62.

SCHAPS, ERIC, AND CLINTON R. SANDERS, "Purposes, Patterns, and Protection in a Campus Drug Using Community," *Journal of Health and Social Behavior*, 11 (June, 1970), 135–45.

SCHULMAN, SAM, AND ANNE M. SMITH, "The Concept of 'Health' Among Spanish-Speaking Villagers of New Mexico and Colorado," *Journal of Health and Human Behavior*, 4 (Winter, 1963), 226–35.

SHANAS, ETHEL, "A Note on Restriction of Life Space: Attitudes of Age Cohorts," *Journal of Health and Social Behavior*, 9 (March, 1969), 86–90.

SIMMONS, OZZIE G., "The Sociocultural Integration of Alcohol Use: A Peruvian Study," *Quarterly Journal of Studies on Alcohol*, 29 (March, 1968), 152–71.

SMART, REGINALD G., AND DIANNE FEJER, "Illicit LSD Users: Their Social Backgrounds, Drug Use and Psychopathology," *Journal of Health and Social Behavior*, 10 (December, 1969), 297–308.

SUCHMAN, EDWARD A., "Social Patterns of Illness and Medical Care," *Journal of Health and Human Behavior*, 6 (Spring, 1965), 2–16.

SWANSON, ROBERT M., AND STEPHEN P. SPITZER, "Stigma and the Psychiatric Patient Career," *Journal of Health and Social Behavior*, 11 (March, 1970), 44–51.

TITLEY, ROBERT W., "Imaginations About the Disabled," *Social Science and Medicine*, 3 (April, 1969), 29–38.

TYROLER, HERMAN A., ALBERT L. JOHNSON, AND JOHN T. FULTON, "Patterns of Preventive Health Behavior in Populations," *Journal of Health and Human Behavior*, 6 (Fall, 1965), 128–40.

VAN ARSDOL, MAURICE D., JR., GEORGES SABAGH, AND FRANCESCA ALEXANDER, "Reality and the Perception of Environmental Hazards," *Journal of Health and Human Behavior*, 5 (Winter, 1964), 144–54.

WAKEFIELD, JOHN, AND LEO BARIC, "Public and Professional Attitudes to a Screening Programme for the Prevention of Cancer of the Uterine Cervix: A Preliminary Study," *British Journal of Preventive and Social Medicine*, 19 (October, 1965), 151–58..

WELLIN, EDWARD, "Cultural Factors in Nutrition," *Nutrition Reviews*, 13 (May, 1955), 129–31.

WHATLEY, CHARLES D., "Social Attitudes Toward Discharged Mental Patients," *Social Problems*, 6 (Spring, 1959), 313–20.

WILLIAMS, J. J., "Patients and Prejudice: Lay Attitudes Toward Women Physicians," *American Journal of Sociology*, 51 (January, 1946), 283–87.

WORLD HEALTH ORGANIZATION, *Social Psychiatry and Community Attitudes*, Report of the Expert Committee on Mental Health of the World Health Organization, Technical Report Series, No. 177. Geneva, 1959.

IV. THE RELATIONSHIP BETWEEN PATIENTS AND HEALTH PROFESSIONALS

BALINT, MICHAEL, *The Doctor, His Patient, and the Illness*. New York: International Universities Press, Inc., 1957.

BLOOM, SAMUEL W., *The Doctor and His Patient: A Sociological Interpretation.* New York: Russell Sage Foundation, 1963.

BLUM, ALAN F., AND LARRY ROSENBERG, "Some Problems Involved in Professionalizing Social Interaction: The Case of Psychotherapeutic Training," *Journal of Health and Social Behavior,* 9 (March, 1969), 72–86.

BLUM, R. H., *The Management of the Doctor-Patient Relationship.* New York: McGraw-Hill Book Company, 1960.

BOLTON, BRIAN, AND PATRICIA SOMMER, "Mode of Address and Patient Satisfaction in Rehabilitation: An Experimental Study," *Journal of Health and Social Behavior,* 11 (September, 1970), 215–19.

BUCK, RODGER L., "Sociocultural Stresses and the Physician-Patient Relationship," *Journal of the American Medical Association,* 170 (August 1, 1959), 1648–51.

CARTWRIGHT, ANN, *Patients and Their Doctors: A Study of General Practice.* New York: Atherton Press, 1967.

CHANCE, E., *Families in Treatment: From the Viewpoint of the Patient, the Clinician, and the Researcher.* New York: Basic Books, Inc., Publishers, 1959.

COGSWELL, BETTY E., "Rehabilitation of the Paraplegic: Processes of Socialization," *Sociological Inquiry,* 37 (Winter, 1967), 11–26.

COSER, ROSE LAUB, *Life in the Ward.* East Lansing, Mich.: Michigan State University Press, 1962.

COSER, ROSE LAUB, "Evasiveness as a Response to Structural Ambivalence," *Social Science and Medicine,* 1 (July, 1967), 203–18.

DANIELS, ARLENE K., "The Captive Professional: Bureaucratic Limitations in the Practice of Military Psychiatry," *Journal of Health and Social Behavior,* 10 (December, 1969), 255–65.

DAVIS, FRED, "Uncertainty in Medical Prognosis, Clinical and Functional," *American Journal of Sociology,* 66 (July, 1960), 41–47.

DECK, JEANETTE R., AND EDITH S. DECK, eds., *A Sociological Framework for Patient Care.* New York: John Wiley & Sons, Inc., 1966.

DODGE, JOAN S., "Nurses' Sense of Adequacy and Attitudes Toward Keeping Patients Informed," *Journal of Health and Human Behavior,* 2 (Fall, 1961), 213–16.

EHRLICH, HOWARD J., AND MARY LOU BAUER, "Therapists' Feelings Toward Patients and Patient Treatment and Outcome," *Social Science and Medicine,* 1 (September, 1967), 283–92.

FIELD, MARK G., "The Doctor-Patient Relationship in the Perspective of 'Fee-for-Service' and 'Third-Party Medicine'," *Journal of Health and Human Behavior,* 2 (Winter, 1961), 252–62.

FOX, R. C., *Experiment Perilous: Physicians and Patients Facing the Unknown.* New York: The Free Press, 1959.

FREIDSON, ELIOT, "Specialties Without Roots: The Utilization of New Services," *Human Organization,* 18 (Fall, 1959), 112–16.

FREIDSON, ELIOT, "Client Control and Medical Practice," *American Journal of Sociology,* 65 (January, 1960), 374–82.

FREIDSON, ELIOT, "The Organization of Medical Practice and Patient Behavior," *American Journal of Public Health,* 51 (January, 1961), 43–51.

FRIEDSAM, H. J., AND HARRY W. MARTIN, "A Comparison of Self and Physician's Health Ratings in an Older Population," *Journal of Health and Human Behavior,* 4 (Fall, 1963), 179–83.

HANEY, C. ALLEN, AND ROBERT MICHIELUTTE, "Selective Factors Operating in the Adjudication of Incompetency," *Journal of Health and Social Behavior*, 9 (September, 1968), 233–42.

HUNT, R. G., O. GURRSLIN, AND J. L. ROACH, "Social Status and Psychiatric Service in a Child Guidance Clinic," *American Sociological Review*, 23 (February, 1958), 81–83.

JONES, NELSON F., AND CARL L. KEENER, "Patient Attitudes and Clinical Judgment as Related to Patients' Course in Hospital," *Social Science and Medicine*, 2 (March, 1968), 55–62.

JOYCE, C. R. B., "Patient Co-operation and the Sensitivity of Clinical Trials," *Journal of Chronic Diseases*, 15 (November, 1962), 1025–26.

KADUSHIN, CHARLES, "Social Distance Between Client and Professional," *American Journal of Sociology*, 67 (March, 1962), 517–31.

LASAGNA, LOUIS, "The Doctor and the Dying Patient," *Journal of Chronic Diseases*, 22 (July, 1969), 65–68.

LIEBERSON, STANLEY, "Ethnic Groups and the Practice of Medicine," *American Sociological Review*, 23 (October, 1958), 542–49.

LINN, LAWRENCE S., "Social Characteristics and Social Interaction in the Utilization of a Psychiatric Outpatient Clinic," *Journal of Health and Social Behavior*, 8 (March, 1967), 3–14.

MECHANIC, DAVID, "Role Expectations and Communication in the Therapist-Patient Relationship," *Journal of Health and Human Behavior*, 2 (Fall, 1961), 190–98.

MELBIN, MURRAY, "Behavior Rhythms in Mental Hospitals," *American Journal of Sociology*, 74 (May, 1969), 650–65.

MILLER, S. M., AND E. G. MISHLER, "Social Class, Mental Illness, and American Psychiatry," *Milbank Memorial Fund Quarterly*, 37 (April, 1959), 174–99.

MIRA, MARY P., "One Team's Record: An Analysis of the Behavior of a Professional Group," *Social Science and Medicine*, 3 (April, 1969), 95–100.

OLESEN, VIRGINIA, AND ELVI WHITTAKER, *The Silent Dialogue*. San Francisco: Jossey–Bass, 1968.

ORT, ROBERT S., AMASA B. FORD, AND RALPH L. LISKE, "The Doctor-Patient Relationship as Described by Physicians and Medical Students," *Journal of Health and Human Behavior*, 5 (Spring, 1964), 25–34.

PALMER, J. W., "Staff-Patient Communications in a Chest Hospital," *British Journal of Preventive and Social Medicine*, 20 (October, 1966), 195–201.

PAPPER, SOLOMON, "The Undesirable Patient," *Journal of Chronic Diseases*, 22 (May, 1970), 777–79.

PARSONS, TALCOTT, "Social Structure and Dynamic Process: The Case of Modern Medical Practice," in *The Social System*. New York: The Free Press, 1951, pp. 428–79.

PARSONS, TALCOTT, "Illness and the Role of the Physician: A Sociological Perspective," *American Journal of Orthopsychiatry*, 21 (July, 1951), 452–60.

PEARLIN, LEONARD I., AND MORRIS ROSENBERG, "Nurse-Patient Social Distance and the Structural Context of a Mental Hospital," *American Sociological Review*, 27 (February, 1962), 56–66.

PLAJA, ANTONIO ORDONEZ, LUCY M. COHEN, AND JULIAN SAMORA, "Communication Between Physicians and Patients in Outpatient Clinics: Social and Cultural Factors," *Milbank Memorial Fund Quarterly*, 46 (April, 1968), 161–215.

PRESS, IRWIN, "Urban Illness: Physicians, Curers and Dual Use in Bogota," *Journal of Health and Social Behavior*, 10 (September, 1969), 209–18.

QUINT, JEANNE C., *The Nurse and the Dying Patient.* New York: The Macmillan Company, 1967.

READER, GEORGE G., LOIS PRATT, AND MARGARET C. MUDD, "What Patients Expect from Their Doctors," *Modern Hospital*, 89 (July, 1957), 88–94.

REVANS, R. W., "The Adjustment of Nurse and Patient to Hospital Life," *Journal of Chronic Diseases*, 15 (September, 1962), 857–65.

SCHRODER, DAVID, AND DANUTA EHRLICH, "Rejection by Mental Health Professionals: A Possible Consequence of Not Seeking Appropriate Help for Emotional Disorders," *Journal of Health and Social Behavior*, 9 (September, 1968), 222–32.

SEGAL, BERNARD E., "Nurses and Patients: Time, Place and Distance," *Social Problems*, 9 (Winter, 1962), 257–64.

SEGAL, BERNARD E., "Nurses and Patients: A Case Study in Stratification," *Journal of Health and Human Behavior*, 5 (Spring, 1964), 54–61.

SHADER, RICHARD I., WILLIAM A. BINSTOCK, AND DOROTHY SCOTT, "Psychiatrists' Biases: Who Get Drugs?" *Social Science and Medicine*, 2 (June, 1968), 213–16.

SHADER, RICHARD I., AND FREDERIC M. LEVINE, "Staff-Patient Interaction Patterns and Opinions About Mental Illness," *Social Science and Medicine*, 3 (April, 1969), 101–4.

SHUVAL, JUDITH T., AARON ANTONOVSKY, AND A. MICHAEL DAVIES, "The Doctor-Patient Relationship in an Ethnically Heterogeneous Society," *Social Science and Medicine*, 1 (July, 1967), 141–54.

SKIPPER, JAMES K., JR., DAISY L. TAGLIACOZZO, AND HANS O. MAUKSCH, "Some Possible Consequences of Limited Communication Between Patients and Hospital Functionaries," *Journal of Health and Human Behavior*, 5 (Spring, 1964), 34–40.

SUDNOW, DAVID, *Passing On: The Social Organization of Dying.* Englewood Cliffs, N.J.: Prentice-Hall, Inc., 1967.

SUSSMAN, MARVIN B., ed., *Sociology and Rehabilitation.* Washington, D.C.: American Sociological Association, 1966.

TURNER, R. JAY, AND LAWRENCE J. ZABO, "Social Competence and Schizophrenic Outcome: An Investigation and Critique," *Journal of Health and Social Behavior*, 9 (March, 1969), 41–51.

TYRON, PHYLLIS A., AND ROBERT C. LEONARD, "A Clinical Test of Patient-Centered Nursing," *Journal of Health and Human Behavior*, 7 (Fall, 1966), 183–92.

WALSH, JAMES LEO, "Nurses, Professional Striving and the Poor: A Case of Incompatibility," *Social Science and Medicine*, 3 (August, 1969), 217–27.

WAXLER, NANCY E., AND ELLIOTT G. MISHLER, "Hospitalization of Psychiatric Patients: Physician-Centered and Family-Centered Influence Patterns," *Journal of Health and Human Behavior*, 4 (Winter, 1963), 250–58.

V. THE ORGANIZATION OF THE DELIVERY OF MEDICAL CARE

ABRAMSON, ARTHUR S., et al., "A Therapeutic Community in a General Hospital: Adaptation to a Rehabilitation Service," *Journal of Chronic Diseases*, 16 (February, 1963), 179–86.

ACHESON, ROY M., et al., "Factors Influencing Referrals to the Out-Patients Department of a London Teaching Hospital," *British Journal of Preventive and Social Medicine*, 17 (April, 1963), 81–84.

AIKEN, MICHAEL, AND JERALD HAGE, "Organizational Interdependence and Intra-Organizational Structure," *American Sociological Review*, 33 (December, 1968), 912–32.

AKERS, RONALD L., AND RICHARD QUINNEY, "Differential Organization of Health Professions: A Comparative Analysis," *American Sociological Review*, 33 (February, 1968), 104–22.

ALDERSON, M. R., "Terminal Care in Malignant Disease," *British Journal of Preventive and Social Medicine*, 24 (May, 1970), 120–23.

ANDERSEN, RONALD, AND ODIN W. ANDERSON, *A Decade of Health Services: Social Survey Trends in Use and Expenditures.* Chicago: University of Chicago Press, 1968.

ANDERSON, ODIN W., *The Uneasy Equilibrium: Private and Public Financing of Health Services in the U.S., 1875–1965.* New Haven, Conn.: College and University Press, 1968.

ANDERSON, THEODORE R., AND S. WARKOV, "Organizational Size and Functional Complexity: A Study of Administration in Hospitals," *American Sociological Review*, 26 (February, 1961), 23–28.

ARGYRIS, CHRIS, *Diagnosing Human Relations in Organizations: A Case Study of a Hospital.* New Haven, Conn.: Yale University Labor and Management Center, 1956.

ARMOR, DAVID J., AND GERALD L. KLERMAN, "Psychiatric Treatment Orientations and Professional Ideology," *Journal of Health and Social Behavior*, 9 (September, 1968), 243–55.

ARNOLD, ARTHUR, "The Implication of Two-Person and Three-Person Relationships for Family Psychotherapy," *Journal of Health and Human Behavior*, 3 (Summer, 1962), 94–97.

ARTISS, COL. KENNETH L., *Milieu Therapy in Schizophrenia.* New York: Grune & Stratton, Inc., 1962.

BADGLEY, ROBIN F., AND SAMUEL WOLFE, "Medical Care and Conflict in Saskatchewan," *Milbank Memorial Fund Quarterly*, 43 (October, 1965), 463–80.

BADGLEY, ROBIN F., AND SAMUEL WOLFE, *Doctors' Strike: Medical Care and Conflict in Saskatchewan.* New York: Atherton Press, 1967.

BALES, ROBERT FREED, "Types of Social Structure as Factors in 'Cures' for Alcohol Addiction," *Applied Anthropology*, 1 (1942), 1–13.

BARNES, E., *People in Hospitals.* London: Macmillan & Co., Ltd., 1961.

BARRELL, ROBERT P., ALAN S. DEWOLFE, AND FRED E. SPANER, "Some Changes During the Initial Phase of the Unit System in a Large Mental Hospital," *Social Science and Medicine*, 2 (December, 1968), 475–80.

BART, PAULINE B., "Social Structure and Vocabularies of Discomfort: What Happened to Female Hysteria?" *Journal of Health and Social Behavior*, 9 (September, 1968), 188–93.

BARTLETT, HARRIET, *Social Health Practices in the Health Field.* New York: National Association of Social Workers, 1961.

BATES, FREDERICK L., AND RODNEY F. WHITE, "Differential Perceptions of Authority in Hospitals," *Journal of Health and Human Behavior*, 2 (Winter, 1961), 262–67.

BELKNAP, IVAN, *Human Problems of a State Mental Hospital.* New York: McGraw-Hill Book Company, 1956.

BELKNAP, IVAN, AND JOHN G. STEINLE, *The Community and Its Hospitals: A Comparative Analysis.* Syracuse, N.Y.: Syracuse University Press, 1963.

Bennett, Ruth, and Lucille Nahemow, "Institutional Totality and Criteria of Social Adjustment in Residences for the Aged," *Journal of Social Issues*, 21 (October, 1965), 44–78.

Bennis, Warren G., et al., "Reference Groups and Loyalties in the Out-Patient Department," *Administrative Science Quarterly*, 2 (March, 1958), 481–500.

Berkowitz, Norman H., Mary F. Malone, and Malcolm W. Klein, "Patient Care as a Criterion Problem," *Journal of Health and Human Behavior*, 3 (Fall, 1962), 171–76.

Bierman, Pearl, et al., "Health Services Research in Great Britain," *Milbank Memorial Fund Quarterly*, 46 (January, 1968), 9–102.

Blankenship, L. Vaughn, and Ray H. Elling, "Organizational Support and Community Power Structure: The Hospital," *Journal of Health and Human Behavior*, 3 (Winter, 1962), 257–69.

Bracht, Neil F., "The Contribution of Public Health Social Work in Academic Departments of Community Medicine," *Milbank Memorial Fund Quarterly*, 47 (January, 1969), 73–91.

Brewster, Agnew W., Scott I. Allen, and Lucy M. Kramer, "Experience with a Pre-paid Drug Benefit," *Journal of Health and Human Behavior*, 4 (Spring, 1963), 14–22.

Bright, Margaret, and Abraham Lilienfield, eds., "Symposium on Behavioral Problems in Community Cancer Control Activities," *Journal of Chronic Diseases*, 16 (May, 1963), entire issue.

Brodoff, Bernard N., Martin Cherkasky, and William Adelman, "The Affiliation of an Institute for the Care of the Long-Term Sick (Beth Abraham Home) with a Neighboring General Hospital (Montefiore Hospital)," *Journal of Chronic Diseases*, 16 (October, 1963), 1115–21.

Brown, Esther Lucile, *Newer Dimensions of Patient Care: Part II: Improving Staff Motivation and Competence in the General Hospital,* New York: Russell Sage Foundation, 1962.

Bucher, Rue, and L. Schatzman, "The Logic of the State Mental Hospital," *Social Problems*, 9 (Spring, 1962), 337–49.

Bucher, Rue, and Anselm Strauss, "Professions in Process," *American Journal of Sociology*, 66 (January, 1961), 325–35.

Burling, Temple E., Edith M. Lentz, and Robert N. Wilson, *The Give and Take in Hospitals: A Study in Human Organization.* New York: G. P. Putnam's Sons, 1956.

Burnand, G., "A Study of the Concept of Change at Work for Senior Hospital Staff, via the Semantic Differential Technique," *Social Science and Medicine*, 3 (April, 1970), 627–37.

Burney, Leroy E., William A. Steiger, and Thomas Georges, "Implications for Comprehensive Health Care," *Milbank Memorial Fund Quarterly*, 42 (October, 1964), 45–56.

Burrow, James G., *AMA: Voice of American Medicine.* Baltimore: The Johns Hopkins Press, 1963.

Bynder, Herbert, "Physicians Choose Psychiatrists: Medical Social Structure and Patterns of Choice," *Journal of Health and Human Behavior*, 6 (Summer, 1965), 83–91.

Caplan, Eleanor K., and Marvin B. Sussman, "Rank Order of Important Variables for Patient and Staff Satisfaction," *Journal of Health and Human Behavior*, 7 (Summer, 1966), 133–38.

Cates, Judith N., "Conflict Resolution in the Mental Hospital," *Journal of Health and Human Behavior*, 7 (Summer, 1966), 138–43.

Caudill, William, *The Psychiatric Hospital as a Small Society*. Cambridge, Mass.: Harvard University Press, 1958.

Caudill, William, "Around the Clock Patient Care in Japanese Psychiatric Hospitals: The Role of the Tsukisoi," *American Sociological Review*, 26 (April, 1961), 204–14.

Caudill, William, et al., "Social Structure and Interaction Process on a Psychiatric Ward," *American Journal of Orthopsychiatry*, 22 (April, 1952), 314–34.

Caudill, William, and Edward Stainbrook, "Some Covert Effects of Communication Difficulties in a Psychiatric Hospital," *Psychiatry*, 17 (February, 1954), 27–40.

Chambers, Leslie A., "National Problems of Environmental Health," *Journal of Health and Human Behavior*, 5 (Winter, 1964), 133–36.

Clark, A. W., "Conditions Influencing Patient Response to Treatment in a Therapeutic Community," *Social Science and Medicine*, 1 (September, 1967), 309–21.

Coleman, James S., Elihu Katz, and Herbert Menzel, *Medical Innovation: A Diffusion Study*. Indianapolis: The Bobbs–Merrill Co., Inc., 1966.

Coleman, James S., Herbert Menzel, and Elihu Katz, "Social Processes in Physician's Adoption of a New Drug," *Journal of Chronic Diseases*, 9 (January, 1959), 1–19.

Collver, Andrew, Ralph Ten Have, and Mary C. Speare, "Factors Influencing the Use of Maternal Health Services," *Social Science and Medicine*, 1 (September, 1967), 293–308.

Colombotos, John, "Physicians and Medicare: A Before-After Study of the Effects of Legislation on Attitudes," *American Sociological Review*, 34 (June, 1969), 318–34.

Coser, Rose Laub, "Authority and Decision-Making in a Hospital: A Comparative Analysis," *American Sociological Review*, 23 (February, 1958), 56–63.

Coser, Rose Laub, "Insulation from Observability and Types of Social Conformity," *American Sociological Review*, 26 (February, 1961), 28–39.

Costonis, Anthony F., "The Mental Hospital Unit System: A Critical Evaluation and Research Statement," *Journal of Health and Human Behavior*, 7 (Summer, 1966), 75–83.

Cumming, Elaine, "Phase Movement in the Support and Control of the Psychiatric Patient," *Journal of Health and Human Behavior*, 3 (Winter, 1962), 235–42.

Cumming, Elaine, and John Cumming, "The Locus of Power in a Large Mental Hospital," *Psychiatry*, 19 (November, 1956), 361–69.

Cutler, S. J., et al., "The Role of Hypothesis Testing in Clinical Trials," *Journal of Chronic Diseases*, 19 (August, 1966), 857–82.

Darsky, Benjamin J., Nathan Sinai, and Solomon J. Axelrod, *Comprehensive Medical Services Under Voluntary Health Insurance: A Study of Windsor Medical Services*. Cambridge, Mass.: Harvard University Press, 1958.

Denman, Loretta, "Mental Patients as 'Line Workers,' 'Machines,' and 'Outputs,'" *Journal of Health and Human Behavior*, 4 (Fall, 1963), 211–14.

Deuschle, Kurt W., et al., "The Kentucky Experiment in Community Medicine," *Milbank Memorial Fund Quarterly*, 44 (January, 1966), 9–23.

Devereaux, George, "The Social Structure of a Schizophrenia Ward and Its Therapeutic Fitness," *Journal of Clinical Psychopathology*, 6 (October, 1944), 231–65.

Devereaux, George, "The Social Structure of the Hospital as a Factor in Total Therapy," *American Journal of Orthopsychiatry*, 19 (July, 1949), 492–500.

DREW, FRANCIS L., AND ALVIN P. SHAPIRO, "Sociological Determinants of Drug Utilization in a University Hospital," *Journal of Chronic Diseases*, 11 (November, 1964), 983–90.

DUNHAM, H. W., AND S. K. WEINBERG, *The Culture of the State Hospital*. Detroit: Wayne State University Press, 1960.

DYKENS, JAMES W., et al., *Strategies of Mental Hospital Change*. Boston: Commonwealth of Massachusetts, Department of Mental Health, 1964.

EATON, JOSEPH W., "Social Processes of Professional Teamwork," *American Sociological Review*, 16 (October, 1951), 707–13.

EILENBERG, M. D., M. J. PRITCHARD, AND P. B. WHATMORE, "A 12-Month Survey of Observation Ward Practice," *British Journal of Preventive and Social Medicine*, 16 (January, 1962), 22–29.

ELINSON, JACK, "The Physician's Dilemma in Puerto Rico," *Journal of Health and Human Behavior*, 3 (Spring, 1962), 14–21.

ELLENBOGEN, BERT L., CHARLES E. RAMSEY, AND ROBERT A. DANLEY, "Health Need, Status, and Subscription to Health Insurance," *Journal of Health and Human Behavior*, 7 (Spring, 1966), 59–63.

ELLING, RAY H., AND S. HALEBSKY, "Organizational Differentiation and Support: A Conceptual Framework," *Administrative Science Quarterly*, 6 (September, 1961), 185–209.

ELLING, RAY H., AND OLLIE J. LEE, "Formal Connections of Community Leadership to the Health System," *Milbank Memorial Fund Quarterly*, 44 (July, 1966), 294–307.

EVANG, KARL, D. STARK MURRAY, AND WALTER J. LEAR, *Medical Care and Family Security*. Englewood Cliffs, N.J.: Prentice-Hall, Inc., 1964.

FALK, LESLIE A., "Group Health Plans in Coal Mining Communities," *Journal of Health and Human Behavior*, 4 (Spring, 1963), 4–14.

FELDMAN, DANIEL J., "Medical Rehabilitation: The Clinical Management of Disability," *Journal of Chronic Diseases*, 16 (December, 1963), 1313–16.

FERSTER, C. B., AND MARIAN K. DEMYER, "The Development of Performances in Autistic Children in an Automatically Controlled Environment," *Journal of Chronic Diseases*, 13 (April, 1961), 312–45.

FIELD, M. G., "Approaches to Mental Illness in Soviet Society: Some Comparisons and Conjectures," *Social Problems*, 7 (Spring, 1960), 277–97.

FINK, RAYMOND, AND SAM SHAPIRO, "Patterns of Medical Care Related to Mental Illness," *Journal of Health and Human Behavior*, 7 (Summer, 1966), 91–98.

FISCHER, GLORIA J., "Socio-Economic Factors and Outcome of Released Mental Patients: Influence of Type of Placement, Occupational Adjustment, Compensation, and Type of Hospital," *Journal of Health and Human Behavior*, 6 (Summer, 1965), 105–10.

FOLLMANN, J. F., JR., *Medical Care and Health Insurance: A Study in Social Progress*. Homewood, Ill.: Richard D. Irwin, Inc., 1963.

FORSYTH, GORDON, *Doctors and State Medicine*. Philadelphia: J. B. Lippincott Co., 1967.

FREEMAN, HOWARD E., AND CAMILLE LAMBERT, JR., "The Influence of Community Groups on Health Matters," *Human Organization*, 24 (Winter, 1965), 353–57.

FREEMAN, HOWARD E., AND OZZIE G. SIMMONS, "Consensus and Coalition in the Release of Mental Patients: A Research Note," *Human Organization*, 20 (Summer, 1961), 89–91.

FREEMAN, HOWARD E., AND OZZIE G. SIMMONS, "Treatment Experiences of Mental Patients and Their Families," *American Journal of Public Health*, 51 (September, 1961), 1266–73.

FREIDSON, ELIOT, *Patients' Views of Medical Practice: A Study of Subscribers to a Prepaid Medical Plan in The Bronx*. New York: Russell Sage Foundation, 1961.

FREIDSON, ELIOT, ed., *The Hospital in Modern Society*. New York: The Free Press, 1963.

FRIEDMAN, JAY W., "Dental Care Programs: Prospects and Perspectives," *Journal of Health and Human Behavior*, 7 (Winter, 1966), 255–65.

FRIEDMAN, JAY W., "Multiple Determinants of Hospital Programs," *Social Science and Medicine*, 3 (April, 1969), 49–63.

GARRETT, S. A. G., et al., "The Need for Intensive Nursing Care," *British Journal of Preventive and Social Medicine*, 20 (January, 1966), 34–41.

GEORGOPOULOS, BASIL S., AND FLOYD C. MANN, *The Community General Hospital*. New York: The Macmillan Company, 1962.

GIBSON, THOMAS C., "Community Health Services in the Management of Congestive Heart Failure," *Journal of Chronic Diseases*, 19 (February, 1966), 133–40.

GIEL, R., YOSEPH GEZAHEGN, AND J. N. VAN LUIJK, "Faith-healing and Spirit-possession in Ghion, Ethiopia," *Social Science and Medicine*, 2 (March, 1968), 63–80.

GORDON, EDWARD E., AND KATE H. KOHN, "Evaluation of Rehabilitation Methods in the Hemiplegic Patient," *Journal of Chronic Diseases*, 19 (January, 1966), 3–16.

GOSS, MARY E. W., "Influence and Authority Among Physicians in an Outpatient Clinic," *American Sociological Review*, 26 (February, 1961), 39–51.

GOSS, MARY E. W., "Administration and the Physician," *American Journal of Public Health*, 52 (February, 1962), 183–91.

GREENBLATT, MILTON, D. J. LEVINSON, AND R. H. WILLIAMS, eds., *The Patient and the Mental Hospital*. New York: The Free Press, 1957.

GREENBLATT, MILTON, et al., *Drug and Social Therapy in Chronic Schizophrenia*. Springfield, Ill.: Charles C Thomas, Publisher, 1965.

GREENBLUM, J., "The Control of Sick-Care Functions in the Hospitalization of a Child: Family Versus Hospital," *Journal of Health and Human Behavior*, 2 (Spring, 1961), 32–38.

GRUENBERG, ERNEST M., ed., "Evaluating the Effectiveness of Mental Health Service," *Milbank Memorial Fund Quarterly*, 44 (January, 1966, Part 2), entire issue.

GRUER, ROSAMOND, "Hospital Discharges in Relation to Area of Residence," *British Journal of Preventive and Social Medicine*, 24 (May, 1970), 124–28.

HALEVI, H. S., "Patterns of Hospitalization in England and Israel," *British Journal of Preventive and Social Medicine*, 23 (August, 1969), 196–202.

HALL, OSWALD, "The Informal Organization of the Medical Profession," *Canadian Journal of Economic and Political Science*, 12 (February, 1946), 30–44.

HALL, P., AND W. L. TONGE, "Long-Standing Continuous Unemployment in Male Patients with Psychiatric Symptoms," *British Journal of Preventive and Social Medicine*, 17 (October, 1963), 191–96.

HAMLIN, ROBERT H., "The Role of Voluntary Agencies in Meeting the Health Needs of Americans," *Annals of the American Academy of Political and Social Science*, 337 (September, 1961), 93–102.

HANSON, ROBERT C., "Administration Responsibilities in Large and Small Hospitals in a Metropolitan Community," *Journal of Health and Human Behavior*, 2 (Fall, 1961), 199–204.

HANSON, ROBERT C., "The Systemic Linkage Hypothesis and Role Consensus Patterns in Hospital-Community Relations," *American Sociological Review*, 27 (June, 1962), 304–13.

HARVARD MEDICAL SCHOOL AND PSYCHIATRIC SERVICE, MASSACHUSETTS GENERAL HOSPITAL, *Community Mental Health and Social Psychiatry: A Reference Guide*. Cambridge, Mass.: Harvard University Press, 1962.

HARVEY, JOHN COLLINS, AND JULAN W. REED, "A Two-Year Study in Intensive Rehabilitation of 50 Chronically Ill Indigent Medical Outpatients," *Journal of Chronic Diseases*, 15 (February, 1962), 141–56.

HENRY, JULES, "The Culture of Interpersonal Relations in a Therapeutic Institution for Emotionally Disturbed Children," *American Journal of Orthopsychiatry*, 27 (October, 1957), 725–34.

HIMES, JOSEPH S., "Social Distance to Three Types of Hospitals," *Journal of Health and Human Behavior*, 2 (Fall, 1961), 210–13.

HOCHSTRASSER, DONALD L., Gifford S. Nickerson, and Kurt W. Deschle, "Sociomedical Approaches to Community Health Programs," *Milbank Memorial Fund Quarterly*, 44 (July, 1966), 345–60.

HOGARTH, JAMES, *The Payment of the Physician: Some European Comparisons*. New York: The Macmillan Company, 1963.

HOLLOWAY, ROBERT G., JAY W. ARTIS, AND WALTER E. FREEMAN, "The Participation Patterns of 'Economic Influence' and Their Control of a Hospital Board of Trustees," *Journal of Health and Human Behavior*, 4 (Summer, 1963), 88–99.

HUNTLEY, ROBERT R., et al., "The Quality of Medical Care: Techniques and Investigation in the Outpatient Clinic," *Journal of Chronic Diseases*, 14 (December, 1961), 630–42.

HURWITZ, JACOB I., B. R. HUTCHESON, AND SAUL COOPER, "Problems in Refining the Psychiatric Assessment of Juvenile Delinquents," *Journal of Health and Human Behavior*, 2 (Winter, 1961), 276–82.

JEFFREYS, MARGOT, "Social Class and Health Promotion: Some Obstacles in Britain," *Health Education Journal*, 15 (May, 1957), 109–18.

JENNEY, E. ROSS, AND OZZIE G. SIMMONS, "Human Relations and Technical Assistance in Public Health," *Scientific Monthly*, 78 (June, 1954), 365–71.

JOINT COMMISSION ON MENTAL ILLNESS AND HEALTH, *Action for Mental Health: Final Report of the Joint Commission on Mental Illness and Health*. New York: Basic Books, Inc., Publishers, 1961.

JONES, KATHLEEN, AND ROY SIDEBOTHAM, *Mental Hospitals at Work*. London: Routledge & Kegan Paul, Ltd., 1962.

JONES, MAXWELL, *Social Psychiatry*. Springfield, Ill.: Charles C Thomas, Publishers, 1962.

JONES, MAXWELL, et al., *The Therapeutic Community*. New York: Basic Books, Inc., Publishers, 1953.

JOURNAL OF SOCIAL ISSUES, "Socio-Cultural Approaches to Medical Care," 8 (October, 1952), entire issue.

JOURNAL OF SOCIAL ISSUES, "New Pathways from the Mental Hospital," 16 (1960), entire issue.

JULIAN, JOSEPH, "Compliance Patterns and Communication Blocks in Complex Organizations," *American Sociological Review*, 31 (June, 1966), 382–90.

KAHNE, MERTON J., "Suicides in Mental Hospitals: A Study of the Effects of Personnel and Patient Turnover," *Journal of Health and Social Behavior*, 9 (September, 1968), 255–66.

KALISH, RICHARD A., "Life and Death: Dividing the Indivisible," *Social Science and Medicine*, 2 (September, 1968), 249–61.

KEITH, ROBERT ALLEN, "The Need for a New Model in Rehabilitation," *Journal of Chronic Diseases*, 21 (July, 1968), 281–86.

KELMAN, HOWARD R., "Evaluation of Rehabilitation for the Long Term Ill and Disabled Patient: Some Persistent Research Problems," *Journal of Chronic Diseases*, 7 (July, 1964), 631–39.

KELMAN, HOWARD R., AND ARTHUR WILLNER, "Problems in Measurement and Evaluation of Rehabilitation," *Archives of Physical Medicine and Rehabilitation*, 43 (April, 1962), 172–81.

KISSICK, WILLIAM L., ed., "Dimensions and Determinants of Health Policy," *Milbank Memorial Fund Quarterly*, 46 (January, 1968, Part 2), entire issue.

KLARMAN, HERBERT E., "Characteristics of Patients in Short-Term Hospitals in New York City," *Journal of Health and Human Behavior*, 3 (Spring, 1962), 46–52.

KLARMAN, HERBERT E., "The Distinctive Economic Characteristics of Health Services," *Journal of Health and Human Behavior*, 4 (Spring, 1963), 44–49.

KLARMAN, HERBERT E., *Hospital Care in New York City: The Roles of Voluntary and Municipal Hospitals.* New York: Columbia University Press, 1963.

KLARMAN, HERBERT E., *The Economics of Health.* New York: Columbia University Press, 1965.

KNUTSON, ANDIE L., "Frames of Reference in Public Health Communication," *Journal of Health and Social Behavior*, 8 (June, 1967), 107–15.

KOHN, ROBERT M., AND BERTHA CUTCHER, "The Community Impact of a Work Evaluation Unit: A Controlled Study," *Journal of Chronic Diseases*, 8 (August, 1964), 659–66.

KRAENZEL, CARL F., "Pillars of Service for the Emerging Community of the Plains, with Special Emphasis upon Health Services," *Journal of Health and Human Behavior*, (Summer and Fall, 1964), 67–74.

KRAMER, BERNARD M., *Day Hospital.* New York: Grune & Stratton, Inc., 1962.

KRAMER, MORTON, et al., "National Approach to the Evaluation of Community Mental Health Programs," *American Journal of Public Health*, 51 (July, 1961), 969–79.

KRAUSS, IRVING, "An Approach to Evaluating the Effectiveness of a Public Health Program," *Journal of Health and Human Behavior*, 3 (Summer, 1962), 141–46.

KRIESBERG, LOUIS, "Careers, Organization Size, and Succession," *American Journal of Sociology*, 68 (November, 1962), 335–60.

LEFTON, MARK, SIMON DINITZ, AND BENJAMIN PASAMANICK, "Decision-Making in a Mental Hospital: Real, Perceived and Ideal," *American Sociological Review*, (December, 1959), 822–29.

LEFTON, MARK, AND WILLIAM R. ROSENGREN, "Organizations and Clients: Lateral and Longitudinal Dimensions," *American Sociological Review*, 31 (December, 1966), 802–11.

LEIGHTON, ALEXANDER H., *An Introduction to Social Psychiatry.* Springfield, Ill.: Charles C Thomas, Publishers, 1960.

LEVINE, SOL, ODIN W. ANDERSON, AND GERALD GORDON, *Non-Group Enrollments for Health Insurance: A Study of Administrative Approaches of Blue Cross Plans.* Cambridge, Mass.: Harvard University Press, 1957.

LEVINE, SOL, AND PAUL E. WHITE, "Exchange as a Conceptual Framework for the Study of Interorganizational Relationships," *Administrative Science Quarterly*, 5 (March, 1961), 583–601.

LEVINE, SOL, NORMAN A. SCOTCH, AND GEORGE J. VLASAK, "Unravelling Technology and Culture in Public Health," *American Journal of Public Health*, 59 (February, 1969), 237–44.

LIGHT, HAROLD L., AND W. J. BROWN, "The Gouverneur Health Services Program: An Historical View," *Milbank Memorial Fund Quarterly*, 45 (October, 1967), 375–91.

LINDSEY, ALMONT, *Socialized Medicine in England and Wales: The National Health Service 1948–1961*. Chapel Hill: University of North Carolina Press, 1962.

LINN, E. L., "Patients' Socioeconomic Characteristics and Release from a Mental Hospital," *American Journal of Sociology*, 65 (November, 1959), 280–86.

LINN, LAWRENCE S., "Social Characteristics and Social Interaction in the Utilization of a Psychiatric Outpatient Clinic," *Journal of Health and Social Behavior*, 8 (March, 1967), 3–14.

LINN, LOUIS, ed., *Frontiers in General Hospital Psychiatry*. New York: International Universities Press, Inc., 1961.

LYNCH, MATTHEW J., AND STANLEY S. RAPHAEL, *Medicine and the State*. Springfield, Ill.: Charles C Thomas, Publisher, 1963.

MACEACHERN, M. T., *Hospital Organization and Management*. Chicago: Physician's Record Company, 1957.

MACMAHON, BRIAN, THOMAS F. PUGH, AND GEORGE B. HUTCHISON, "Principles in the Evaluation of Community Mental Health Programs," *American Journal of Public Health*, 51 (July, 1961), 963–68.

MADIGAN, FRANCIS, "Role Satisfactions and Length of Life in a Closed Population," *American Journal of Sociology*, 67 (May, 1962), 640–50.

MANNING, JANE, AND BETTY ANN GLASSER, "The Home Visit in the Treatment of Psychiatric Patients Awaiting Hospitalization," *Journal of Health and Human Behavior*, 3 (Summer, 1962), 97–104.

MARKS, JOHN, HAYDEN L. MEES, AND EDWARD SIMMEL, "Ideology, Social Change, and Violence in a Mental Hospital," *Journal of Health and Human Behavior*, 4 (Winter, 1963), 258–66.

MARTIN, J. P., *Social Aspects of Prescribing*. Melbourne: William Heinemann, Ltd., 1957.

MAYS, EDWARD E., "Oxygen Therapy in Hypoxic Chronic Bronchitis: Feasibility of Nocturnal Oxygen Supplementation at Home After Hospital-Induced Improvement," *Journal of Chronic Diseases*, 22 (December, 1969), 421–30.

MCELRATH, DENNIS C., "Perspective and Participation of Physicians in Prepaid Group Practice," *American Sociological Review*, 26 (August, 1961), 596–608.

MCKEOWN, THOMAS, AND J. R. TERVEL, "An Assessment of the Feasibility of Discharge of Patients in Hospitals for the Subnormal," *British Journal of Preventive and Social Medicine*, 24 (May, 1970), 116–19.

MCKINLAY, JOHN B., "The New Late Comers for Antenatal Care," *British Journal of Preventive and Social Medicine*, 24 (February, 1970), 52–57.

MCKUSICK, VICTOR A., "Family-Oriented Follow-Up," *Journal of Chronic Diseases*, 22 (June, 1969), 1–7.

MCNERNEY, WALTER J., et al., *Hospital and Medical Economics: A Study of Policies, Services, Costs, Methods of Control*. Chicago: Hospital Research and Educational Trust, 1962.

MCNERNEY, WALTER J., et al., *Regionalization and Health Care*. Ann Arbor: University of Michigan Press, 1962.

MEDALIA, NAHUM Z., "Air Pollution as a Socio-Environmental Health Problem: A Survey Report," *Journal of Health and Human Behavior*, 5 (Winter, 1964), 154–66.

MENZEL, HERBERT, JAMES COLEMAN, AND ELIHU KATZ, "Dimensions of Being 'Modern' in Medical Practice," *Journal of Chronic Diseases*, 9 (January, 1959), 20–40.

MESSING, SIMON D., "Social Problems Related to the Development of Health in Ethiopia," *Social Science and Medicine*, 3 (January, 1970), 331–37.

MESSING, SIMON D., AND JULIUS S. PRINCE, "Health Practices in Ethiopian Pre-Urban Communities," *Journal of Health and Human Behavior*, 7 (Winter, 1966), 272–76.

MESSING, SIMON D., JULIUS S. PRINCE AND TSEGHE YOHANNES, "A Method of Health Culture Research in an African Country," *Journal of Health and Human Behavior*, 6 (Winter, 1965), 261–63.

MEYER, HENRY H., AND EDGAR F. BORGATTA, *An Experiment in Mental Patient Rehabilitation.* New York: Russell Sage Foundation, 1959.

MILBANK MEMORIAL FUND, "Mental Hospitals Join the Community," *Milbank Memorial Fund Quarterly*, 42 (July, 1964, Part 2), entire issue.

MILLER, CHARLES J., LEO G. REEDER, AND HARTLEY E. MANNING, "Every Doctor's Office: A Cancer Detection Center?" *Journal of Chronic Diseases*, 19 (November–December, 1966), 1211–19.

MISHLER, ELLIOT G., AND NANCY E. WAXLER, "Decision Processes in Psychiatric Hospitalization: Patients Referred, Accepted, and Admitted to a Psychiatric Hospital," *American Sociological Review*, 28 (August, 1963), 576–88.

MIZRUCHI, EPHRAIM H., AND ROBERT PERRUCCI, "Norm Qualities and Differential Effects of Deviant Behavior: An Exploratory Analysis," *American Sociological Review*, 27 (June, 1962), 391–400.

MONCK, ELIZABETH M., "Employment Experiences of 127 Discharged Schizophrenic Men in London," *British Journal of Preventive and Social Medicine*, 17 (April, 1963), 101–10.

MULLER, CHARLOTTE, "Medical Review of Prescribing," *Journal of Chronic Diseases*, 18 (July, 1965), 689–96.

MUMFORD, EMILY, AND J. K. SKIPPER, JR., *Sociology in Hospital Care.* New York: Harper & Row, Publishers, Inc., 1967.

NEW, PETER KONG-MING, AND J. THOMAS MAY, "Organization Under Stress: An Analysis of the Local Board of Health," *Journal of Health and Human Behavior*, 6 (Winter, 1965), 226–34.

NEW, PETER KONG-MING, et al., "The Support Structure of Heart and Stroke Patients: A Study of the Role of Significant Others in Patient Rehabilitation," *Social Science and Medicine*, 2 (June, 1968), 185–201.

NIELSEN, JOHANNES, WILLIAM WILSNACK, AND ERIK STROMGREN, "Some Aspects of Community Psychiatry," *British Journal of Preventive and Social Medicine*, 19 (April, 1965), 85–93.

OPLER, MARVIN K., *Culture and Social Psychiatry.* New York: Atherton Press, 1967.

OPLER, MARVIN K., ed., *Culture and Mental Health.* New York: The Macmillan Company, 1959.

OSBORNE, OLIVER H., "The Yoruba Village as a Therapeutic Community," *Journal of Health and Social Behavior*, 10 (September, 1969), 187–200.

PALLEY, HOWARD A., "The 'Health Insurance Plan' Controversy: Ideology and the Organization of Medical Care," *Journal of Health and Human Behavior*, 6 (Winter, 1965), 218–26.

PALOLA, ERNEST G., AND JOSEPH F. JONES, "Contrasts in Organization Features and Role Strains Between Psychiatric and Pediatric Wards," *Journal of Health and Human Behavior*, 6 (Fall, 1965), 155–63.

PARSONS, A., "Some Comparative Observations on Ward Social Structure: Southern Italy, England and the United States," *L'Ospedale Psichiatrico*, 2 (April–June, 1959), 3–23.

PASAMANICK, BENJAMIN, FRANK R. SCARPITTI, AND SIMON DINITZ, *Schizophrenics in the Community*. New York: Appreton–Century–Crofts, 1967.

PATTEN, THOMAS, JR., "Health and Behavior in Homes for Veterans: Some Old and New Patterns," *Journal of Health and Human Behavior*, 2 (Spring, 1961), 47–58.

PEARLIN, LEONARD I., "Sources of Resistance to Change in a Mental Hospital," *American Journal of Sociology*, 68 (November, 1962), 325–35.

PERROW, CHARLES, "Organizational Prestige: Some Functions and Dysfunctions," *American Journal of Sociology*, 66 (January, 1961), 335–41.

PERROW, CHARLES, "The Analysis of Goals in Complex Organizations," *American Sociological Review*, 26 (September, 1961), 854–66.

PERRUCCI, ROBERT, "Social Distance Strategies and Intra-Organizational Stratification: A Study of the Status System on a Psychiatric Ward," *American Sociological Review*, 28 (December, 1963), 951–63.

PFAUTZ, HAROLD W., AND GITA WILDER, "The Ecology of a Mental Hospital," *Journal of Health and Human Behavior*, 3 (Summer, 1962), 67–73.

PHANEUF, MARIA C., "Home Care Following Hospitalization," *Journal of Health and Human Behavior*, 4 (Spring, 1963), 22–29.

PSATHAS, GEORGE, AND DENNIS J. ARP, "Characteristics of Private Practice in Psychiatry and Clinical Psychology," *Journal of Health and Social Behavior*, 8 (September, 1967), 209–22.

PURDOM, P. W., "The Environmental Health Challenge: Environmental Health in the Metropolitan Setting," *Journal of Health and Human Behavior*, 5 (Winter, 1964), 136–41.

RABINOWITZ, HERBERT S., AND SPIRO B. MITSOS, "Rehabilitation vs. Planned Social Change: A Conceptual Framework," *Journal of Health and Human Behavior*, 5 (Spring, 1964), 2–14.

RAPOPORT, ROBERT N., *Community as Doctor*. Springfield, Ill.: Charles C Thomas, Publisher, 1961.

RAUSH, HAROLD L., AND CHARLOTTE L. RAUSH, *The Halfway House Movement: A Search for Sanity*. New York: Appleton–Century–Crofts, 1968.

READER, GEORGE G., "Medical Care," *Journal of Health and Human Behavior*, 3 (Spring, 1962), 3–4.

READER, GEORGE G., AND MARY E. W. GOSS, "Medical Sociology with Particular Reference to the Study of Hospitals," *Transactions of the Fourth World Congress of Sociology*, 2 (1959), 139–52.

READER, GEORGE G., AND MARY E. W. GOSS, eds., *Comprehensive Medical Care and Teaching: A Report on the New York Hospital– Cornell Medical Center Program*. Ithaca, N.Y.: Cornell University Press, 1968.

WALTER REED INSTITUTE OF RESEARCH, *Symposium on Preventive and Social Psychiatry*. Washington, D.C.: Government Printing Office, 1957.

REEDER, LEO G., "Employment Practices and the Cardiac," *Journal of Chronic Diseases*, 18 (September, 1965), 951–63.

REEDER, LEO G., AND GEORGE DONOHUE, *Employer Attitudes Toward Heart Disease.* Minneapolis: Minnesota Heart Association, 1954.

REEDER, LEO G., DON H. ZIMMERMAN, AND ELEANOR BERNETT SHELDON, "Improving Nursing Home Administration," *Journal of Health and Human Behavior*, 4 (Spring, 1963), 29–36.

REITZES, D. C., *Negroes and Medicine.* Cambridge, Mass.: Harvard University Press, 1958.

RICHARDSON, ARTHUR H., et al., "Use of Medical Resources of Spancos II.: Social Factors and Medical Care Experience," *Milbank Memorial Fund Quarterly*, 45 (January, 1967), 61–77.

ROBINSON, IRA E., HAROLD BRONFIN, AND JACK O. BALSWICK, "Nursing Home Resources and Rural and Urban Needs," *Journal of Health and Social Behavior*, 11 (June, 1970), 146–51.

ROBINSON, R., D. F. DEMARCHE, AND M. K. WAGLE, *Community Resources in Mental Health.* New York: Basic Books, Inc., Publishers, 1960.

ROEMER, MILTON I., "On Paying the Doctor and the Implications of Different Methods," *Journal of Health and Human Behavior*, 3 (Spring, 1962), 4–14.

ROEMER, MILTON I., "On Medical Care and Human Behavior," *Journal of Health and Human Behavior*, 4 (Spring, 1963), 3–4.

ROEMER, MILTON I., AND RAY H. ELLING, "Sociological Research on Medical Care," *Journal of Health and Human Behavior*, 4 (Spring, 1963), 49–68.

ROEMER, RUTH, "Legal Systems Regulating Health Personnel: A Comparative Analysis," *Milbank Memorial Fund Quarterly*, 46 (October, 1968), 432–73.

ROGLER, LLOYD H., AND A. B. HOLLINGSHEAD, "The Puerto Rican Spiritualist as a Psychiatrist," *American Journal of Sociology*, 67 (July, 1961), 17–22.

ROGOFF, JOSEPH B., DONALD V. COONEY, AND BERNARD KUTNER, "Hemiplegia: A Study of Home Rehabilitation," *Journal of Chronic Diseases*, 17 (June, 1964), 539–50.

ROHRER, WAYNE C., "Demographic and Social Changes Affecting the Community Hospital," *Hospital Administration*, 7 (Summer, 1962), 32–51.

ROSEN, GEORGE, "Some Substantive Limiting Conditions in Communication Between Health Officers and Medical Practitioners," *American Journal of Public Health*, 51 (December, 1961), 1085–16.

ROSENBAUM, MAX, AND MILTON BERGER, *Group Psychotherapy and Group Function.* New York: Basic Books, Inc., Publishers, 1963.

ROSS, JOHN A., "Social Class and Medical Care," *Journal of Health and Human Behavior*, 3 (Spring, 1962), 35–40.

ROSSMAN, I., AND MARGARET CLARKE, "Recreational and Work Therapy on a Home Care Program," *Journal of Chronic Diseases*, 14 (December, 1961), 643–54.

RUSK, HOWARD A., ed., "Symposium: Selected Papers Presented at the Eighth World Congress of the International Society for Rehabilitation of the Disabled," *Journal of Chronic Diseases*, 13 (March, 1961), entire issue.

RYAN, MICHAEL, "Health Centre Policy in England and Wales," *British Journal of Sociology*, 19 (March, 1968), 34–46.

SAMPSON, HAROLD, SHELDON L. MESSINGER, AND ROBERT D. TOWNE, "The Mental Hospital and Marital Family Ties," *Social Problems*, 9 (Fall, 1961), 141–55.

SANDERS, BARKEV S., "Completeness and Reliability of Diagnosis in Therapeutic Practice," *Journal of Health and Human Behavior*, 5 (Summer and Fall, 1961), 84–95.

SANDERS, RICHARD, ROBERT S. SMITH, AND BERNARD S. WEINMAN, *Chronic Psychoses and Recovery: An Experiment in Socio-Environmental Treatment.* San Francisco: Jossey–Bass, 1967.

Sasuly, Richard, and Milton I. Roemer, "Health Insurance Patterns: A Conceptualization from the California Scene," *Journal of Health and Human Behavior*, 7 (Spring, 1966), 36–45.

Sathe, Y., M. Zelen, and J. Zweifel, "The Interpretation of Clinical Trials," *Journal of Chronic Diseases*, 18 (April, 1965), 385–95.

Schaffer, L., and L. K. Myers, "Psychotherapy and Social Stratification: An Empirical Study of Practice in a Psychiatric Out-Patient Clinic," *Psychiatry*, 17 (February, 1954), 83–93.

Scheff, Thomas J., "Control Over Policy by Attendants in a Mental Hospital," *Journal of Health and Human Behavior*, 2 (Summer, 1961), 93–105.

Schwartz, Lola Romanucci, "The Hierarchy of Resort in Curative Practices: The Admiralty Islands, Melanesia," *Journal of Health and Social Behavior*, 10 (September, 1969), 201–09.

Scott, Frances Gillespie, "A Study of Exclusions in a Mental Rehabilitation Program," *Journal of Health and Human Behavior*, 4 (Fall, 1963), 183–94.

Seeman, M. and J. W. Evans, "Stratification and Hospital Care," *American Sociological Review*, 26, Part I (February, 1961), 67–79; Part II (April, 1961), 193–203.

Segal, Bernard E., "Dissatisfaction and Desire for Change Among Chilean Hospital Workers," *American Journal of Sociology*, 75 (November, 1969), 375–88.

Seham, Max, "An American Doctor Looks at 11 Foreign Health Systems," *Social Science and Medicine*, 3 (April, 1969), 65–81.

Shapiro, Sam, "End Result Measurements of Quality of Medical Care," *Milbank Memorial Fund Quarterly*, 45 (April, 1967), 7–31.

Shapiro, Sam, and Raymond Fink, "Methodological Considerations in Studying Patterns of Medical Care Related to Mental Illness," *Milbank Memorial Fund Quarterly*, 41 (October, 1963), 371–99.

Sheldon, Alan, Carol Pierson Ryser, and Melvin J. Krant, "An Integrated Family Oriented Cancer Care Program: The Report of a Pilot Project in the Socio-Emotional Management of Chronic Disease," *Journal of Chronic Diseases*, 22 (April, 1970), 743–55.

Shiloh, Ailon, "The Interaction Between the Middle Eastern and Western Systems of Medicine," *Social Science and Medicine*, 2 (September, 1968), 235–49.

Shryock, R. H., *National Tuberculosis Association, 1904–1954: A Study of the Voluntary Health Movement in the United States.* New York: National Tuberculosis Association, 1957.

Sills, D. L., *The Volunteers: Means and Ends in National Organization.* New York: The Free Press, 1958.

Silver, George A., *Family Medical Care: A Report on the Family Health Maintenance Demonstration.* Cambridge, Mass.: Harvard University Press, 1963.

Simmons, Ozzie G., James A. Davis, and Katherine Spencer, "Interpersonal Strains in Release from a Mental Hospital," *Social Problems*, 4 (July, 1956), 21–28.

Smith, Harvey L., "Psychiatry: A Social Institution in Process," Social Forces, 33 (May, 1955), 310–16.

Solon, Jerry A., et al., "Delineating Patterns of Medical Care," *American Journal of Public Health*, 50 (August, 1960), 1105–31.

SOLON, JERRY A., et al., "Patterns of Medical Care: Validity of Interview Information on Use of Hospital Clinics," *Journal of Health and Human Behavior*, 3 (Spring, 1962), 21–30.

SOMERS, HERMAN M., AND ANNE R. SOMERS, *Doctors, Patients, and Health Insurance: The Organization and Financing of Medical Care*. Washington, D.C.: The Brookings Institution, 1961.

SOMMER, R., AND N. OSMOND, "Symptoms of Institutional Care," *Social Problems*, 8 (Winter, 1960–61), 254–63.

SPECIAL COMMITTEE TO STUDY COMMITTMENT PROCEDURES, *Mental Illness and Due Process: Report and Recommendations on Admission to Mental Hospitals Under New York Law*. Ithaca, N.Y.: Cornell University Press, 1962.

SPIVACK, MAYER, AND HAROLD W. DEMONE, JR., "Mental Health Facilities: A Model for Physical Planning," *Social Science and Medicine*, 3 (April, 1970) 513–28.

STANTON, ALFRED H., AND MORRIS S. SCHWARTZ, *The Mental Hospital*. New York: Basic Books, Inc., Publishers, 1954.

STEIN, H., "Socio-Cultural Factors in Psychiatric Clinics for Children," *Social Service Review*, 30 (March, 1956), 9–19.

STENSLAND, PER G., "The Health Profession and the Changing Community," *Milbank Memorial Fund Quarterly*, 43 (October, 1965), 439–50.

STEPHENS, LINDA COOGLE, "Staff Communications on the Medical and Surgical Services: A Research Note," *Journal of Health and Social Behavior*, 8 (June, 1967), 148–53.

STEVENS, ROSEMARY, *Medical Practice in Modern England: The Impact of Specialization and State Medicine*. New Haven, Conn.: Yale University Press, 1966.

STEVENSON, GEORGE S., *Mental Health Planning for Social Action*. New York: McGraw-Hill Book Company, 1956.

STOLL, CLARICE S., "Ward Deviance and Psychiatric Decisions," *Journal of Health and Social Behavior*, 9 (December, 1968), 336–45.

STRAUS, ROBERT, "Planning a University Medical Center for the Student and the Patient," *Journal of Health and Human Behavior*, 4 (Spring, 1963), 36–44.

STRAUSS, ANSELM L., "Medical Organization, Medical Care and Lower Income Groups," *Social Science and Medicine*, 3 (August, 1969), 143–77.

STRAUSS, ANSELM, et al., *Psychiatric Ideologies and Institutions*. New York: The Free Press, 1964.

SUCHMAN, EDWARD A., "Stages of Illness and Medical Care," *Journal of Health and Human Behavior*, 6 (Fall, 1965), 114–28.

SUCHMAN, EDWARD A., "Preventive Health Behavior: A Model for Research on Community Health Campaigns," *Journal of Health and Social Behavior*, 8 (September, 1967), 197–209.

SUSSER, MERVYN, "Teaching Social Medicine in the United States," *Milbank Memorial Fund Quarterly*, 44 (October, 1966), 389–414.

SUSSMAN, MARVIN B., et al., *The Walking Patient: A Study in Outpatient Care*. Cleveland: Press of Western Reserve University, 1967.

TOOBERT, SAUL, FRANCES GILLESPIE SCOTT, AND JOHN D. LEWIS, "Relations of Various Indicators of Ward Management to Measures of Staff Attitudes in a Large Mental Hospital," *Journal of Health and Human Behavior*, 3 (Fall, 1962), 185–93.

TORREY, E. FULLER, "Health Services in Ethiopia," *Milbank Memorial Fund Quarterly*, 45 (July, 1967), 275–87.

TUCKMAN, JACOB, AND RICHARD A. REGAN, "Problems Referred to Children's Outpatient Psychiatric Clinics," *Journal of Health and Human Behavior*, 7 (Spring, 1966), 54–59.

TURK, HERMAN, "Social Cohesion through Variant Values: Evidence from Medical Role Relations," *American Sociological Review*, 28 (February, 1963), 28–37.

ULLMANN, ALICE, "Social Work in a Home-Care Program," *Journal of Chronic Diseases*, 15 (September, 1962), 925–34.

ULLMANN, LEONARD P., *Institution and Outcome: A Comparative Study of Psychiatric Hospitals*. Oxford: Pergamon Press, 1967.

VAYDA, EUGENE, "The Potential of Prepaid Group Practice in Community Medicine Teaching Programs," *Milbank Memorial Fund Quarterly*, 48 (April, 1970), 129–43.

VON MERING, OTTO, AND STANLEY H. KING, *Remotivating the Mental Patient*. New York: Russell Sage Foundation, 1957.

WARREN, M. D., JANE COOPER, AND JOAN L. WARREN, "Problems of Emergency Admissions to London Hospitals," *British Journal of Preventive and Social Medicine*, 21 (October, 1967), 141–49.

WECHSLER, HENRY, AND T. F. PUGH, "Fit of Individual and Community Characteristics and Rates of Psychiatric Hospitalization," *American Journal of Sociology*, 73 (November, 1967), 331–39.

WEEKS, H. ASHLEY, et al., *Family Spending Patterns and Health Care*. Cambridge, Mass.: Harvard University Press, 1961.

WEINER, HYMAN J., AND SHELLEY AKABAS, "The Impact of Chronic Illness on a Union Population: Implications for Labor Health Programs," *Journal of Health and Human Behavior*, 5 (Summer and Fall, 1964), 103–8.

WELLIN, EDWARD, "Implications of Local Culture for Public Health," *Human Organization*, 16 (Winter, 1958), 16–18.

WESSEN, ALBERT F., ed., *The Psychiatric Hospital as a Social System*, Proceedings of the Third Annual Conference on Community Mental Health Research, Social Science Institute, Washington University, St. Louis, Mo. Springfield, Ill.: Charles C Thomas, Publishers, 1964.

WHITE, KERR L., ed., "Symposium on Medical Care Research," *Journal of Chronic Diseases*, 9 (September, 1964), entire issue.

WHITE, PAUL E., "Myth and Reality in Interorganizational Behavior: A Study of Competition Between Two National Voluntary Health Agencies," *American Journal of Public Health*, 58 (February, 1968), 289–304.

WILDE, WILLIAM A., "Decision-Making in a Psychiatric Screening Agency," *Journal of Health and Social Behavior*, 9 (September, 1968), 215–21.

WING, J. K., AND G. W. BROWN, "Social Treatment of Chronic Schizophrenia: A Comparative Survey of Three Mental Hospitals," *Journal of Mental Science*, 107 (September, 1961), 847–61.

WINOKUR, GEORGE, ed., "Mental Health and Preventive Medicine," *Human Organization*, 16 (Winter, 1958), entire issue.

WOLFE, SAMUEL, et al., "The Work of a Group of Doctors in Saskatchewan," *Milbank Memorial Fund Quarterly*, 46 (January, 1968), 103–29.

WOLKON, GEORGE H., "Role Discontinuity and Resocialisation of the Psychiatric Patient," *Social Science and Medicine*, 3 (April, 1970), 679–87.

YERACARIS, CONSTANTINE, "Social Factors Associated with the Acceptance of Medical Innovations: A Pilot Study," *Journal of Health and Human Behavior*, 3 (Fall, 1962), 193–98.

ZANDER, A. F., et al., *Role Relations in the Mental Health Professions.* Ann Arbor: Institute for Social Research, University of Michigan, 1957.

VI. THE HEALTH PROFESSIONS

ABEL-SMITH, B., *A History of the Nursing Profession.* London: William Heinemann, Ltd., 1960.

ACHESON, ROY M., AND A. M. PAYNE, "Preventive Medicine at the Yale School of Medicine: 1950–1965," *Milbank Memorial Fund Quarterly,* 45 (July, 1967), 287–303.

ADAMS, STUART, "Trends in Occupational Origins of Physicians," *American Sociological Review,* 18 (August, 1953), 404–9.

ANDERSON, ODIN W., AND FREMONT J. LYDEN, "Physicians, Third Party Payments, and Professional Prerogatives," *Journal of Health and Human Behavior,* 4 (Fall, 1963), 195–99.

ANDERSON, ODIN W., AND MILVOY S. SEACAT, *An Analysis of Personnel in Medical Sociology,* Health Information Foundation Research Series, No. 21. New York, 1962.

ARAN, LYDIA, AND JOSEPH BEN-DAVID, "Socialization and Career Patterns as Determinants of Productivity of Medical Researchers," *Journal of Health and Social Behavior,* 9 (March, 1969), 3–15.

BACK, KURT W., et al., "Public Health as a Career in Medicine: Secondary Choice Within a Profession," *American Sociological Review,* 23 (October, 1958), 533–41.

BADGLEY, ROBIN F., ed., "Medical Careers in Public Health," *Milbank Memorial Fund Quarterly,* 44 (April, 1966), entire issue.

BAKER, SHELDON R., "Attitudes Toward Patient Care and Child Rearing Practices by Student Nurses: A Research Note," *Journal of Health and Human Behavior,* 7 (Summer, 1966), 63–65.

BECKER, HOWARD S., et al., *Boys in White: Student Culture in Medical School.* Chicago: University of Chicago Press, 1691.

BEN-DAVID, JOSEPH, "The Professional Role of the Physician in Bureaucratized Medicine: A Study in Role-Conflict," *Human Relations,* 11 (1958), 255–74.

BEN-DAVID, JOSEPH, "Roles and Innovations in Medicine," *American Journal of Sociology,* 65 (May, 1960), 557–68.

BLOOM, SAMUEL W., "The Sociology of Medical Education: Some Comments on the State of a Field," *Milbank Memorial Fund Quarterly,* 43 (April, 1965), 143–85.

BLOOM, SAMUEL W., et al., "The Sociologist as a Medical Educator: A Discussion," *American Sociological Review,* 25 (February, 1960), 95–101.

BUCHER, RUE, "The Psychiatric Residency and Professional Socialization," *Journal of Health and Human Behavior,* 6 (Winter, 1965), 197–207.

BUCK, RODGER L., "Behavioral Scientists in Schools of Medicine," *Journal of Health and Human Behavior,* 2 (Spring, 1961), 59–64.

CAHALAN, DON, PATRICIA COLLETTE, AND NORMAN A. HILMAR, "Career Interests and Expectations of U.S. Medical Students," *Journal of Medical Education,* 32 (August, 1957), 557–63.

CLEVELAND, SIDNEY E., "Personality Patterns Associated with the Professions of Dietitian," *Journal of Health and Human Behavior,* 2 (Summer, 1961), 113–23.

CLUTE, KENNETH F., *The General Practitioner: A Study of Medical Education and Practice in Ontario and Nova Scotia.* Toronto: University of Toronto Press, 1963.

COE, RODNEY M., "Processes in the Development of Established Professions," *Journal of Health and Social Behavior*, 11 (March, 1970), 59–67.

COGSWELL, BETTY E., AND D. D. WEIR, "A Role in Process: The Development of Medical Professionals' Role in Long-Term Care of Chronically Diseased Patients," *Journal of Health and Human Behavior*, 5 (Summer and Fall, 1964), 95–103.

COKER, ROBERT E., JR., et al., "The Medical Student: Specialization and General Practice," *North Carolina Medical Journal*, 21 (March, 1960), 96–101.

COKER, ROBERT E., JR., et al., "Patterns of Influence: Medical School Faculty Members and the Values and Specialty Interests of Medical Students," *Journal of Medical Education*, 35 (June, 1960), 518–27.

CORWIN, RONALD G., "Role Conception and Career Aspiration: A Study of Identity in Nursing," *The Sociological Quarterly*, 2 (April, 1961), 69–86.

CORWIN, RONALD G., "The Professional Employee: A Study of Conflict in Nursing Roles," *American Journal of Sociology*, 66 (May, 1961), 604–15.

DAVIS, FRED, ed., *The Nursing Profession: Five Sociological Essays.* New York: John Wiley & Sons, Inc., 1966.

DAVISON, R. L., "Opinion of Nurses on Cancer, Its Treatment and Curability: A Survey Among Nurses in Public Health Service," *British Journal of Preventive and Social Medicine*, 19 (January, 1965), 24–29.

DEUTSCHER, IRWIN, AND ANN MONTAGUE, "Professional Education and Conflicting Value Systems: The Role of Religious Schools in the Educational Aspirations of Nursing Students," *Social Forces*, 32 (December, 1956), 126–31.

DEVEREUX, GEORGE, AND FLORENCE R. WEINER, "The Occupational Status of Nurses," *American Sociological Review*, 15 (October, 1950), 628–34.

DODGE, JOAN S., "Nurses' Sense of Adequacy and Attitudes Toward Keeping Patients Informed," *Journal of Health and Human Behavior*, 2 (Fall, 1961), 213–16.

ELINSON, JACK, "The Physician's Dilemma in Puerto Rico," *Journal of Health and Human Behavior*, 3 (Spring, 1962), 14–20.

EVANS, LESTER J., *The Crisis in Medical Education.* Ann Arbor: University of Michigan Press, 1964.

FIELD, MARK G., "Structured Strain in the Role of the Soviet Physician," *American Journal of Sociology*, 58 (March, 1953), 493–502.

FISCHER, ANN, "The Importance of Sibling Position in the Choice of a Career in Pediatric Nursing," *Journal of Health and Human Behavior*, 3 (Winter, 1962), 283–88.

FORD, AMASA B., RALPH E. LISKE, AND ROBERT S. ORT, "Reactions of Physicians and Medical Students to Chronic Illness," *Journal of Chronic Diseases*, 15 (August, 1962), 785–94.

FOX, RENÉE C., "Physicians on the Drug Industry Side of the Prescription Blank: Their Dual Commitment to Medical Science and Business," *Journal of Health and Human Behavior*, 2 (Spring, 1961), 3–15.

FREDERICKS, MARCEL A., AND PAUL MUNDY, "The Relationship Between Social Class and National Board Scores of Students in a Medical School," *Social Science and Medicine*, 3 (April, 1969), 104–10.

FRENCH, KATHERINE S., "Research Interviewers in a Medical Setting," *Human Organization*, 21 (Fall, 1962), 219–24.

GILLIN, JOHN, "The Making of a Witch Doctor," Psychiatry, 19 (May, 1956), 131–36.

Gish, Oscar, and James A. Wilson, "Emigrating British Physicians," *Social Science and Medicine*, 3 (April, 1970), 495–511.

Glaser, W. A., "Doctors and Politics," *American Journal of Sociology*, 66 (November, 1960), 230–45.

Goode, William J., "Encroachment, Charlatanism, and the Emerging Profession: Psychology, Sociology, and Medicine," *American Sociological Review*, 25 (December, 1960), 902–14.

Grace, Harry A., "A Systematic Perspective on Health Manpower," *Journal of Health and Human Behavior*, 6 (Winter, 1965), 234–38.

Gray, Robert M., and W. R. Elton Newman, "The Relationship of Medical Students' Attitudes of Cynicism and Humanitarianism to Performances in Medical School," *Journal of Health and Human Behavior*, 3 (Summer, 1962), 147–51.

Gray, Robert M., W. R. Elton Newman, and Adina M. Reinhardt, "The Effect of Medical Specialization on Physicians' Attitudes," *Journal of Health and Human Behavior*, 7 (Summer, 1966), 128–33.

Haavio-Mannila, Elina, "The Occupational Value Structure of the Finnish Medical Profession," *Social Science and Medicine*, 1 (January, 1968), 425–40.

Hall, Oswald, "Types of Medical Careers," *American Journal of Sociology*, 55 (November, 1949), 243–53.

Hall, Oswald, "Half Medical Man, Half Administrator: A Medical Dilemma," *Canadian Public Administration*, 2 (December, 1959), 185–94.

Hammond, Kenneth R., and F. Kern, Jr., *Teaching Comprehensive Medical Care.* Cambridge, Mass.: Harvard University Press, 1959.

Hooper, Douglas, and John Roberts, "Teaching Behavioral Science to Medical Students in Some U.S. Medical Schools: A Report," *Social Science and Medicine*, 2 (June, 1968), 217–21.

Hughes, Everett C., "The Making of a Physician: A General Statement of Ideas and Problems," *Human Organization*, 14 (Winter, 1956), 21–25.

Hughes, Everett C., "Stress and Strain in Professional Education," *Harvard Educational Review*, 29 (Fall, 1959), 319–29.

Hughes, Everett C., H. M. Hughes, and Irwin Deutscher, *Twenty Thousand Tell Their Story.* Philadelphia: J. B. Lippincott Co., 1958.

Hummell, Hans J., Heidron Kaupen-Haas, and Wolfgang Kaupen, "The Referring of Patients as a Component of the Medical Interaction System," *Social Science and Medicine*, 3 (April, 1970), 597–607.

Irish, Donald P., and Daniel W. McMurry, "Professional Oaths and American Medical Colleges," *Journal of Chronic Diseases*, 18 (March, 1965), 275–89.

Jaco, E. Gartly, "Evaluation of Teaching in Chronic Illness and the Handicapped in Dental Education," *Journal of Health and Human Behavior*, 6 (Spring, 1965), 35–48.

Joyce, C. R. B., J. M. Last, and M. Weatherall, "Personal Factors as a Cause of Differences in Prescribing by General Practitioners," *British Journal of Preventive and Social Medicine*, 22 (July, 1968), 170–77.

Kendall, Patricia L., "The Relationship Between Medical Educators and Medical Practitioners," *Journal of Health and Human Behavior*, 6 (Summer, 1965), 79–82.

Knutson, Andie L., "Body Transplants and Ethical Values: Viewpoints of Public Health Professionals," *Social Science and Medicine*, 2 (December, 1968), 393–415.

Kramer, Marlene, "Nurse Role Deprivation: A Symptom of Needed Change," *Social Science and Medicine*, 2 (December, 1968), 461–75.

KRAUSE, ELLIOTT A., "Structured Strain in a Marginal Profession: Rehabilitation Counseling," *Journal of Health and Human Behavior*, 6 (Spring, 1965), 55–63.

KRIESBERG, LOUIS, "The Bases of Occupational Prestige: The Case of Dentists," *American Sociological Review*, 27 (April, 1962), 238–45.

KRIESBERG, LOUIS, AND BEATRICE R. TREIMAN, "The Public Views on Dentistry as a Profession," *Journal of Dental Education*, 25 (September, 1961), 247–68.

KRIESBERG, LOUIS, AND LATHROP V. BEALE, "Career Specifications Among Medical Students," *Journal of Health and Human Behavior*, 3 (Fall, 1962), 204–13.

LEHMANN, JUSTUS F., "Patient Care Needs as a Basis for Development of Objectives of Physical Medicine and Rehabilitation Teaching in Undergraduate Medical Schools," *Journal of Chronic Diseases*, 21 (January, 1968), 3–12.

LEVINSON, DANIEL J., "Medical Education and the Theory of Adult Socialization," *Journal of Health and Social Behavior*, 8 (December, 1967), 253–65.

LIFE, HAROLD I., VICTOR F. LIEF, AND NINA R. LIEF, eds., *The Psychological Basis of Medical Practice: By 52 Authors*. New York: Harper & Row, Publishers, Inc., 1963.

MACGREGOR, FRANCES C., *Social Science in Nursing*. New York: Russell Sage Foundation, 1960.

MARTIN, HARRY W., AND FRED E. KATZ, "The Professional School as a Molder of Motivation," *Journal of Health and Human Behavior*, 2 (Summer, 1961), 106–12.

MCCORKLE, THOMAS, "Chiropractic: A Deviant Theory of Disease and Treatment in Contemporary Western Culture," *Human Organization*, 20 (Spring, 1961), 20–23.

MCCORMACK, THELMA H., "The Druggists' Dilemma: Problems of a Marginal Occupation," *American Journal of Sociology*, 61 (January, 1956), 308–15.

MECHANIC, DAVID, "Correlates of Frustration among British General Practitioners," *Journal of Health and Social Behavior*, 11 (June, 1970), 87–104.

MECHANIC, DAVID, AND MARGARET NEWTON, "Social Considerations in Medical Education Points of Convergence Between Medicine and Behavioral Science," *Journal of Chronic Diseases*, 18 (March, 1965), 291–301.

MELBIN, MURRAY, "Organization Practice and Individual Behavior: Absenteeism Among Psychiatric Aides," *American Sociological Review*, 26 (February, 1961), 14–23.

MENSH, IVAN N., "Orientations of Social Values in Medical Student Assessment," *Social Science and Medicine*, 3 (January, 1970), 339–48.

MENZEL, HERBERT, "Innovation, Integration, and Marginality: A Survey of Physicians," *American Sociological Review*, 25 (October, 1960), 704–13.

MERTON, ROBERT K., SAMUEL BLOOM, AND NATALIE ROGOFF, "Studies in the Sociology of Medical Education," *Journal of Medical Education*, 31 (August, 1956), 552–64.

MERTON, ROBERT K., GEORGE G. READER, AND PATRICIA L. KENDALL, eds., *The Student-Physician: Introductory Studies in the Sociology of Medical Education*. Cambridge, Mass.: Harvard University Press, 1957.

MONGEAU, BEATRICE, H. L. SMITH, AND A. C. MANEY, "The 'Granny' Midwife: Changing Roles and Functions of a Fold Practitioner," *American Journal of Sociology*, 66 (March, 1961), 497–506.

MONTAGUE, JOEL B., JR., "Medicine and the Concept of Professionalism," *Sociological Inquiry*, 33 (Winter, 1963), 45–50.

MONTAGUE, JOEL B., JR., "Professionalism among American, Australian, and English Physicians," *Journal of Health and Human Behavior*, 7 (Winter, 1966), 284–89.

MORE, D. M., "The Dental Student," *Journal of the American College of Dentists*, 28 (March, 1961), 1–93.

Myerhoff, Barbara, G., and William R. Larson, "The Doctor as Culture Hero: The Routinization of Charisma," *Human Organization*, 24 (Fall, 1965), 187–91.

New, Peter Kong-Ming, and J. Thomas May, "Teaching Activities of Social Scientists in Medical and Public Health Schools," *Social Science and Medicine*, 2 (December, 1968), 447–61.

Orzack, Louis M., and John R. Uglum, "Sociological Perspectives of the Profession of Optometry," *American Journal of Optometry and Archives of American Academy of Optometry*, (August, 1958).

Otterland, Anders, "Effect of Thailidomide Warning on Medicine Prescribed for Pregnant Women: Analysis of Free Medicines Delivered to Expectant Mothers in the Västerbotten County of Sweden During 1961 and 1962," *British Journal of Preventive and Social Medicine*, 19 (April, 1965), 94–96.

Palec, Rudolf, "The Regional System and Postgraduate Medical Training in Czechoslovakia," *Milbank Memorial Fund Quarterly*, 44 (October, 1966), 414–26.

Pearlin, Leonard I., "Alienation from Work: A Study of Nursing Personnel," *American Sociological Review*, 27 (June, 1962), 314–26.

Piedmont, Eugene B., "Referrals and Reciprocity: Psychiatrists, General Practitioners, and Clergymen," *Journal of Health and Social Behavior*, 9 (March, 1969), 29–41.

Psathas, George, "The Fate of Idealism in Nursing School," *Journal of Health and Social Behavior*, 9 (March, 1969), 52–64.

Quarantelli, Enrico L., "The Career Choice Patterns of Dental Students," *Journal of Health and Human Behavior*, 2 (Summer, 1961), 124–32.

Quarantelli, Enrico L., "The Dental Student Image of the Dentist-Patient Relationship," *American Journal of Public Health*, 51 (September, 1961), 1312–19.

Rawnsley, K., and J. B. Loudon, "Factors Influencing the Referral of Patients to Psychiatrists by General Practitioners," *British Journal of Preventive and Social Medicine*, 16 (October, 1962), 174–82.

Reissman, Leonard, and John H. Rohrer, eds., *Change and Dilemma in the Nursing Profession*. New York: G. P. Putnam's Sons, 1957.

Reissman, Leonard, et al., "The Motivation and Socialization of Medical Students," *Journal of Health and Human Behavior*, 1 (Fall, 1960), 174–82.

Richard, Michel Paul, "The Negro Physician: Babbitt or Revolutionary?" *Journal of Health and Social Behavior*, 10 (December, 1969), 265–74.

Rosenblatt, Daniel, and Edward A. Suchman, "Awareness of Physician's Social Status Within an Urban Community," *Journal of Health and Human Behavior*, 7 (Fall, 1966), 146–53.

Rosengren, W. R., "Status, Stress and Role Contradictions: Emergent Professionalization in Psychiatric Hospitals," *Mental Hygiene*, 45 (January, 1961), 28–39.

Rushing, William A., *The Psychiatric Professions: Power, Conflict, and Adaptation in a Psychiatric Hospital Staff*. Chapel Hill: University of North Carolina Press, 1964.

Samora, Julian, "The Social Scientist as Teacher and Researcher in the Medical School," *Journal of Health and Human Behavior*, 1 (Spring, 1960), 42–46.

Saunders, Lyle, "The Changing Role of Nurses," *American Journal of Nursing*, 54 (September, 1954), 1094–98.

Seeman, Melvin, and John W. Evans, "Stratification and Hospital Care: I. The Performance of the Medical Interne," *American Sociological Review*, 26 (February, 1961), 67–80.

Seeman, Melvin, and John W. Evans, "Stratification and Hospital Care: II. The Objective Criteria of Performance," *American Sociological Review*, 26 (February, 1961), 193–204.

SEEMAN, MELVIN, AND JOHN W. EVANS, "Apprenticeship and Attitude Change," *American Journal of Sociology*, 67 (January, 1962), 365–78.

SEGAL, BERNARD E., "Psychiatrist and Sociologist: Social System, Subculture, and Division of Labor," *Journal of Health and Human Behavior*, 6 (Winter, 1965), 207–18.

SHEPARD, WILLIAM P., AND JAMES G. RONEY, JR., ed., "The Teaching of Preventive Medicine in the United States," *Milbank Memorial Fund Quarterly*, 42 (October, 1964), Part 2), entire issue.

SHERLOCK, BASIL, AND ALAN COHEN, "The Strategy of Occupational Choice: Recruitment to Dentistry," *Social Forces*, 44 (March, 1966), 303–13.

SHERLOCK, BASIL J., AND RICHARD T. MORRIS, "The Evolution of the Professional: A Paradigm," *Sociological Inquiry*, 37 (Winter, 1967), 27–46.

SHRYOCK, R. H., *The History of Nursing: An Interpretation of the Social and Medical Factors Involved.* Philadelphia: W. B. Saunders Co., 1959.

SHUVAL, JUDITH T., "Perceived Role Components of Nursing in Israel," *American Sociological Review*, 28 (February, 1963), 37–47.

SHUVAL, JUDITH T., "Sex Role Differentiation in the Professions: The Case of Israeli Dentists," *Journal of Health and Social Behavior*, 11 (September, 1970), 236–44.

SIMPSON, IDA HARPER, "Patterns of Socialization into Professions: The Case of Student Nurses," *Sociological Inquiry*, 37 (Winter, 1967), 47–54.

SIMPSON, RICHARD L., "The Psychiatric Attendant: Development of an Occupational Self-Image in a Low-Status Occupation," *American Sociological Review*, 24 (June, 1959), 389–92.

SISTAK, ZVONKO, "Teaching Comprehensive Medical Care in Yugoslavia," *Milbank Memorial Fund Quarterly*, 44 (October, 1966), 437–51.

SKIPPER, JAMES K., "Functional Significance of the Nurse Role: An Evaluation," *Journal of Health and Human Behavior*, 3 (Spring, 1962), 41–45.

SMITH, HARVEY L., "Contingencies of a Professional Differentiation," *American Journal of Sociology*, 63 (January, 1958), 410–14.

SOLOMON, DAVID N., "Ethnic and Class Differences among Hospitals as Contingencies in Medical Careers," *American Journal of Sociology*, 66 (March, 1961), 463–71.

STOLLEY, PAUL D., AND LOUIS LASAGNA, "Prescribing Patterns of Physicians," *Journal of Chronic Diseases*, 22 (December, 1969), 395–405.

TAYLOR, JAMES BENTLEY, "The Organization of Physician Attitudes Towards the Emotionally Disturbed Patient," *Journal of Health and Human Behavior*, 6 (Summer, 1965), 99–104.

THORNER, ISIDOR, "Pharmacy: The Functional Significance of an Institutional Pattern," *Social Forces*, 20 (March, 1942), 321–28.

THORNER, ISIDOR, "Nursing: The Functional Significance of an Institutional Pattern," *American Sociological Review*, 20 (October, 1955), 531–38.

TURK, HERMAN, AND THELMA INGLES, *Clinic Nursing: Explorations in Role Innovation.* Philadelphia: F. A. Davis Company, 1963.

VERBEEK-HEIDA, P. M., "General Practitioners' Attitudes Towards Group Practice in the Netherlands," *Social Science and Medicine*, 3 (August, 1969), 249–58.

WAGNER, NATHANIEL N., "Psychologists in Medical Education: A 9-Year Comparison," *Social Science and Medicine*, 2 (March, 1968), 81–86.

WALSH, JAMES LEO, AND RAY H. ELLING, "Professionalism and the Poor: Structural Effects and Professional Behavior," *Journal of Health and Social Behavior*, 9 (March, 1969), 16–28.

WARDWELL, WALTER I., "The Reduction of Strain in a Marginal Social Role," *American Journal of Sociology*, 61 (July, 1955), 16–25.

WEINBERG, MARTIN S., AND ELINA HAAVIO MANNILA, "The Medical Profession in Finland," *Journal of Health and Social Behavior*, 8 (September, 1967), 228–33.

WILLIAMS, J. J., "The Woman Physician's Dilemma," *Journal of Social Issues*, 6 (1950), 38–44.

WILLIAMS, THOMAS RHYS, AND MARGARET M. WILLIAMS, "The Socialization of the Student Nurse," *Nursing Research*, 8 (Winter, 1959), 18–25.

WILLIAMSON, HELEN M., WILLIAM E. EDMONSTON, JR., AND JOHN A. STERN, "Use of the EPPS for Identifying Personal Role Attributes Desirable in Nursing," *Journal of Health and Human Behavior*, 4 (Winter, 1963), 266–76.

WILLIE, CHARLES V., "The Social Class of Patients That Public Health Nurses Prefer to Serve," *American Journal of Public Health*, 50 (August, 1960), 1126–36.

WILSON, A. T. M., "Hospital Nursing Auxiliaries: Notes on a Background Survey and Job-Analysis," *Human Relations*, 3 (1950), 89–105.

WILSON, ROBERT N., "The Physician's Changing Hospital Role," *Human Organization*, 18 (Winter, 1959–60), 177–83.

WYLIE, CHARLES M., "Participation of General Practitioners in a Rehabilitation Program," *Journal of Chronic Diseases*, 17 (April, 1964), 359–69.

YOUNG, DONALD, "Sociology and the Practicing Professions," *American Sociological Review*, 20 (December, 1955), 641–48.

ZOLA, IRVING KENNETH, AND SYDNEY H. CROOG, "Work Perceptions and Their Implications for Professional Identity: An Exploratory Analysis of Public Health Nurses," *Social Science and Medicine*, 2 (March, 1968), 15–28.

VII. SOCIAL EPIDEMIOLOGY

ABRAMSON, J. H., et al., "Cornell Medical Index as a Health Measure in Epidemiological Studies: A Test of the Validity of a Health Questionnaire," *British Journal of Preventive and Social Medicine*, 19 (July, 1965), 103–10.

ACHESON, ROY, ed., "Comparability in International Epidemiology," *Milbank Memorial Fund Quarterly*, 43 (April, 1965, Part 2), entire issue.

ADELSTEIN, A. M., "Some Aspects of Cardiovascular Mortality in South Africa," *British Journal of Preventive and Social Medicine*, 17 (January, 1963), 29–40.

AGER, ERNEST A., et al., "An Epidemiological Study of Childhood Leukemia," *Journal of Chronic Diseases*, 18 (February, 1965), 113–32.

AGUALIMPIA M., CARLOS, et al., "Demographic Facts of Colombia: The National Investigation of Morbidity," *Milbank Memorial Fund Quarterly*, 47 (July, 1969), 255–96.

ALDERSON, M. R., "Data on Sickness Absence in Some Recent Publications of the Ministry of Pensions and National Insurance," *British Journal of Preventive and Social Medicine*, 21 (January, 1967), 1–6.

ANDERSON, ODIN W., AND G. GORDON, "Social Research in Respiratory Disease," *Bulletin of the National Tuberculosis Association*, 47 (February, 1961), 11–12.

ANTONOVSKY, AARON, "Social Class and Illness: A Reconsideration," *Sociological Inquiry*, 37 (Spring, 1967), 311–22.

ANTONOVSKY, AARON, "Social Class, Life Expectancy and Overall Mortality," *Milbank Memorial Fund Quarterly*, 45 (April, 1967), 31–75.

ANTONOVSKY, AARON, "Social Class and Major Cardiovascular Diseases," *Journal of Chronic Diseases*, 21 (May, 1968), 65–106.

ANTONOVSKY, AARON AND RACHEL KATS, "The Life Crisis History as a Tool in Epidemiological Research," *Journal of Health and Social Behavior*, 8 (March, 1967), 15–21.

ARCHER, MORTON, SEYMOUR RINZLER, AND GEORGE CHRISTAKIS, "Social Factors Affecting Participation in a Study of Diet and Coronary Heart Disease," *Journal of Health and Social Behavior*, 8 (March, 1967), 22–31.

ASHLEY, DAVID J. B., AND H. DUNCAN DAVIES, "Lung Cancer and Chronic Bronchitis in Wales," *British Journal of Preventive and Social Medicine*, 20 (July, 1966), 148–51.

AUSUBEL, DAVID P., *Drug Addiction: Physiological, Psychological and Sociological Aspects.* New York: Random House, Inc., 1958.

BACON, SELDEN D., *Sociology and the Problems of Alcohol*, Memoirs of the Section on Alcohol Studies, No. 1. New Haven, Conn.: Hillhouse Press, 1946.

BACON, SELDEN D., "Social Settings Conducive to Alcoholism," *Journal of the American Medical Association*, 164 (May 11, 1957), 177–81.

BACON, SELDEN D., ed., "Understanding Alcoholism," *Annals of the American Academy of Political and Social Science*, 315 (January, 1958), entire issue.

BAHR, HOWARD M., "Drinking, Interaction, and Identification: Notes on Socialization into Skid Row," *Journal of Health and Social Behavior*, 8 (December, 1967), 272–85.

BEADENKOPF, WILLIAM G., et al., "Some Demographic Characteristics of an Autopsied Population," *Journal of Chronic Diseases*, 18 (April, 1965), 333–51.

BENNETT, F. J., G. A. SAXTON, AND V. JUNOD, "Family Structure and Health at Kasangati," *Social Science and Medicine*, 2 (September, 1968), 261–83.

BERLE, B. B., *Eighty Puerto Rican Families in New York City: Health and Disease Studied in Context.* New York: Columbia University Press, 1958.

BIÖRCK, GUNNAR, "Epidemiological Studies on Cardiovascular Diseases in Sweden," *Journal of Chronic Diseases*, 18 (June, 1965), 519–26.

BLACKARD, WILLIAM G., YOSKIAKI OMORI, AND LAWRENCE R. FREEDMAN, "Epidemiology of Diabetes Mellitus in Japan," *Journal of Chronic Diseases*, 18 (May, 1965), 415–27.

BOEK, WALTER E., AND JEAN K. BOEK, "Health, Social Status, and the Life Cycle," *Journal of Chronic Diseases*, 14 (August, 1961), 272–82.

BORTNER, RAYMAN W., AND RAY H. ROSENMAN, "The Measurement of Pattern A Behavior," *Journal of Chronic Diseases*, 20 (July, 1967), 525–33.

BOWMAN, CLAUDE C., "Eufunctional Aspects of Stress-Producing Situations," *Journal of Health and Human Behavior*, 6 (Winter, 1965), 243–47.

BRONKS, I. G., AND E. K. BLACKBURN, "A Socio-Medical Study of Haemophilia and Related States," *British Journal of Preventive and Social Medicine*, 22 (April, 1968), 68–72.

BRUHN, JOHN G., "An Epidemiological Study of Myocardial Infractions in an Italian-American Community," *Journal of Chronic Diseases*, 18 (April, 1965), 353–65.

BRUHN, JOHN G., "Sociological Factors Related to Participation in a Screening Clinic for Heart Disease," *Social Science and Medicine*, 3 (April, 1969), 85–93.

BRUHN, JOHN G., et al., "Social Aspects of Coronary Heart Disease in a Pennsylvania German Community," *Social Science and Medicine*, 2 (June, 1968), 201–13.

BUEHLER, JOHN, "Two Experiments in Psychiatric Interrator Reliability," *Journal of Health and Human Behavior*, 7 (Fall, 1966), 192–203.

BURNIGHT, ROBERT G., "Chronic Morbidity and the Socio-Economic Characteristics of Older Urban Males," *Milbank Memorial Fund Quarterly*, 43 (July, 1965), 311–22.

DUDLEY, EUGENE, RICHARD A. BELDIN, AND BENJAMIN C. JOHNSON, "Climate, Water Hardness and Coronary Heart Disease," *Journal of Chronic Diseases*, 22 (June, 1969), 25–48.

EISENBERG, HENRY, et al., "The Epidemiology of Coronary Heart Disease in Middlesex County, Connecticut," *Journal of Chronic Diseases*, 14 (August, 1961), 221–35.

EPSTEIN, FREDERICK H., E. P. BOAS, AND RITA SIMPSON, "The Epidemiology of Atherosclerosis Among a Random Sample of Clothing Workers of Different Ethnic Origins in New York City," *Journal of Chronic Diseases*, 5 (March, 1957), 300–28.

EPSTEIN, LEON M., "Validity of a Questionnaire for Diagnosis of Peptic Ulcer in an Ethnically Heterogeneous Population," *Journal of Chronic Diseases*, 22 (June, 1969), 49–55.

EVANS, ANNE S., AND MARGARET M. WESSLER, "The Research-Oriented Single Home Follow-up Interview: Its Validity and Effectiveness as a Methodological Tool," *Journal of Health and Human Behavior*, 4 (Fall, 1963), 214–17.

FELDMAN, HARVEY W., "Ideological Supports to Becoming and Remaining a Heroin Addict," *Journal of Health and Social Behavior*, 9 (June, 1969), 131–39.

FELDMAN, JACOB J., "The Household Interview Survey as a Technique for the Collection of Morbidity Data," *Journal of Chronic Diseases*, 2 (May, 1960), 535–57.

FIELD, PETER B., "Mortality Rates and Aggression Management Indices," *Journal of Health and Human Behavior*, 4 (Summer, 1963), 99–105.

FISCHER, A., AND J. L. FISCHER, "Culture and Epidemiology: A Theoretical Investigation of Kuru," *Journal of Health and Human Behavior*, 2 (Spring, 1961), 16–25.

FORT, TWILA, AND AUSTIN L. PORTERFIELD, "Some Backgrounds and Types of Alcoholism Among Women," *Journal of Health and Human Behavior*, 2 (Winter, 1961), 283–92.

FREEDMAN, RONALD, LOLAGENE C. COOMBS, AND JUDITH FRIEDMAN, "Social Correlates of Fetal Mortality," *Milbank Memorial Fund Quarterly*, 44 (July, 1966), 327–45.

GAMPEL, B., et al., "Urbanization and Hypertension Among Zulu Adults," *Journal of Chronic Diseases*, 15 (January, 1962), 67–70.

GARNER, A. M., AND C. WENAR, *The Mother-Child Interaction in Psychosomatic Disorders*. Urbana: University of Illinois Press, 1959.

GARRETT, H. LEON, ROY V. FLANGLE, AND GEORGE V. MANN, "Physical Conditioning and Coronary Risk Factors," *Journal of Chronic Diseases*, 19 (August, 1966), 899–908.

GELBER, IDA, *Alcoholism in New York City*. New York: New York City Department of Health, 1960.

GILL, D. G., R. ILLSLEY, AND L. H. KOPLIK, "Pregnancy in Teenage Girls," *Social Science and Medicine*, 3 (April, 1970), 549–74.

GORDIS, LEON, ABRAHAM LILIENFELD, AND ROMEO RODRIGUEZ, "Studies in the Epidemiology and Preventability of Rheumatic Fever: I. Demographic Factors and the Incidence of Acute Attacks," *Journal of Chronic Diseases*, 21 (February, 1969), 645–54.

GORDIS, LEON, ABRAHAM LILIENFELD, AND ROMEO RODRIGUEZ, "Studies in the Epidemiology and Preventability of Rheumatic Fever: II. Socio-Economic Factors and the Incidence of Acute Attacks," *Journal of Chronic Diseases*, 21 (February, 1969), 655–66.

GORDON, NORMAN B., AND BERNARD KUTNER, "Long Term and Fatal Illness and the Family," *Journal of Health and Human Behavior*, 6 (Winter, 1965), 190–97.

GRAHAM, SAXON, "Ethnic Background and Illness in a Pennsylvania County," *Social Forces*, 4 (July, 1956), 76–82.

BURNIGHT, ROBERT G., AND P. G. MARDEN, "Social Correlates of Weight in an Aging Population," *Milbank Memorial Fund Quarterly*, 45 (April, 1967), 75–93.

BURNS, B. H., "Chronic Chest Disease, Personality and Success in Stopping Cigarette Smoking," *British Journal of Preventive and Social Medicine*, 23 (February, 1969), 23–27.

CAFFREY, BERNARD, "Reliability and Validity of Personality and Behavioral Measures in a Study of Coronary Heart Disease," *Journal of Chronic Diseases*, 21 (June, 1968), 191–204.

CHAPMAN, JOHN M., et al., "Relationships of Stress, Tranquilizers, and Serum Cholesterol Levels in a Sample Population Under Study for Coronary Heart Disease," *American Journal of Epidemiology*, 83 (May, 1966), 537–47.

CHAZAN, JOSEPH A., AND WARREN WINKELSTEIN, JR., "Household Aggregation of Hypertension: Report of a Preliminary Study," *Journal of Chronic Diseases*, 17 (January, 1964), 9–18.

COBB, SIDNEY, PATRICIA HUNT, AND ERNEST HARBURG, "The Intrafamilial Transmission of Rheumatoid Arthritis: II. An Interview Measure of Rheumatoid Arthritis," *Journal of Chronic Diseases*, 22 (September, 1969), 203–15.

COBB, SIDNEY, et al., "Some Psychological and Social Characteristics of Patients Hospitalized for Rheumatoid Arthritis, Hypertension and Duodenal Ulcer," *Journal of Chronic Diseases*, 18 (December, 1965), 1259–78.

COBB, SIDNEY, et al., "The Intrafamilial Transmission of Rheumatoid Arthritis: I. Design of the Study," *Journal of Chronic Diseases*, 22 (September, 1969), 195–202.

COHEN, JACOB, AND RUTH STEINITZ, "Underlying and Contributory Causes of Death of Adult Males in Two Districts," *Journal of Chronic Diseases*, 22 (June, 1969), 17–24.

COMMISSION ON CHRONIC ILLNESS, *Chronic Illness in the United States*. Vols. 1–4. Cambridge, Mass.: Harvard University Press, 1956–1959.

CONANT, ROGER G., JOSEPH A. PERKINS, AND ALLAN B. AINLEY, "Stroke Morbidity, Mortality and Rehabilitative Potential," *Journal of Chronic Diseases*, 18 (April, 1965), 397–403.

COOMBS, LOLAGENE C., et al., "Premarital Pregnancy and Status Before and After Marriage," *American Journal of Sociology*, 75 (March, 1970), 800–20.

COUCHMAN, K. G., R. D. WIGLEY, AND I. A. M. PRIOR, "Autoantibodies in the Carterton Population Survey: The Prevalence of Thyroid and Gastric Antibodies, Antinuclear and Rheumatoid Factors, in a Probability Based Population Sample," *Journal of Chronic Diseases*, 23 (June, 1970), 45–53.

CRAMER, MARY JANE, AND EDWARD BLACKER, "Social Class and Drinking Experience of Female Drunkenness Offenders," *Journal of Health and Human Behavior*, 7 (Winter, 1966), 276–84.

DAMON, ALBERT, AND ANTHONY P. POLEDNAK, "Constitution, Genetics, and Body Form in Peptic Ulcer: A Review," *Journal of Chronic Diseases*, 20 (October, 1967), 787–802.

DEASY, LEILA CALHOUN, "Some Reflections on Coronary Heart Disease: Socio-Medical Implications for Patients and Their Families," *Social Science and Medicine*, 3 (April, 1970), 659–67.

DIETHELM, OSKAR, ed., *Etiology of Chronic Alcoholism*. Springfield, Ill.: Charles C Thomas, Publisher, 1955.

DOBSON, H. L., et al., "Socioeconomic Status and Diabetes Mellitus," *Journal of Chronic Diseases*, 7 (May, 1958), 413–21.

DOVENMUEHLE, ROBERT H., "Health and Aging," *Journal of Health and Human Behavior*, 1 (Winter, 1960), 273–78.

GRAHAM, SAXON, AND ABRAHAM M. LILIENFELD, "Genetic Studies of Gastric Cancer in Humans: An Appraisal," *Cancer*, 11 (September, 1958).

GRAHAM, P. J., et al., "Childhood Asthma: A Psychosomatic Disorder? Some Epidemiological Considerations," *British Journal of Preventive and Social Medicine*, 21 (April, 1967), 78–85.

GREENWALD, ISIDOR, "Studies of Exophthalmic Goitre: V. The Course of Mortality in Canada, 1921–1965, and its Significance," *Journal of Chronic Diseases*, 22 (May, 1970), 811–17.

GROEN, J. J., et al., *Psychosomatic Research*. New York: Pergamon Press, 1964.

GUERRIN, ROBERT F., AND EDGAR F. BORGATTA, "Socio-economic and Demographic Correlates of Tuberculosis Incidence," *Milbank Memorial Fund Quarterly*, 43 (July, 1965), 269–90.

GUSSOW, ZACHARY, "Behavioral Research in Chronic Disease: A Study of Leprosy," *Journal of Chronic Diseases*, 17 (February, 1964), 179–89.

HAENSZEL, WILLIAM, "Cancer Mortality Among the Foreign Born in the United States," *Journal of the National Cancer Institute*, 26 (January, 1961), 37–132.

HARBURG, ERNEST, et al., "Personality Traits and Behavioral Patterns Associated with Systolic Blood Pressure Levels in College Males," *Journal of Chronic Diseases*, 17 (May, 1964), 405–14.

HARBURG, ERNEST, et al., "The Intrafamilial Transmission of Rheumatoid Arthritis: IV. Recalled Parent-Child Relations by Rheumatoid Arthritics and Controls," *Journal of Chronic Diseases*, 22 (September, 1969), 223–38.

HAWTHORNE, VICTOR M., "Population Screening as a Personalized Method of Health Education," *Social Science and Medicine*, 3 (April, 1970), 653–58.

HAYBRITTLE, J. L., "Mortality Rates from Cancer and Tuberculosis," *British Journal of Preventive and Social Medicine*, 17 (January, 1963), 23–28.

HEASMAN, M. A., AND D. D. REID, "Theory and Observation in Family Epidemics of the Common Cold," *British Journal of Preventive and Social Medicine*, 15 (January, 1961), 12–17.

HIGGINS, I. T. T., A. L. COCHRANE, AND A. J. THOMAS, "Epidemiological Studies of Coronary Disease," *British Journal of Preventive and Social Medicine*, 17 (October, 1963), 153–65.

HIGGINS, I. T. T., et al., "Coronary Disease in Mining Communities in Marion County, West Virginia," *Journal of Chronic Diseases*, 22 (August, 1969), 165–79.

HINKLE, LAWRENCE E., JR., "Ecological Observations on the Relation of Physical Illness, Mental Illness, and the Social Environment," *Psychosomatic Medicine*, 23 (July–August, 1961), 289–97.

HINKLE, LAWRENCE E., JR., "Some Social and Biological Correlates of Coronary Heart Disease," *Social Science and Medicine*, 1 (July, 1967), 129–40.

HINKLE, LAWRENCE E., JR., "Social Factors and Coronary Heart Disease: Some General Introductory Remarks," *Social Science and Medicine*, 2 (June, 1968), 107–10.

HINKLE, LAWRENCE, E., AND HAROLD G. WOLFF, "Ecologic Investigations of the Relationship between Illness, Life Experiences and the Social Environment," *Annals of Internal Medicine*, 49 (December, 1958), 1373–88.

HINKLE, LAWRENCE E., et al., "An Investigation of the Relation Between Life Experience, Personality Characteristics, and General Susceptibility to Illness," *Psychosomatic Medicine*, 20 (July–August, 1958), 278–95.

HOLMES, T. H., et al., "Psychosocial and Psychophysiologic Studies of Tuberculosis," *Psychosomatic Medicine*, 19 (March–April, 1957), 134–43.

HOSKIN, J. O., L. G. KILOH, AND J. E. CAWTE, "Epilepsy and *Guria*: The Shaking Syndromes of New Guinea," *Social Science and Medicine*, 3 (April, 1969), 39–48.

HOWARD, JAN, "Race Differences in Hypertension Mortality Trends: Differential Drug Exposure as a Theory," *Milbank Memorial Fund Quarterly*, 43 (April, 1965), 202–19.

HOWARD, JAN, AND BARBARA L. HOLMAN, "The Effects of Racê and Occupation on Hypertension Mortality," *Milbank Memorial Fund Quarterly*," 48 (July, 1970), 263–96.

HUGHES, CHARLES C., AND JOHN M. HUNTER, "Disease and 'Development' in Africa," *Social Science and Medicine*, 3 (April, 1970), 443–93.

HUNTER, D., *The Diseases of Occupations.* Boston: Little, Brown and Company, 1957.

IBRAHIM, MICHEL A., et al., "Personality Traits and Coronary Heart Disease Utilization of a Cross-Sectional Study Design to Test Whether a Selected Psychological Profile Precedes or Follows Manifest Coronary Heart Disease," *Journal of Chronic Diseases*, 19 (March, 1966), 255–71.

IBRAHIM, MICHEL A., et al., "Psychological Patterns and Coronary Heart Disease: An Appraisal of the Determination of Etiology by Means of a Stochastic Process," *Journal of Chronic Diseases*, 20 (November–December, 1967), 931–40.

JACKMAN, NORMAN, et al., "Interaction, Emotion and Physiologic Change," *Journal of Health and Human Behavior*, 4 (Summer, 1963), 83–88.

JACKSON, ELTON F., "Status Consistency and Symptoms of Stress," *American Sociological Review*, 27 (August, 1962), 469–80.

JACKSON, ELTON F., AND PETER J. BURKE, "Status and Symptoms of Stress: Additive and Interaction Effects," *American Sociological Review*, 30 (August, 1965), 556–64.

JACOBSON, PAUL H., "Cohort Survival for Generations Since 1840," *Milbank Memorial Fund Quarterly*, 42 (July, 1964), 36–54.

JELLINEK, E. M., *The Disease Concept of Alcoholism.* New Haven, Conn.: Hillhouse Press, 1960.

JENKINS, C. DAVID, "Components of the Coronary-Prone Behavior Pattern: Their Relation to Silent Myocardial Infarction and Blood Lipids," *Journal of Chronic Diseases*, 19 (May, 1966), 599–609.

JENKINS, C. DAVID, RAY H. ROSENMAN, AND MEYER FRIEDMAN, "Development of an Objective Psychological Test for the Determination of the Coronary-Prone Behavior Pattern in Employed Men," *Journal of Chronic Diseases*, 20 (June, 1967), 371–79.

JENKINS, C. DAVID, RAY H. ROSENMAN, AND MEYER FRIEDMAN, "Replicability of Rating the Coronary-Prone Behaviour Pattern," *British Journal of Preventive and Social Medicine*, 22 (January, 1968), 16–22.

JOHNSON, BENJAMIN, AND RICHARD D. REMINGTON, "A Sampling Study of Blood Pressure Levels in White and Negro Residents of Nassau, Bahamas," *Journal of Chronic Diseases*, 13 (January, 1961), 39–51.

JOHNSON, BENJAMIN C., FREDERICK H. EPSTEIN, AND MARCUS O. KJELSBERG, "Distributions and Familial Studies of Blood Pressure and Serum Cholesterol Levels in a Total Community: Tecumseh, Michigan," *Journal of Chronic Diseases*, 18 (February, 1965), 147–60.

KADUSHIN, CHARLES, "Social Class and the Experience of Ill Health," *Sociological Inquiry*, 34 (Winter, 1964), 67–80.

KEITH, ROBERT ALLEN, "Personality and Coronary Heart Disease: A Review," *Journal of Chronic Diseases*, 19 (November–December, 1966), 1231–43.

KELLER, MARK, AND VERA EFRON, "The Prevalence of Alcoholism," *Quarterly Journal of Studies on Alcohol*, 16 (December, 1955), 619–44.

DUDLEY, EUGENE, RICHARD A. BELDIN, AND BENJAMIN C. JOHNSON, "Climate, Water Hardness and Coronary Heart Disease," *Journal of Chronic Diseases*, 22 (June, 1969), 25–48.

EISENBERG, HENRY, et al., "The Epidemiology of Coronary Heart Disease in Middlesex County, Connecticut," *Journal of Chronic Diseases*, 14 (August, 1961), 221–35.

EPSTEIN, FREDERICK H., E. P. BOAS, AND RITA SIMPSON, "The Epidemiology of Atherosclerosis Among a Random Sample of Clothing Workers of Different Ethnic Origins in New York City," *Journal of Chronic Diseases*, 5 (March, 1957), 300–28.

EPSTEIN, LEON M., "Validity of a Questionnaire for Diagnosis of Peptic Ulcer in an Ethnically Heterogeneous Population," *Journal of Chronic Diseases*, 22 (June, 1969), 49–55.

EVANS, ANNE S., AND MARGARET M. WESSLER, "The Research-Oriented Single Home Follow-up Interview: Its Validity and Effectiveness as a Methodological Tool," *Journal of Health and Human Behavior*, 4 (Fall, 1963), 214–17.

FELDMAN, HARVEY W., "Ideological Supports to Becoming and Remaining a Heroin Addict," *Journal of Health and Social Behavior*, 9 (June, 1969), 131–39.

FELDMAN, JACOB J., "The Household Interview Survey as a Technique for the Collection of Morbidity Data," *Journal of Chronic Diseases*, 2 (May, 1960), 535–57.

FIELD, PETER B., "Mortality Rates and Aggression Management Indices," *Journal of Health and Human Behavior*, 4 (Summer, 1963), 99–105.

FISCHER, A., AND J. L. FISCHER, "Culture and Epidemiology: A Theoretical Investigation of Kuru," *Journal of Health and Human Behavior*, 2 (Spring, 1961), 16–25.

FORT, TWILA, AND AUSTIN L. PORTERFIELD, "Some Backgrounds and Types of Alcoholism Among Women," *Journal of Health and Human Behavior*, 2 (Winter, 1961), 283–92.

FREEDMAN, RONALD, LOLAGENE C. COOMBS, AND JUDITH FRIEDMAN, "Social Correlates of Fetal Mortality," *Milbank Memorial Fund Quarterly*, 44 (July, 1966), 327–45.

GAMPEL, B., et al., "Urbanization and Hypertension Among Zulu Adults," *Journal of Chronic Diseases*, 15 (January, 1962), 67–70.

GARNER, A. M., AND C. WENAR, *The Mother-Child Interaction in Psychosomatic Disorders.* Urbana: University of Illinois Press, 1959.

GARRETT, H. LEON, ROY V. FLANGLE, AND GEORGE V. MANN, "Physical Conditioning and Coronary Risk Factors," *Journal of Chronic Diseases*, 19 (August, 1966), 899–908.

GELBER, IDA, *Alcoholism in New York City.* New York: New York City Department of Health, 1960.

GILL, D. G., R. ILLSLEY, AND L. H. KOPLIK, "Pregnancy in Teenage Girls," *Social Science and Medicine*, 3 (April, 1970), 549–74.

GORDIS, LEON, ABRAHAM LILIENFELD, AND ROMEO RODRIGUEZ, "Studies in the Epidemiology and Preventability of Rheumatic Fever: I. Demographic Factors and the Incidence of Acute Attacks," *Journal of Chronic Diseases*, 21 (February, 1969), 645–54.

GORDIS, LEON, ABRAHAM LILIENFELD, AND ROMEO RODRIGUEZ, "Studies in the Epidemiology and Preventability of Rheumatic Fever: II. Socio-Economic Factors and the Incidence of Acute Attacks," *Journal of Chronic Diseases*, 21 (February, 1969), 655–66.

GORDON, NORMAN B., AND BERNARD KUTNER, "Long Term and Fatal Illness and the Family," *Journal of Health and Human Behavior*, 6 (Winter, 1965), 190–97.

GRAHAM, SAXON, "Ethnic Background and Illness in a Pennsylvania County," *Social Forces*, 4 (July, 1956), 76–82.

Burnight, Robert G., and P. G. Marden, "Social Correlates of Weight in an Aging Population," *Milbank Memorial Fund Quarterly*, 45 (April, 1967), 75–93.

Burns, B. H., "Chronic Chest Disease, Personality and Success in Stopping Cigarette Smoking," *British Journal of Preventive and Social Medicine*, 23 (February, 1969), 23–27.

Caffrey, Bernard, "Reliability and Validity of Personality and Behavioral Measures in a Study of Coronary Heart Disease," *Journal of Chronic Diseases*, 21 (June, 1968), 191–204.

Chapman, John M., et al., "Relationships of Stress, Tranquilizers, and Serum Cholesterol Levels in a Sample Population Under Study for Coronary Heart Disease," *American Journal of Epidemiology*, 83 (May, 1966), 537–47.

Chazan, Joseph A., and Warren Winkelstein, Jr., "Household Aggregation of Hypertension: Report of a Preliminary Study," *Journal of Chronic Diseases*, 17 (January, 1964), 9–18.

Cobb, Sidney, Patricia Hunt, and Ernest Harburg, "The Intrafamilial Transmission of Rheumatoid Arthritis: II. An Interview Measure of Rheumatoid Arthritis," *Journal of Chronic Diseases*, 22 (September, 1969), 203–15.

Cobb, Sidney, et al., "Some Psychological and Social Characteristics of Patients Hospitalized for Rheumatoid Arthritis, Hypertension and Duodenal Ulcer," *Journal of Chronic Diseases*, 18 (December, 1965), 1259–78.

Cobb, Sidney, et al., "The Intrafamilial Transmission of Rheumatoid Arthritis: I. Design of the Study," *Journal of Chronic Diseases*, 22 (September, 1969), 195–202.

Cohen, Jacob, and Ruth Steinitz, "Underlying and Contributory Causes of Death of Adult Males in Two Districts," *Journal of Chronic Diseases*, 22 (June, 1969), 17–24.

Commission on Chronic Illness, *Chronic Illness in the United States*. Vols. 1–4. Cambridge, Mass.: Harvard University Press, 1956–1959.

Conant, Roger G., Joseph A. Perkins, and Allan B. Ainley, "Stroke Morbidity, Mortality and Rehabilitative Potential," *Journal of Chronic Diseases*, 18 (April, 1965), 397–403.

Coombs, Lolagene C., et al., "Premarital Pregnancy and Status Before and After Marriage," *American Journal of Sociology*, 75 (March, 1970), 800–20.

Couchman, K. G., R. D. Wigley, and I. A. M. Prior, "Autoantibodies in the Carterton Population Survey: The Prevalence of Thyroid and Gastric Antibodies, Antinuclear and Rheumatoid Factors, in a Probability Based Population Sample," *Journal of Chronic Diseases*, 23 (June, 1970), 45–53.

Cramer, Mary Jane, and Edward Blacker, "Social Class and Drinking Experience of Female Drunkenness Offenders," *Journal of Health and Human Behavior*, 7 (Winter, 1966), 276–84.

Damon, Albert, and Anthony P. Polednak, "Constitution, Genetics, and Body Form in Peptic Ulcer: A Review," *Journal of Chronic Diseases*, 20 (October, 1967), 787–802.

Deasy, Leila Calhoun, "Some Reflections on Coronary Heart Disease: Socio-Medical Implications for Patients and Their Families," *Social Science and Medicine*, 3 (April, 1970), 659–67.

Diethelm, Oskar, ed., *Etiology of Chronic Alcoholism*. Springfield, Ill.: Charles C Thomas, Publisher, 1955.

Dobson, H. L., et al., "Socioeconomic Status and Diabetes Mellitus," *Journal of Chronic Diseases*, 7 (May, 1958), 413–21.

Dovenmuehle, Robert H., "Health and Aging," *Journal of Health and Human Behavior*, 1 (Winter, 1960), 273–78.

KELLERT, STEPHEN, et al., "Culture Change and Stress in Rural Peru: A Preliminary Report," *Milbank Memorial Fund Quarterly*, 45 (October, 1967), 391–417.

KEYES, ANCEL, "The Diet and the Development of Coronary Heart Disease," *Journal of Chronic Diseases*, 4 (October, 1956), 364–80.

KEYES, ANCEL, "Arteriosclerotic Heart Disease in a Favored Community," *Journal of Chronic Diseases*, 19 (March, 1966), 245–54.

KING, HAITUNG, AND JOHN C. BAILAR, III, "Mortality Among Lutheran Clergymen," *Milbank Memorial Fund Quarterly*, 46 (October, 1968), 527–49.

KING, HAITUNG, EARL DIAMON, AND JOHN C. BAILAR, III, "Cancer Mortality and Religious Preference: A Suggested Method in Research," *Milbank Memorial Fund Quarterly*, 43 (July, 1965), 269–90.

KING, STANLEY H., AND SIDNEY COBB, "Psychosocial Factors in the Epidemiology of Rheumatoid Arthritis," *Journal of Chronic Diseases*, 7 (June, 1958), 466–75.

KNOX, GEORGE, "Epidemiology of Childhood Leukemia in Northumberland and Durham," *British Journal of Preventive and Social Medicine*, 18 (January, 1964), 17–24.

LAHAR, ELKHANAN, "Methodological Problems in Behavioral Research on Disease," *Journal of Chronic Diseases*, 20 (May, 1967), 333–40.

LAUGHTON, KATHERINE B., CAROL W. BUCK, AND G. E. HOBBS, "Socio-Economic Status and Illness," *Milbank Memorial Fund Quarterly*, 36 (January, 1958), 46–57.

LEAVELL, HUGH R., "Chronic Disease and the Behavioral Sciences," *Journal of Chronic* Diseases, 2 (July, 1955), 113.

LEGG, SUSAN, et al., "Patterns of Low Birth Weight in West Jerusalem with Special Reference to Maternal Origin," *British Journal of Preventive and Social Medicine*, 24 (May, 1970), 89–96.

LEHRMAN, EDWARD W., "Social Class and Coronary Heart Disease: A Sociological Assessment of the Medical Literature," *Journal of Chronic Diseases*, 20 (June, 1967), 381–91.

LELLOUCH, J., et al., "The Relationships Between Smoking and Levels of Serum Urea and Uric Acid: Results of an Epidemiological Survey," *Journal of Chronic Diseases*, 22 (June, 1969), 9–15.

LEWIS, CHARLES E., "Factors Influencing the Return to Work of Men with Congestive Heart Failure," *Journal of Chronic Diseases*, 19 (November–December, 1966), 1193–1209.

LEWIS, J. G., AND D. A. CHAMBERLAIN, "Alcohol Consumption and Smoking Habits in Male Patients with Pulmonary Tuberculosis," *British Journal of Preventive and Social Medicine*, 17 (July, 1963), 149–52.

LEYS, D. G., et al., "Mothers at Work: A Study of the Health of Primary School Children Carried Out for the Kent Pediatric and Child Health Society," *British Journal of Preventive and Social Medicine*, 17 (July, 1963), 145–48.

LILIENFELD, ABRAHAM M., ed., "Symposium on Epidemiology of Cardiovascular Diseases," *Journal of Chronic Diseases*, 18 (August, 1965), entire issue.

LINDESMITH, ALFRED R., *Opiate Addiction*. Bloomington, Ind.: Principia Press, 1947.

LUDWIG, EDWARD G., AND JERE WYSONG, "Work, Heart Disease and Mental Health," *Journal of Chronic Diseases*, 21 (February, 1969), 687–89.

MACGREGOR, FRANCES COOKE, *Facial Deformities and Plastic Surgery*. Springfield, Ill.: Charles C Thomas, Publisher, 1956.

MATSUMOTO, Y. SCOTT, "Social Stress and Coronary Heart Disease in Japan," *Milbank Memorial Fund Quarterly*, 48 (January, 1970), 9–36.

McCord, William, Joan McCord, and P. Verden, "Familial Correlates of 'Psychosomatic' Symptoms in Children," *Journal of Health and Human Behavior*, 1 (Fall, 1960), 192–99.

McChlloch, J. W., and P. G. Fawcett, "Some Factors Affecting the Prevalence of Stammering," *British Journal of Preventive and Social Medicine*, 18 (July, 1964), 146–51.

McDonough, J. R., et al., "Coronary Heart Disease Among Negroes and Whites in Evans County, Georgia," *Journal of Chronic Diseases*, 18 (May, 1965), 443–68.

McFarland, David D., and Sidney Cobb, "Causal Interpretations from Cross-Sectional Data: An Examination of the Stochastic Processes Involved in the Relationship Between a Personality Characteristic and Coronary Heart Disease," *Journal of Chronic Diseases*, 20 (June, 1967), 393–406.

McKenzie, Herman I., et al., "Child Mortality in Jamaica," *Milbank Memorial Fund Quarterly*, 45 (July, 1967), 303–21.

Mechanic, David, and Margaret Newton, "Some Problems in the Analyses of Morbidity Data," *Journal of Chronic Diseases*, 18 (June, 1965), 569–80.

Meile, Richard L., and Philip N. Haese, "Social Status, Status Incongruence and Symptoms of Stress," *Journal of Health and Social Behavior*, 10 (September, 1969), 237–44.

Mendelson, M., S. Hirsch, and C. S. Webber, "A Critical Examination of Some Recent Theoretical Models in Psychosomatic Medicine," *Psychosomatic Medicine*, 18 (October, 1956), 363–73.

Meyer, A. S., *Social and Psychological Factors in Opiate Addiction: A Review of Research Findings Together with an Annotated Bibliography*. New York: Bureau of Applied Social Research, Columbia University, 1952.

Miller, F. J. W., et al., *Growing Up in Newcastle Upon Tyne: A Continuing Study of Health and Illness in Young Children Within Their Families*. London: Oxford University Press, 1960.

Modan, Baruch, Uri Mintz, and Jacob Finkelman, "Male Breast Cancer in Israel: Selected Epidemiological and Clinical Aspects," *Journal of Chronic Diseases*, 23 (June, 1970), 55–60.

Modan, Baruch, Brian P. Moore, and Batia Paz, "Mortality from Renal Disease in Israel: Some Epidemiological Aspects," *Journal of Chronic Diseases*, 22 (April, 1970), 727–32.

Monk, Mary, et al., "An Epidemiological Study of Ulcerative Colitis and Regional Enteritis Among Adults in Baltimore: III. Psychological and Possible Stress-Precipitating Factors," *Journal of Chronic Diseases*, 22 (February, 1970), 565–78.

Moos, Rudolf H., "Personality Factors Associated with Rheumatoid Arthritis: A Review," *Journal of Chronic Diseases*, 17 (January, 1964), 41–55.

Moos, Rudolf H., and George F. Solomon, "Personality Correlates of the Degree of Functional Incapacity of Patients with Physical Disease," *Journal of Chronic Diseases*, 18 (October, 1965), 1019–38.

Moriyama, Iwao M., "Vital and Health Statistics of the Future," *Milbank Memorial Fund Quarterly*, 44 (July, 1966), 318–27.

Murphy, H. B. M., "Personality and the Vermiform Appendix," *Journal of Health and Human Behavior*, 7 (Fall, 1966), 153–62.

Myrianthopoulos, Ntinos, and Katherine S. French, "An Application of the U.S. Bureau of the Census Socioeconomic Index to a Large, Diversified Patient Population," *Social Science and Medicine*, 2 (September, 1968), 283–99.

NAUGHTON, JOHN, AND JOHN F. MCCOY, "Observations on the Relationship of Physical Activity to the Serum Cholesterol Concentration of Healthy Men and Cardiac Patients," *Journal of Chronic Diseases*, 19 (July, 1966), 727–33.

NEWCOMBE, HOWARD B., "Familial Tendencies in Diseases of Children," *British Journal of Preventive and Social Medicine*, 20 (April, 1966), 49–57.

NEWELL, DAVID J., et al., "Use of Cohort Life Tables in Family Studies of Disease," *Journal of Chronic Diseases*, 13 (May, 1961), 439–52.

NORMAN-TAYLOR, W., AND W. H. REES, "Blood Pressures in Three New Hebrides Communities," *British Journal of Preventive and Social Medicine*, 17 (July, 1963), 141–44.

O'DONNELL, JOHN A., AND JUDITH P. JONES, "Diffusion of the Intravenous Technique Among Narcotic Addicts in the United States," *Journal of Health and Social Behavior*, 9 (June, 1969), 120–30.

OSTFIELD, A. M., et al., "A Prospective Study of the Relationship Between Personality and Coronary Heart Disease," *Journal of Chronic Diseases*, 17 (March, 1964), 265–76.

PAFFENBARGER, RALPH S., et al., "The Picture Puzzle of the Postpartum Psychoses," *Journal of Chronic Diseases*, 13 (February, 1961), 161–73.

PHILLIPS, LESLIE, *Human Adaptation and Its Failures*. New York: Academic Press, Inc., 1968.

PITTMAN, DAVID J., ed., *Alcoholism: An Interdisciplinary Approach*. Springfield, Ill.: Charles C Thomas, Publisher, 1959.

POSNER, MARGERY, AND HAROLD B. HOUSER, "Economic Aspects of Multiple Sclerosis: I. A Method for Classification of Income of Families of Different Sizes and Compositions and Its Application in a Longitudinal Study of Multiple Sclerosis," *Journal* of Chronic Diseases, 22 (December, 1969), 473–83.

RAUTSHARJU, PENTTI M., M. J. KARVONEN, AND ANCEL KEYES, "The Frequency of Arteriosclerotic and Hypertensive Heart Disease Among Ostensibly Healthy Working Populations in Finland," *Journal of Chronic Diseases*, 13 (May, 1961), 426–38.

REAVES, LEONARD E., "Concepts in the Etiology of Alcoholism," *Journal of Chronic Diseases*, 17 (June, 1964), 551–56.

REEDER, LEO G., "Social Factors in Heart Disease: A Preliminary Research Report on the Relationship of Certain Social Factors to Blood Pressure in Males," *Social Forces*, 34 (May, 1956), 367–71.

REEDER, LEO G., "The Socio-Economic Effects of Heart Disease," *Social Problems*, 4 (July, 1956), 51–55.

REEDER, LEO G., "Occupation and Socioeconomic Status as a Variable in Heart Disease Research: A Critique," *American Journal of the Medical Sciences*, 238 (September, 1959), 297–307.

RICHARDS, I. D. GERALD, "Congenital Malformations and Environmental Influences in Pregnancy," *British Journal of Preventive and Social Medicine*, 23 (November, 1969), 218–25.

ROBINSON, J. O., AND M. M. WOOD, "Symptoms and Personality in the Diagnosis of Physical Illness," *British Journal of Preventive and Social Medicine*, 22 (January, 1968), 23–26.

ROOM, ROBIN, "Cultural Contingencies of Alcoholism: Variations Between and Within Nineteenth-Century Urban Ethnic Groups in Alcohol-Related Death Rates," *Journal of Health and Social Behavior*, 9 (June, 1969), 99–113.

ROSE, GEOFFREY, "Familial Patterns in Ischaemic Heart Disease," *British Journal of Preventive and Social Medicine*, 18 (April, 1964), 75–80.

SAPIRA, JOSEPH D., JOHN C. BALL, AND HARRY PENN, "Causes of Death among Institutionalized Narcotic Addicts," *Journal of Chronic Diseases*, 22 (April, 1970), 733–42.

SCHULL, WILLIAM J., AND SIDNEY COBB, "The Intrafamilial Transmission of Rheumatoid Arthritis: III. The Lack of Support for a Genetic Hypothesis," *Journal of Chronic* Diseases, 22 (September, 1969), 217–22.

SCOTCH, NORMAN A., AND H. JACK GEIGER, "The Epidemiology of Rheumatoid Arthritis," *Journal of Chronic Diseases*, 15 (November, 1962), 1037–67.

SCOTCH, NORMAN A., AND H. JACK GEIGER, "The Epidemiology of Essential Hypertension, A Review with Special Attention to Psychologic and Sociocultural Factors: II. Psychologic and Sociocultural Factors in Etiology," *Journal of Chronic Diseases*, 16 (November, 1963), 1183–1213.

SEELEY, J. R., "Estimating the Prevalence of Alcoholism: A Critical Analysis on the Jellinek Formula," *Quarterly Journal of Studies on Alcohol*, 20 (June, 1959), 245–55.

SELYE, HANS, *The Stress of Life*. New York: McGraw-Hill Book Company, 1956.

SHAPIRO, ALVIN P., "An Experimental Study of Comparative Responses of Blood Pressure to Different Noxious Stimuli," *Journal of Chronic Diseases*, 13 (April, 1961), 293–311.

SHAPIRO, SAM, EVE WEINBLATT, AND PAUL M. DENSEN, "Longitudinal versus Cross-Sectional Approaches in Studying Prognostic Factors in Coronary Heart Disease," *Journal of Chronic Diseases*, 19 (August, 1966), 935–45.

SHAPIRO, SAM, et al., "The H.I.P. Study of Incidence and Prognosis of Coronary Heart Disease: Preliminary Findings on Incidence of Myocardial Infarction and Angina," *Journal of Chronic Diseases*, 18 (June, 1965), 527–58.

SHAPIRO, SAMUEL, et al., "The Epidemiology of Digoxin: A Study in Three Boston Hospitals," *Journal of Chronic Diseases*, 22 (November, 1969), 361–71.

SHAPIRO, SAM, et al., "Social Factors in the Prognosis of Men Following First Myocardial Infarction," *Milbank Memorial Fund Quarterly*, 48 (January, 1970), 37–50.

SHEKELLE, RICHARD B., ADRIAN M. OSTFELD, AND OGLESBY PAUL, "Social Status and Incidence of Coronary Heart Disease," *Journal of Chronic Diseases*, 22 (December, 1969), 381–94.

SHEPS, MINDEL C., "On the Person Years Concept in Epidemiology and Demography," *Milbank Memorial Fund Quarterly*, 44 (January, 1966), 69–92.

SKIPPER, JAMES K., JR., AND ROBERT C. LEONARD, "Children, Stress, and Hospitalization: A Field Experiment," *Journal of Health and Social Behavior*, 9 (December, 1968), 275–87.

SKINNER, JAMES S., et al., "Social Status, Physical Activity, and Coronary Proneness," *Journal of Chronic Diseases*, 19 (July, 1966), 773–83.

SKLAROFF, STANLEY A., "Use of National Health Service General Practice Records in Epidemiological Inquiries: Duodenal Ulcer, A Test Case," *British Journal of Preventive and Social Medicine*, 17 (October, 1963), 177–84.

SKYRING, A., et al., "Some Epidemiological and Familial Aspects of Coronary Heart Disease: Report of a Pilot Study," *Journal of Chronic Diseases*, 16 (December, 1963), 1267–79.

SMITHURST, B. A., "Epidemiological Survey of Diabetes in Toowoomba, Queensland," *Journal of Chronic Diseases*, 22 (August, 1969), 153–64.

SPARER, P. J., ed., *Personality, Stress, and Tuberculosis.* New York: International Universities Press, Inc., 1956.

SPENCE, JAMES C., et al., *A Thousand Families in Newcastle Upon Tyne: An Approach to the Study of Health and Illness in Children.* New York: Oxford University Press, 1954.

STAFF OF THE BENJAMIN ROSE HOSPITAL, "Multidisciplinary Studies of Illness in Aged Persons," *Journal of Chronic Diseases,* 13 (May, 1961), 453–64.

STAMLER, J., et al., "Epidemiologic Studies of Cardiovascular Renal Diseases: I–III," *Journal of Chronic Diseases,* 12 (October, 1960), 440–75.

STEIN, ZENA A., AND MERVYN W. SUSSER, "Socio-Medical Study of Enuresis Among Delinquent Boys," *British Journal of Preventive and Social Medicine,* 19 (October, 1965), 174–81.

STEIN, ZENA A., AND MERVYN W. SUSSER, "The Social Dimensions of a Symptom. A Sociomedical Study of Enuresis," *Social Science and Medicine,* 1 (July, 1967), 183–202.

STOCKS, PERCY, "Lung Cancer and Bronchitis in Relation to Cigarette Smoking and Fuel Consumption in Twenty Countries," *British Journal of Preventive and Social Medicine,* 21 (October, 1967), 181–85.

STOCKWELL, EDWARD G., "Infant Mortality and Socio-Economic Status: A Changing Relationship," *Milbank Memorial Fund Quarterly,* 40 (January, 1962), 101–11.

STOECKLE, JOHN D., IRVING K. ZOLA, AND GERALD E. DAVIDSON, "The Quantity and Significance of Psychological Distress in Medical Patients," *Journal of Chronic Diseases,* 10 (October, 1964), 959–70.

STOECKLE, JOHN D., et al., "Respiratory Disease in U.S. Soft Coal Miners: Clinical and Etiological Considerations," *Journal of Chronic Diseases,* 15 (September, 1962), 887–905.

SUSSER, MERVYN, "Causes of Peptic Ulcer: A Selective Epidemiological Review," *Journal of Chronic Diseases,* 20 (June, 1967), 435–56.

SYME, S. LEONARD, MERTON H. HYMAN, AND PHILIP E. ENTERLINE, "Sociocultural Factors and Coronary Heart Disease," *Sociological Inquiry,* 34 (Winter, 1964), 81–91.

SYME, S. LEONARD, MERTON M. HYMAN, AND PHILIP E. ENTERLINE, "Some Social and Cultural Factors Associated with the Occurrence of Coronary Heart Disease," *Journal of Chronic Diseases,* 17 (March, 1964), 277–89.

SYME, S. LEONARD, MERTON M. HYMAN, AND PHILIP E. ENTERLINE, "Cultural Mobility and the Occurrence of Coronary Heart Disease," *Journal of Health and Human Behavior,* 6 (Winter, 1965), 178–90.

SYME, S. LEONARD AND LEO G. REEDER, eds., "Social Stress and Cardiovascular Disease," *Milbank Memorial Fund Quarterly,* 45 (April, 1967, Part 2), entire issue.

TALBERT, ROBERT H., "Ecological Variations in Dental Health in a Metropolitan Community," *Journal of Health and Human Behavior,* 3 (Summer, 1962), 128–32.

TAYLOR, P. J., AND A. J. FAIRRIE, "Chronic Disability in Men of Middle Age: A Study of 165 Men in a General Practice and a Refinery," *British Journal of Preventive and Social Medicine,* 22 (October, 1968), 183–92.

THOMAS, CAROLINE BEDELL, "Psychophysiological Aspects of Blood Pressure Regulation: A Clinician's View," *Journal of Chronic Diseases,* 7 (July, 1964), 599–607.

TIBBITTS, HELEN G., NICHOLAS J. DEMERATH, AND ALBERT F. WESSEN, "Sociology and Staphylococcus," *American Journal of Sociology,* 54 (November, 1959), 298–300.

TUNBRIDGE, R. E., "Sociomedical Aspects of Diabetes Mellitus," *Lancet* (October, 1953), 893–99.

Tyroler, H. A., and John Cassel, "Health Consequences of Culture Change: II. The Effect of Urbanization on Coronary Heart Mortality in Rural Residents," *Journal of Chronic Diseases*, 17 (February, 1964), 167–77.

Van Kammen-Wijnmalen, E. H. W., et al., "Prevalence of Pneumoconiosis in Diabetic Coal-Miners," *Journal of Chronic Diseases*, 22 (February, 1970), 609–15.

Vaughan, D. H., "Some Social Factors in Perinatal Mortality," *British Journal of Preventive and Social Medicine*, 22 (July, 1968), 138–45.

Wardwell, Walter I., Claus B. Bahnson, and Herbert S. Caron, "Social and Psychological Factors in Coronary Heart Disease," *Journal of Health and Human Behavior*, 4 (Fall, 1963), 154–65.

Wardwell, Walter I., Merton Hyman, and Claus B. Bahnson, "Stress and Coronary Heart Disease in Three Field Studies," *Journal of Chronic Diseases*, 17 (January, 1964), 73–84.

Wardwell, Walter I., Merton Hyman, and Claus B. Bahnson, "Socio-environmental Antecedents to Coronary Heart Disease in 87 White Males," *Social Science and Medicine*, 2 (June, 1968), 165–85.

Willicos, R. R., "Factors Leading to a Failure of Control of Gonorrhea," *British Journal of Preventive and Social Medicine*, 16 (July, 1962), 113–22.

Willie, Charles V., and William B. Rothney, "Racial, Ethnic, and Income Factors in the Epidemiology of Neonatal Mortality," *American Sociological Review*, 27 (August, 1962), 522–26.

Wilner, Daniel M., and Gene C. Kassebaum, eds., *Narcotics*. New York: McGraw-Hill Book Company, 1965.

Wilner, Daniel M., et al., "The Baltimore Study on the Effects of Housing on Health," *Baltimore Health News* (Baltimore City Health Department), 37 (June, 1960), 45–52.

Wolf, Stewart et al., *Life Stress and Essential Hypertension*. Baltimore: Williams & Wilkins Co., 1955.

Wolff, Harold G., *Stress and Disease*. Springfield, Ill.: Charles C Thomas, Publisher, 1953.

Wylie, Charles M., "Recent Trends in Mortality from Cerebrovascular Accidents in the United States," *Journal of Chronic Diseases*, 14 (August, 1961), 213–20.

VIII. EPIDEMIOLOGICAL AND ETIOLOGICAL ASPECTS OF MENTAL PROBLEMS

Abramson, J. H., "Emotional Disorder, Status Inconsistency and Migration," *Milbank Memorial Fund Quarterly*, 44 (January, 1966), 23–49.

Banks, E. P., "Methodological Problems in the Study of Psychiatric Wards," *Social Forces*, 34 (March, 1956), 277–80.

Bateson, Gregory, et al., "Toward a Theory of Schizophrenia," *Behavioral Science*, 1 (October, 1956), 251–64.

Beck, S. J., "Families of Schizophrenic and of Well Children: Methods, Concepts and Some Results," *American Journal of Orthopsychiatry*, 30 (April, 1960), 247–75.

Becker, Ernest, "Socialization, Command of Performance, and Mental Illness," *American Journal of Sociology*, 67 (March, 1962), 494–517.

Beiser, Morton, "Poverty, Social Disintegration and Personality," *Journal of Social Issues*, 21 (January, 1965), 56–78.

BELKNAP, IVAN AND HIRAM J. FRIEDSAM, "Age and Sex Categories as Sociological Variables in the Mental Disorders of Late Maturity," *American Sociological Review*, 14 (June, 1949), 367–76.

BELLIN, SEYMOUR, AND ROBERT H. HARDT, "Mental Status and Mental Disorders among the Aged," *American Sociological Review*, 23 (April, 1958), 155–62.

BIANCHI, G. N., J. E. CAWTE, AND L. G. KILOH, "Cultural Identity and the Mental Health of Australian Aborigines," *Social Science and Medicine*, 3 (January, 1970), 371–87.

BIRTCHNELL, JOHN, "Parent Death in Relation to Age and Parental Age at Birth in Psychiatric Patients and General Population Controls," *British Journal of Preventive and Social Medicine*, 23 (November, 1969), 244–50.

BLUM, RICHARD H., "Case Identification in Psychiatric Epidemiology," *Milbank Memorial Fund Quarterly*, 40 (July, 1962), 253–88.

BOWEN, M., R. H. DYSINGER, AND B. BASAMANIA, "The Role of the Father in Families with a Schizophrenic Patient," *American Journal of Psychiatry*, 115 (May, 1959), 1017–20.

BROWN, GEORGE W., AND J. L. T. BIRLEY, "Crises and Life Changes and the Onset of Schizophrenia," *Journal of Health and Social Behavior*, 9 (September, 1968), 203–14.

BROWN, G. W., et al., "Influence of Family Life on the Course of Schizophrenic Illness," *British Journal of Preventive and Social Medicine*, 16 (April, 1962), 55–68.

BRUHN, JOHN G., "Comparative Study of Attempted Suicides and Psychiatric Outpatients," *British Journal of Preventive and Social Medicine*, 17 (October, 1963), 197–201.

CAWTE, J. E., AND L. G. KILOH, "Language and Pictorial Representation in Aboriginal Children. Implications for Transcultural Psychiatry," *Social Science and Medicine*, 1 (April, 1967), 67–76.

CHAMBLISS, WILLIAM, "The Negative Self: An Empirical Assessment of a Theoretical Assumption," *Sociological Inquiry*, 34 (Winter, 1964), 108–12.

CLARK, ROBERT E., "Psychoses, Income, and Occupational Prestige," *American Journal of Sociology*, 54 (March, 1949), 433–40.

CLAUSEN, JOHN A., AND MELVIN L. KOHN, "Parental Authority Behavior and Schizophrenia," *American Journal of Orthopsychiatry*, 26 (April, 1956), 297–313.

CROCETTI, GUIDO M., et al., "Selected Aspects of the Epidemiology of Schizophrenia in Croatia (Yugoslavia)," *Milbank Memorial Fund Quarterly*, 42 (April, 1964), 9–37.

CUMMING, JOHN M., "The Family and Mental Disorder: An Incomplete Essay," *Milbank Memorial Fund Quarterly*, 39 (April, 1961), 185–228.

DESOLE, DANIEL E., PHILIP SINGER, AND JACOB ROSEMAN, "Community Psychiatry and the Syndrome of Psychiatric Culture Shock: The Emergence of a New Functional Disorder," *Social Science and Medicine*, 1 (January, 1968), 401–18.

DOHRENWEND, BRUCE P., "Social Status and Psychological Disorder: An Issue of Substance and an Issue of Method," *American Sociological Review*, 31 (February, 1966), 14–35.

DOWNES, JEAN, AND KATHERINE SIMON, "Characteristics of Psychoneurotic Patients and Their Families as Revealed in a General Morbidity Study," *Milbank Memorial Fund Quarterly*, 32 (January, 1954), 42–64.

DUNHAM, H. WARREN, *Sociological Theory and Mental Disorder*. Detroit: Wayne State University Press, 1959.

DUNHAM, H. WARREN, "Social Structures and Mental Disorders: Competing Hypotheses of Explanation," *Milbank Memorial Fund Quarterly*, 39 (April, 1961), 259–311.

DUNHAM, H. WARREN, *Community and Schizophrenia: An Epidemiological Analysis.* Detroit, Mich.: Wayne State University Press, 1965.

DUNHAM, H. WARREN, PATRICIA PHILLIPS, AND BARBARA SRINISASAN, "A Research Note on Diagnosed Mental Illness and Social Class," *American Sociological Review*, 31 (April, 1966), 223–27.

FABREGA, HORACIO, JR., DUANE METZGER, AND GERALD WILLIAMS, "Psychiatric Implications of Health and Illness in a Maya Indian Group," *Social Science and Medicine*, 3 (April, 1970), 609–26.

FARIS, ROBERT E. L., AND H. WARREN DUNHAM, *Mental Disorders in Urban Areas.* Chicago: University of Chicago Press, 1939.

FEIBLEMAN, JAMES K., *Biosocial Factors in Mental Illness.* Springfield, Ill.: Charles C Thomas, Publisher, 1962.

FISHER, S., et al., "Parents of Schizophrenics, Neurotics, and Normals," *A.M.A. Archives of General Psychiatry*, 1 (August, 1959), 149–66.

FLECK, STEPHEN, "Family Dynamics and Origin of Schizophrenia," *Psychosomatic Medicine*, 22 (September–October, 1960), 333–44.

FOLKARD, STEVEN, BERTRAM MENDELBROTE, AND MAY MONRO, "Personal Problems Associated with Mental Health and Mental Illness," *British Journal of Preventive and Social Medicine*, 16 (April, 1962), 69–75.

FRANK, JEROME D., *Persusasion and Healing: A Comparative Study of Psychotherapy.* Baltimore: Johns Hopkins Press, 1963.

FREEMAN, HOWARD E., AND OZZIE G. SIMMONS, "The Use of the Survey in Mental Illness Research," *Mental Hygiene*, 34 (July, 1960), 400–10.

FREEMAN, HOWARD E., OZZIE G. SIMMONS, AND BERNARD J. BERGEN, "Possessiveness as a Characteristic of Mothers of Schizophrenics," *Journal of Abnormal and Social Psychology*, 58 (March, 1959), 271–73.

FREEMAN, HOWARD E., OZZIE G. SIMMONS, AND BERNARD J. BERGEN, "Residential Mobility Inclinations among Families of Mental Patients," *Social Forces*, 38 (May, 1960), 320–24.

FRENCH, JOHN R. P., JR., "SPSSI Presidential Address, 1963: The Social Environment and Mental Health," *Journal of Social Issues*, 19 (October, 1963), 39–56.

FRUMKIN, ROBERT M., "Social Factors in Schizophrenia," *Sociology and Social Research*, 38 (July–August, 1954), 383–86.

GATLIN, FRANCIS I., "Noise and Emotional Stress," *Journal of Chronic Diseases*, 18 (June, 1965), 509–18.

GIBBS, JACK P., "Rates of Mental Hospitalization: A Study of Societal Reaction to Deviant Behavior," *American Sociological Review*, 27 (December, 1962), 782–92.

GOLDHAMER, HERBERT, AND ANDREW MARSHALL, *Psychosis and Civilization.* New York: Free Press, 1953.

GOVE, WALTER R., "Sleep Deprivation: A Cause of Psychotic Disorganization," *American Journal of Sociology*, 75 (March, 1970), 782–99.

GOVE, WALTER, AND JOHN E. LUBACH, "An Intensive Treatment Program for Psychiatric Inpatients: A Description and Evaluation," *Journal of Health and Social Behavior*, 10 (September, 1969), 225–36.

GREGORY, IAN, "An Analysis of Familial Data on Psychiatric Patients: Parental Age, Family Size, Birth Order, and Ordinal Position," *British Journal of Preventive and Social Medicine*, 12 (January, 1958), 42–59.

GROSSACK, MARTIN M., ed., *Mental Health and Segregation.* New York: Springer Publishing Company, 1963.

HALLOWELL, A. IRVING, "Culture and Mental Disorder," *Journal of Abnormal and Social Psychology,* 29 (April–June, 1934), 1–9.

HALLOWELL, A. IRVING, "Values, Acculturation, and Mental Health," *American Journal of Orthopsychiatry,* 20 (October, 1950), 732–43.

HAMILTON, JAMES ALEXANDER, *Postpartum Psychiatric Problems.* St. Louis, Mo.: The C. V. Mosby Co., 1962.

HENRY, JULES, "Family Structure and the Transmission of Neurotic Behavior," *American Journal of Orthopsychiatry,* 21 (October, 1951), 800–18.

HOCH, PAUL H., AND JOSEPH ZUBIN, eds., *Comparative Epidemiology of the Mental Disorders,* New York: Grune and Stratton, Inc., 1961.

HOLLINGSHEAD, AUGUST B., "Some Issues in the Epidemiology of Schizophrenia," *American Sociological Review,* 26 (February, 1961), 5–13.

HOLLINGSHEAD, AUGUST B., AND FREDERICK C. REDLICH, *Social Class and Mental Illness: A Community Study.* New York: John Wiley & Sons, Inc., 1958.

HUGHES, C. C., et al., *People of Cove and Woodlot.* New York: Basic Books, Inc., Publishers, 1960.

HUNT, RAYMOND G., "Socio-Cultural Factors in Mental Disorder," *Behavioral Science,* 4 (April, 1959), 96–106.

HUNT, RAYMOND G., "Social Class and Mental Illness: Some Implications for Clinical Theory and Practice," *American Journal of Psychiatry,* 116 (June, 1960), 1065–69.

IKEDA, KIYOSHI, H. V. BALL, AND D. S. YAMAMURA, "Ethnocultural Factors in Schizophrenia: The Japanese in Hawaii," *American Journal of Sociology,* 68 (September, 1962), 242–79.

JACKSON, DON D., ed., *The Etiology of Schizophrenia.* New York: Basic Books, Inc., Publishers, 1960.

JACO, E. GARTLY, "The Social Isolation Hypothesis and Schizophrenia," *American Sociological Review,* 19 (October, 1954), 567–77.

JACO, E. GARTLY, *The Social Epidemiology of Mental Disorders.* New York: Russell Sage Foundation, 1960.

JAHODA, MARIE, *Race Relations and Mental Health.* Paris: UNESCO, 1960.

KAPLAN, BERT, AND THOMAS F. A. PLAUT, *Personality in a Communal Society: An Analysis of the Mental Health of the Hutterites.* Lawrence: University of Kansas Publications, 1956.

KAPLAN, BERT, ROBERT B. REED, AND WYMAN RICHARDSON, "A Comparison of the Incidence of Hospitalized and Non-Hospitalized Cases of Psychosis in Two Communities," *American Sociological Review,* 21 (August, 1956), 472–79.

KIDD, CECIL B., "Psychiatric Morbidity Among Students," *British Journal of Preventive and Social Medicine,* 19 (October, 1965), 143–50.

KLEINER, ROBERT J., AND SEYMOUR PARKER, "Migration and Mental Illness: A New Look," *American Sociological Review,* 24 (October, 1959), 687–90.

KLEINER, ROBERT J., AND SEYMOUR PARKER, "Goal-Striving, Social Status, and Mental Disorder: A Research Review," *American Sociological Review,* 28 (April, 1963), 189–203.

KOGAN, KATE L., AND JOAN K. JACKSON, "Personality Adjustment and Childhood Experiences," *Journal of Health and Human Behavior,* 5 (Spring, 1964), 50–54.

KOLE, DELBERT M., "A Cross-Cultural Study of Medical-Psychiatric Symptoms," *Journal of Health and Human Behavior,* 7 (Fall, 1966), 162–75.

Kornhauser, Arthur, and Otto M. Reid, *Mental Health of the Industrial Worker.* New York: John Wiley & Sons, Inc., 1965.

Kramer, Morton, et al., *A Historical Study of the Disposition of First Admissions to a State Mental Hospital: Experience of the Warren State Hospital During the Period 1916–50,* U.S. Public Health Service, Public Health Monograph, No. 32. Washington, D.C.: Government Printing Office, 1955.

Krupinski, J., "Sociological Aspects of Mental Ill-Health in Migrants," *Social Science and Medicine,* 1 (September, 1967), 267–82.

Langner, Thomas S., "A Twenty-Two Item Screening Score of Psychiatric Symptoms Indicating Impairment," *Journal of Health and Human Behavior,* 3 (Winter, 1962), 269–77.

Langner, Thomas S., and Stanley T. Michael, *Life Stress and Mental Health: The Midtown Manhattan Study,* A. C. Rennie Series in Social Psychiatry, Vol. II. New York: The Free Press, 1963.

Lazarus, Judith, Ben Z. Locke, and Dorothy Swaine Thomas, "Migration Differentials in Mental Disease: State Patterns in First Admissions to Mental Hospitals for All Disorders and for Schizophrenia, New York, Ohio and California, as of 1950," *Milbank Memorial Fund Quarterly,* 41 (January, 1963), 25–42.

Lee, Everett S., "Socio-Economic and Migration Differentials in Mental Disease: New York State, 1949–1951," *Milbank Memorial Fund Quarterly,* 41 (July, 1963), 249–68.

Leighton, Alexander H., *My Name is Legion.* New York: Basic Books, Inc., Publishers, 1959.

Leighton, Dorothea C., et al., *The Character of Danger: Psychiatric Symptoms in Selected Communities,* New York: Basic Books, Inc., Publishers, 1963.

Lemert, Edwin M., "Paranoia and the Dynamics of Exclusion," *Sociometry,* 25 (March, 1962), 2–20.

Linton, Ralph, *Culture and Mental Disorders.* Springfield, Ill.: Charles C Thomas, Publisher, 1956.

Little, Alan, "An 'Expectancy' Estimate of Hospitalization Rates for Mental Illness in England and Wales," *British Journal of Sociology,* 16 (September, 1965), 221–31.

Lowe, C. R., and F. N. Garratt, "Sex Pattern of Admissions to Mental Hospitals in Relation to Social Circumstances," *British Journal of Preventive and Social Medicine,* 13 (April, 1959), 88–102.

Lowenthal, Marjorie Fiske, *Lives in Distress: The Paths of the Elderly to the Psychiatric Ward.* New York: Basic Books, Inc., Publishers, 1964.

Lowenthal, Marjorie Fiske, "Social Isolation and Mental Illness in Old Age," *American Sociological Review,* 29 (February, 1964), 54–71.

Lowenthal, Marjorie, and Paul L. Berkman, "The Problem of Rating Psychiatric Disability in a Study of Normal and Abnormal Aging," *Journal of Health and Human Behavior,* 5 (Spring, 1964), 40–45.

Lu, Yi-Chuang, "Contradictory Parental Expectations in Schizophrenia," *Archives of General Psychiatry,* 6 (March, 1962), 219–34.

Lystad, M. H., "Social Mobility Among Selected Groups of Schizophrenic Patients," *American Sociological Review,* 22 (June, 1957), 288–92.

Malzberg, Benjamin, and Everett S. Lee, *Migration and Mental Disease: A Study of First Admissions to Hospitals for Mental Disease, New York 1939–1941.* New York: Social Science Research Council, 1956.

MANIS, JEROME G., et al., "Validating a Mental Health Scale," *American Sociological Review*, 28 (February, 1963), 108–17.

MANIS, JEROME G., et al., "Estimating the Prevalence of Mental Illness," *American Sociological Review*, 29 (February, 1964), 84–90.

MILBANK MEMORIAL FUND, *Interrelations Between the Social Environment and Psychiatric Disorders*. New York, 1953.

MILBANK MEMORIAL FUND, *Causes of Mental Disorders: A Review of Epidemiological Knowledge*. New York, 1961.

MILLER, KENT S., AND CHARLES M. GRIGG, *Mental Health and the Lower Social Classes*. Tallahassee: Florida State University, 1966.

MYERS, JEROME K., AND BERTRAM H. ROBERTS, *Family and Class Dynamics in Mental Illness*. New York: John Wiley & Sons, Inc., 1959.

MYERS, JEROME K., AND LEE L. BEAN, *A Decade Later: A Follow-up of Social Class and Mental Illness*. New York: John Wiley & Sons, Inc., 1968.

MYERS, JEROME K., LEE L. BEAN, AND MAX P. PEPPER, "Social Class and Psychiatric Disorders: A Ten Year Follow-up," *Journal of Health and Human Behavior*, 6 (Summer, 1965), 74–79.

NICKOLS, JOHN, "Self-Image Ratings of Normal and Disturbed Subjects," *Journal of Health and Human Behavior*, 7 (Spring, 1966), 28–36.

OFFER, DANIEL, AND MELVIN SABSHIN, *Normality: Theoretical and Clinical Concepts of Mental Health*. New York: Basic Books, Inc., Publishers, 1966.

PAFFENBERGER, RALPH S., JR., "Epidemiological Aspects of Parapartum Mental Illness," *British Journal of Preventive and Social Medicine*, 18 (October, 1964), 189–95.

PARKER, SEYMOUR, AND ROBERT J. KLEINER, *Mental Illness in the Urban Negro Community*. New York: The Free Press, 1966.

PARKER, SEYMOUR, ROBERT J. KLEINER, AND BERT NEEDELMAN, "Migration and Mental Illness. Some Reconsiderations and Suggestions for Further Analysis," *Social Science and Medicine*, 3 (April, 1969), 1–9.

PARKES, C. MURRAY, Interhospital and Intrahospital Variations in the Diagnosis and Severity of Schizophrenia," *British Journal of Preventive and Social Medicine*, 17 (April, 1963), 85–89.

PARSONS, P. L., "Mental Health of Swansea's Old Folk," *British Journal of Preventive and Social Medicine*, 19 (January, 1965), 43–47.

PASAMANICK, BENJAMIN, *Epidemiology of Mental Disorder*, American Association for the Advancement of Science, Publication, No. 60. Washington, D.C., 1959.

PHILIP, A. E., AND J. W. MCCULLOCH, "Use of Social Indices in Psychiatric Epidemiology," *British Journal of Preventive and Social Medicine*, 20 (July, 1966), 122–26.

PHILLIPS, DEREK L., AND KEVIN J. CLANCY, "Response Biases in Field Studies of Mental Illness," *American Sociological Review*, 35 (June, 1970), 503–15.

PHILLIPS, DEREK L., AND BERNARD F. SEGAL, "Sexual Status and Psychiatric Symptoms," *American Sociological Review*, 34 (February, 1969), 58–73.

PLUNKETT, RICHARD J., AND JOHN E. GORDON, *Epidemiology and Mental Illness*. New York: Basic Books, Inc., Publishers, 1960.

REDLICH, FREDERICK C., "The Concept of Normality," *American Journal of Psychotherapy*, 6 (July, 1952), 551–76.

ROBINS, LEE N., "Social Correlates of Psychiatric Disorders: Can We Tell Causes from Consequences?" *Journal of Health and Social Behavior*, 10 (June, 1969), 95–104.

Rosenberg, Morris, "The Dissonant Religious Context and Emotional Disturbance," *American Journal of Sociology,* 68 (July, 1962), 1–11.

Rosengren, William R., "The Self in the Emotionally Disturbed," *American Journal of Sociology,* 66 (March, 1961), 454–63.

Rosenthal, David, ed., *The Genain Quadruplets: A Case Study and Theoretical Analysis of Heredity and Environment in Schizophrenia.* New York: Basic Books, Inc., Publishers, 1964.

Rogler, Lloyd H., and August B. Hollingshead, "Class and Disordered Speech in the Mentally Ill," *Journal of Health and Human Behavior,* 2 (Fall, 1961), 178–85.

Rowden, David W., et al., "Judgments about Candidates for Psychotherapy: The Influence of Social Class and Insight-Verbal Ability," *Journal of Health and Social Behavior,* 11 (March, 1970), 51–58.

Rutter, Michael, "Some Current Research Issues in American Child Psychiatry," *Milbank Memorial Fund Quarterly,* 41 (October, 1963), 339–70.

Sampson, Harold, S. L. Messinger, and R. D. Towne, "Family Processes and Becoming a Mental Patient," *American Journal of Sociology,* 68 (July, 1962), 88–97.

Sanua, Victor D., "Sociocultural Factors in Families of Schizophrenics: A Review of the Literature," *Psychiatry,* 24 (August, 1961), 246–65.

Sarbin, Theodore R., *Studies in Behavior Pathology.* New York: Holt, Rinehart & Winston, Inc., 1961.

Scheff, Thomas J., *Being Mentally Ill: A Sociological Theory.* Chicago: Aldine Publishing Company, 1966.

Scheff, Thomas J., and Eric Sundstrom, "The Stability of Deviant Behavior Over Time: A Reassessment," *Journal of Health and Social Behavior,* 11 (March, 1970), 37–43.

Scott, Marvin B., and Stanford M. Lyman, "Paranoia, Homosexuality and Game Theory," *Journal of Health and Social Behavior,* 9 (September, 1968), 179–87.

Scott, William A., "Social Psychological Correlates of Mental Illness and Mental Health," *Psychological Bulletin,* 55 (March, 1958), 65–87.

Segal, Bernard E., Robert J. Weiss, and Robert Sokol, "Emotional Adjustment, Social Organization, and Psychiatric Treatment Rates," *American Sociological Review,* 30 (August, 1965), 548–56.

Simmons, Ozzie G., *Work and Mental Illness: Eight Case Studies.* New York: John Wiley & Sons, Inc., 1965.

Singer, Benjamin D., "Some Implications of Differential Psychiatric Treatment of Negro and White Patients," *Social Science and Medicine,* 1 (April, 1967), 77–84.

Slotkin, J. S., "Culture and Psychopathology," *Journal of Abnormal and Social Psychology,* 51 (September, 1955), 269–75.

Smith, M. Brewster, "'Mental Health' Reconsidered: A Special Case of the Problem of Values in Psychology," *American Psychologist,* 16 (June, 1961), 299–306.

Soddy, Kenneth, ed., *Mental Health and Value Systems: Cross-Cultural Studies in Mental Health.* Chicago: Quadrangle Books, 1962.

Sommer, Robert, and Robert Hall, "Alienation and Mental Illness," *American Sociological Review,* 23 (August, 1958), 418–20.

Srole, Leo, et al., *Mental Health in the Metropolis: The Midtown Manhattan Study.* New York: McGraw-Hill Book Company, 1962.

Stein, Lilli, "'Social Class' Gradient in Schizophrenia," *British Journal of Preventive and Social Medicine,* 11 (October, 1957), 181–95.

Stein, Zena, and Mervyn Susser, "Widowhood and Mental Illness," *British Journal of Preventive and Social Medicine,* 23 (May, 1969), 106–10.

TEELE, JAMES E., "Sociocultural Factors Relating to Mild Mental Retardation," *Social Science and Medicine*, 3 (January, 1970), 363–69.

THOMAS, DOROTHY SWAINE, AND BEN Z. LOCKE, "Marital Status, Education and Occupational Differentials in Mental Disease: State Patterns in First Admissions to Mental Hospitals for all Disorders and for Schizophrenia, New York and Ohio as of 1950," *Milbank Memorial Fund Quarterly*, 41 (April, 1963), 145–60.

TUCKMAN, JACOB, DAVID M. GRAY, AND WILLIAM F. YOUNGMAN, "Some Correlates of Psychiatric Readmission," *Social Science and Medicine*, 1 (September, 1967), 321–32.

TUCKMAN, JACOB, AND RICHARD A. REGAN, "Ordinal Position and Behavior Problems in Children," *Journal of Health and Social Behavior*, 8 (March, 1967), 32–39.

TURNER, R. JAY, "Social Mobility and Schizophrenia," *Journal of Health and Social Behavior*, 9 (September, 1968), 194–203.

TURNER, R. JAY, et al., "Field Survey Methods in Psychiatry: The Effects of Sampling Strategy Upon Findings in Research on Schizophrenia," *Journal of Health and Social Behavior*, 10 (December, 1969), 289–97.

VENESS, H., AND J. O. HOSKIN, "Psychiatry in New Britain: A Note on the 'Fruit-Tree Experiment' as a Measure of the Effect of Language on Association Processes," *Social Science and Medicine*, 1 (January, 1968), 419–24.

WECHSLER, HENRY, "Community Growth, Depressive Disorders, and Suicide," *American Journal of Sociology*, 67 (July, 1961), 9–17.

WEINBERG, S. KIRSON, *Society and Personality Disorders*. Englewood Cliffs, N.J.: Prentice-Hall, Inc., 1952.

WEINBERG, S. KIRSON, "Cultural Aspects of Manic-Depression in West Africa," *Journal of Health and Human Behavior*, 6 (Winter, 1965), 247–53.

WEINBERG, S. KIRSON, *The Sociology of Mental Disorders: Analyses and Readings in Psychiatric Sociology*. Chicago: Aldine Publishing Company, 1967.

WERTHEIMER, NANCY M., "A Psychiatric Follow-up of Children with Rheumatic Fever and Other Chronic Diseases," *Journal of Chronic Diseases*, 16 (March, 1963), 223–37.

WOLMAN, BENJAMIN B., "Family Dynamics and Schizophrenia," *Journal of Health and Human Behavior*, 6 (Fall, 1965), 163–69.

World Health Organization, Expert Committee on Mental Health, *Epidemiology of Mental Disorders*, Technical Report Series, No. 185. Geneva, 1960.

YOKOYAMA, SADAO T., "Industrialization and Mental Health in Japan," *Social Science and Medicine*, 3 (April, 1970), 689–91.

ZENTNER, HENRY, "Durkheim, Mental Health and Religious Socialization," *Sociological Inquiry*, 34 (Winter, 1964), 92–107.

ZUBIN, JOSEPH, ed., *Field Studies in the Mental Disorders*. New York: Grune & Stratton, Inc., 1961.

IX. SOURCES OF INFORMATION ABOUT MEDICAL SOCIOLOGY

Those readers who wish to pursue developments in medical sociology should be aware of the following sources:

Journals:

American Sociological Review
American Journal of Sociology

Journal of Health and Social Behavior
Social Science and Medicine
Sociological Inquiry
Journal of Social Issues
Journal of Chronic Diseases
British Journal of Preventive and Social Medicine

Bibliographic sources:

Index Medicus, National Library of Medicine, U.S. Public Health Service, Washington, D.C.

Sociological Abstracts, American Sociological Association, New York

Psychological Abstracts, American Psychological Association, Washington, D.C.

Biological Abstracts, Bioscience Information Service

Current Bibliography of Epidemiology, American Public Health Association, New York, N.Y.

NAME INDEX

The names included in the bibliography in chapter 22 do not appear in this index.

T

SUBJECT INDEX